STUDENT EDITION

Third Edition
BSCS

5415 Mark Dabling Boulevard
Colorado Springs, CO 80918-3842

BSCS

Biology
A Human Approach

Includes *SCLINKS*
NSTA

KENDALL/HUNT PUBLISHING COMPANY
4050 Westmark Drive   Dubuque, Iowa 52002

BSCS ADMINISTRATIVE STAFF, THIRD EDITION

Carlo Parravano, *Chair, Board of Directors*
Rodger W. Bybee, *Executive Director*
Janet Carlson Powell, *Director and Chief Science Education Officer*
Pamela Van Scotter, *Director, The BSCS Center for Curriculum Development*
Marcia Mitchell, *Director of Finance*

BSCS THIRD EDITION PROJECT STAFF

Anne L. Westbrook, *Project Director*
Dottie Watkins, *Revision Coordinator*
Barbara Perrin, *Production Manager*
Stacey Luce, Lisa Rasmussen, *Production Staff*
Steve Getty, *Unit 1, Review*

BSCS SECOND EDITION PROJECT STAFF

Hedi F. Baxter, *Project Director*
April Gardner, *Curriculum Developer*
Sherry Herron, *Curriculum Developer*
Rose M. Johnson, *Project Assistant*
Janet Carlson Powell, *Science Education Advisor*
Pamela Van Scotter, *Director of Curriculum Development*

BSCS SECOND EDITION PRODUCTION STAFF

Richard Bascobert, *Editor*
Joan Bolen, *Production Assistant*
Diane Gionfriddo, *Photo Researcher*
Barbara Perrin, *Production Manager*
Lisa Rasmussen, *Graphic Designer*

SECOND EDITION CONTRIBUTORS

Edward Drexler, Pius XI High School, Milwaukee, WI
The Jane Goodall Institute, Silver Spring, MD
Tim Myles, University of Toronto, Toronto, Ontario
Douglas Niles, Delavan, WI

SECOND EDITION ARTISTS AND EDITORS

Fran Sevin
Susan Bartel
Marjorie C. Leggitt
Robert F. Schwengel
Paige Louis Thomas
MiRobin Webster

FIRST EDITION BSCS DEVELOPMENT TEAM

Rodger W. Bybee, *Principal Investigator*
Michael J. Dougherty, *Project Director 1995–1996*
Janet Carlson Powell, *Project Director, 1993–1995*
Gordon E. Uno, *Project Director, 1992*

Staff Associates

Randall K. Backe, Wilbur Bergquist, William J. Cairney, Michael J. Dougherty, B. Ellen Friednan, Philip Goulding, David A. Hanych, Laura J. Laughran, Lynda B. Micikas, Jean P. Milani, Josina Romero-O'Connell, Jenny Sigsted, Pamela Van Scotter.

FIRST EDITION ARTISTS AND EDITORS

Jan Chatlain Girard
Mark Handy
Becky Hill
Brent Sauerhagen

Credits can be found on page 775
Editorial, design, and production services provided by
LaurelTech, New Hampshire
sciLinks® is owned by the National Science Teachers Association. All rights resered.
Cover image provided by Corbis

This material is based on work supported by the National Science Foundation under Grant No. ESI 925274. Any opinions, findings, conclusions, or recommendations expressed in this publication are those of the authors and do not necessarily reflect the views of the granting agency.

Printed in the United States of America
5 6 7 8 9 10   11 10 09 08 07

Acknowledgments

Second Edition Contributors

Pedagogical Advisors

Scott Charleton, Lebanon High School, Lebanon, OH

Frank Girolami, Mason High School, Mason, OH

Barbara Grosz, Pine Crest Preparatory School, Fort Lauderdale, FL

Melanie Hardel, Hartford Union High School, Hartford, WI

Terry Houchens, Joliet Central High School, Joliet, IL

Mary McClellan, Seattle School District, Seattle, WA

Kimberly Noethen, Cornell University, Ithaca, NY

Eugene O'Brien, Hartford Union High School, Hartford, WI

Members of the BSCS-Human listserv

Content Reviewers

Dr. John G. Bailey, College of Veterinary Medicine, Mississippi State, MS (Chapter 7)

Dr. Marvin Druger, Syracuse University, Syracuse, NY (Chapter 1)

Dr. Diane Ebert-May, Michigan State University, East Lansing, MI (Chapter 9)

Dr. James J. Gallagher, Michigan State University, East Lansing, MI (Chapter 3)

Dr. Burnette W. Hamil, Mississippi State University, Mississippi State, MS (Chapter 16)

Dr. Craig Hanke, University of Wisconsin, Green Bay, Green Bay, WI (Chapter 5)

Dr. Ross Jilk, Rochester University, Kansas City, MO (Chapter 12)

Carolyn W. Keys, The University of Georgia, Athens, GA (Engage, Explain, Evaluate)

Dr. Norman G. Lederman, Illinois Institute of Technology, Chicago, IL (Chapter 2)

Dr. Sarah H. Martin, University of Southern Mississippi, Hattiesburg, MS (Chapters 13 and 14)

Dr. Rhonda A. Patterson, University of Southern Mississippi, Hattiesburg, MS (Chapter 6)

Dr. Montgomery Slatkin, University of California, Berkeley, CA (Chapter 11)

Dr. Marshall Sundberg, Emporia State University, Emporia, KS (Chapter 15)

Dr. James H. Wandersee, Louisiana State University, Baton Rouge, LA (Chapter 8)

Dr. Richard E. Wilson, Rockhurst University, Kansas City, MO (Chapter 4)

Consultants

Dr. Robert D. Carlson, Marshfield Clinic, Marshfield, WI

Ms. Diana Gordon, Vernier Software & Technology, Beaverton, OR

Dr. Eileen M. Lento, PASCO Scientific, Roseville, CA

Dr. Gerald Saunders, University of Northern Colorado, Greeley, CO

Mr. Geof Smith, Ward's Natural Science Establishment, Inc., Rochester, NY

Dr. Edward B. Whitney, Colorado Department of Labor, Denver, CO

First Edition Contributors

Contributors

Robert A. Bouchard, College of Wooster, Wooster, OH; Edward Drexler, Pius XI High School, Milwaukee, WI; Kim Finer, Kent State University, Canton, OH; Ann Haley-Oliphant, Miami University, Oxford, OH; Laura J. Laughran, New Directions, Tucson, AZ.

Consultants

Susan Speece, External Evaluator, Fresno City College, Fresno, CA; Constance Bouchard, College of Wooster, Wooster, OH; Ted Dunning, New Mexico State University, Las Cruces, NM; Irene Pepperberg, University of Arizona, Tucson, AZ; Bert Kempers, Media Design Associates, Inc., Boulder, CO; Will Allgood, Media Design Associates, Inc., Boulder, CO; Mark Viner, Media Design Associates, Inc., Boulder, CO; Larry N. Norton, Quantum Technology, Inc., Evergreen, CO; Chester Penk, Quantum Technology, Inc., Evergreen, CO; Ward's Natural Science Establishment, Inc., Rochester, NY.

Advisory Board

Judy Capra, Jefferson County Public Schools, Golden, CO; Mack Clark, Academy School District 20, Colorado Springs, CO; Diane Ebert-May, Northern Arizona University, Flagstaff, AZ; Philip R. Elliott, The Colorado College, Colorado Springs, CO; April Gardner (*Executive Committee*), University of Northern Colorado, Greeley, CO; Michele Girard, Peyton High School, Peyton, CO; Eville Gorham, University of Minnesota, Minneapolis, MN; Joseph Graves, Arizona State University—West, Phoenix, AZ; Ann Haley-Oliphant (*Executive Committee*), Miami University, Oxford, OH; Paul DeHart Hurd, Prof. Emeritus, Stanford University, Stanford, CA; Mary Kiely, Stanford University, Stanford, CA; Douglas Kissler, Douglas County High School, Castle Rock, CO; Carole Kubota, University of Washington, Seattle, WA; Douglas Lundberg, Air Academy High School, United States Air Force Academy, CO; Michael E. Martinez (*Executive Committee*), University of California, Irvine, CA; Donald E. Mason, Mitchell High School, Colorado Springs, CO; Laurence McCullough, Baylor College of Medicine, Houston, TX; Martin K. Nickels, Illinois State University, Normal, IL; Floyd Nordland, Prof. Emeritus, Purdue University, West Lafayette, IN; S. Scott Obenshain, University of New Mexico, Albuquerque, NM; William O'Rourke, Harrison School District, Colorado Springs, CO; Ann Pollet, Pueblo County High School, Pueblo, CO; Jerry Resnick, Clara Barton High School, Brooklyn, NY; Parker A. Small, Jr., University of Florida, Gainesville, FL; Gordon E. Uno, University of Oklahoma, Norman, OK; Betty M. Vetter, Commission on Professionals in Science and Technology, Washington, DC; Bruce Wallace (*Executive Committee*), Virginia Polytechnic Institute and State University, Blacksburg, VA; Harry Zimbrick, School District 11, Colorado Springs, CO.

Reviewers

Field-Test Site Centers and Coordinators

Field-Test Schools and Teachers

First Edition

Colombia, South America

Haydée Bejardno de Cadena, Marcela Melendez, Monica Sarmiento, Colegio Los Nogales, Bogotá

Arizona

Marcia Fisher, Arcadia High School, Scottsdale; Doug Davis, Dub Manis, Dee Schwartz, Chinle High School, Chinle; Geri Fisher, Jo Quintenz, Desert View High School, Tucson; Kathy Thayer, Ray High School, Ray; Clyde Christensen, Scott Greenhalgh, Ray Pool, Mary Southall, Elizabeth Stone, Tempe High School, Tempe; Willie Long Reed, Tuba City High School, Tuba City; Jack Johnson, Williams High School, Williams; Carlos Estrada, Karen Steele, Window Rock High School, Fort Defiance

Colorado

Don Born, Peggy Wickliff, Air Academy High School, United States Air Force Academy; Linda Lynch, Douglas County High School, Castle Rock; Doug Hewins, Liberty High School, Colorado Springs; Barbara Andrews, Mitchell High School, Colorado Springs; Rata Clarke, Ray Coddington, Jean Orton, Jim Snare, Palmer High School, Colorado Springs; Rod Baker, Michele Girard, Peyton High School, Peyton; Kathy Dorman, Malcom Hovde, Ponderosa High School, Parker; Ann Pollet, Deborah Walters, Pueblo County High School, Pueblo; Glen Smith, Sabin Junior High School, Colorado Springs; Jeff Cogburn, B.J. Stone, Valley High School, Gilcrest; Bill Bragg, Wasson High School, Colorado Springs; Larry Jakel, Doug Steward, Weld Central High School, Keenesburg; Jay Matheson, West Center for Intergenerational Learning, Colorado Springs; Christy Beauprez, Glenn Peterson, Windsor High School, Windsor

Florida

James Happel, Constance Hopkins, Manatee High School, Bradenton; Scott MacGregor, Joe Martin, Palmetto High School, Palmetto; Barbara Grosz, Pine Crest School, Fort Lauderdale

Hawaii

Jamie Nekoba, Waiákea High School, Hilo; Jennifer Busto, Maryknoll Schools, Honolulu

Illinois

Shelly Peretz, Thornridge High School, Dolton

Kansas

J.D. Hand, Chuck Mowry, Gina Whaley, Junction City Senior High School, Junction City

Minnesota

Clyde Cummins, St. Paul Academy Summit School, St. Paul

Missouri

David Jungmeyer, California R-1 High School, California

New Jersey

Judith Jones, Saint John Vianney High School, Holmdel; Margaret Sheldon, West Morris Central High School, Chester; Karen Martin, West Morris Mendham High School, Mendham

Ohio

Barbara Blackwell, Susan Keiffer-Barone, Aiken High School, Cincinnati; Scott Popoff, Sycamore High School, Cincinnati

Texas

Peter Mariner, Francis Mikan, Dean Mohlman, Tom Stege, St. Stephen's Episcopal School, Austin

Washington

Kathleen Heidenrich, Vicky Lamoreaux, River Ridge High School, Lacey; Larry Bencivengo, Mary Margaret Welch, Mercer Island High School, Mercer Island; Mary Ketchum, Jeannie Wenndorf, Lindberg High School, Renton; Gro Buer, Carol Nussbaum, B.E.S.T. Alternative School, Kirkland; Connie Kelly, Diane Lashinsky, Patrick Taylor, Shorecrest High School, Seattle

Wisconsin

Gene O'Brien, Hartford Union High School, Hartford

Contents

Unit 2   Homeostasis: Maintaining Dynamic Equilibrium in Living Systems 146

Unit 2   *Essays*

Unit 3 — Energy, Matter, and Organization: Relationships in Living Systems

Unit 5   Development: Growth and Differentiation in Living Systems

Unit 6   Ecology: Interaction and Interdependence in Living Systems

Unit 6 *Essays*

Evaluate

Appendix A

Appendix B

Appendix C

Dear Learners:

The staff at BSCS developed BSCS Biology: A Human Approach for students first. Not all of the books you use are developed this way. But we feel that focusing on the student is the only way to provide you with the best biology learning experience possible. As you glance through the book, notice that this is not a passive, encyclopedic approach to biology. You will not sit day after day in lectures. Instead, this book helps you learn biology through active involvement.

BSCS cares about the quality of its books because we care about students and teachers. We are a nonprofit organization where scientists and educators are dedicated to improving science education. This book is the result of BSCS's study of the research in biology and learning. It is our interpretation of what we think is a better way to help students learn biology. When we defined the word "better," we decided that a better high school biology program would mean the following:

- More emphasis on the big concepts of biology and less emphasis on the vocabulary words of biology
- More opportunities to conduct investigations that you design
- More connections between biological concepts and your life

In the program overview on the next several pages, you can read about how we put these differences into practice in BSCS Biology: A Human Approach. The overview describes the key features of the program that we think make it noticeably different from and better than other texts. To make sure our ideas worked in classrooms, we spent 2 1/2 school years testing our ideas in classrooms with approximately 80 teachers and 5,000 students. Then, after students and teachers used our textbook and program for several years, we took all the feedback we received from classrooms around the nation. We combined that with current research on how people learn and used that information to improve the book. In addition, many biologists and educators reviewed the materials to make sure they were accurate and current at the time we went to press. We list these contributors and reviewers at the front of the book.

Hundreds of people work together to create one new BSCS program. This process never ends as long as the program is in print. If you read something that you think is confusing or inaccurate, or if you have suggestions for improving an activity, please write to us. We will consider your comments when we revise the book in later editions. Our mailing address is

BSCS Biology: A Human Approach Revision Team
BSCS
5415 Mark Dabling Boulevard
Colorado Springs, CO 80918-3842

We hope you enjoy learning biology in this new way. We enjoyed putting this program together for you because learners are the most important people in schools.

Sincerely,

The Project Staff

BSCS

Program Overview

The letter from the project staff states that *BSCS Biology: A Human Approach* is a better way to learn biology. Six key features of the program help explain why we think this program is better. We describe each feature below.

I. Unifying Themes

We organized the program into three sections and six core units. The three sections are the Engage, Explain, and Evaluate Sections. They come at the beginning, middle, and end of the program and are described under the *Instructional Model* heading. We organized the six core units around six major biological concepts. These concepts are recurring themes that unify all of biology. Although you will see these themes in every unit, we focus on one theme in each unit.

Evolution: Patterns and Products of Change in Living Systems

What does it mean to be human? This is the central question of Unit 1. You will assess the unique qualities of humans and the diversity of life while trying to place humans in the scheme of living systems. Then you will consider characteristics that are common to all living systems as well as those that are unique to humans. You will grapple with the question of whether life is definable. Unity, diversity, genetic variation, and evolution, including cultural evolution, are the major conceptual themes in Unit 1.

Homeostasis: Maintaining Dynamic Equilibrium in Living Systems

Unit 2 explores the controlled internal environment that all organisms require to function well. You will use familiar examples to develop an understanding of the concepts of response, regulation, and feedback. Then you will examine the division between internal and external conditions. You will look at the processes by which internal conditions are maintained in spite of changes in external conditions. In the final chapter of the unit, you will expand these concepts by analyzing the way health and disease affects both the individual human and society as a group.

Energy, Matter, and Organization: Relationships in Living Systems

Unit 3 begins by letting you explain the requirements of physical performance and consider the effects of fitness, drugs, and alcohol on performance. You will develop an understanding of the relationship between structure and function. You also will explore the interplay between energy and matter. You will do this through such metabolic processes as photosynthesis and cellular respiration as well as through interactions in a community. Finally, you will consider the role of producers, consumers, and decomposers in the flow of energy and cycling of matter in a community.

Continuity: Reproduction and Inheritance in Living Systems

Unit 4 focuses on reproduction, patterns of inheritance, and the role of genes and DNA in inheritance. The discussion of human sexual reproduction includes reproductive systems and cycles, reproductive behavior, and ethical issues, such as contraception and sexually transmitted diseases. You will consider the role inheritance plays in continuity and variation and how genes are a source of coded information. In conclusion, you will study the dynamics of gene expression and replication at a molecular level. This provides a basis for understanding genetic engineering.

Development: Growth and Differentiation in Living Systems

As Unit 5 begins, you will consider development as a process that involves differentiation and growth and that requires regulation. You will explore patterns of development. These appear in stages such as reproductive maturity, aging, and death. Development is affected by evolutionary history and provides opportunities for evolutionary change. It also depends on communication. Finally, you will consider human life stages. You will look at biologically programmed events as well as the cultural environment in which they take place.

Ecology: Interaction and Interdependence in Living Systems

Unit 6 centers on issues in the area of ecology. We include dilemmas about the interactions among populations, resources, and environments. You will examine the concepts involved in population dynamics. This sets the stage for studying the interactions between humans and their environment. Next, you will focus on how human actions can modify the environment, especially by using technology. The final emphasis is an analysis of the ethical issues raised when humans share a common resource.

II. Subthemes

Two subthemes, or background ideas, are woven through the entire program. They help to establish connections between biology and your life. They improve your reasoning ability. The Science as Inquiry subtheme refers to the discovery process by which information is obtained and evaluated. It also refers to the changing body of knowledge that characterizes scientific understanding. This theme systematically exposes you to the processes of science. This includes making observations, making inferences, assembling evidence, developing hypotheses, designing experiments, collecting data, analyzing and presenting results, and communicating and evaluating conclusions.

The Science and Humanity subtheme makes your study of biology more relevant and approachable. It does this by incorporating the critical elements of human culture; the history of science; the place of ethics, ethical analysis, and decision making in today's controversial science world; and the importance of human technology as a way of adapting. We define technology as the use of knowledge to achieve a practical solution to a perceived problem. We also recognize that the ultimate effects of the technological process or product on society and the biosphere may extend beyond the intended effects.

III. Instructional Model

We organized the instruction of major concepts in this book around a model of learning that recognizes how individuals build or construct new ideas. We call this type of instructional model the "5Es." The program is organized around five phases of learning that we best can describe using words that begin with E: Engage, Explore, Explain, Elaborate, and Evaluate. You will get an overview of the program by completing the Engage Section. Units 1 to 3 let you explore the big ideas of scientific inquiry. The Explain Section then sets you up to conduct your own scientific inquiry. Units 4 to 6 are designed to help you elaborate your understanding of the processes of science. The Evaluate Section provides several opportunities for you to evaluate your progress in learning biology.

IV. Cooperative Learning

Cooperative learning is an educational strategy that helps you increase your responsibility for your own learning. Cooperative learning also models the processes that scientists use when collaborating. It helps you develop the working relationship skills necessary for today's workforce.

V. Assessment

Assessment opportunities allow you to evaluate your progress. These activities are embedded throughout the program, and the assessments themselves are learning experiences. The following assessment strategies are included in the program:

- Assessments of your performance, such as experiments
- Written tests that have a variety of short-answer and essay questions
- Assessments of cooperative learning skills
- Debates
- Presentations, both by teams and by individuals
- Written assignments, both by teams and by individuals
- Journal assignments that include short-term and long-term work
- Projects, both ongoing and one-time
- An ongoing activity about a newly discovered organism
- Opportunities for self-assessment and peer assessment
- Discussions, both by teams and by the whole class
- The computer testbank CD-ROM, which includes an on-line student test-taking module

VI. Educational Technology

Educational technology is integral to the program. It is used as a tool to enhance learning and understanding. The program includes the following major electronic technologies:

- DVDs: interactive video activities for the chapters
- SciLinks: directions to Internet sites selected to complement the topics in activities (SciLinks icons appear in the margin)
- Probe ware: experimental protocols include instructions for using probe ware and microcomputer-based laboratory options
- Computer simulations on the interactive CD *The Commons:* allow exploration of complex biological interactions

Third Edition

BSCS
Biology
A Human Approach

5415 Mark Dabling Boulevard
Colorado Springs, CO 80918-3842

BSCS

Includes SciLINKS
NSTA

KENDALL/HUNT PUBLISHING COMPANY
4050 Westmark Drive   Dubuque, Iowa 52002

> "The whole of science is nothing more than a refinement of everyday thinking."
>
> *Albert Einstein,* Out of My Later Years, *1950*

Being a Scientist

When faced with a problem or a puzzle, how do you figure things out? You might answer, "I think about them." But are you aware of *how* you think? This biology program focuses on science as one of the ways humans understand and explain their world. The activities throughout this program encourage you to think as a scientist does. This short section is titled *Engage* because it engages you in the type of experiences that you will have in this course.

ACTIVITIES

Engage	Cooperating like a Scientist
Explore	Communicating like a Scientist
Explain	Thinking as a Scientist Thinks
Elaborate	Recording Data in Your Scientific Journal
Evaluate	You and the Science of Biology

Cooperating like a Scientist

Engage

Imagine a scientist at work. Do you see a man in a white coat working alone? Scientists come in all shapes and sizes—men and women from all cultures—and they rarely work in isolation. This picture shows a group of scientists working together. Usually, two or more scientists work cooperatively to make scientific breakthroughs possible. In this activity, we will look at the role that cooperation plays in science.

PROCESS AND PROCEDURES

1. Write a paragraph in response to this question: How do we do science?

2. Your teacher will assign lab partners randomly. Exchange paragraphs with your lab partner and discuss the differences among your ideas.

3. Join another pair of lab partners as directed by your teacher so that you have a team of 4 together at 1 table to play the radar game.

4. Choose 2 people to be "blinds" (persons wearing blindfolds) and 2 people to be "helpers." The people who are blinds will stay blindfolded and remain seated for this entire activity.

5. Have the 2 students who will be the blinds sit on the same side of the table. Helpers sit on the opposite side of the table. Blinds must stay seated.

6. From this point on, you must follow these rules:

NEED TO KNOW

Game Rules

a. Helpers may not touch any materials or the blinds. (If a blind drops something, however, helpers may retrieve the material and give it back to the blinds.)

b. Helpers may not talk. They may not talk to the teacher, their blinds, or other helpers or blinds from other teams. Helpers may not speak to answer a question even if a blind asks. Helpers pretend that they are completely mute.

c. Helpers and blinds may not use any materials other than those your teacher instructed you to get after the blindfolds were in place.

d. Blinds *may* talk. They may talk to each other, to the teacher, to their helpers, and to helpers and blinds from other teams.

e. Blinds may touch the materials.

7. Obtain a clean blindfold from your teacher. Now, helpers blindfold their blinds. Your teacher will give instructions to the helpers as soon as all the blinds in the class are blindfolded.

8. Follow the instructions given by your teacher.

9. Participate in a class discussion of your success rate with the radar activity. Answer the following questions:

   a. How did you do?

   b. How did you feel?

   c. Why did you feel the way you did?

   d. If you could change the rules of the radar game, how would you change them?

   e. How does this game relate to the work that scientists do?

10. Look back at the paragraph you wrote in step 1. Write another short paragraph that explains the role that communication plays in doing science.

Communicating like a Scientist

The radar game required cooperation. You will continue to develop and use cooperation skills throughout this program. You will also develop other skills of working like a scientist, such as strong communication habits. One of the most important jobs for a scientist is to accurately record ideas and data to share with other scientists and the public.

Like a scientist, you will keep a scientific journal throughout this course. The accuracy with which you describe events in your journal is important because this will enable you to compare your observations with those of others. For example, your records should provide important information about what might have caused differences in investigations that you and your classmates do in your classroom.

A scientific journal also helps scientists communicate with others about their work so that their peers and the public can review their work. Accurate record-keeping makes it possible for scientists to repeat experiments and see if they can obtain the same results. This replication process is essential for scientists and society to trust an investigator.

Your classmates depend on you to keep accurate records of your investigations so that your class can analyze results effectively. In addition, your teacher will evaluate your journal. It is important for your journal to be well organized and to represent your work thoroughly so that your teacher can give you credit for your accomplishments.

Materials

spiral notebook   soft pencil (#2)
blank drawing paper   unknown objects

PROCESS AND PROCEDURES

Part A   Your Scientific Journal: Recording Your Thoughts and Observations

1. Read Appendix B, *Technique 1 Journals*, on page 690.
2. From your reading, list the key points that you need to remember about
   a. recording data,
   b. responding to questions,
   c. taking notes,
   d. keeping track of your questions,
   e. keeping track of your responsibilities, and
   f. using your journal during assessment.

3. Your teacher will provide you with a rubric to help you evaluate your journal techniques. Read and discuss the rubric with your partner. Record any questions you have about journal evaluation.

4. Participate in a class discussion about journal techniques. Think about the following questions:

   a. What are the differences between keeping a science journal and writing a laboratory report?

   b. What do you think sounds the most interesting about keeping a science journal?

   c. What part of keeping a science journal sounds the most challenging?

Part B   Using Drawings to Record Observations

"A picture is worth a thousand words." This familiar saying can be true when you are recording scientific observations. In your journal, you must carefully describe the observations that you make, and a drawing can be an excellent way to describe an object. In this activity, you will work on the art of making careful observations. You do not need any drawing skills to be able to learn to sketch what you see.

Observing and Describing

1. You and your partner are going to work as a team. One person will be the observer, and the other will identify an object without seeing or touching it.

2. The observer will select an object in the room without showing it to his or her partner.

NEED TO KNOW

Art Terms

◆ **Line:** This can be horizontal, vertical, diagonal, broken, wavy, and so forth. Length is the most important dimension of line.

◆ **Space:** The area between, around, above, below, or within.

◆ **Shape:** Shapes can be geometric or lack a specific form. Shape is the length and width of an object.

◆ **Form:** There are five fundamental forms in nature: sphere, cube, cone, pyramid, and cylinder.

◆ **Texture:** The surface quality of an object. This can either be a real texture that you can feel or a visible texture that you see. It is the look and feel of the surface of an object.

◆ **Value:** The relative lightness or darkness of areas.

◆ **Color:** Comprised of three distinct properties:

   a. hue: the name of a color

   b. value: the lightness (tint) or darkness (shade)

   c. intensity: the quality of brightness or dullness

3. Sit back-to-back with your partner. The observer holds the selected object.

4. The observer will describe the object to his or her partner but can only describe the object with the art terms listed in the need to know box titled Art Terms.*

5. After the partner has correctly identified the object, switch roles and obtain a new, unknown object for the second observer to describe.

6. Record in your journal which 3 art terms you found most useful for describing the object. Explain which terms you found the most difficult to use.

A Blind Drawing

In this exercise, you will work by yourself to draw an object that you can touch, but cannot see.

1. Obtain a sheet of plain paper, a soft pencil (#2), and 1 brown paper bag that contains an object from your teacher. Do not look in the bag!

2. With 1 hand, create a line drawing of what you feel as you trace the outline of the object in your bag with your fingers. Carefully feel the edges of your object and draw its outline at the same time. Take your time and concentrate.

3. When your drawing is complete, compare it to the object in the bag. Make this comparison by explaining 3 ways that your drawing is like the object and 3 ways it is different.

4. How long did it take you to make your blind drawing? When you think about how long you should take to make a drawing in your science journal, remember your blind drawing. Any drawing that you make to accurately record your observations will take time and concentration as well.

Experimenting with the Pencil Line

For this task, you will use your pencil and 1 sheet of paper. You will have 3 minutes to make a variety of marks on the paper. Be imaginative and feel free to experiment. Use the point and the side of the pencil to create lines of varying length, thickness, and shape, and to create shading effects. Your objective is to become familiar with the pencil and the various effects you can create with it.

Making a Detailed Drawing

A detailed drawing records accurate information about the material. In this type of drawing, keep your interpretation to a minimum. The goal is to draw only what is visible and to select those details that are the most important observations to capture in a drawing.

1. Work individually to draw the object that was in your brown bag for the blind drawing.

2. Begin by making a simple line drawing that accurately captures the basic shape, size, and proportion of the object. Add details to your line drawing using some of the effects that you developed in your pencil-line experimentation.

Figure En.1
Experiment with your pencil.

*Adapted from Stoops & Samuelson, 1983.

3. When your drawing is complete, label it to indicate the relative size of the drawing to the real object (for example, ½ actual size or 10× magnification).

4. Attach your completed drawing to a page in your journal.

Analysis

1. Answer the following questions in your journal:

    a. Had you ever seen an object like the one that you just finished drawing?

    b. How did your previous experience of either having seen or not having seen an object like this influence your drawing?

2. Explain whether or not you think that scientific observations are completely objective. Provide an example to illustrate your point of view.

Explain

Thinking as a Scientist Thinks

To think as a scientist thinks, you need to

- ask questions,
- gather information,
- use logical reasoning, and
- apply your creativity to develop predictions and explanations that make sense of the evidence that you collect.

You will practice these skills in this activity.

Scientists are often inspired by an incident that happens while they are doing something else. For example, anyone who eats or prepares meat might observe that maggots (immature flies) soon cover a piece of meat that is left out for too long. People once thought that maggots spontaneously came to life from the meat. In 1668, however, a biologist named Francesco Redi *questioned* whether it was possible for life to come from nonliving matter. He *gathered information* by making careful observations and experimenting. Redi placed some meat under gauze and left some uncovered. He found that only the uncovered meat developed maggots. After analyzing his careful observations and data, Francesco Redi *reasoned* that flies were laying eggs on the uncovered meat, and that maggots came from the fly eggs, not the rotting meat. In this way, Redi used scientific inquiry to *explain his observations* and questions about the natural world. Scientists propose explanations based on evidence.

In this activity, imagine that something happened while you were writing in your science journal that caused you to ask questions. You will use this situation to learn about the basic processes of science. You will collect relevant evidence and use logical reasoning to propose explanations based on that evidence. Throughout the year, you will continue to build your understandings and abilities to conduct scientific inquiries. This will continue until you can design and conduct your own independent investigations.

Materials (per team of 2)

set of color pens   termite
blank white paper   small paintbrush or cotton swab

PROCESS AND PROCEDURES

1. Listen to or read to yourself the following scenario.

SCENARIO

Late One Night

You are a scientist, and you were working late last night. You drew a diagram in different colors of ink, and it looked similar to the drawing below. While you were writing and drawing the diagram in your journal, you nodded off.

    When you awoke, you found there was a termite in the middle of the diagram. You watched the termite's response to the ink on the page, and it made you wonder. Next, you called in your friend, who is also a scientist. Together you made a prediction about what the termite was doing. Questions about the termite and its behavior led you to start experimenting and making careful observations to see if your prediction was correct.

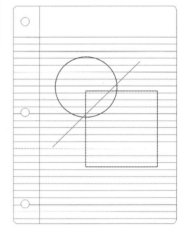

Figure En.2 A simple line diagram

2. Pick up 1 set of materials for you and your partner.

3. Using your colored pens, create a simple line diagram like the one that might have been found in the journal (see Figure En.2). Observe your termite's behavior.

Note: Termites are soft-bodied insects and must not be pinched. Use the soft bristles of the paintbrush or a cotton swab to block your termite and redirect it. *Do not* try to pick up your termite with your fingers or push it around with the paintbrush.

4. The first step in thinking scientifically is to identify the questions you are trying to answer. Begin this process by thinking about the questions that come to mind as you watch your termite on the diagram. Identify 3 questions and record them in your journal.

5. Work with your partner to select 1 question about the termite's behavior that you think you might be able to answer through experimentation.

6. In your journal, predict the answer to your question. Also, explain briefly why you think that your prediction may be reasonable.

7. Discuss with your partner how you will experiment and make observations to learn more about your question. Save all test diagrams that you use, and record your observations in your journal. Pay attention to the amount of time you are given to conduct your experiment.

8. Use the information and observations that you gather to develop a possible explanation for what you observe and a possible answer to your question. Include any additional questions that come up while you are experimenting.

Figure En.3 To move the termite without harming it, block the termite's path without touching it.

9. Be prepared to report to the class what question you tested, the results of your experimentation, and your explanation or additional questions.

Analysis

1. Participate in a class discussion of the questions, experiments, and ideas about termites.

2. Read the terms below and identify two additional terms that could be used to describe the way scientists think:

   explanation   evidence   prediction   logic

3. Write a paragraph in your journal to summarize the statement, *science is a way of knowing*. Include the four terms from question 2 and the two terms that you added.

4. In your journal, explain whether you agree or disagree with each of the following statements:

   ◆ Scientists observe without making any judgments; scientific observations are objective and value free.

   ◆ If two scientists run the same experiment and have similar observations, they will develop the same explanation for the results.

Elaborate

Recording Data in Your Scientific Journal

Scientists communicate information and ideas through speaking and writing. Data tables and graphs are two forms of writing that help scientists report information clearly and accurately. Because you will be designing your own investigations in this course, you also will need to work like a scientist to design appropriate data tables and graphs.

PROCESS AND PROCEDURES

1. In your journal, explain 3 steps that you think are most important when making a data table.

2. What do you find is the hardest decision that you have to make when you construct a data table? Why is it difficult to decide?

3. Participate in a class discussion about how your class will make data tables to report results clearly and accurately to each other and to your teacher. Consider the following questions:

   a. What are the terms that you use to describe data?

   b. Why is it important for your class to agree to use the same terms when you describe data in tables, graphs, conclusions, analysis questions, and presentations?

c. Why is it useful for scientists to have a particular format that is always used when making data tables and graphs? What is useful about having standard formats for data in a high school biology class?

   d. What table and graph formats will be standardized in your class?

4. Read Appendix B, *Technique 2 Graphing*, on page 692, and follow the instructions to practice graphing.

You and the Science of Biology Evaluate

Imagine yourself doing one or more of the following:

- Understanding the choices a doctor offers for treatment of an illness
- Deciphering nutritional information on a food package label
- Voting on an issue involving science and technology
- Serving on a jury that has to listen to an expert describe DNA evidence
- Deciding whether or not to support the construction of a new dam

These are examples of actions that happen in the United States. Will you be one of the people making informed decisions and choices because you have learned to think scientifically? Or, will you be one of the people who acts and hopes for the best, despite a lack of information and understanding? By participating in this biology program, you are taking a big step toward joining the first group of people.

In this course, we use six main ideas to organize your study of biology. We also integrate these ideas with opportunities to think about and use the methods of science. As a result, you can learn how to think scientifically while you learn biology.

PROCESS AND PROCEDURES

Read *A Human Approach to Biology* on page 12, and identify at least 1 reason why each of the following is relevant:

- the study of biology now
- the study of biology in the future

Analysis

Use your experiences from the activities you have just completed and your general life experiences to answer the following questions in your journal. After each answer, leave room to revise your response following a class discussion of the questions.

1. What role does science play in your life?
2. What role do you think science will play in your future?
3. How can science help you make decisions about yourself, your lifestyle, your community, and your planet?
4. How do the decisions that we make today influence future generations, generations that could include your children and grandchildren?

A Human Approach to Biology

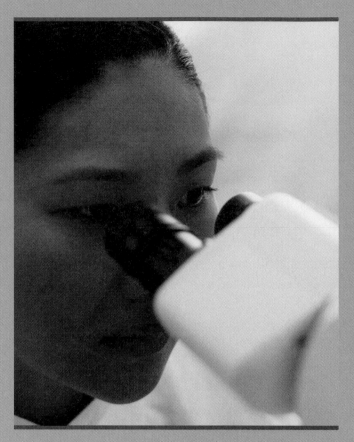

The scientist in the photograph above represents the visual image many people have of scientists. While this is one example of what doing science looks like, there are many other examples. Think about the activities listed at the beginning of this Evaluate Section: making choices in the doctor's office and voting, for example. All of those activities can be conducted using the methods of science.

Biology is a way of explaining by scientific processes what living organisms do and how they do it. There are other ways to look at life. You could describe living things in poetry, by paintings, or in a written story. These activities have great value and add an important dimension to human life. These ways of describing life, however, would not be a scientific approach. In a scientific approach, the explanations are based on asking questions that can be answered by gathering information and evidence and then analyzing what we

know in a logical manner. (See the summary of the processes of science in Figure En.4.) In this program, you will be practicing "Science as Inquiry" when you learn and use the processes of science.

Biology is a challenging scientific study because all of life is very complex and shows variety and intricate connections. Fortunately, living things also share some very important characteristics that can be summarized as large ideas. In this program, these large and universal ideas are the topics of each of the six units.

This program is called *BSCS Biology: A Human Approach* because we have focused your activities around human interactions. You will experience this human approach in several ways. You will complete experiments that involve yourself. You will read examples of the unifying principles that point out the

- Asking questions
- Gathering information
- Proposing explanations

Figure En.4 **The processes of science.** The processes of science help you learn more about biology.

connection between humans and evolution; homeostasis; matter, energy, and organization; continuity; development; and ecology. Also, you will understand "Science and Humanity" when you experience connections to biology content that point out the following:

- Humans use technology to help solve problems. Consequently, we are able to improve our ability to survive in the near future.
- Technology varies from culture to culture and changes across time.
- Science takes place within a cultural and historical context as well as within a set of constraints often dictated by the culture and time period.
- Humans can use ethical analysis to make decisions and solve problems. This applies to both scientific investigations and questions because humans themselves conduct these endeavors.

As you study the biology in this course, you will learn about living systems. If you can understand how you learn, you will further enjoy the process of learning and be more successful at it. Scientists who study how people learn are called **cognitive psychologists**. These scientists have proposed an explanation for learning that suggests that, in order to learn, one first must be engaged in an idea. Then the learner must explore the idea. Next, the learner develops an explanation of the idea. Finally, the learner elaborates his or her understanding and is able to evaluate what he or she has learned.

As you look through this book, you will notice the use of five words that start with the letter "E." This program uses these "E words" to organize the instructional flow in each chapter. This instructional flow is designed to help you construct an understanding of each big idea in biology.

The essays for most of the program are grouped together at the end of each unit in this book, while the assessment opportunities are embedded within the program. These physical placements reflect two aspects of BSCS's approach to science and learning. First, because our understanding of the content changes frequently, we designed a program that acknowledges this. The essays provided give you a place to begin your research, but they are intended to be only one resource of the many resources available to you. For example, you may supplement your research with other books, magazines, and the Internet. A second aspect of the approach is reflected in the embedded assessment. We think you should have continual opportunities to evaluate your understanding and growth, so you will notice frequent chances to monitor your own learning.

Unifying Principles of Biology

Evolution: Patterns and Products of Change in Living Systems

Homeostasis: Maintaining Dynamic Equilibrium in Living Systems

Energy, Matter, and Organization: Relationships in Living Systems

Continuity: Reproduction and Inheritance in Living Systems

Development: Growth and Differentiation in Living Systems

Ecology: Interaction and Interdependence in Living Systems

BSCS

Unifying principles of biology These six big ideas are one way to organize the discipline of biology. These ideas are also the titles of the six units in *BSCS Biology: A Human Approach.*

UNIT 1

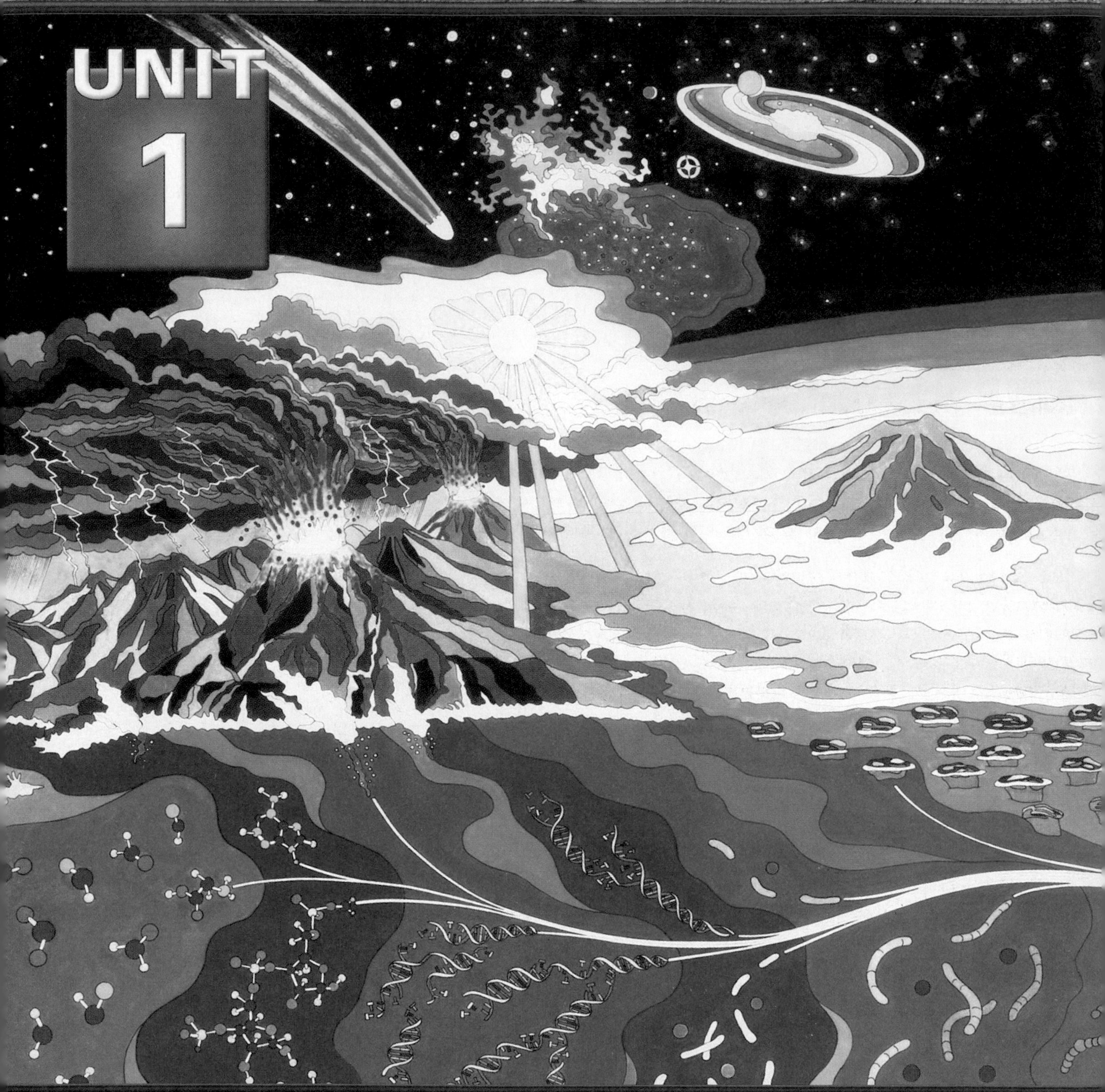

Evolution: Patterns and Products of Change in Living Systems

1 The Human Animal

2 Evolution: Change across Time

3 Products of Evolution: Unity and Diversity

How did the great diversity of life on earth come to be? What do the organisms living on earth have in common with each other? As we reflect on ourselves as living organisms, what does it mean to be human, and how did humans come to be?

These questions do not have simple answers. Scientists and philosophers have been asking these questions for hundreds of years. In particular, biologists have been studying the diversity of living systems and looking for patterns. They have found patterns in the information, sequences of events, and chemical and physical structures of living things. Scientists learn more about these patterns by asking questions, gathering information, and proposing explanations.

In this unit, you will explore change in living systems in much the same way. The following goals will help you learn the big ideas in this unit. By the end of Unit 1, you will be able to

- explain that humans have characteristics that distinguish them from other organisms;
- compare the many characteristics that humans share with other living systems and organisms;
- recognize the diversity of living systems on earth;
- demonstrate how evolution provides a scientific explanation for this diversity;
- apply the methods of science, such as critical thinking, making observations, asking questions, collecting data, and recording and analyzing data; and
- use evidence, inference, and inquiry appropriately.

> "... and this is the weaving of human living: of whose fabric each individual is a part ..."
>
> *James Agee and Walker Evans*, Let Us Now Praise Famous Men, *1941*

The Human Animal

Consider for a moment the vast differences among humans, as depicted by the people in these photographs. We differ in stature, in the shape of our eyes, in the texture of our hair, and in the color of our skin. We differ in our ways of living, the languages that we speak, the foods that we grow and eat, and our concept of the universe. Yet, we share the common bond of humanness, and we see some of ourselves reflected in each of a thousand other faces.

As you begin the first chapter of this unit, you will find yourself looking at humans in a way that may be new to you. You will look at humans the way scientists do. To do this, you will build a range of knowledge and skills that illustrates science as a way of knowing. You will examine some physical characteristics that humans share with other primates. You will also examine the ways in which humans are different from other primates. This chapter also explores humans as social and cultural animals that use language and have a great capacity for learning. Your experiences in these activities will help you begin to develop a scientific understanding of the human animal and what it means to be human.

ACTIVITIES

Engage	How Different Are We?
Explore	Primates Exploring Primates
Explain	Tony's Brain
Explain	Portraying Humankind
Elaborate	A Long Childhood
Evaluate	What Does It Mean to Be Human?

How Different Are We?

In the previous Engage Section, you began to explore science as a way of learning about the natural world. Remember, before you began your experiments with termites, you thought about termite behavior and made careful observations to gain a sense of what the termite was doing. These processes—observing and thinking—always precede experimental work. Careful observations help us collect information about the world around us. Thinking about those observations helps us understand the information that we have gathered. Thoughtful observations also tend to point to other questions.

To begin your study of humans, make some preliminary observations and do some thinking about them. Look around you—what evidence do you have that humans are unique?

PROCESS AND PROCEDURES

1. Your teacher will assign teams. With your teammates, conduct a brainstorming session to consider the question, What is it about humans that makes us unique? Imagine that you are describing a human to an alien in outer space. How would you describe humans so that the alien could tell them apart from other animals?

2. Write your team's responses on a large piece of paper and post it in the front of the room. Participate in a class discussion. What common ideas did all teams have? What ideas are unique to each team? What other animals show the same characteristics that you listed as being unique to humans?

3. After the class discussion, choose at least 6 characteristics that all teams agree describe humans.

4. Consider these human characteristics while you listen to or read the narrative that describes Jane Goodall's observations of a family of chimpanzees at the

Figure 1.1
Jane Goodall.
As Goodall studied chimpanzees in the wild, she recorded their every move, interaction, gesture, and grunt. See a page from Dr. Goodall's journal in the essay *The Chimp Scientist* on page 84.

SCENARIO

Chimps at Gombe

Gombe Stream Chimpanzee Reserve, Tanzania, Africa

1980: Nope and Pom, two wild chimpanzees, are feeding quietly. Suddenly a chimp screams in the distance. Pom stares toward the sound, turns to Nope, and grimaces. Then the calls break out again. Now at least two chimps are screaming, one an infant. Above the screams, the observer can hear male barks and whoops of attack. Instantly, Pom leaps to her feet and charges toward the sounds of battle. By the time the observer arrives, it is quiet again, and Pom and her mother, Passion, are grooming each other intently. Pom's little brother, Pax, is close beside them. Both Passion and Pax have fresh, bleeding wounds, but the family is safe and together.

1981: On a blustery morning, Pom's new baby clings tightly to her hair. As the wind starts to die down, he begins to play, venturing out on the limb that he and his mother are sharing. Just then, a violent gust sweeps through the tree and his little body falls spread-eagle through the air. The observer hears a thud and then nothing but silence. Pom looks down at her infant son. Slowly she climbs out of the tree and gathers the tiny form into her arms. For the next 2 hours, she grooms and nurses him. He leans against her body with his eyes closed. Finally, she carries his battered body away. Three days later, he is dead.

1982: Pom is 17 and her brother Pax is still a youngster when their mother, Passion, dies. Passion has been ill for weeks, and now she trembles with every movement. One morning, she is dead. She must have fallen in the night; her body hangs in a tangle of vines. Pom and Pax sit staring at their mother's body. Little Pax repeatedly approaches her and tries to nurse from her cold breasts. Then he starts to scream and pull at her dangling hand. So frantic are his efforts that finally he succeeds in pulling her loose. As Passion sprawls lifeless on the wet ground, her children inspect her body many times. Pax cries softly. At last, just before darkness, Pom and Pax move off together.

1983: Having lost both her baby and her mother, a weak and listless Pom finally leaves the community and is not seen at Gombe again. Pax, on the other hand, attaches himself to an older brother, Prof, who provides the care that a mother chimpanzee would. One day, Pax sneezes loudly. Before the astonished observer can get out the camera, Prof hurries over to Pax and stares at his runny nose. Then, picking up a handful of leaves, Prof carefully wipes the mess away.

Gombe Stream Chimpanzee Reserve in Tanzania, Africa. Think about whether the chimpanzees that Dr. Goodall studied show some of those characteristics. (See *Chimps at Gombe*, above.)

Jane Goodall is a British scientist who began studying chimpanzees in the wild in the 1960s.

5. With your classmates, discuss what thoughts crossed your mind as you listened to this account. Consider the following questions:

   a. Were you surprised by anything that Dr. Goodall observed? If so, what?

   b. Did you find yourself reflecting more on the similarities or on the differences between humans and chimps? Explain your response.

PAGE 84

c. If you had been Dr. Goodall observing this group of chimpanzees, what questions would you now have about these animals? Record in your journal at least 2 questions that you would like to research if you were Dr. Goodall.

Use the essay *The Chimp Scientist* (page 84) as a resource for this discussion.

Analysis

Use the following tasks to analyze the list that you created with your classmates of characteristics that make humans different from other animals. Record your responses in your journal.

1. For each characteristic you have listed, identify and describe a nonhuman animal that also displays that characteristic to some degree.

2. Do you think there is any *one* characteristic that sets humans apart from all other animals? Explain your answer.

Further Challenges

To learn more about Dr. Jane Goodall, check your library for the many books that Dr. Goodall has written and look for information at the Jane Goodall Institute Web site http://www.janegoodall.org. You also may be interested in other scientists who have done or are doing similar work. The American Society for Primatologists maintains a Web site with links to many interesting research projects, scientists, and general information about primates.

Explore

Primates Exploring Primates

In *How Different Are We?*, you read and thought about observations that someone else has made. You have just considered how humans are like and are different from other animals. Now you will have a chance to explore these ideas in more depth and to make some observations of your own. You will observe humans and other related animals as they move about and use tools. You also will compare human brains to those of other organisms. Remember, your goal is to look at humans in the way scientists do. In this activity, you are gathering evidence about the characteristics that set humans apart from other animals and which are shared to some degree.

Materials   (per team of 2)

assortment of objects to grip	padlock and key	DVD and player
masking tape	sheep brain	

PROCESS AND PROCEDURES

Part A   Get a Grip!

1. Spend 10 minutes observing how humans move from place to place. Make a record of these observations in your journal.

   Take the time to notice such things as the different types of strides that are possible and the differences in the way humans use their arms, legs, and feet. You can record observations with words and drawings.

2. Now work with a partner to observe how humans use their hands. Use the objects that your teacher provides to explore the different ways that humans hold and use objects. Record these observations in detail in your journal.

CAUTION: Do not swing, throw, drop, or fool around with any of the objects in a way that might harm you or your classmates.

Warning

3. Watch the DVD segment "Observing Primates." Record your observations of how each primate moves about and uses its arms, legs, hands, and feet. Make the same type of observations for each primate as you made for humans. As you observe humans in this segment on the DVD, add any new observations to those that you made in steps 1 and 2.

   Primates are the group of animals that includes humans, apes, and monkeys, along with a few lesser-known animals. Record as much detail as you can and be sure to label your journal entries clearly so you can tell which observations go with each primate. Pay particular attention to how each primate uses its fingers and thumbs so you can compare those motions to the human grip observations you made earlier.

Topic: scientific investigation
Go to: www.scilinks.org
Code: human3E21

4. With your partner, have a brainstorming session to create a list of all the questions that come to mind about how primates move about and use their hands. Record this list in your journal.

   Come up with at least 5 questions.

5. Science begins with observing and asking questions about the world around us. Then it moves to a stage in which we begin to answer those questions by using a combination of further observation and experimentation. Scientists often have many questions that they would like to answer, but usually they focus their efforts on those that are testable.

   Use the criteria in the need to know box titled Testable Questions to determine which of the questions on your list are testable. Mark these questions with a *T*. Continue to work with your partner.

6. To gain a clearer sense of the nature of a testable question, compare these 2 questions:

   a. What is the importance of an opposable thumb for the ways in which humans use their hands?

   b. Without using your thumbs, can you use a key to open a lock?

      With your partner, discuss which question is easier to test. Explain the reasons for your choice in your journal.

NEED TO KNOW

Testable Questions

a. A question is likely to be testable if it uses question words like *whether, when, where, what, how many, how much,* and *how often,* rather than question words like *why.*

For example, the question, *How many fingers does a gorilla have on its right hand?* suggests an easy way to answer. Yet the question, *Why does a gorilla have four fingers on its right hand?,* does not.

b. If the specific issue to be tested is stated in your question and you list the specific items that will be involved, then your question is likely to be testable.

The question, *How much do gorillas eat?* is not easily tested. A more easily tested version of this question is, *How many pounds of bananas does the largest adult male gorilla in the Portland Zoo eat?*

c. A question is likely to be testable if it describes the conditions under which to conduct the test.

An even better version of the gorilla and banana question would be, *How many pounds of bananas does the largest adult male gorilla in the Portland Zoo eat in 1 week?* This question specifies the conditions that interest us; we are not asking how many pounds of bananas this gorilla would eat in the wild or during his lifetime.

d. A question is likely to be testable if it describes the criteria that will be used to judge the outcome of the test.

Does a half-eaten banana count as having been eaten? How about a banana that is three-quarters eaten? Can you phrase this gorilla and banana question so that it is easier to test than the other questions listed above?

e. A question is likely to be testable if it can be tested using available resources and procedures.

In the end, questions about gorillas and bananas, however testable by some people in some parts of the world, are not testable questions for us in the classroom. All researchers (students and teachers alike) are limited by the resources that they have available.

7. Read through the 5 questions that you recorded in your journal in step 4. Select 1 of your testable questions to use in an experiment, or select the question you chose as most testable in step 6. If you are choosing one of your own questions, have your teacher check your procedure.

Steps a–k in the following protocol box help you investigate whether you can open a lock without using your thumbs. You may be able to modify this protocol to test one of your own questions.

Use the following protocol to test your question.

PROTOCOL

Protocol for Testing the Question

A protocol is a plan or procedure for a basic investigation that can answer a testable question. The protocol also serves as a standard for controlling variables. When you construct a more challenging or creative testable question, you can modify the standard protocol to collect the data you need to answer or better understand your question.

a. Predict what you think the answer to your testable question will be. Record your prediction in your journal, and explain why you have made this prediction.

b. Obtain a lock, a key, and masking tape as your teacher directs.

c. Decide who will carry out the task first and who will keep track of the time and record observations.

d. Be certain that the lock is locked. Place the lock and the key on the table in front of you and your partner.

e. When the person responsible for keeping track of the time says "begin," the person performing the task will pick up the key and attempt to unlock the lock.

This task lasts 30 seconds. The timer/recorder should keep track of the time and record whether or not the person was successful.

f. Switch places and repeat steps d and e.

g. Have 1 person at a time use the masking tape to tape his or her thumbs to 1 side of each hand as shown in Figure 1.2.

You and your partner may need to help each other tape 1 or both hands.

h. Repeat steps d through f.

i. Share your results with the rest of the class, and record the class data in your journal.

j. Analyze your results and those of the rest of the class. Answer your original question, and explain connections between your results and your prediction.

k. Identify the limits, exceptions, or alternate interpretations of the results.

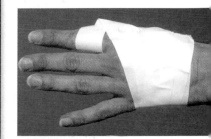

Figure 1.2 Ask your partner to help you tape your thumbs to the sides of your hands as shown. You should not be able to use your thumb at all, but you should be able to move and use each of your other fingers.

8. Read the essay *Do You Have a Grip on That?* on page 86, and with your partner, complete the following in your journal:

PAGE 86

   a. Use the class results to formulate an answer and an explanation to the question you tested.

   b. In what ways do you think the thumb is important to the way humans use their hands?

   c. Look back in your journal at the record of your observations of the way other primates use their hands.

   1) In what ways do they use their thumbs?

   2) How are those ways different from what you just discovered about how humans use their thumbs?

   d. Review the observations of posture and stride that you made for humans and other primates. How is human movement and posture different from that of other primates?

Part B   All Brains on Board

In Part A of this activity, you observed primates by using observational science techniques similar to the ones that Jane Goodall used. In this part of the activity, you will observe the brains of various organisms and compare them to each other. You will use both drawings and the DVD segment "Comparing Brains" for your observations and comparisons. *Mapping the Brain*, page 88 in the essay section, presents general information about the brain that will help you make your observations. Continue to work with your partner throughout this part of the activity; you will need to share sheep brains with other teams.

Warning

1. Examine the sheep brain that your teacher provides. **Be sure to wear gloves when handling the brain and to wash your hands thoroughly at the end of class.**

2. Use the drawing of the sheep brain (Figure 1.3) to study the 2 color-coded regions of the brain. Locate the same 2 regions on the sheep brain that you are examining.

3. As you continue to study the sheep brain, read the essay *Brains and More Brains* (page 89) to learn about the basic functions of these regions of the brain.

4. Compare the color-coded regions of the sheep brain to the color-coded brains of 6 additional organisms. Record your observations in your journal.

   Use the drawings in Figure 1.4 on pages 25 and 26 and the images of brains in the DVD segment "Comparing Brains" to make these comparisons.

5. Create a table in your journal to record your observations so that you can make comparisons more easily. Compare the relative sizes, shapes, and textures of the different regions of the brains. Also, record any unique or distinguishing characteristics that you observe.

6. Using your observations of the various brains, participate in a class discussion of the following questions:

   a. Consider the sheep brain. Which brain of those that you have studied is most like the sheep brain?

   b. Why are some brains similar?

      Use the information you collected in step 4. Make sure you can explain your choices.

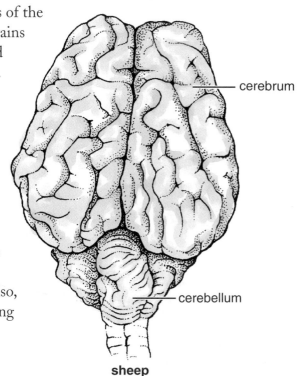

Figure 1.3   Sheep brain (life-sized). Can you find each of these regions on the sheep brain that you are examining?

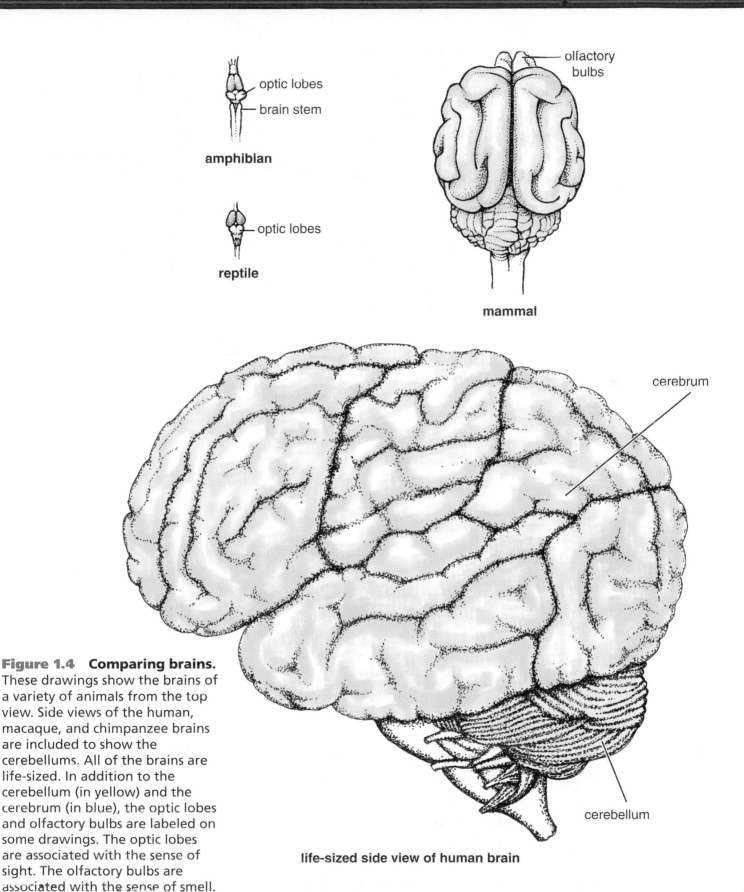

amphibian

optic lobes

brain stem

reptile

optic lobes

mammal

olfactory bulbs

cerebrum

cerebellum

life-sized side view of human brain

Figure 1.4   Comparing brains.
These drawings show the brains of a variety of animals from the top view. Side views of the human, macaque, and chimpanzee brains are included to show the cerebellums. All of the brains are life-sized. In addition to the cerebellum (in yellow) and the cerebrum (in blue), the optic lobes and olfactory bulbs are labeled on some drawings. The optic lobes are associated with the sense of sight. The olfactory bulbs are associated with the sense of smell.

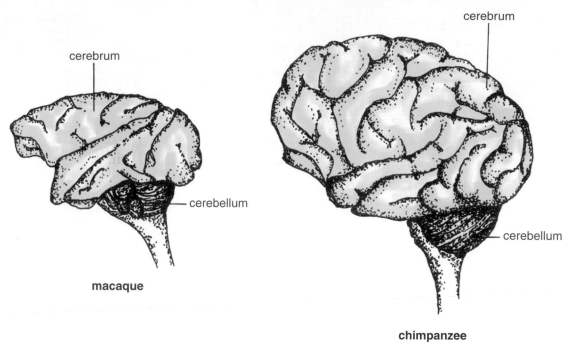

cerebrum

cerebrum

cerebellum

cerebellum

macaque

chimpanzee

Figure 1.4   Comparing brains.   *(continued)*

c. Consider the cerebrum of each animal. Do you observe anything about the human cerebrum that makes it distinctive from the others? If so, what?

d. What did you learn about the function of the cerebrum as you read the essay *Brains and More Brains* that helps you understand why the cerebrum makes humans distinctive?

e. Consider the cerebellum of each animal. Which animals would you expect to have well-developed cerebellums and why?

f. Consider the other observations you made about the brains. What inferences might you make about an animal that has a brain that has very large optic lobes or olfactory bulbs?

Analysis

Discuss the following with your partner, and then record your own answers in your journal:

1. How might the differences that you notice in the behaviors of the animals you studied be related to the differences that you noticed in their brains? Explain your answer.

   To answer this question, use what you know about the behavior of fish, amphibians, reptiles, birds, sheep, other nonhuman mammals, and humans. Think about what you have learned from the observations that you made during this activity.

2. List two additional questions that you have about the brain as a result of your observations and readings in this activity.

Further Challenges

1. If you want to learn more about the way humans use their hands, revisit the essay *Do You Have a Grip on That?* (page 86). When you have finished reading, review the DVD segment "Observing Primates" and see which grips you observe other primates using.

2. Visit a zoo and make detailed observations of the way various primates or other animals move. You could record your observations in writing, drawings, or video.

3. Develop an experiment designed to answer another one of your testable questions from this activity.

Tony's Brain

Explain

"Have you lost your mind?"
"Make up your mind."
"Do you mind?"
"Mind your manners!"
"I'll give you a piece of my mind!"

The meanings of these common phrases might seem obvious, but consider whether the location or the function of the human mind is obvious. In the last activity, you observed the brains of many animals, but did you observe their minds? Could you infer something about the animals' minds from the brain observations that you made? Moreover, what is the relationship between the mind and the large complex brain that is one of the distinguishing characteristics of humans?

In this activity, you will explore the relationship of the human brain to the mind by trying to discover the causes for a problem involving the mind and the brain of a teenager named Tony. To complete this task, you will need to make observations and gather evidence. You will use the observations that you make and the evidence that you gather to make inferences about Tony's problem. That is, you will use evidence to develop an explanation of what caused the particular problem with his mind. You also will explore how explanations can change when more observations and evidence become available.

Materials

DVD and player

PROCESS AND PROCEDURES

Part A   Making Sense of Words

1. With your team of 4, consider the words *brain* and *mind*. Try to develop 1 consensus definition for each word. The definition should be acceptable to all members of your team. Record your definitions for both brain and mind in your journal.

2. Meet with another team to compare your definitions. Explain why your team defined brain and mind as it did.

Part B   A Problem and Possible Explanations

1. Read the following scenario:

SCENARIO

Tony's Unusual Behavior

Tony is one of your best friends. For years, you have known him as a happy, generous, and sometimes shy person. For most of his life, Tony has enjoyed relatively good health. He is active in your school's drama club and plays on the baseball team.

Recently, Tony celebrated his 15th birthday. Soon afterward, you noticed that he began to exhibit strange behaviors. His sister told you that he has nightmares, repeated insomnia, and an overall nervousness. At times, you see that Tony is ecstatically happy. At other times, he seems depressed and sad. You are very worried about your friend.

During the course of several months, Tony continues to show increasing signs of unusual behavior. His mood swings become more dramatic and more frequent. During his winter vacation, Tony doesn't even get out of bed.

2. Think of explanations that might account for Tony's behavior and contribute them to a class list.

Generate as many explanations as possible. At this point, do not discuss which explanations are better than others.

3. Discuss the following question with your team:
Why would it be unscientific to strongly support 1 of these explanations over all the others?

Each member of the team should take a turn giving his or her reasons.

4. Read the information on Copymaster *Personal Interview with Tony* to help you understand more about Tony's condition. Then, with your teammates, modify the list of explanations so it contains only those that are still reasonable in light of this new information.

Where possible, support an explanation by including evidence that you found in the conversation.

5. With your class, watch the DVD segment "Behavioral Disorders and the Brain." Then, with your team, decide whether to revise your list again.

Information in Copymaster *Some Disorders of the Mind and Brain* may help you with this task. Use what you have learned to determine the part of Tony's brain that is most likely affected by the illness. You can draw a diagram of the brain or write an explanation on your worksheet, but be certain to include evidence that supports your decision.

6. Read the additional information on Copymaster *Results of the Doctors' Investigations of Tony's Behavior.* Revise your list again by crossing out any explanations that are no longer consistent with the new evidence.

7. With your team, draw a conclusion about which disorders from the table in *Some Disorders of the Mind and Brain* that Tony most likely suffers from. List 3 pieces of evidence that support your conclusion. On your team's worksheet, record your team's consensus conclusion.

8. Imagine that your team is the group of doctors treating Tony. Develop a plan to determine if your diagnosis is correct.

Analysis

Topic: mind/brain
Go to: www.scilinks.org
Code: human3E29

With your team, consider the following questions and record your responses in your journal:

1. It appears that Tony's mind was affected by his illness because his feelings and behaviors changed so dramatically. At the same time, there is medical evidence of physical changes in his brain. Based on your analysis of the brain/mind connection, explain whether or not you would now change your original definitions for brain and mind.

2. In this activity, you conducted an analysis using **inductive reasoning**. This means that you made observations and collected evidence in an effort to explain Tony's unusual behavior. How does new information affect the conclusions that people might draw through inductive reasoning? When can you be certain that you have arrived at the correct explanation for a problem like Tony's?

   It might help to consider where the mind and brain are located and what their relationship is. Also, consider these questions: Under what conditions does the brain cease to exist? Under what conditions does the mind cease to exist?

3. As humans age, the brain undergoes changes that, in some individuals, can affect a person's memory. Some people might also respond more slowly to certain things. These difficulties can be caused by a slight decrease in the number of neurons or in their connections in some areas of the brain. These changes are normal.

   In the brains of people who have Alzheimer's disease, however, more extensive changes take place. Changes that happen in the producton of two proteins lead to the buildup of plaque and "tangles" that affect the neurons' ability to function. These neurons cannot communicate normally with other neurons. As a result of this buildup, the neurons eventually die from impaired function. We see evidence of this neuron death as shrinkage of the cerebral hemispheres.

   Think about what you have learned about the brain and mind in the last two activities. Explain how the changes in the brain of a person with Alzheimer's disease relate to the changes in the function of the person's mind.

Portraying Humankind

By now, you have some idea of the range and subtlety of characteristics that make humans human. You have made observations of humans, other primates, and a collection of brains, and you have reflected on the similarities and differences that emerged. In the upcoming activity, *A Long Childhood*, you will continue to learn about characteristics that are unique to humans. When you have completed this chapter, you will present a special project to your class to show that you understand what it means to be human.

Select a medium that you are comfortable with to create your project. Some possibilities include a poster, a diorama, a poem, a story, a report, a musical piece, a play, a TV show, or a video. As you think about and plan your project, use the criteria in the rubric provided by your teacher to guide your work.

Materials   (per person or team of 2)

You may need an assortment of materials to help you create your project.

poster board	old photographs	tape recorder	DVD and player
markers	musical instruments	magazines	
glue	video camera	cardboard boxes	

PROCESS AND PROCEDURES

1. Think about designing a project to illustrate your understanding of what it means to be human.

   Think of an activity that you enjoy doing and consider what it is about being human that makes it possible for you to do this activity. Perhaps you can incorporate a demonstration or description of this activity into your project and presentation.

2. When you have a general idea in mind, share your idea with your partner.

3. Obtain a copy of the rubric that your teacher will use to evaluate your project. To meet the criteria for this project, be sure that you understand and can explain the following ideas to your partner:

   ◆ How humans are structured to be bipedal.

   ◆ How the human hand is similar to and different from the hands of other primates.

   ◆ How different parts of the cerebrum are associated with various behaviors.

   ◆ How different parts of the human brain are similar to and different from the brains of other primates.

   ◆ How nerves transmit information.

   ◆ Why the human brain is responsible for complex human behavior.

   The essays *On Being Human* (page 92) and *Brains and a Lot of Nerve* (page 95) and the DVD segment "More About the Brain" will help broaden your understanding of these ideas. As you watch the DVD segments, practice your observation skills. Record notes in your journal.

PAGE 92   PAGE 95

4. Write a short description of your project in your journal. List 4 or 5 concepts from the essays and the previous activities that you plan to incorporate into your project.

Analysis

Complete this analysis according to your teacher's directions.

1. Meet with your partner and exchange written descriptions of your projects.

    a. Read your partner's description.

    b. If something about your partner's project is unclear to you, ask questions of him or her.

    c. Review the criteria for the project that are listed in the rubric provided by your teacher. Tell your partner how well you think his or her proposed project meets them.

    d. Make suggestions that you think would contribute to your partner's project.

2. According to the feedback that you receive from your partner, revise or add to your description.

You will present your project to the class as the evaluate activity for this chapter.

A Long Childhood

Elaborate

Have you noticed that puppies may be separated from their mother within 2 months of birth, and a newborn foal will be up and walking around within minutes of its birth? A human child, however, usually will stay with its mother for years and does not begin to walk until it is close to 1 year old. Have you ever wondered why this is so?

The collection of physical characteristics that sets humans apart from other organisms results in some behavioral differences as well. You have explored various aspects of the human brain and have compared it with the brains of other organisms. But what does that really mean? How do the features of the human brain contribute to behaviors that make us different? Could these differences have anything to do with our long childhoods? In this activity, you will explore some possible answers to those questions and no doubt will come up with more intriguing questions of your own.

Materials

You will need resources on the development of other animals after birth.

PROCESS AND PROCEDURES

1. Participate in a class discussion and answer the following questions as they apply to humans:

    a. What is the length of pregnancy?

	Length of pregnancy	Get food	Completely mobile	Sexually mature
Humans				

Figure 1.5 Sample table of information on animals. A table similar to this one will help you organize your information in a way that makes it easy to use.

   b. At what age do the young stop nursing or are able to get food on their own?

   c. At what age are the young completely and independently mobile?

   d. At what age do individuals become sexually mature?

2. Record the answers to those questions in your journal.

   You also will collect this information for other animals, so create a table in which to organize and record all of the information. You may want to arrange the questions across the top and list the animals in the left column as in Figure 1.5.

3. Select another animal and answer the questions in step 1 for that animal.

   Use the resources that your teacher provides or resources from the library.

4. Contribute your answers to a class data table.

   Record the class data in your own data table.

5. With your classmates, discuss what patterns emerge as you compare the data for humans with those of the other animals.

   Use the data to identify the animals that have long "childhoods."

PAGE 98

6. With a partner, discuss the question, What are some of the things that happen as the result of a long childhood in humans? Record your ideas in your journal.

   Use the essay *The Importance of Being Children* (page 98) as a resource.

Analysis

   Think about how you will fold your ideas developed in this activity into the project you began in the activity *Portraying Humankind*.

   1. To help you do this, discuss the following questions with a classmate:

      a. How does a long childhood help humans develop complex culture?

      b. How does our language ability help us develop complex culture?

c. How does our ability to learn help us develop complex culture?

d. Give three examples of different ways that humans learn. How do you learn best?

e. Give two examples of other animals that exhibit a certain capacity for learning, language, and culture.

f. How different are humans and other animals? How alike are they? Support your answers with new information that you have learned in this activity.

2. Decide how you will fold some of these expanded ideas into your project. Then add this information to your written description for the project.

3. Have your teacher approve your completed plan for the project.

4. Work on your project as your teacher directs.

Topic: animal adaptations
Go to: www.scilinks.org
Code: human3E33

Further Challenges

1. Together with other interested classmates, find out about the existence of culture and society in other animals.

2. Do further library research on the learning abilities of other primates or dolphins.

3. Learn more about your own learning style. Your teacher may have some resources to get you started.

    Your learning style is the way you prefer to learn. There are questionnaires you can take to find out more about how your brain works best for learning new information.

What Does It Mean to Be Human?

Evaluate

In this activity, you will demonstrate what you have learned in Chapter 1. You will use your projects to show how this new knowledge helped you answer the question, What does it mean to be human?, from a scientific perspective.

PROCESS AND PROCEDURES

1. Present the project that you began in the activity *Portraying Humankind* to your classmates according to your teacher's directions.

2. Using the criteria given to you by your teacher, identify what you think are the 3 strongest projects in your class. List these in your journal and justify your choices.

Analysis

Use the same criteria to rate your own project and presentation. Explain your rating in your journal.

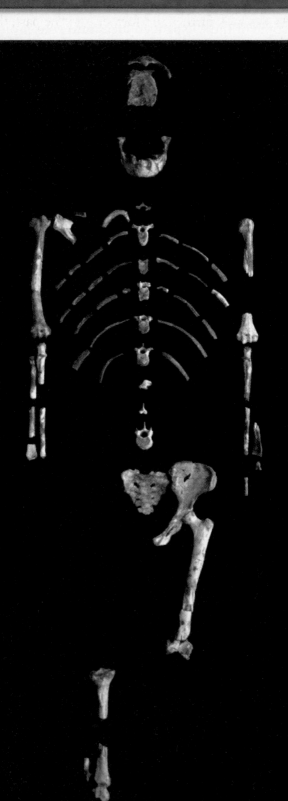

"... just as he was about to quit searching for the day, he noticed part of a fossilized arm bone just lying on the ground partway up the slope of a gully."

Evolution: Change across Time

Fossil skeletons like the one shown here provide a tremendous opportunity for scientists to study the physical characteristics of organisms that lived long ago. Such studies reveal an interesting fact. As you look further and further into the past, the skeletons of ancient organisms look less and less like organisms that are alive today. This is because populations of living organisms change across time. In this chapter, you will begin to understand how living organisms change and why change is important to understanding the relationships between biological systems.

We begin the chapter with a look at Lucy, the fossil skeleton of an ancient humanlike organism shown here. We ask that you imagine how she may have looked and behaved at the time she lived. Next, you will construct a timeline of earth's history and in doing so, gain an appreciation for the vast time spans required for geological and evolutionary change. After modeling geologic time, you will explore some of the biological, geological, and anthropological evidence for evolution by becoming a specialist in one of these scientific disciplines. Your studies will lead you to think about cultural evolution—the rapid, nonbiological changes at which humans excel. Finally, you will evaluate your understanding of evolution by analyzing an important modern example of evolution in action.

ACTIVITIES

Engage	Lucy
Explore	Modeling the Earth's History
Explore **Explain**	Evidence for Change across Time
Explain	Explaining Evolution
Elaborate	Modeling Natural Selection
Elaborate	A Cold Hard Look at Culture
Evaluate	Evolution in Action

Digging Up the Past

No one knows how Lucy died. She apparently died quietly. If a lion or a leopard had killed her, her bones probably would have been splintered and crushed. Hyenas had not scavenged her, or her skeletal parts would have been scattered over a wide area. Instead, she died by the edge of an ancient lake where mud and sand covered her. She remained buried for almost 3.5 million years.

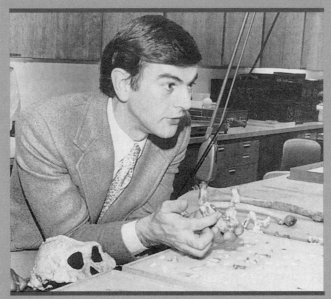

Lucy lived in what is today the Afar desert, a remote region of northeastern Ethiopia in East Africa (see map in Figure 2.1). The large lake that once existed there has long since dried up, and the area is now hot and desertlike. Even though she was fully grown and probably in her 20s when she died, Lucy stood only three and one-half feet tall. Her head was a bit larger than a softball, and her brain could not have been much larger than that of a modern chimpanzee. The shapes of her knee joint and pelvis bones indicate that she walked upright on two legs. For more than 3 million years, Lucy remained buried in the ancient lakebed.

In 1973, Donald Johanson (pictured above), a young anthropologist from the United States, arrived in Ethiopia to look for fossils. Working with two Frenchmen, Maurice Taieb and Yves Coppens, Johanson found a primitive primate knee joint that had washed out of a slope during a rain. It seldom rains in the Afar desert, but when it does, the rain is heavy, cutting gullies into the gravel and bare rock. On very rare occasions, these rains uncover ancient fossils, and as luck would have it, such a rain occurred not long before Johanson's arrival. This fossil knee joint was intriguing because it was about 3 million years old, and its structure indicated that this individual had walked erect.

Because of this find, Johanson decided to return to the same ancient lakebed the following year to continue the search. If any more humanlike fossils were embedded in the ground, they might be of a similar age. Johanson and his colleague, Tom Gray, had been searching all fall with no success when they parked their vehicle on the slope of a gully on the morning of November 30, 1974.

The temperature had reached 43°C (110°F), and they were about to return to camp when Johanson noticed part of a fossilized arm bone lying on the ground partway up the slope of a gully. As he searched further, he found pieces of a skull, thighbone, and pelvis, along with other skeletal parts but no evidence of any tools. Remarkably, the skeletal parts all seemed to be from one individual, and a very humanlike individual at that. The two scientists barely could contain their excitement. They named the skeleton "Lucy," after a song that was popular at the time. This skeleton (shown in the opening photo) has become one of the most famous fossils found of an early humanlike animal.

What did this new find mean in terms of human origins? Did gradual changes in animals such as Lucy eventually lead to modern humans? Some of the answers had to wait until Johanson returned to his lab at the Cleveland Museum of Natural History. There, he and his colleagues spent many months in painstaking detective work, comparing Lucy with other fossils of more recent human ancestors as well as with modern human and ape skeletons. Johanson's conclusions sharpened the debate within the scientific community about exactly when the human line split from the ape line. Most scientists agree that at a very early time, there was a single primate ancestor to both modern humans and modern apes.

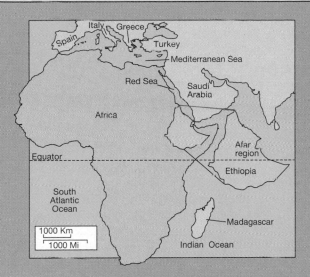

Figure 2.1 Map of the Afar region in Ethiopia.

Recent fossil discoveries continue to add evidence to the scientific explanation of human origins. In 1994, paleontologist Tim White discovered a new species of hominid in Ethiopia. Named *Ardipithecus ramidus*, it dates from 4.4 million years ago. In 2000, a team led by Brigitte Senut and Martin Pickford found another fossil that dates from 6 million years ago. Scientists are debating whether this fossil is a hominid or a chimp ancestor. In the summer of 2002, paleontologists from France discovered another hominid fossil in Chad, a country in north central Africa, that dates from 6–7 million years ago. Scientists are still working to resolve when both chimps and humans split from a common ancestor. The recent find of fossils from about 6 million years ago suggests that a common ancestor was at least that old.

Will we discover more fossil remains that link humans and our most ancient ancestors? If so, will those remains help to resolve the dispute about this timing? Perhaps a future anthropologist will discover more clues and new ways to examine our existing evidence to clarify further the details of our origins.

Lucy

Since the mid-1800s, scientists have been piecing together the puzzle of human evolution. Some of the most important pieces of this complex puzzle are the fossilized skeletal remains of individuals who lived millions of years ago. Dated at about 3.4 million years old, Lucy is one of the oldest and most complete hominid fossils. **Hominids** are erect-walking primates that include modern humans, earlier human species, and early humanlike species.

In this activity, you will think about how Lucy may have looked and behaved while she was alive, and you will begin to appreciate how much humans have changed across time.

PROCESS AND PROCEDURES

1. Describe in your journal how Lucy may have looked. Explain 3 things she might have done during a typical day and how she would have gone about doing them.

   Use the photograph of the fossil skeleton in the opening photo to this chapter and your notes from Chapter 1 to help you develop your description. Pay particular attention to Lucy's hands, feet, posture, and way of moving. Try to describe how she may have communicated with family members and others living in her group.

2. Consider the following question and record your answer in your journal:

   What evidence from the Lucy find could help scientists develop an explanation about the gap between modern humans and early nonhuman primates?

NEED TO KNOW

Evidence and Inference

When scientists find skeletal remains, they work carefully to gather as much information as possible from their findings. Often the skeletal remains are incomplete, but such remains are **evidence** from which the scientists can draw conclusions about the individual. Scientists try to be aware of their own strong beliefs, moods, and prior experiences when they search for and find evidence because these factors can influence their observations. Conclusions that follow logically from some form of direct evidence are known as **inferences**. (Conclusions that do not follow logically from evidence are just guesses. Guessing is not an acceptable way to draw scientific conclusions.) For example, scientists have made inferences based on skeletal evidence about how tall an individual was and whether or not the individual was bipedal. Fossil evidence and inferences based on this evidence may support a current theory about human origins or may point to new ideas.

Analysis

Use the information from your description to answer the following questions as part of a class discussion:

1. Compare hominids from Lucy's lifetime to your own. Do you think there have been more changes in physical characteristics of the body (such as hands, feet, head, posture) or more changes in how hominids lived (types of shelter, ways of getting around, ways of gathering food)?

2. Use the information in the need to know box to help you answer these questions:

   a. Which aspects of your descriptions did you base on evidence?

   b. Which aspects of your descriptions were inferences related to evidence?

   c. Which aspects of your descriptions were guesses?

Explore

Modeling the Earth's History

The Lucy fossil is extremely old, more than 3 million years old. According to geologists, however, the earth formed 4.6 billion years ago. This is a time span that is difficult to comprehend because time for humans generally means tens and hundreds of years. The time span of the earth's history is called **geologic time**. One way to grasp the immensity of the earth's history is through a timeline. In this activity, you will develop a timeline of the earth's history to help you better understand when certain human events and major geological and biological events occurred. This timeline should help you appreciate geologic time and the changes that have taken place since the formation of the earth.

Materials   (per team of 4)

10 clothespins or paper clips (optional)
event cards that your teacher provides

PROCESS AND PROCEDURES

1. Discuss the following question with your teammates:
   How long ago do you think each of the following events took place and in what sequence?

   ◆ First dinosaurs
   ◆ Formation of Rocky Mountains
   ◆ First hominids
   ◆ First life (bacteria)
   ◆ First modern humans
   ◆ First oxygen in atmosphere
   ◆ First land plants

2. Make a list of the events in the order that your team thinks they happened.

   List the most recent event first. Write large enough that the class will be able to read your list when you post it at the front of the class. Next to each event, record the number of years ago that your team thinks each event took place.

3. Post your team's list of events at the front of the class as your teacher directs. Compare your team's estimated times and sequence with those of other teams. Then discuss the questions below with your teammates.

   a. Consider your estimates. Explain whether they were guesses or logical conclusions based on evidence.

   b. Why did your team's estimates differ from those of other teams?

4. Examine the table *Major Events in the Earth's History* that your teacher provides, and answer the following question in your journal:

   Which times or sequences of occurrence surprised you?

   Scientists use several tools to think about geologic time. One of these tools is the use of evidence and inference. This table is based on inferences from evidence that scientists have gathered about the history of the earth and its living organisms. It also is based on theories that geologists and paleontologists have developed about the time spans and patterns of change in the earth's history. For those reasons, the dates in this table are more accurate than guesses.

5. Study the marked clothesline that your teacher has prepared. Discuss with your teammates how it might be used to represent the events listed in Copymaster *Major Events in the Earth's History*.

6. Study the event cards that your teacher provides.

   Fold each card in half, crosswise, to form a tent.

NEED TO KNOW

A Type of Model

A second tool used by scientists to think about geologic time is a **model**—that is, a simple system or situation that mimics a more complex system or situation.

You can make a more useful comparison of the events in the table by constructing a timeline. A timeline is a type of model that shows when events took place in relationship to each other. Because the length of a timeline corresponds to time, a timeline offers a simple, visual way to picture how much time separated certain events in the past. Figure 2.2 is a small version of the timeline that you will work with in class.

The distance between the red marks on the clothesline represents 1 billion years. The distance between the short black marks represents 100 million years. Your teacher has marked the timeline at 5 billion years ago and at the present.

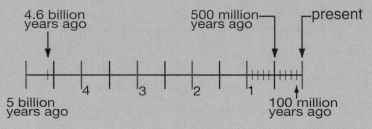

Figure 2.2 Timeline of earth's history.

7. Decide where on the timeline each event card should go, and place your cards in the appropriate locations.

   Use the information in the table of events to help you decide. Beneath the name of the event on each card, write the number of years ago that each event occurred. Carefully locate the correct time on the timeline. Fasten your event cards to the timeline as your teacher directs.

Analysis

Use the timeline that you just created to answer the following questions with your teammates, and then participate in a class discussion:

1. Look for and describe the following patterns on the timeline:
   a. Relationships between geological and biological events
   b. Relationships between plant and animal events
   c. One or two additional patterns that you see on the timeline
2. Is it likely that these patterns occurred separately, or do you think they might be related? Explain.
3. Are the patterns that you chose to describe evidence, or were there inferences involved in finding and describing the patterns?
4. What did the timeline (a model) help you understand about the earth's history?

Evidence for Change across Time

Explore

Explain

What has changed in your lifetime? Throughout history, people have found the changes that take place around them intriguing. For thousands of years, people have been noticing, recording, and trying to explain the various changes that they observe in nature. These changes include routine changes, such as the patterns of day and night, the phases of the moon, and the changing seasons. They also include devastating changes, such as erupting volcanoes, earthquakes, and floods.

Changes may be rapid (a 30-second earthquake changes the environment), or they may be slow (leaves changing color in the fall and falling off the trees). The biological changes of evolution generally are very slow. The story of Lucy and other hominids provides us with an idea of some biological changes that have taken place during the past 6 million years. To appreciate those changes, we first must understand the process of biological change across time.

In this activity, you will assume the role of a specialist and work with other specialists to study the evidence that scientists have accumulated about biological change. As you and your teammates study your data, you will begin to see how combinations of evidence from several branches of science can support an explanation. Your team of specialists will use this collection of evidence to develop a presentation about the theory of evolution.

After you have learned about the jobs that each of the specialists do, you will write a story about a fossil find. In your story, you will explain how scientists from each of the four scientific fields that you have studied would contribute to finding and analyzing the fossil.

PROCESS AND PROCEDURES

1. Each member of your team will take on a different job. You will each become a specialist and learn about a different field of science.

    Each team member from your group will join team members from other groups who are studying the same field of science. After everyone has had time to study his or her special field of science, your original team will get back together so that you can teach each other what you have learned.

2. With your team, decide who will become each specialist:

    ◆ Paleontologist: The scientist who investigates biological change by studying fossils and the history of the earth.

    ◆ Evolutionary biologist: The scientist who studies the origins and relatedness of living organisms.

    ◆ Developmental biologist: The scientist who studies how the processes of growth and development occur and change over time.

    ◆ Physical anthropologist: The scientist who studies the biological evolution of humans.

3. Meet with the members of other teams who have assumed the same role that you have, and together read and study the information assigned to your role. As you work with your team, make certain that everyone contributes ideas. *Then go to the procedural section that follows step 7.*

   You will be responsible for sharing the information with your original teammates.

4. When you complete your specialist work, return to your team and begin step 5.

5. Share your information with your original team. Discuss how each set of information represents evidence that supports the concept of change across time. Also, discuss how the collection of evidence is stronger than any of the separate pieces.

6. Create a data table or diagram, like the one shown in Figure 2.3, to help you keep track of this collection of information.

   Make certain that you learn all about the scientific evidence for evolution that is contributed by each type of scientist.

7. After all team members have taught their teams about their scientific specialty, you will write a short story about a fossil find. In the story that you write, you will show what you have learned in this activity by explaining the evidence that a paleontologist, evolutionary biologist, developmental biologist, and physical anthropologist would gain from such a fossil find.

	Developmental biologist	Evolutionary biologist	Paleontologist	Physical anthropologist
Evidence				

Figure 2.3 Evidence for change across time. Draw a table like this in your journal to help you keep track of each specialist's evidence for change across time.

PROCEDURES FOR THE SPECIALISTS

 Paleontologists

Paleontologists are scientists who specialize in the study of fossils and the history of life. Much as detectives reconstruct a crime from the evidence left behind, paleontologists search for clues to biological change by studying the fossils. Geologists are scientists who study the origin, history, and structure of the earth. In your role as a paleontologist, you will examine both geologic and fossil evidence because understanding biological change requires an understanding of geological change.

Materials

glass beaker with strata (prepared by your teacher)
empty glass beaker (1 for 2 students)
strata materials
set of colored envelopes (1 for 2 students)
poster board (1 piece for 2 students)
DVD and player (watch as a team)

1. Read the Copymaster *Interview with a Paleontologist*. Think about how you will explain the job of a paleontologist to your teammates.

2. Complete the following activities with the other paleontologist in your group. Geologists use an indirect method of dating rocks and fossils called **stratigraphy**. Stratigraphy is the study of strata on earth. **Strata** are layers. For this task, you will study a model of earth's strata.

   a. Observe the beaker of strata provided by your teacher. Work with 1 other team member to make an exact copy of the strata and its markers in your own beaker.

      Look closely at the layers. Make your beaker's layers match as closely as possible.

   b. Answer the following questions about your beaker and its strata:

      1) Which layer of materials is the oldest (has been in the beaker the longest)?

      2) If these strata were layers in the earth's surface, what inferences might you make about the relationship between the depth of the layer and the amount of time that has passed?

   c. Consider the locations of the 3 colored markers that you placed in the strata. If you found these colored markers in earth's strata, which would you infer to be oldest?

Topic: paleontology
Go to: www.scilinks.org
Code: human3E43

Topic: fossils
Go to: www.scilinks.org
Code: human3E44a

Topic: radioactive dating
Go to: www.scilinks.org
Code: human3E44b

PAGE 102   PAGE 104

Topic: plate tectonics
Go to: www.scilinks.org
Code: human3E44c

d. Obtain 3 colored envelopes from your teacher. Each envelope corresponds to 1 of the colored markers in your strata.

e. Imagine that each envelope represents a fossil discovery. Which "fossil" would be the oldest? Which would have formed most recently?

f. Open the envelopes and carefully observe the fossil pictures in each.

g. In your journal, compare each fossil with each of the others and with modern-day organisms. What similarities and differences do you observe?

   Hint: Consider how the fossils look and their relative ages.

3. Work with another paleontologist to create a poster that you can use to explain to your classmates how fossils form and how they can be dated.

   Use the essays *Fossils: Traces of Life Gone By* (page 102) and *Technologies That Strengthen Fossil Evidence* (page 104) as resources.

4. When the DVD player becomes available, watch the DVD about plate tectonics (formerly thought of as continental drift) and think about the changes that the continents have undergone over time.

   a. In your journal, explain how the movement and separation of continents affected the organisms living on land in earth's distant past.

   b. Add information to your poster about how the evidence for plate tectonics contributes to the theory of evolution.

5. Check that you have completed all the steps for the paleontologists. Finish preparing your poster to use as a visual aid when you teach your original team about paleontology. Return to step 5 in the general procedure.

◆ Evolutionary Biologists

Evolutionary biologists are scientists who study how living organisms change physically over time.

Materials

Topic: evolutionary biology
Go to: www.scilinks.org
Code: human3E44d

dissecting tray and tools
chicken wing (1 wing for 2 students)
animal limbs handout
colored pencils
envelope containing examples of vestigial structures
poster board (1 piece for 2 students)

1. Read the Copymaster *Interview with an Evolutionary Biologist*. Think about how you will explain the job of an evolutionary biologist to your teammates.

2. Complete the following activities with the other evolutionary biologists in your group:

   a. Work with a partner from your group to dissect a chicken wing carefully.

   As you complete the dissection, compare the bones that you find with the chicken wing anatomy diagram provided by your teacher.

   b. Locate the bones listed in the bird wing anatomy diagram, and color them in using the colored pencils.

   Color-code the diagram so that each of the underlined bones is a different color.

   c. Wash your hands with soap. Next, obtain 1 bat wing diagram and 1 human hand diagram and their keys.

   d. With your partner, color the bones of the bat wing and human hand with the same color coding that you used on the chicken wing diagram.

   e. In your journal, explain the similarities that you found between a human hand, a bat wing, and a chicken wing.

   f. Mount your diagrams on a poster board to share with your classmates.

3. Read about homologous structures and vestigial structures in the essay *Modern Life: Evidence for Evolutionary Change* on page 107.

   a. On the diagram that you colored, are the parts of the animal limbs homologous or vestigial? Why do you think so?

   b. Title your poster with the correct term (homologous or vestigial structures), and write a definition for the term in your own words beneath the title.

4. Obtain an envelope containing examples of vestigial structures. Study the structures inside.

   a. On the handout showing human vestigial structures, write a brief, logical explanation about why each of the structures is considered vestigial.

   b. On the handout showing vestigial hind limbs in whales and snakes, write a brief, logical explanation for why these hind limb bones are considered vestigial.

   Use the information in the essay *Modern Life: Evidence for Evolutionary Change* on page 107 to help you write your explanations.

5. Make a poster about vestigial structures on the back of your poster about homologous structures.

6. Check over your posters. You will use your posters to teach your original team about the evidence contributed by evolutionary biologists to the theory of evolution. Return to step 5 in the general procedure.

◆ Developmental Biologists

Developmental biologists are scientists who study the stages of growth and development that living organisms pass through as they grow from fertilized egg to mature adult and beyond.

Topic: homologous and vestigial structures
Go to: www.scilinks.org
Code: human3E45

PAGE 107

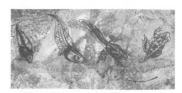

Materials

embryo puzzle (1 per 2 students)
DNA handout
poster board (1 piece per 2 students)
DVD and player (watch as a team)

1. Read the Copymaster *Interview with a Developmental Biologist*. Think about how you will explain the job of a developmental biologist to your teammates.

2. Complete these activities with the other developmental biologists in your group.

   a. Read the information in the need to know box in your group.

NEED TO KNOW

EMBRYOLOGY

Embryology is the branch of developmental biology that focuses on the early development of organisms before they are born or hatched. During this prebirth or prehatching stage, scientists call the developing organisms *embryos*. Scientists can compare the developing embryos of organisms as diverse as fish, amphibians, reptiles, birds, and mammals. They find that the embryos of these vertebrate animals (animals that have backbones) resemble each other.

Make certain that everyone understands these concepts before continuing to step b.

   b. Study the individual drawings of embryos that your teacher provides. Try to arrange all of the embryonic stages in a developmental order for each animal. When you have finished, your arrangement should show 3 stages of embryonic development for a fish, a frog, a chicken, a calf, and a human.

   These drawings depict various embryonic stages of 5 different vertebrates. These stages are relative. They do not represent the same point in time, but rather the same relative amount of development.

   c. Compare your arrangement with the illustration that your teacher provides.

   d. Discuss the following questions in your group, and record your answers in your journal:

   1) In general, which organisms have embryonic stages that are the most similar? The least similar? Explain your answers.

   2) What do you think these similarities and differences tell scientists about how these organisms have changed across time and how they are related?

   Consider whether you expect related organisms to look similar or not. Would you also expect related organisms to go through similar stages of development? Consider the later stages of development. Do the more closely related organisms look more or less similar?

e. Study the segment "Embryology" on the DVD. Compare the images to the ones you have assembled by answering the following questions:

   1) Do the images on the DVD help you to see other similarities and differences that are not apparent in the drawings? Record your observations in your journal.

   2) Work with 1 other developmental biologist from your team to make a poster that you will use to teach your original team about embryology.

      Your poster should show the embryo stages that you studied. It also should include a summary of how comparing the development of embryos contributes to scientists' understandings of how populations of species have changed over time.

3. Read the essay *Modern Life: Evidence for Evolutionary Change* on page 107.

  a. In your journal, explain where DNA is located and what its purpose is.

  b. Obtain a handout from your teacher that shows a comparison of the DNA that codes for the α and β hemoglobin proteins that are found in primate blood.

    Compare the DNA from the different primate species. Determine which primates are most similar and which are most different.

  c. Discuss this information with your partner and summarize your understanding of this evidence in your journal.

    Use the information in the essay *Modern Life: Evidence for Evolutionary Change* on page 107 to help you interpret the DNA handout.

  d. Add to your poster the DNA handout and a brief summary about how DNA analysis contributes evidence to the theory of evolution.

4. Review your poster and your journal notes. You will use this information to teach your original team about how developmental biologists contribute to understanding evolution. Return to step 5 in the general procedure.

◆ Physical Anthropologists

Physical anthropologists are scientists who study how humans have changed biologically over time.

Materials

DVD and player (watch as a team)
small rulers
protractors
pictures of selected human, chimpanzee, and mystery bones (1 set per 2 students)
poster board (1 piece per 2 students)

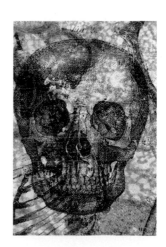

1. Read the Copymaster *Interview with a Physical Anthropologist*. Think about how you will explain the job of an anthropologist to your teammates.

The SciLinks box reads:
SCLINKS
NSTA
Topic: DNA
Go to: www.scilinks.org
Code: human3E47

2. Complete the following activities with the other physical anthropologists in your group:

   a. Obtain an envelope that contains pictures of selected human, chimpanzee, and mystery bones for yourself and 1 partner.

      1) Carefully observe the human and chimpanzee bones for similarities and differences.

      2) Compare each of the mystery bones to the human and chimpanzee bones. Make a table in your journal. List each mystery bone as either more like human bones, more like chimpanzee bones, or not like either human or chimpanzee bones.

      3) Based on your observations, write a feasible explanation in your journal for how the mystery fossil bones might be related to humans and chimpanzees.

   b. When available, view the image sequence "Hominid Skulls" on the DVD and make observations. As you compare the skulls, focus on the features listed below, make measurements where appropriate, and record the information in your journal.

      ◆ Size of lower jaw

      ◆ Prominence of brow ridges

      ◆ Slope of face

      ◆ Width of face

      ◆ Size of forehead

      ◆ Size of brain case

      ◆ Size of molars

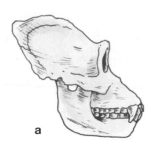

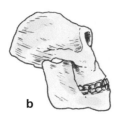

Figure 2.4 Compare the features on these gorilla (**a**) and early hominid (**b**) skulls.

Use the sketches of skulls in Figure 2.4 to help you determine which measurements to make. Create a data table like the one in Figure 2.5 to record your results. Review the sequence of skulls or individual frames as many times as necessary to make your comparisons.

Trait	Fossil name
Jaw size	
Brow ridge	
Slope of face	
Face width	
Forehead size	
Brain case size	
Molar size	

Figure 2.5   Record of fossil measurements.

c. Read the essay *Primates Show Change across Time* (page 110), and discuss the following questions in your group. Record your ideas in your journal.

PAGE 110

1) What evidence did you find in the essay and in your observations of the hominid skulls that indicates change between early and modern hominids?

2) What evidence indicates relatedness between early and modern hominids?

d. Summarize the pattern of changes that you observe in the hominid skulls from *Australopithecus afarensis* to *Homo sapiens*.

e. Use the evidence that you have examined to draw an inference about the ancestors of modern humans and modern primates.

f. Work with your partner to make a poster. You will use this information to teach your original team about the evidence that physical anthropologists contribute to our understanding of how species change over time.

Topic: human evolution
Go to: www.scilinks.org
Code: human3E49

g. Glue the human, chimpanzee, and mystery bones onto a poster board. Add a summary, in your own words, for how humans have changed over time.

3. Return to step 5 in the general procedure.

Further Challenges

Plate tectonics, the movement of continents, and the ice ages had a tremendous effect on the distribution of living organisms throughout the earth's history. The movement of continents and the rising and falling of sea levels created and destroyed many land bridges. These land bridges connected one continent to another. Think about these concepts as you use the fossil data in Figure 2.5 to complete the following tasks:

1. Propose a place of origin and a migration route for marsupial mammals.

   Mammals are animals characterized, in part, by hair, sweat glands, and the nursing of young with milk secreted by mammary glands. Marsupials are mammals that produce embryos that spend only a short time in the mother's uterus. At birth, the immature infants must crawl into the mother's pouch, where they continue to mature while nursing from the mother.

2. Consider what the fossil record indicates about ancient distributions of marsupial mammals. Then propose an explanation for the present marsupial mammal distribution.

Continent	Oldest marsupial fossil (mya = million years ago)	Present marsupial distribution (number of families)
North America	110 mya	1
South America	75 mya	2
Antarctica	55 mya	0
Europe/Asia	52–58 mya	1
Africa	50 mya	0
Australia	30 mya	10

Figure 2.6 Distribution of marsupials.

Explaining Evolution

Landmasses separate and come together again. The sea level rises and falls with each ice age and with the movement of the tectonic plates. Species of organisms live in one environment. They sometimes migrate to other environments and change gradually into related but physically distinct forms. Then they usually become extinct. You have explored much about the changes that occur across geologic time. Now you will have the opportunity to explain how biological changes take place.

To develop an explanation of evolution, you will assume the role of a newspaper reporter. You will uncover the story behind the theory of evolution. For example, you may have heard of Charles Darwin. Darwin, a 19th-century naturalist, is famous for writing *On the Origin of Species by Means of Natural Selection*, first published in 1859. But do you really know who he was? What did he do, how did he do it, and why did it matter? The story you write will help answer some of the questions that you may have had about evolution. How does evolution take place? Why are biologists so interested in it?

Materials   (per team of 2)

large piece of butcher paper

PROCESS AND PROCEDURES

You may have heard that newspaper reporters are taught to include the most important information in the first few sentences of their news stories. This information is the *who, what, when, where, why,* and *how* of the breaking story. Imagine that it is the year 2034, and you and your partner are rookie newspaper reporters. Here is your first assignment: put together a short article about the theory of evolution in recognition of the 175th anniversary of the publication of Darwin's book *On the Origin of Species.* Your teacher is your editor and is pleased with your enthusiasm for journalism. But do you have the scientific and investigative skills required to nose out the story? Can you use your reporting skills to identify the highlights of the story, right up front?

1. Write the 6 italicized words listed above along the left side of your large piece of paper.

2. Now write 6 questions, 1 for each question word, about Darwin and his work.

   Choose questions that you find interesting. Remember, you are acting as a reporter, so think of questions that will attract your readers' interests as well.

3. Develop these question words into complete questions that are more specific. Remember, you and your partner need to think of and answer questions that will impress your editor.

   For example, you might develop your "who" question as follows: Who first wrote about the theory of evolution?

4. Decide how you will divide the responsibility for finding answers to each of these 6 questions.

   Questions about who, when, where, and what are likely to be easier to answer than questions about how and why. You may wish to divide the easy and more difficult questions evenly between you and your partner.

5. Work individually or with your partner (as determined in step 4) to gather and summarize the information required to answer your assigned questions. Record notes in your journal.

   One source of information about Darwin's work can be found in the essays *Darwin Proposes Descent with Modification* on page 111 and *Evolution by Natural Selection* on page 114.

6. Work with your partner to develop short but interesting and informative answers to each of the questions. Write those answers on the large paper.

   Share with your partner the information that you gathered for each of your questions. Discuss and agree upon the team answers before writing them on the paper.

PAGE 111

PAGE 114

7. Post your answers as your teacher directs.

8. How did your summary compare with those of your classmates? Be prepared to share your response to this question in a short class discussion.

Analysis

Your editor is impressed with your work but doubts whether the story is important enough to print. "After all," the editor argues, "we refer to it as the 'theory' of evolution. If it's just a theory, it means that we aren't sure about it. Why should we pay attention to it? What makes Darwin's theory any more convincing than a theory that you or I might suggest?" You, of course, are horrified at the editor's lack of understanding about the nature of scientific theories.

SCI LINKS®
NSTA

Topic: Darwin
Go to: www.scilinks.org
Code: human3E51

1. Work with your partner to prepare a rebuttal to the editor's criticism. Your response should include

   a. a definition of a scientific theory that demonstrates the error in the editor's argument, and

   b. an explanation of the importance of the theory of evolution to modern biology.

   Information in the essay *Just a Theory?* on page 119 will help you develop your response.

PAGE 119

2. Choose one member of your team to offer the rebuttal orally to your editor (your teacher). Although one person should present the team's response, both members should be prepared to answer further questions about the issue if your editor is not convinced by your initial comments.

Further Challenges

To create a real journalism article, take the summary of your story and craft it into a smooth, informative article that answers the important questions about evolution.

Modeling Natural Selection

Darwin developed his theory of evolution—a theory that explains how organisms change over time—by analyzing his observations during a 20-year period. In his theory, he proposed natural selection as the mechanism of evolution. You can model years of natural selection in the classroom in 1 or 2 days by modeling just one of the many types of selective pressures. In this case, predation is the selective pressure that you will model. Predation is important to evolution because it places a limit on one of the key requirements of natural selection—the ability of organisms to survive long enough to reproduce.

In this activity, you will model the effects of predation on a prey population. When you modeled geologic time, your class used the clothesline as a model. In this example, you will use fabric to model an environment and paper dots to model a population of prey in that environment. The different-colored paper dots (the prey population) will represent a variation in the color of individuals within a species. You and your classmates will be the predators. By analyzing the selective effects of predation in this model, you will gain a better understanding of how natural selection can change the average characteristics of a population.

Materials   (per team of 4)

record sheet
3 petri dish halves
36 × 44-in piece of fabric A or fabric B
4 sheets of graph paper
zip plastic sandwich bag containing
    120 paper dots, 20 each of 6 colors
    (labeled *Starting Population*)

masking tape
6 colored pencils similar to the dot colors
6 zip plastic sandwich bags, each
    containing 100 paper dots of a
    single color
watch or clock with a second hand
3 forceps (optional)

PROCESS AND PROCEDURES

1. Decide which team member will be the game warden and which team members will be the predators.

    Three members of your team will play the role of predators. As predators, each will hunt paper dots (the prey) in their habitat (the piece of fabric). The 4th member will be the game warden, who will keep track of the hunting.

2. Examine the paper dots in the bag labeled *Starting Population*. Record the number of individuals (dots) of each color.

    The colored dots represent individuals of a particular species. The individuals of this species can be 1 of 6 colors.

    The game warden should record the starting population as the *Hunt 1 Starting Population* on the record sheet that your teacher provides.

3. Spread out the piece of fabric on a desk or tabletop. Tape the corners of the fabric to the table.

    Half of the teams will have pieces of fabric A, and half will have pieces of fabric B.

4. Read the information in the need to know box to learn the rules the predators must follow. Set up the model as follows:

   Predators: Obtain a petri dish half. Turn to face away from the habitat.

   Game warden: Obtain a petri dish half. Pour the dots from the bag labeled *Starting Population* into your petri dish. When the predators turn their backs, spread the *Hunt 1 Starting Population* throughout the habitat.

   Spread the dots over the fabric as uniformly as possible so that no dots stick together or cover other dots.

5. Put the model into action as follows:

   Game warden: Direct the predators to face the habitat and begin picking up dots (prey); say "stop" after 20 seconds.

6. Finish round 1 of predation in your model as follows:

   Predators: Sort the paper dots you collected by color, and record the number of each color that you "ate."

   Game warden: Subtract the total number of each color that was "eaten" from the *Hunt 1 Starting Population* to determine how many survivors remain in the "habitat." Record the number of survivors for each color of the paper dots. Label this *Hunt 1 Surviving Population*.

7. Prepare for round 2 of predation in your model as follows:

   Predators: Simulate reproduction among the survivors. For every colored dot remaining on the fabric, add 3 dots of the same color to the warden's petri dish. In this model, we are saying that each survivor has 3 offspring before the next hunting season.

   The 3 paper dots of each color represent offspring. Obtain these offspring from the bags containing single colors of dots.

   Game warden: Record the total number of each color of paper dot that will now be in the habitat as *Hunt 2 Starting Population*.

Figure 2.7
Ptarmigan. Many animals, including this ptarmigan, are camouflaged so that they don't stand out in their environment. This can help them avoid predation.

NEED TO KNOW

Rules for Predators

a. Obey the warden. When the warden instructs you, turn your back to the habitat and look away while she or he is placing the prey on the fabric.

b. Wait until the warden says "start" to begin hunting.

c. *Use only your eyes* to locate your prey. *Do not feel the fabric* for dots.

d. Use only one hand (or one forceps).

e. Pick up one dot at a time and put it in your petri dish half before taking another dot.

f. Pick up as many paper dots (prey) as possible until the game warden says "stop." You will have 20 seconds to hunt.

8. *Predators*: Again, turn away from the habitat.

   Game warden: When the predators turn their backs, spread the "offspring" from the *Hunt 1 Surviving Population* throughout the habitat and mix them in with their "parents." (The offspring are the dots that were added to your petri dish in step 7.)

   Spread the dots as uniformly as possible so that no dots stick together or cover other dots.

9. Repeat steps 5 and 6 for round 2 of predation.

10. *Do not* repeat steps 4 through 6 for a 3rd round of predation. Calculate the number of each color of paper dot by assuming that each surviving paper dot would produce 3 offspring. Add the number of survivors (parents) to the number of offspring for each color. Record this information as *Hunt 4 Starting Population*.

    Each team member should record this information in his or her journal.

11. As a team, use colored pencils and graph paper to prepare bar graphs that show the number of each color of paper dots in each of the 4 starting populations (see Figure 2.8).

    Use colored pencils that correspond to the colors of the paper dots. You should have 4 bar graphs when you are finished with this step. If you need help making bar graphs, refer to Appendix B, *Technique 2 Graphing*.

12. Study the bar graphs of each starting population (or generation). With your teammates, consider the following questions and record your team's responses in your journal:

    a. Which, if any, colors of paper dots had a better survival rate than other dots in the 2nd-, 3rd-, and 4th-generation starting populations?

    b. What might be the reason that predators did not select these colors as often as they did other colors?

    c. What effect did capturing a particular color dot have on the numbers of that color in the following generations?

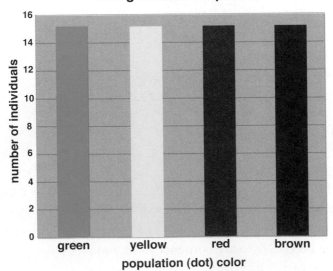

First-generation Population

Figure 2.8 Sample graph of starting population data.

13. Now that your predator/prey investigation is complete, clean up by sorting the colored dots into their respective plastic bags as you found them.

Analysis

At the location that your teacher indicates, post your team's bar graph for the *Hunt 4 Starting Population* beside the fabric that you used. Compare the bar graphs of teams who used fabric A with the bar graphs of teams who used fabric B. Complete the following tasks as a team. Record your team's responses in your journal.

1. How well do the class data support your team's conclusions in step 12?

2. Imagine one real-life predator/prey relationship (for example, wolves and rabbits).

   a. Record in your journal the predator/prey relationship that you select as your example.

   b. Write a paragraph that describes how one characteristic of the prey population might change because of natural selection.

   c. Write a second paragraph that explains how one characteristic of the predator population might change because of natural selection.

   Base your explanations on what you have learned in this model of natural selection by predation.

3. When you and your classmates studied paleontologists, evolutionary biologists, developmental biologists, and physical anthropologists, you learned about the evidence and inference that each of these sciences contributes to the theory of evolution. Understanding the process of natural selection also adds to the collection of evidence and inference that helps scientists interpret change over time.

   Write a paragraph that explains why knowing about the process of natural selection adds more evidence and inference to support the theory of evolution.

4. Explain what *biological evolution* means. Use terms and ideas that you have learned from this chapter, including the following:

adaptation	natural selection	species
population	variation	mutation

A Cold Hard Look at Culture

Elaborate

There are sea horses that look like marine plants, bacteria that live in hot springs, and giant pandas that feed almost exclusively on bamboo. Through biological evolution, all of these organisms have changed and passed their unique characteristics to offspring in generation after generation. Many of these changes are adaptations that enable these organisms to survive in very specific habitats. Humans, however, are not restricted to a single habitat. We can survive in extreme heat, extreme cold, under water, and even in space. What allows humans to live in so many environments when most other organisms have such a narrow range of suitable habitats?

The answer is culture. We have an exceptional ability to develop behaviors and technologies that permit us to cope with new situations in nonbiological ways. For instance, we can minimize the effects of an extremely hot and unpleasant environment by using the technology of air-conditioning to modify part of that environment. This ability is called **cultural adaptation** or **cultural evolution**. It is one of the distinguishing characteristics of humans. Cultural evolution differs significantly from biological evolution because *acquired* traits, like learned behaviors, can be passed on to future generations through culture. In fact, the cultural transmission of information and values from person to person and generation to generation happens through communication and learning. This is the primary reason that the experience of being human has changed so dramatically in the last 10,000 years.

A biological adaptation is different from a cultural adaptation. A biological adaptation is an inherited trait. A cultural adaptation is an acquired trait. Biological adaptations are beneficial traits that an organism inherits genetically. Individuals that are better equipped to survive in a particular environment are more likely to reproduce and leave behind offspring with these same biological adaptations. Cultural adaptations can be learned and must be taught to the next generation or they may be lost.

In this activity, you and your teammates will be archaeologists. An archaeological society has asked your team to help its members study the remains of a human who died more than 5,000 years ago. They also want help studying the items that were found with him. Because he was buried in ice and snow high in the Alps, his body and his belongings were unusually well preserved. Your assignment is to determine whatever you can about his life and his culture. Decide whether you think he was physically similar to, or distinctly different from, humans living today.

Materials

DVD and player

PROCESS AND PROCEDURES

1. Read the following paragraphs by yourself:

> A man died high in the Alps, above tree line. His body was frozen into a glacier and remained there for more than 5,000 years. Then, in 1991, some hikers who had veered slightly off course discovered the well-preserved corpse. They assumed that it was a modern hiker who was killed the previous winter, and they notified authorities. Because the authorities did not realize that they were dealing with something very old, they removed the body from the ice somewhat carelessly and in a way that resulted in the loss of valuable evidence.
>
> Imagine the surprise of the authorities and the hikers when they found out that the body was really that of a human from an ancient time. He and his possessions are some of the most valuable archaeological evidence ever found.

Topic: iceman
Go to: www.scilinks.org
Code: human3E56

Usually the types of evidence that are preserved from humans who lived 5,000 years ago are hard substances, such as teeth or bones and the stone or metal parts of tools. Pottery, too, may survive, but decay generally destroys soft tissues such as skin, hair, plant materials, and leather.

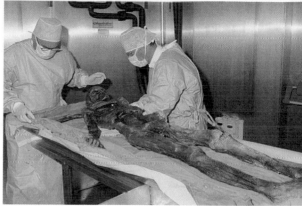

Just as scientists must infer ideas about the skin and outward appearance of a dinosaur from its fossil remains, so must they infer details about the appearance or culture of early humans from whatever is preserved. The term **artifact** is used to describe material remains, such as pieces of pottery, tools, and textiles that scientists use for evidence to infer the details of culture.

In this activity, you will use inference to interpret a situation with many artifacts that usually do not preserve well. You also will consider some particular aspects of biological evolution.

2. Examine the table in Figure 2.9. This table lists many of the artifacts that authorities and scientists found with the Iceman and gives a general description of his body.

This list will help you get a general idea of the types of clothing and tools the Iceman had.

> *General description of body*: General age: 5,300 years; mostly intact; X-rays revealed that he died of an arrow wound; he was shot from behind in the left shoulder; 5 feet, 2 inches tall; 20 to 30 years old at time of death; a series of markings on skin—several sets of blue parallel lines on lower back, stripes on right ankle, and a cross behind left knee; medium-length hair (cut); physical features similar to humans today.

3. The artifacts listed in Figure 2.9 are evidence of how the iceman lived. What inferences about his lifestyle can you make based on the evidence?

Artifact	Comments
Grass cape	Carefully stitched together; isolated repairs made with grass thread
Arrows and leather quiver (carrying case for arrows)	Oldest leather quiver ever found; some arrows with flint arrowheads; other arrows unfinished
Very long bow	Unstrung
Pouch with worked bits of flint	Flint is a type of stone that flakes easily into sharp pieces.
Clothing and boots	Made of leather; grass stuffed inside boots
Copper-bladed axe with wooden handle	One of the oldest axes of its type and first with handle intact; attached by leather ties and glue; copper blade
Mushrooms strung on a leather strip	A type of fungus with medicinal (antibiotic) properties
Flint dagger and grass sheath	Worked flint blade on wooden handle; first sheath of this age recovered
Bone needle	
Grass rope	
Stone disk threaded with a leather strap	
Bits of a primitive wheat and wheat pollen	This type of wheat grew only at low altitudes.

Figure 2.9 Artifacts recovered with the Iceman.

4. Watch the DVD segment "A Glimpse of the Iceman."

5. With your team of 4, discuss what each artifact is and how the Iceman might have used it. Select 3 artifacts that you find most interesting. Record your ideas about their possible uses in a table in your journal.

6. Consider the artifacts, and select 2 of the following questions to answer in your journal:

    a. What might the bow and the finished and unfinished arrows and arrowheads indicate about his way of life?

    b. What might the copper-bladed axe with the wooden handle indicate about his culture?

    c. What can you tell from the bits of wheat and wheat pollen present?

    d. What might the different markings on his body indicate?

    Refer back to the descriptive paragraphs in step 1 and to Figure 2.9 if you wish.

7. How did you use evidence or make inferences to answer the questions in step 6? Explain.

8. Did your personal opinions and previous experiences influence how you interpreted the evidence? Explain whether you think that happens when scientists examine evidence. How might such influences affect their work?

9. If you could have 3 more pieces of evidence or 3 more bits of information to help you complete your understanding of the Iceman, what would they be? Explain.

Analysis

Answer the following questions in your journal. Be prepared to share your ideas in a class discussion.

1. What particular physical features of the Iceman would you compare with modern humans if you were looking for evidence of biological evolution? Explain.

2. What artifacts from the Iceman would you compare with artifacts from modern humans as evidence of cultural evolution?

3. Do you think there have been greater changes in humans physically or culturally in the last 5,000 years? Explain your answer.

Evaluate # Evolution in Action

You have been studying the evidence, inferences, and mechanism for change over time in living organisms for the last two chapters. In this evaluate activity, you will apply your knowledge to explain three possible endings to a story about a teenage girl who had surgery. Use the vocabulary and concepts that you have learned to write well-reasoned explanations for the three possible outcomes to the scenario.

SCENARIO

A Turn for the Worse

The attendants wheel the teenage girl into the operating room as her mother waits anxiously in the sitting room at the end of the hall. The girl's appendix is so severely inflamed that her doctor worries that it might rupture before she can perform the operation. In spite of the danger, the operation goes smoothly, and the surgeon removes the girl's inflamed appendix without mishap. After surgery, nurses take the patient to the recovery room. In about 30 minutes, she regains consciousness and speaks to her mother.

All seems to be going well in the first 24 hours after surgery. However, on the following day, the girl begins to run a fever, which quickly rises. Her doctor realizes that she has contracted an internal infection during the surgery.

The girl in this story has a bacterial infection. A strain of *Staphylococcus* bacteria contaminated the open wound during surgery, and it continued to multiply inside her body. Will she survive this infection? Use your knowledge of evolution and your scientific thinking skills to propose an explanation for what happens next. As you complete this activity, you will evaluate what you have learned about the way living organisms change across time.

PROCESS AND PROCEDURES

Read the following 3 descriptions of possible outcomes for the opening scenario. Each description takes place in a different time period in the history of Western medicine.

Scenario 1

The year is 1925: The girl becomes delirious from fever; in a few days, she dies.

Scenario 2

The year is 1945: The girl receives an injection of the antibiotic penicillin, followed by repeated doses. Within 24 hours, her fever is reduced. In a week, she is released from the hospital, well on her way to recovery.

Scenario 3

The year is 1965: The girl receives an injection of the antibiotic penicillin, followed by repeated doses. Despite this treatment, her fever continues, and she becomes delirious. In a few days, she dies.

1. Read the background information on antibiotics in the need to know box. Study the graph in Figure 2.10. Decide why the outcomes for the 3 scenarios are different.

2. For each outcome, write 1 paragraph that explains why that outcome is possible at that time in history.

   Base your explanations on your experiences in this chapter. Give a basic overview of how these scenarios could have happened.

Figure 2.10

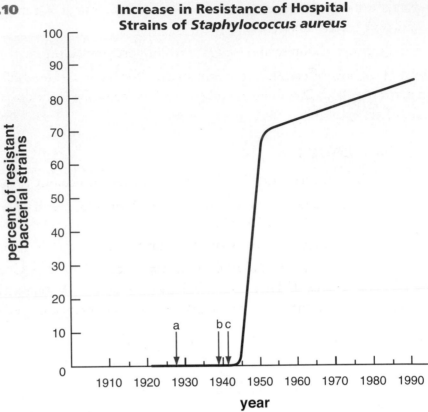

Increase in Resistance of Hospital Strains of *Staphylococcus aureus*

a. 1928: In the laboratory, Sir Alexander Fleming observed that the mold *Penicillium* kills the bacterium *Staphylococcus*.

b. 1939: Ernest Chain, Sir Howard Florey, and researchers at Oxford University isolated the antibiotic penicillin from the mold *Penicillium*.

c. 1941: Large-scale production of penicillin begins.

Analysis

1. The example of a bacterial infection in this activity can serve as a model of evolution. In a short essay, explain how this example illustrates evolution in action in modern times. Write your essay to explain the evolutionary change represented by the three scenarios. Explain what changed over time and how it happened. Along with other terms that you have learned in the last chapter, be sure to include the following terms in your essay:

   evolution   variation   adaptation
   natural selection   mutation

   A good description of this model of evolution must include these points:

   ◆ Describes the evolutionary change that occurs in this model

   ◆ Identifies the factor in the bacteria's environment that exerts a pressure for natural selection

   ◆ Explains the role that variation in individual characteristics plays in the evolution of resistant populations

- Explains how new generations of offspring play a role in the evolution of resistant bacterial populations
- Uses specific examples and evidence to support your response

2. Explain how the difference in generation time for humans (about 20 years) and bacteria (about 20 minutes) makes a difference in their rates of evolutionary change.

Further Challenges

1. Describe in two or three sentences the interaction between culture and medicine.

   You do not need to refer to the scenarios that you wrote about in the general procedure or in question 1 of the Analysis.

2. What effect might antibacterial soaps have on the evolution of bacteria?

3. You might want to read the *Scientific American* article called "The Challenge of Antibiotic Resistance" (March 1998). Briefly summarize how human behavior can influence the evolution of certain disease-causing organisms (pathogens).

NEED TO KNOW

Antibiotics

An antibiotic is a medicine that is toxic to certain bacteria. Antibiotics are used to fight bacterial infections. You may have heard of antibiotics such as penicillin, amoxicillin, tetracycline, or erythromycin. Researchers discovered a few antibiotics in the 1920s and some, such as penicillin, were in limited use by the late 1930s. Mass production of penicillin in the 1940s made this powerful therapy against bacterial infections a widespread tool in medicine. Before that time, doctors had few options to fight a bacterial infection once it started. Patients often died if they suffered from serious infections such as bacterial pneumonia, gangrene, or a staph infection.

Today, doctors have a wide range of antibiotics from which to choose. They use them to treat a variety of illnesses such as sore throats (which are sometimes caused by a *Streptococcus* bacterium), bacterial pneumonia (a serious lung infection), and even acne. This range of antibiotic choices is relatively recent in the history of medicine and human illnesses. In fact, the dependence of Western medicine on technology, such as the development of antibiotics, is a relatively recent cultural development. This dependence has dramatically changed the way we think about health care and physicians. Many patients now demand an antibiotic prescription when they are sick, even if an antibiotic will not cure their problem.

Every antibiotic is not effective against every type of bacterium. A particular antibiotic can kill only a limited number of bacterial species. In addition, the genetic material (DNA) of some bacteria can change in a way that allows these bacteria to resist the killing effects of an antibiotic that was once effective. These bacteria are said to be *resistant* to that antibiotic. Such genetic changes do not occur very often. But because bacteria with these changes can survive in the presence of the antibiotic, they are more likely to reproduce than nonresistant bacteria. If the resistant bacteria pass their genetic changes along to future generations, an entire population of resistant bacteria can arise. When that happens, the antibiotic becomes ineffective against that bacterial population.

"Great biological diversity takes long stretches of geological time and the accumulation of large reservoirs of unique genes."

E. O. Wilson, The Diversity of Life, *1992*

Products of Evolution: Unity and Diversity

How many different types of life can you find in this coral reef? How many different types do you think you would find if you actually went snorkeling among the soft coral, feather starfish, and fairy basslets of this coral reef?

One of the most remarkable aspects of life is its enormous diversity. Think of the differences, for example, between the tiny microorganisms that fill this ocean water and the huge blue whales that feed on them. Think as well of the differences between the towering trees that may grow along streets in your neighborhood and the insects and worms that live in the soil that anchors the roots of the trees.

Your challenge in this chapter is to look at life's diversity as a scientist might. To do that, you will consider not only the enormous differences that exist among organisms, but also the ways in which all living organisms are alike. You will examine how the unity that underlies all of life helps scientists understand and explain life's diversity. You will also explore the ways in which scientists organize the knowledge that they have accumulated about living systems. In addition, as you complete these activities, you should find, as most scientists do, that a close study of the variety of life on earth will increase your appreciation for life's diversity and complexity.

ACTIVITIES

Engage	Strange Encounters
Explore	
Explain	Describing Life
Explain	A Look at Diversity
Explain	
Elaborate	Adaptation, Diversity, and Evolution
Elaborate	Using Unity to Organize Diversity
Elaborate	Explaining the Zebra's Stripes
Evaluate	First Encounter with the Critter

Strange Encounters

In Chapter 2, you examined evolution, a process of change across time. You have looked at how long biological evolution has been going on and how evolution takes place. But have you ever thought about its remarkable results? Think of the wide variety of organisms on earth: lions on the Serengeti, bacteria that live in near-boiling water, delicate roses in a beautiful garden. . . .

In this chapter, you will observe and think about all of the variety on earth: the products of evolution. How is it that the life around us (and even in us) occurs in so many different forms? How do scientists identify and keep track of all of life's variations?

 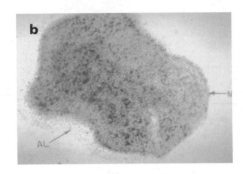 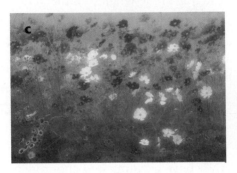

Figure 3.1 **(a)** This pair of lions (*Panthera leo*) watches prey in the distance. **(b)** This thermophile (*Sulfolobus brierlexi*) is part of a group of bacteria that thrive in hot water (60°C–90°C [140°F–194°F]). **(c)** These flowers can live in moderate to warm climates.

As a starting point for your study of the diversity that resulted from evolution, let's consider how it is that, in general, we can easily recognize life. Although living organisms occur in a wide variety of shapes, sizes, colors, and habitats, can you usually tell whether or not an object you encounter is alive?

Materials   (per person)

question card   DVD and player

PROCESS AND PROCEDURES

1. Observe the DVD segment "Unusual Creatures." As you watch, keep in mind the question written on the card that your teacher has given you.

    Make notes in your journal to help you answer the question on your card.

2. As a class, discuss your responses to the questions on the question cards.

3. Read the scenario *What Is It?* Imagine that you are Katrina, suddenly confronted with a strange object that you have never seen before. Write in your journal a short 2- or 3-paragraph ending to her story that describes how she finally determines whether the object really *is* alive. Resolve the issue for her (that is,

What *Is* It?

Katrina peered at the . . . thing . . . in front of her. Definitely unusual. Peculiar, even. She has walked this path a thousand times in the 3 months she's lived here and had never seen anything like this before.

She walked around it, once, slowly. It had a regular shape, sort of like a hexagon, but its surface didn't look shiny and synthetic like plastic, metal, or glass. Instead, it looked almost biological: sort of scaly and wrinkled and, well, something like a snake's skin. The

object had strange colors, too: sort of purplish-greenish, with amber highlights. It looked out of place in the weeds and low shrubs along the path, yet somehow it didn't look manufactured either.

What was it? An egg? A cocoon? A mushroom? Some type of dormant reptile? Or maybe it wasn't alive at all. It really didn't look alive, but neither did it look dead. She almost expected it to . . . but then again, she also wouldn't have been surprised if it. . . .

describe how she finally discovers the object's identity). Be creative (for example, you may want to give the story a surprise ending). Be sure that your story ending addresses the following questions:

- What characteristics make her think that it is alive?
- What characteristics make her think that it is not alive?
- How does she finally make her decision?

4. Share your ending as your teacher directs.

Describing Life

Explore

Explain

It is one thing for us to have such a good, intuitive sense of what is alive and what is not alive *here on earth*. It is quite another thing, however, to describe life so clearly that it would enable us to identify it in a very different setting. Scientists faced this problem in 1976 and again in 1997 and 2004 as they designed experiments to search for life on Mars. What characteristics of life are so general, so basic, that if we observed them, we would be ready to say that life really was present?

This activity will help you think about this question. You will probe the fundamental characteristics that all organisms on earth share. Considered together, they provide the best general description of life that we have been able to construct.

Materials (per team of 4)

large sheet of paper   felt-tipped marker

PROCESS AND PROCEDURES

1. Work with your team to develop a comprehensive list of characteristics that you think are common to all living organisms on earth. Record your list on a large sheet of paper.

   Refer to the scenario from the previous activity for ideas to get you started.

2. With your team, identify the 1 characteristic from your list that you think would be easiest to look for if you were to mount a search for life on another planet. Mark this characteristic with a check mark, and be prepared to explain why your team selected it.

   The list that you have created is really a description of living systems as you understand them now. Notice, however, that you also can use your description as a checklist to try to determine whether some unknown object is or is not alive.

PAGE 121

3. Follow your teacher's instructions for displaying your team's list so other class members can see it.

4. Scientists actually have searched for evidence of life on Mars. Prior to the 1976 and 2004 robotic surface explorations on Mars, scientists had to decide on a method for trying to detect the presence of life, whatever form it might have there.

   Work with your team to learn about the Mars experiments and to answer the questions below. Record your answers in your journal. The essay *Describing Life: An Impossible Challenge?* on page 121 includes information about the Mars experiments that will help you answer these questions.

   a. How do scientists describe life? (That is, what list of characteristics do scientists associate with life?)

   b. How does the list of characteristics that scientists associate with life compare with your list and the lists developed by other teams?

   c. What were 2 difficulties your group faced in making your list of characteristics? For example, how would you classify something like a feather found on the ground or pieces of loose hair?

   d. What specific characteristics of life did the scientists involved in the Mars mission look for?

   e. Why do you think that they chose these characteristics and not others?

   f. How did their choice of searchable characteristics compare with the choice that you and your teammates made in step 2?

   g. If you were trying to solve Katrina's question (page 65), what would you do to determine whether or not the object was living?

Figure 3.2 The Stream. Our living and nonliving surroundings combine to make the familiar landscapes that we enjoy on earth.

Analysis

Complete the following tasks in your journal:

1. Evaluate each of the following statements as either true or false. Support your thinking with a short explanation and an example drawn from this or the previous activity.

a. We usually can recognize life on earth because our experience of life has taught us that living things possess certain characteristics that things that are not alive do not have.

b. The way in which scientists tried to recognize life on Mars was very similar to the way in which we recognize life, but it was more systematic.

c. Our preconceived notions about an issue may affect the questions that we ask and the ways in which we are prepared to interpret the data that we collect.

2. Examine the following list of unifying principles. What justification can you offer for organizing a biology course around these principles?

NEED TO KNOW

Unifying Principles of Biology

Evolution: Patterns and Products of Change in Living Systems

Homeostasis: Maintaining Dynamic Equilibrium in Living Systems

Energy, Matter, and Organization: Relationships in Living Systems

Continuity: Reproduction and Inheritance in Living Systems

Development: Growth and Differentiation in Living Systems

Ecology: Interaction and Interdependence in Living Systems

A Look at Diversity

Explain

As you saw in the previous two activities, to say that an object is alive is to say something quite significant about it. Think about all the characteristics that living systems and species share in common (the unifying principles): evolution, mechanisms for assuring internal homeostasis, complex organization, genetic continuity, growth and development, and interaction and interdependence with other organisms and with the nonliving world. If we know that an object is alive, then we know that in some way it displays each of these features.

The organization for this course uses these ideas to help you make sense of, and draw meaning from, the sometimes overwhelming amount of information in biology. In addition, these "big ideas" will be useful throughout your life as you interpret and give meaning to observations you make and experiences that you have with living things.

Recognizing the ways in which all organisms are alike—recognizing the underlying unity of life—gives us a common starting point from which we can ask and answer questions about life's diversity. Organisms on earth often are very different from one

Figure 3.3 Black algae at Yellowstone.

another. They can differ in appearance, structure, behavior, and the environments that they occupy. However, they all exhibit certain fundamental characteristics, and they all face similar challenges. To understand diversity, then, we need to understand these characteristics and challenges. We need to consider how different evolutionary pressures have resulted in organisms that have responded to these challenges in widely different ways.

Materials (per team of 6)

large sheet of paper
6 unifying principle cards

colored felt-tipped markers
DVD and player

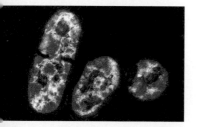

PROCESS AND PROCEDURES

1. Your teacher will give you a unifying principle to consider for this activity. Join the other members of your team. Each of you will have a different unifying principle.

   Take turns reading your unifying principles aloud. Then discuss them with the other members of your team.

   You will study each of these principles in detail later. For now, work with your team members to summarize the big idea for your assigned unifying principles.

   These questions may help to guide your team's discussion. How would you explain this characteristic of life to someone in middle school? What examples would you use to illustrate its importance to humans? to other organisms? Record your ideas in your journal.

   The essay *Describing Life: An Impossible Challenge?* on page 121 may help you think about your principle.

2. Now, meet with the other members of your class who received the same unifying principle. Compare your summaries about the big idea for your principle. Add any new ideas that this discussion raises to the notes in your journal.

   Make sure that you all share the same understanding of your assigned principle. Refer to your teacher any questions that your group cannot answer.

3. Select a spokesperson to summarize your group's understanding of its unifying principle to your teacher.

   Your teacher will want to hear examples of how some living organisms that you are familiar with show your unifying principle.

4. List the following 5 types of organisms down the left column of a table in your journal. Provide plenty of space to make notes about how different types of organisms display the principle. Use your unifying principle as the title to your table.

   ◆ bacteria   ◆ protoctists   ◆ fungi   ◆ plants   ◆ animals

5. Watch the DVD segment "A Diversity of Organisms." Complete the following tasks:

a. In the note section of your table, begin describing how different types of organisms display the principle that you are tracking.

Avoid taking notes on all of the specific examples and details that the segment provides. Instead, concentrate on understanding in general how each major type of organism displays the principle. Say, for example, you are tracking the principle of interaction and interdependence. You might record the fact that plants supply the oxygen to the air that both plants and animals require for life. You likely would not record the name of the specific places in the world where you would find each type of plant.

Do not be concerned if you are unable to complete your table from the information presented in the DVD segment. Some principles are easier to observe in such images than others are. Step 6 offers another opportunity to complete your table.

b. List 1 organism from each group that you find particularly interesting or surprising with respect to the principle that you are tracking. Be prepared to explain why you chose each organism.

6. Your teacher will stop the DVD after each major type of organism. This will allow you to briefly discuss your notes for that group with your classmates who tracked the same unifying principle. Use this discussion to help you expand or modify the information in your notes. That way, you will be able to represent your principle more effectively when you rejoin your original team.

The essay *Five Kingdoms* on page 127 contains information that may help you complete your table.

Topic: biodiversity
Go to: www.scilinks.org
Code: human3E69

PAGE 127

7. Join the members of your original team, and take turns sharing the information that each of you has gathered.

8. Construct a summary diagram, table, or drawing that illustrates how each of the 5 major groups of organisms expresses or has expressed each of the 6 unifying principles of life.

Do all 5 major groups of organisms exhibit all of the principles? What does this tell you about the principles?

9. Add to your diagram a few specific organisms in each kingdom. Identify 1 interesting fact about how each displays 1 of the 6 unifying principles of life.

Analysis

Use the information presented in your summary diagram to answer the following questions. Record your answers in your journal.

1. Which of the six unifying principles seems to have been most useful to biologists in grouping organisms into different large categories, or kingdoms? Explain your answer.

Think about (a) the major difference that distinguishes prokaryotes from all other organisms on earth; (b) how plants differ from both fungi and animals by the way they obtain the energy required for life; and (c) how organisms in each of the kingdoms reproduce.

2. How do these large categories by which biologists organize their thinking about life illustrate both its unity and diversity? Explain your answer.

Further Challenges

Read these observations about a virus, called a *bacteriophage* (see Figure 3.4), that infects bacteria.

A bacteriophage

- contains genetic material,
- reproduces only when inside another organism,
- has an outer case made of protein,
- injects genetic material into a bacterial cell, and
- uses the energy and the structure of the bacterial cell to make parts that assemble into copies of itself (and often kills the bacterial cell).

You may have noticed that neither the DVD segment nor the essay contained any reference to viruses. Yet, we often think about viruses in relation to life. For example, have you ever heard someone complain about being *attacked* by a virus?

1. Use your knowledge of the unifying principles of life to construct a well-reasoned argument to answer the question, Is the bacteriophage alive?

2. For a moment, assume that scientists have decided that a virus *should* be considered alive. Select one of the five kingdoms in which scientists would likely categorize viruses. Support your answer with specific references to the unifying principles and to the information about the bacteriophage listed above.

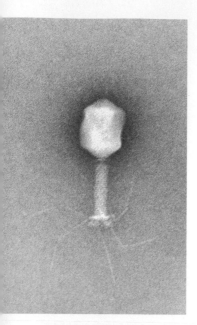

Figure 3.4 The bacteriophage (photographed at 240,000×) is a virus that attacks bacteria.

Explain
Elaborate

Adaptation, Diversity, and Evolution

Think back to the organisms you saw in the previous activity, *A Look at Diversity*. Each one shares the general characteristics of the kingdom in which it is categorized, yet each is uniquely its own creature. Every living organism has peculiarities of structure, function, and behavior that make it distinctly different from all of the others.

In Chapter 2, you learned about evolution—the process of change and selection that can introduce and spread biological differences through a population of organisms. Can that process explain all of the structural, functional, and behavioral diversity that we find on earth?

Let's examine the relationship between evolution and diversity more closely. We will need to consider the more fundamental relationship between a species and the environment in which it lives. Recall from Chapter 2 that inherited characteristics that help an organism survive and reproduce within a particular environment are called **adaptations**. What happens to organisms with adaptations that equip them to live in a particular set of environmental conditions when that environment changes? Is it possible that new characteristics that appear in a species through mutation would allow organisms to live in new environments?

To discover some answers to those questions, consider life in two very different settings: first, across a series of oceanic life zones, and second, across a series of eras in the earth's history.

Materials (per team of 4)

slides and coverslips

hand lens

dissecting needles with corks on tips

large sheet of paper

plant specimens

compound microscope

forceps

scalpel

4 felt-tipped markers

DVD and player

PROCESS AND PROCEDURES

Part A   Diversity and Adaptation in a Marine Environment

1. Observe the DVD segment "Marine Life."

    a. Pay particular attention to the conditions that are present in each of the different environments described. Indicate these conditions in a few words at the appropriate places on Copymaster *Oceanic Life Zones*.

    b. Work with the other members of your team to write on your copymaster the names of several organisms that live in each life zone.

2. For each species, briefly describe 1 adaptation that appears to make it better able to survive in the particular environment where it is usually found.

    Adaptations may be structural, functional, behavioral, or a combination of these. Examples of adaptations that you might use include lungs, gills, internal skeleton, external skeleton, structural protections against predation, behavioral protections against predation, and feeding habits.

    The information on Copymaster *Marine Organisms* will help you complete this task.

SC*LINKS*®
NSTA

Topic: evolution
Go to: www.scilinks.org
Code: human3E71

3. Work with the other members of your team to answer the following questions. Record your responses in your journal.

    a. In general, do most of these marine organisms appear to be well-suited to survival in their environments? Support your answer with specific examples.

    b. Are all inherited characteristics adaptations? Explain your answer, and support it with specific examples.

    c. Name a characteristic that is an adaptation in 1 environment but would not be an adaptation in another environment.

    d. What explanation can you offer for the presence of characteristics that may not be particularly adaptive for a modern organism in its current environment?

Part B   Diversity and Adaptation across Time

1. Work with the members of your team to examine the plant specimens that your teacher has provided.

Manipulate, dissect, or otherwise examine the specimens to gather as much information as possible.

CAUTION: Scalpel blades and needles are sharp; handle with care. Replace cork on needle tip after use.

2. Record your plant observations in your journal. Use your sketching skills to record the observations that are best recorded through drawings.

3. Respond to the following items. Record your answers in your journal.

   a. Identify at least 1 characteristic that all of these organisms share.

   b. Are these organisms as diverse as those in the DVD segment "Marine Life," or are they more similar to each other? Explain your answer.

PAGE 134

4. Read the essay *From Cell to Seed* on page 134 for a short description of the evolution of modern plants. In your journal, make a list of the major adaptations that took place during the evolution of modern plants.

5. For each plant specimen that you observed, use your list of adaptations from step 4 to help you identify at least 1 characteristic that biologists might use to distinguish that plant from all of the others. Record these characteristics in your journal.

6. Arrange your plant specimens in groups that represent those that are most closely related. Discuss and identify at least 1 characteristic that each group shares.

7. Study the branching diagram in Figure 3.5. This diagram shows the relatedness of some vertebrates.

   The points where branches separate represent where new lineages evolved from a common ancestor.

8. What do scientists call the characteristics that enable organisms to function better in their environment?

9. As a team, create a branching pattern on your large sheet of paper that organizes your plant specimens. Think as a biologist would and classify them according to their evolutionary divergence, or separation from an ancestral form.

   Be sure that someone who is not in your team would understand your diagram.

10. Label your diagram with the names of the plant specimens. Include a short statement that identifies the major distinguishing characteristic that caused you to place it at that point in the diagram.

11. Post your diagram in your classroom as your teacher directs. Be prepared to share your ideas in a class discussion.

Analysis

Work with the members of your team to answer the following questions about the relationships among adaptation, diversity, and evolution. Record your answers in your journal.

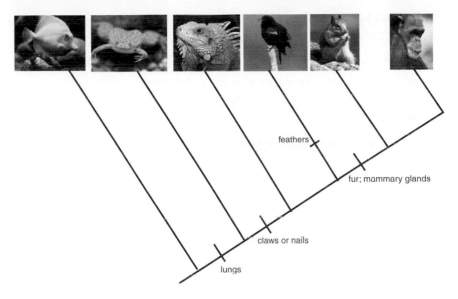

feathers

fur; mammary glands

claws or nails

lungs

Figure 3.5 A branching diagram shows the relatedness of organisms.

1. What are adaptations? Illustrate your answer using examples drawn from the organisms that you studied in Part A and Part B.

2. How is the diversity of organisms on earth related to the diversity of environments in which organisms live? Illustrate your answer using examples drawn from the organisms that you studied in Part A and Part B.

3. If a mutation occurs in a population, it can result in the appearance of a new adaptation. How might this relate to the ability of organisms to colonize new environments? Illustrate your answer using examples drawn from your work in Part B.

4. Explain biological diversity.

5. Propose a general explanation for the appearance of biological diversity on earth.

   Refer to the essay *Mutations Are a Source of Variation* on page 139 for background information that may help you answer this question.

SCi**LINKS**
NSTA

Topic: origin of life
Go to: www.scilinks.org
Code: human3E73

PAGE 139

Elaborate

Using Unity to Organize Diversity

Living systems share different characteristics as a result of their common ancestry. These characteristics provide biologists with a powerful set of guidelines for organizing the millions of different types of life into large categories of similar organisms. This organizing process, called **classification**, plays an important role in biologists' attempts to understand life. First, classification helps them subdivide the numerous types of living (and extinct) organisms into groups of more or less similar types that they can study productively. Second, the act of creating classification categories helps them think about the evolutionary relationships that exist among different types of organisms. In fact, we might say that classification categories represent hypotheses that biologists develop about how different forms of life are related. As scientists change their thinking about these relationships, the ways in which they organize these categories also may change.

This activity offers you a chance to practice biological classification. You will further develop your growing understanding of biological diversity, its origins, and the ways in which scientists study and make sense of it.

Materials   (per team of 4)

set of objects   set of organism cards

PROCESS AND PROCEDURES

Topic: taxonomy/
systematics
Go to: www.scilinks.org
Code: human3E74

Part A   Classification as a Tool

1. Work with your team to examine the set of nonliving objects. What, if anything, do all of these objects share in common? What characteristics do some objects possess that others do not? Record your observations in your journal.

2. Sort the objects in your set into 4 different categories.

   When you sort your objects into categories, you are *classifying* them. The system that you use to sort your objects is called a *classification scheme.*

3. Write your team's classification scheme on a card. Leave the card face down on the table with the sorted objects.

4. When directed by your teacher, go to another team's table and try to guess what their classification scheme is. Compare your classification scheme with that of the other team. Are the categories the same? Could you easily recognize their categories?

5. Answer the following questions in your journal:

   a. Your team and the other team probably used a different basis for the classification schemes. Nevertheless, each team used *some* basis. That is, each team used some general *criteria* to determine what groups they would include in their scheme and what objects would go into each group. Is it possible to classify without establishing such criteria? Support your answer with a different example of classification drawn from your life experience.

   b. Consider the categories of objects that you created in your classification scheme. Could you further separate (or classify) the objects in any of these categories into smaller groups within the large category? Support your answer with specific references to the objects and the classification scheme that you developed.

Part B   Biological Classification

A classification scheme in which objects are sorted first into large categories and then into smaller groups within the large categories is said to be **hierarchical**.

1. Examine the data provided on your organism cards. Work with the other members of your team to create a simple *hierarchical classification scheme* for these organisms.

    Ask yourselves what broad category all of these organisms fit into. Then ask yourselves what criteria you could use to sort them into smaller categories. Continue creating smaller categories until each category contains only 1 type of organism.

2. Figure 3.6 illustrates the hierarchical classification scheme that most biologists use. Compare this classification scheme with the one that you have developed for your organisms. Which levels in Figure 3.6 represent levels in the scheme that you developed? Explain your answer.

3. Complete the classification diagram shown on Copymaster *Biological Classification*. Fill in the names of the organisms that you classified. Then add the names of other appropriate organisms to the remaining lines.

4. Answer the following questions in your journal:

    a. Which group in a hierarchical classification scheme contains
        - the most organisms?
        - the fewest organisms?
        - the most different types of organisms (the greatest diversity)?
        - the fewest different types of organisms (the least diversity)?

    b. What does this classification scheme suggest about evolutionary relationships that exist among these organisms? Explain your answer.

        Information in the essay *Organizing Diversity* on page 141 may help you with this step.

PAGE 141

Analysis

Work with your team to complete the following tasks:

1. Imagine that you are a member of a large publishing company that is writing a new textbook for high school biology classes. Your team has been assigned to write the chapter on the nature and importance of biological classification. Before you can begin to write, of course, you need to decide what the future students should learn about your topic.

    Identify the *three most important ideas* about biological classification that you think a scientifically literate citizen should understand. Summarize these ideas in three concise statements, and record them in your journal.

2. Now, imagine that the editor-in-chief has decided that your team must reduce the size of the book and that there will be no chapter on biological classification. Instead, everything you want the students to learn about the topic has to fit on one page, preferably in the form of a diagram or a drawing (although this can include words or short statements). Luckily, you already have distilled your understanding about the topic into three clear statements (step 1).

    Create a one-page display that communicates and illustrates these ideas in an attractive and interesting manner.

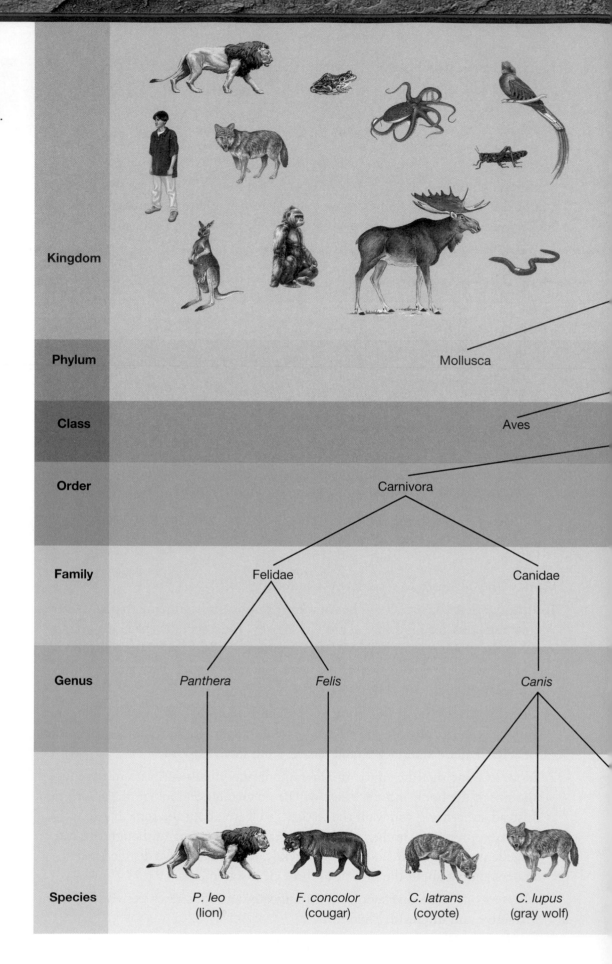

Figure 3.6
Biologists use this hierarchical scheme to classify organisms.

Kingdom

Phylum — Mollusca

Class — Aves

Order — Carnivora

Family — Felidae, Canidae

Genus — *Panthera*, *Felis*, *Canis*

Species — *P. leo* (lion), *F. concolor* (cougar), *C. latrans* (coyote), *C. lupus* (gray wolf)

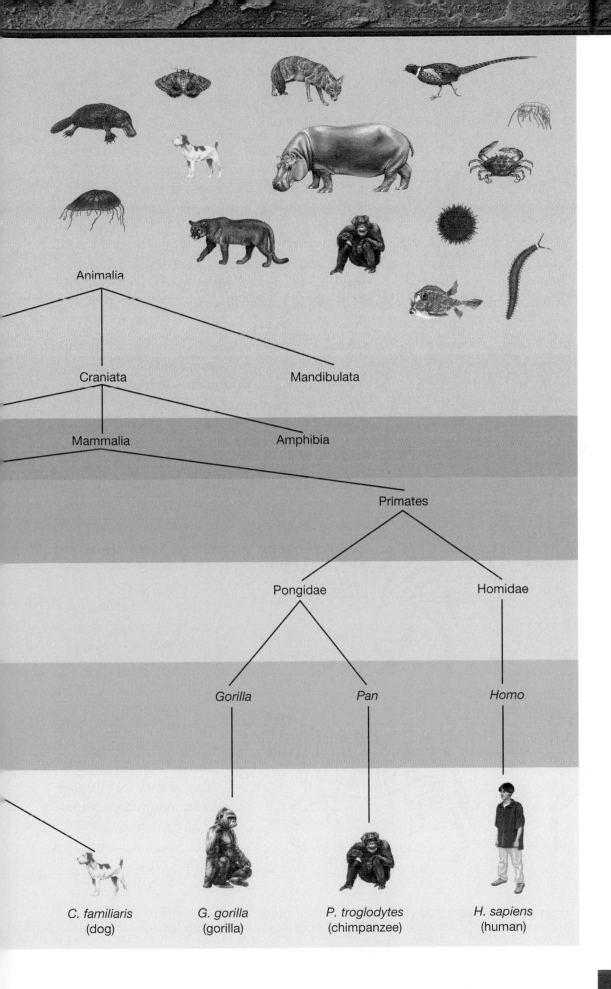

Animalia

Craniata

Mandibulata

Mammalia

Amphibia

Primates

Pongidae

Homidae

Gorilla

Pan

Homo

C. familiaris
(dog)

G. gorilla
(gorilla)

P. troglodytes
(chimpanzee)

H. sapiens
(human)

3. Follow your teacher's instructions and post your display for the class. If you were a textbook editor, which display would you choose to use in the book and why? Record your answer in your journal.

Explaining the Zebra's Stripes

In the last activity, you examined the process of biological classification. Biologists use this as a tool to organize and express the structural and evolutionary relationships that exist among all living things. Think about that idea more closely. Might we expect classification schemes to contain some areas of controversy and question? Certainly, when scientists are classifying an organism about which little is known, you would expect to hear arguments about where to place it in the classification scheme. Perhaps your team encountered such controversies when you created a classification scheme in the last activity. Would you also expect classification schemes to change over time? What happens as scientists discover new information that increases or modifies their understanding of particular relationships and adaptations?

An important characteristic of scientific knowledge is an openness to change and modification. Scientific knowledge is not static. Scientists continuously discover new information and test and reevaluate existing understandings. Usually, changes in scientific knowledge are not so great that we must discard *all* of our previous explanations in favor of new ideas. Nevertheless, as we gain more detailed information about the natural world, our explanations grow and change to reflect it.

Your next activity illustrates this characteristic of growth in scientific knowledge. You will participate in a process to learn about the difficulties that scientists face as they sort through what might appear to be easily answered questions. Can you tell a zebra by its stripes? Is one zebra just like the next?

Chapman's zebra

Grant's zebra

Grevy's zebra

mountain zebra

Figure 3.7 What similarities and differences do you observe among these four zebras?

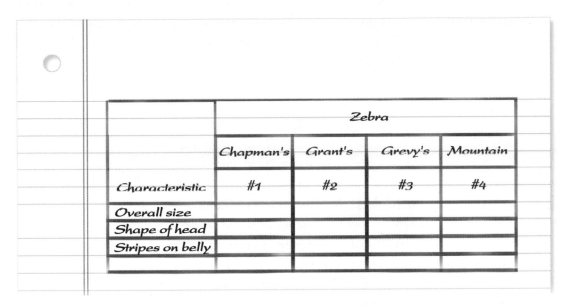

	Zebra			
	Chapman's	Grant's	Grevy's	Mountain
Characteristic	#1	#2	#3	#4
Overall size				
Shape of head				
Stripes on belly				

Figure 3.8   Sample table.   Record your observations in a table similar to this one.

Materials   (per team of 4)

DVD and player

PROCESS AND PROCEDURES

Part A   Looking Closely at the Concept of Species

1. Work with the other members of your team to compare the physical characteristics of the 4 zebras shown in the DVD segment "Zebras" and in Figure 3.7.

   These zebras represent 4 populations that live in Africa; each population has a different common name. Record your observations about these animals in your journal in a table similar to the one in Figure 3.8.

2. Examine the map in Figure 3.9. Compare the ranges of each of these 4 populations of zebras. Add this information to the observations that you recorded in step 1.

3. Discuss with your teammates how you might categorize the 4 zebras into species. Record your answer in your journal.

   The fundamental question here is whether each of these populations of zebras represents a separate species or whether some of them are members of the same species. Develop and support your answer using the information that you collected in steps 1 and 2.

4. Examine the additional information on Copymaster *African Zebras* to make further comparisons among the 4 populations of zebras. How might you categorize these zebras? Support your answer using all of the information you have available to you. Record your answer in your journal.

5. Contribute your ideas to a class discussion about the zebras and about the difficulties involved in assigning species distinctions.

Topic: species/speciation
Go to: www.scilinks.org
Code: human3E79

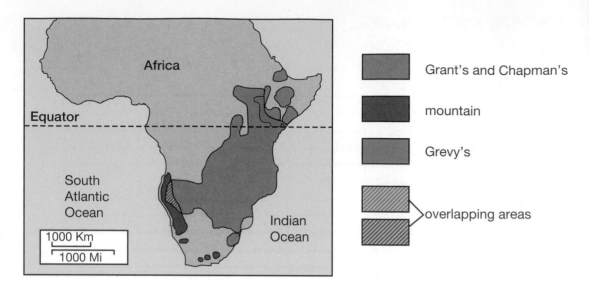

Figure 3.9 How do the ranges of the four zebras compare?

Legend:
- Grant's and Chapman's
- mountain
- Grevy's
- overlapping areas

Africa

Equator

South Atlantic Ocean

1000 Km
1000 Mi

Indian Ocean

Part B   Explaining the Adaptive Significance of Structural Characteristics

One of the most important relationships that you have encountered in this chapter is the relationship between the particular adaptations that a species displays and its environment. In the activity *Adaptation, Diversity, and Evolution*, for example, you looked at some of the different adaptations that various types of marine organisms possess. You then matched these adaptations to the challenges that these organisms face in their particular environments. In the same activity, you looked at the history of the evolution of plants. You noted how the appearance of new adaptations correlated with movements onto land.

How far can we extend this statement: Biological diversity results from random genetic change combined with natural selection? Is all variation among different species the result of selection for adaptive characteristics? Alternatively, are there limitations to the explanations that we can offer about some characteristics?

1. Hold a brainstorming session with the other members of your team about the significance of a zebra's stripes. How might these stripes be adaptations? List your ideas in your journal.

2. Read the 2 explanations on Copymaster *Ideas about the Zebra's Stripes* for the appearance and perpetuation of the zebra's stripes.

3. Work with the other members of your team to analyze the data that relate to each explanation.

    As you read and discuss each explanation, identify and record each bit of evidence, each inference, and all of the assumptions that you recognize. Then decide whether each piece of information supports, does not support, or contradicts each explanation. Take notes in your journal about the results of your discussion. View the DVD segment again if you think it will help you.

4. Discuss the strengths and weaknesses of each of the 2 explanations. Summarize this discussion with a list of the evidence that supports, or fails to support, each explanation.

5. Work with the other members of your team to determine which explanation best accounts for the data presented. Record your answer in your journal.

   Weigh the data that you have collected by asking yourself questions such as, What pieces of information are most relevant to each explanation? What are the most serious flaws of each explanation? Might there be more than 1 explanation to account for the stripes?

6. Participate in a discussion and evaluation of the explanations.

Analysis

Answer the following questions in your journal:

1. Do new species appear on earth because two individuals from separate species mate and their offspring is a new and different species? Explain your answer.

2. Have you ever heard people say, "I don't pay much attention to reports about new scientific findings. After all, scientists say one thing about x, y, or z this year. But they said something else last year, and something different the year before. It's clear that they don't know what's going on"?

   Analyze those statements in light of what you have learned in this activity about the nature of science. In your answer, refer to your experiences in both Part A and Part B of this activity. Record your critique in your journal. Be prepared to share it as your teacher directs.

3. In the essay *Five Kingdoms*, you read about the history of the classification scheme that biologists use to group all living systems into five large kingdoms.

   a. How does that history illustrate this statement: Classification is not an end in itself, but is a means, or a tool, that biologists use to express their understanding about biological diversity?

   b. How does it illustrate this statement: Science is characterized by its openness to change and modification?

   c. What role does the discovery or development of new evidence play in the modification of scientific ideas?

Figure 3.10
U.S. researcher Karla MacEwan collecting plant samples in Costa Rica.

First Encounter with the Critter

Evaluate

Throughout the activities and essays in this chapter, you have focused on how evolution has produced the tremendous diversity of living systems that exist (and have existed) on earth. You also have seen that, in addition to explaining the diversity of life, evolution accounts for its unity. Evolution has produced organisms that are very different from one another, adapted to life in different habitats, and even adapted differently to the same habitat. Evolution *from a common ancestor*, however, also has resulted in organisms that show important similarities to each other.

This activity, the first of six, invites you to use your imagination as you evaluate your understanding of evolution—the process that explains both the unity and the diversity of life—in an unusual way. In this activity, you will "meet" your critter. You will then have a chance to revisit your critter in Units 2–6. In each visit, you will add to your description of the organism as your understanding of the unifying principles of biology increases.

SCENARIO

Keep Your Eyes Open

It was a thrill to hear that the research funds came through. Now you can embark on your long-awaited trip into the wilderness to observe and record data about several endangered species. The conservation organization that is sponsoring your trip has assigned you to a team that will spend several weeks in one location. The organization has given you a list of organisms that you should observe. As a born naturalist, however, you are determined to keep your eyes open for whatever you find of interest.

Materials (per person)

folder with 5 sheets of plain paper   felt-tipped markers   habitat card

PROCESS AND PROCEDURES

1. Study the habitat card that describes where you are going. Mount the card on a page in your folder as a permanent record of the environment in which you will work for the next few weeks.

2. Describe your organism by drawing 1 or more diagrams of it. Include labels with brief descriptions of its distinctive structures.

    Invent an organism, or critter. Use your imagination. The organism that you discover may resemble others found in this habitat or another habitat. Or you might create something quite different from any real species.

    Remember, your critter invention is the evidence that your teacher will use to evaluate what you have learned about evolution, biological diversity, and the unity of life.

3. Write a paragraph about the adaptations you labeled on your critter drawing. Select 1 adaptation as an example to explain your understanding of how adaptations arise in a population and how they can lead to new species.

4. Write a 2nd paragraph that explains what kingdom you would assign your critter to and why. Include an explanation for your critter's placement in a kingdom based on its common ancestry with other organisms in the same kingdom. Explain how your critter's species originated.

SCENARIO

What's That?

After weeks of careful observation and mountains of detailed notes, you have located and studied several of the organisms on your list, although others have eluded you. Then the unexpected happens: you find an organism that scientists have never seen before. You've done it! You have discovered a perviously unknown species.

When you describe the most closely related organisms to your critter, your explanation for the relatedness must provide evidence that you understand how new species evolve.

5. Obtain a rubric from your teacher that explains the grading criteria for your critter. Read the rubric carefully. Use it as a checklist to be certain that you describe your newly discovered critter effectively.

You will know that you have generated a good description if it meets the following criteria:

◆ It describes how your organism resembles all known forms of life.
◆ It describes how your organism is adapted to the habitat in which you found it.
◆ It identifies the known species to which your new organism is most closely related, and it describes the evidence on which you base your answer.

6. One of the most exciting privileges granted to the individual who discovers a new form of life is the honor of naming it. Complete your initial description of this new species by giving it both a common name and a scientific name. (Remember, the scientific name must indicate the organism's relatedness to other organisms.) Add an appropriate caption to each diagram that you have drawn, and record the organism's names in your folder.

Refer to the essay *Organizing Diversity* on page 141 for information about how scientists name new species.

Analysis

Which of the following two statements is most consistent with scientists' understanding of the process of evolution, and why? What is wrong with the other statement? Record your response in your folder.

Statement 1: The habitat that I worked in is very wet and salty. The organism that I discovered evolved a rubberlike skin to keep from shriveling up.

Statement 2: The habitat that I worked in is very wet and salty. The organism that I discovered has a rubberlike skin that may have evolved because it offered protection from the harmful effects of all that salt.

UNIT 1 ESSAYS

Evolution: Patterns and Products of Change in Living Systems

The Chimp Scientist

. . . I have often wondered exactly what it was I felt as I stared at the wild country that so soon I should be roaming. Vanne admitted afterward to have been secretly horrified by the steepness of the slopes and the impenetrable appearance of the valley forests. And David Anstey told me several months later that he had guessed I would be packed up and gone within six weeks. I remember feeling neither excitement nor trepidation but only a curious sense of detachment. What had I, the girl standing on the government launch in her jeans, to do with the girl who in a few days would be searching those very mountains for wild chimpanzees?

Jane Goodall, *In the Shadow of Man*

Dr. Jane Goodall began to observe and study the chimpanzees of Gombe Stream in Tanzania, Africa, more than 30 years ago. At that time, some people thought that it was not scientific to talk about an animal's mind or personality or to give funny names to their subjects. Today, however, we recognize Goodall's work as one of the great contributions to science made during the 20th century.

Thirty years ago, some people thought of science as experiments that men in white coats conducted in laboratories. Indeed, some people still have that mistaken image today. As you have been discovering, however, science is a particular way of knowing and learning about the world. We each can learn the methods of science and put them into practice. It likely is becoming clear to you that observation and reflection are key aspects of science. Dr. Goodall's work is an exemplary model of both of these aspects.

The notes pictured in Figure E1.2 are copied from a page of Dr. Jane Goodall's field journal. Like your journal, her notebook documented her observations. The notes recorded on the page shown here reveal the

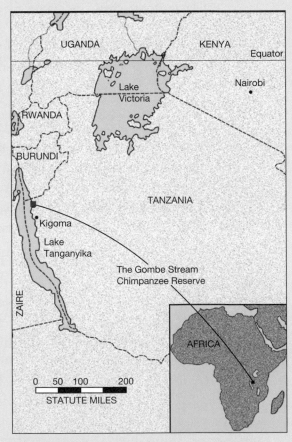

Figure E1.1   The Gombe Stream Chimpanzee Reserve.   The Gombe Stream Chimpanzee Reserve is located near Kigoma, on Lake Tanganyika in Tanzania.

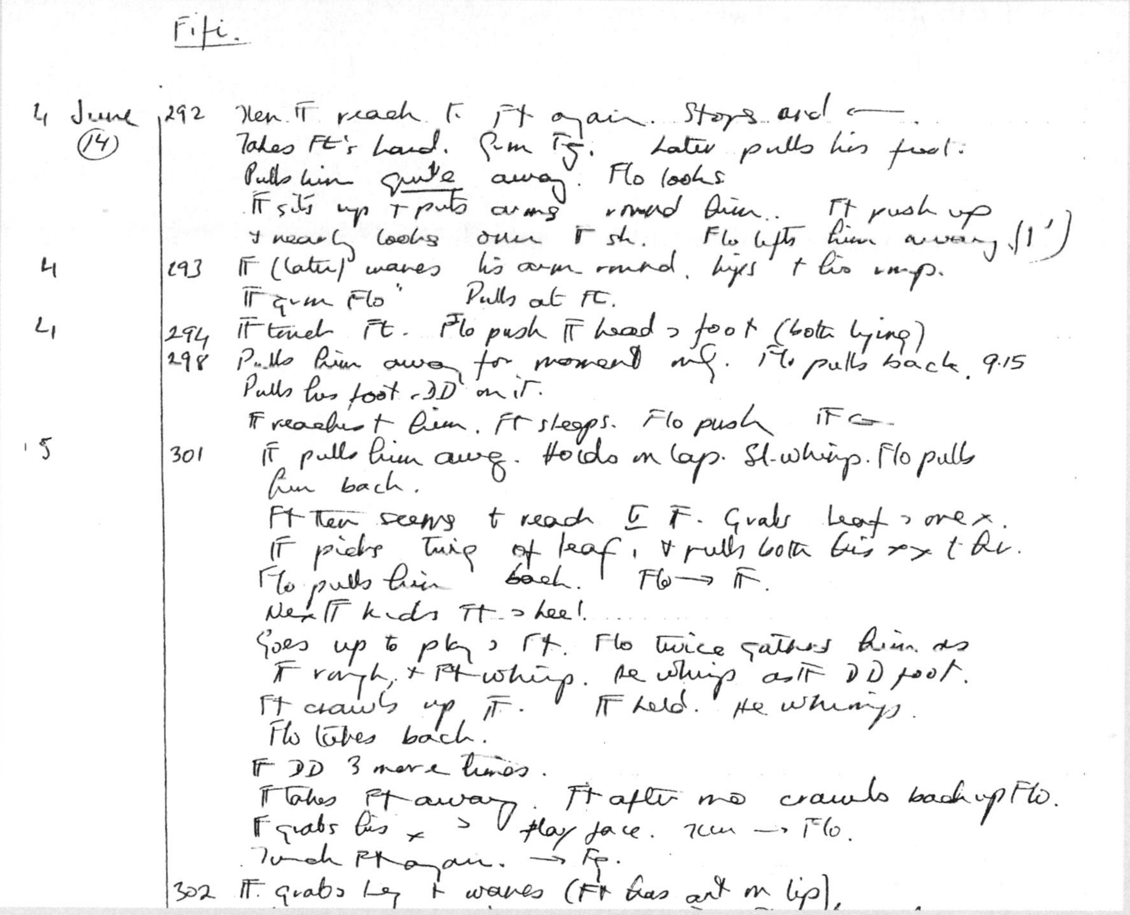

Figure E1.2 Dr. Jane Goodall's field notes. These notes were taken while observing Flo and her children, Fifi (FF) and Flint (Ft). Can you imagine the scene as Fifi tried to take her baby brother, Flint, from Flo before she was ready to entrust him to her care? Flo had at least five children in her lifetime and was an exceptional mother.

value of careful organization for keeping accurate records. Can you tell what Dr. Goodall's notes mean? She made detailed observations while she kept careful watch on her chimpanzee subjects. So she used her own abbreviations and note-taking style that were designed to make it easy to write quickly and understand later.

To learn about the true nature of chimpanzees in the wild, you have to go into the wild—into their natural habitat—and observe them across long periods of time. It took Goodall close to 4 years to collect a significant amount of information. The chimpanzees were hard to find and resisted her presence for the first several years. But eventually they came to trust her—this itself

was a key observation. Goodall carefully recorded their every move, interaction, gesture, and grunt. She discovered the intricacies of their way of living and of their social nature. She found that chimpanzees are caring, clever, and capable of lasting attachments. Through years of observations, she also learned that some individuals are capable of extreme aggression, even cannibalism.

Thirty years ago, scientists thought that humans were the only tool-making animals and generally assumed that humans were the only organisms that could think or have emotions. Today, due to the work of Dr. Goodall and other scientists in related fields, we recognize that many intellectual abilities once thought to be unique to humans are present in other animals. For instance, Goodall observed over and over the ability of chimpanzees not only to use tools, but also to recognize a need for them and make one ahead of time. One such observation involved a chimp named Mike. He finally solved the problem of how to get a banana that Dr. Goodall held out to him. Apparently too nervous to take the banana from her hand, he finally used a stick to knock it to the ground. Only then, did he grab it and run. Even though Mike was not the biggest or strongest male, he was clever. He was able to bluff his way to become the top male by banging together empty kerosene cans that he found in Goodall's camp (see Figure E1.3).

Because of Jane Goodall's long-term study and careful observations, we are able to construct our understanding of the true nature of chimpanzees. This knowledge is important because the chimpanzee is the closest living relative of the human species. Learning more

Figure E1.3   Mike bangs kerosene cans together. Although Mike was not the largest or strongest male, he made his way to the top by creating frightful noise with these empty cans.

about chimpanzees makes it possible to learn more about our common evolutionary heritage. ◆

Do You Have a Grip on That?

Tying a shoe, threading a needle, throwing a baseball, taking notes, or carrying a bucket. Think of all the tasks—large and small—that you do with your hands every day. Have you ever thought about the amazing number of ways in which you can use your hands to grip something?

Scientists have studied the different grips of primates for some time and have more than one way of classifying what they have observed. One school of thought divides grips into two major categories: power grips and precision grips. You use the power grip when you grasp an object with your palm and then curve your fingers around it. The power from the power grip comes as you apply pressure with your whole hand. This power is especially evident in the muscles of your palm that are located at the base of your thumb and

that are responsible for moving your thumb. The power grip requires the full grip of the hand—when you use a hammer or open a tightly closed jar, for example.

The precision grip is a more intricate grip that requires a specific alignment of the thumb with one or more fingers. The thumb applies pressure against another finger or fingers in order to accomplish a precise motion, such as picking up a coin, or to accomplish a precise motion that also requires strength, such as placing a key in a lock and turning it.

Another school of thought subdivides the power and precision grips into as many as 12 categories by defining the grip according to the exact placement of the palm, fingers, and thumb. Figure E1.4 shows seven of the 12 grips.

Hook grasp. The fingers are used as a hook; the thumb is not used.

Cylindric grasp. The palm is used to grasp a cylindrical object; the thumb opposes all of the fingers.

Fist grasp. The fingers are wrapped around a narrow or small object; the thumb opposes the fingers, lying on top of them and securing the grip.

Spheric grasp. The palm is used to grasp a spherical object; the thumb opposes the fingers.

Tip prehension. The tip of the thumb and one or more fingers are used like tweezers to pick up small objects; the thumb opposes one or more fingers.

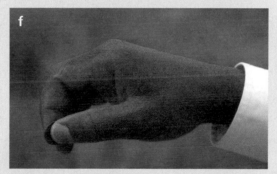

Palmar prehension. The flat surface of the thumb is pressed against the flat surface of the finger or fingers. This grip is similar to the way the tip of a pair of pliers holds an object.

Lateral prehension. The thumb presses against the side of the index finger with other fingers providing additional support. Another type of lateral grip involves the sides of two fingers pressing against each other.

Figure E1.4
Types of Grips. These photographs show seven of the 12 ways humans can grip objects. Which grips did you see the primates use in the DVD "Observing Primates"? Which grip did you test in *Primates Exploring Primates*?

Mapping the Brain

In the mid-1800s, an engineer named Phineas Gage made a spark while tapping a metal rod to set a dynamite charge. In that instant, his whole life changed. The charge exploded, and the metal rod shot up with enormous force and passed through the young man's cheek, eye, and the front part of his brain. He fell backward. The other workers thought he was dead. Remarkably, he survived. It seemed that his only lasting injury would be the loss of sight in one eye. Unfortunately, his loss of sight was only a small part of the lasting effect. As time passed, people who worked with Gage found him to be an entirely different person. His good nature was a thing of the past. He had survived, but not as himself. Instead, he was a foul-mouthed, rude, and untrustworthy person.

For more than 100 years, the strange effects of Gage's remarkable injury and recovery remained a mystery. But in the 1990s, scientists combined their improved understanding of brain function, computer modeling techniques, and new data from Gage's skull to find the answer. The scientists found that the accident damaged both hemispheres of Gage's frontal lobes, which is the part of the brain that influences social behavior (see Figure E1.5).

This dramatic and unusual story is just one example of the way the human brain and the brains of other animals have specialized regions that control different activities. For instance, the victim of a motorcycle accident who sustains a severe brain injury may continue to breathe and to have a regular heartbeat. Yet he or she may have no awareness of the surroundings, no conscious thoughts, and no voluntary control over the movement of arms and legs. In a situation like this, the family members, the physicians, and the legal experts are faced with a difficult question: Is this patient a living person, even though there is no thought and the body can stay alive only through artificial feeding? This dilemma raises many complex ethical questions. But it also shows an important biological fact: the brain has specialized functions, and these functions often can be mapped to specific regions of the brain.

We have learned quite a bit about the role of different parts of animal brains. The drawing in Figure E1.6 shows only some of what we know about the different functions of various regions of the brain. The large upper part of the brain, the cerebrum, is responsible for complex reasoning, thought,

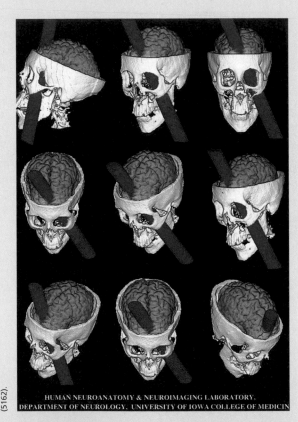

Source: American Association for the Advancement of Science. (1994). The return of Phineas Gage: Clues about the brain from the skull of a famous patient. Reprinted with permission from *Science, 264* (5162).

HUMAN NEUROANATOMY & NEUROIMAGING LABORATORY.
DEPARTMENT OF NEUROLOGY, UNIVERSITY OF IOWA COLLEGE OF MEDICIN

Figure E1.5 In 1994, scientists at the University of Iowa used measurements from Gage's skull along with modern neuroimagery technology to revisit the accident and determine the likely location of damage to the brain. Dr. Hanna Damasio created this series of digital images showing the results of their work from different angles.

language, voluntary movement, and the initial processing of sensations.

The structure at the back of the brain, which in certain views looks like a clamshell, is called the cerebellum. It controls posture and balance. The brain stem directs critical, life-sustaining activities such as breathing and heartbeat. This part of the brain evolved long ago, and it occurs in one form or another in many animals. In the example of the victim of the motorcycle accident, the brain stem may have been uninjured. If this were so, what would happen? The victim would continue to breathe, the heart would continue to beat, and other body functions would continue. But the cerebrum may have been damaged so seriously that the victim would be unable to think. ◆

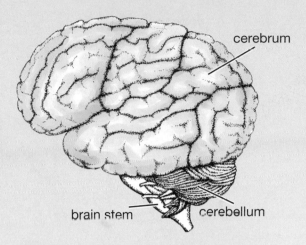

Figure E1.6   Regions of the brain.
The cerebrum is responsible for conscious thought, language, and voluntary movement. The cerebellum is responsible for balance and posture.

Brains and More Brains

Think hard! Add 235 and 25, and then divide by two. Now, which part of the cerebrum did you use? The left half of your cerebrum was probably the most active. On the other hand, if you imagine how to draw a picture, you would probably use more of the right half of your brain. We are just starting to unravel the mysteries about how the brain works. Scientists called **neurobiologists** study the different regions of the brain and work to learn more about how they function and what they control.

Not only are the physical structures of the brain specialized, but also within each of the structures there is further specialization. The cerebrum has two distinct parts, or sides, called the left and right hemispheres (see Figure E1.7). The hemispheres individually control certain behaviors. Sensory and movement functions on the left side of the body are controlled by the right hemisphere of the cerebrum and vice versa. The specific area of the cerebrum that is responsible for controlling the movements of your body is called the motor cortex. The specific area of

the cerebrum that is responsible for letting you feel sensations from your body is called the sensory cortex (see Figure E1.8).

Scientists have been able to map many sites on the motor cortex to a particular part of the human body. They have been able to do the same for the sensory cortex. That is, when you move a certain part of your body, scientists know what part of your motor cortex is making that movement possible. When you smell a rose, scientists know what part of your sensory cortex is allowing you to experience that fragrance.

Figure E1.9 shows the results of this mapping process. The figure of the person looks distorted because the size of the area that is mapped to a particular part of the body is not related to the actual size. Rather, it is related to the amount of precision required for that part of the body to do its job. In humans, a good deal of space is dedicated to the face, tongue, and hands. Why do you think that is so?

In most individuals, the left hemisphere of the human brain controls language and

left hemisphere

right hemisphere

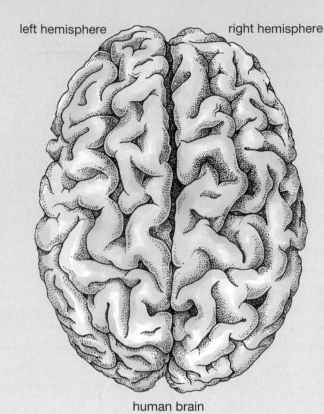

human brain

Figure E1.7
Top view of human brain (approximately 65 percent of lifesize). The human cerebrum is split into halves or hemispheres.

Figure E1.8
Side view of human brain. In humans, the motor cortex and the sensory cortex are located alongside each other, across both hemispheres of the cerebrum. The cortex is the top layer of the cerebrum.

motor cortex

sensory cortex

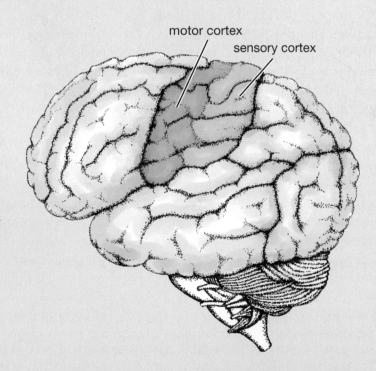

speech, as well as mathematical and other analytical abilities. The right hemisphere is responsible for visual and spatial processing. Many functions, including various aspects of those mentioned above, are controlled jointly by both hemispheres. Communication between the two hemispheres is possible because a bundle of nerve fibers, called the **corpus callosum**, connects them.

An unusual operation on the brain, one that is rarely done, provides evidence for how the corpus callosum makes it possible for the right and left hemispheres to communicate and work together. In extreme cases of epilepsy—a human condition that causes seizures—the fibers of the corpus callosum are surgically cut, separating the two hemispheres. This procedure greatly reduces the number and severity of seizures. Most patients notice no change in their perception

or movement. Their perception, however, is impaired. Messages from their right hand are received only by the left hemisphere. Messages from their left hand are received only by the right hemisphere. Because of the surgery, the hemispheres cannot share information anymore.

The patients generally do not notice this impairment because they make up for it by using their eyes. Unlike messages from the hands, messages from each eye are received in *both* hemispheres. Some patients who had this surgery participated in research that revealed the nature of their impairment. When a researcher places a blindfold on the patient and then places a common object, perhaps a toothbrush, in his or her left hand, the patient can describe what the object feels like. ("It has a long, hard handle and soft bristles at the tip.") Sometimes the patient can describe how

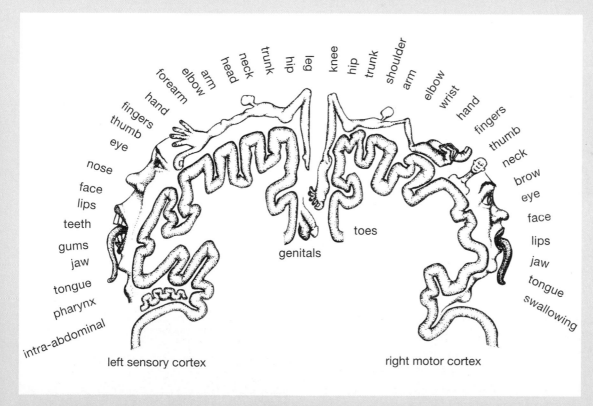

Figure E1.9 Parts of the human body mapped to the motor and sensory cortices. The resulting figure looks distorted because the area of the cortex that is devoted to a particular body part is not related to the actual size of that part. It is instead related to the amount of precision required to control it. In this drawing, only the left sensory cortex and the right motor cortex are shown.

he or she would use the object ("you use it every morning"), but cannot name the object. When the researcher places an object in the patient's right hand, he or she can name it ("it's a toothbrush"), but cannot describe to the researcher how to use it.

Again, under normal circumstances in which the patients are able to use both of their hands and their eyes, their brains compensate. Although the two hemispheres of their brains cannot communicate, they can gather information for each half by using both hands. In that case, the patients experience little difficulty.

This example, and observations made from many other types of surgeries and experiments, provides important evidence for how the brain works. The evidence suggests that the brain can process information in more than one way. In addition, certain functions that are normally performed by one region of the brain can sometimes be taken over by other regions. This is particularly true when the individual is young. For instance, when young children suffer strokes (a blood clot that damages the brain) they tend to recover more quickly than an older individual does. For example, if the stroke damaged a child's left hemisphere, instead of losing some or all of their language ability, the right hemisphere often takes over this function.

Another example of different regions of the brain taking over for a damaged region takes place when input from one of the senses is impaired, for example, when an individual loses his or her sight. In this case, input from another sense will compensate. For these reasons, the brain often is said to be *plastic*—that is, it can be molded by certain events and experiences to accommodate particular circumstances. ◆

On Being Human

Have you ever seen a cow laugh or a cat tap its foot in time to music? Have you ever heard a human purr? Humans are animals, yet humans do things that you would never expect to see in other animals. And other animals do things that you would never expect to see a human do. You are quite capable of *being* human, but you may not have taken time to really *think* about what it means. (The cow and cat haven't thought about themselves either, but as far as we know, they cannot do so. The fact that you can is just one of many ways in which humans can do unusual things.)

A surgeon reaches carefully past his assistant to suture in a small bit of vein that will bypass a block in the coronary artery on the patient's heart. The assistant firmly places the correct steel tool in the surgeon's palm and watches as the delicate procedure is completed.

Across town, in a concert hall, a guitarist waits for the applause to subside before she begins the next song. The fingers of her left hand push against the frets to produce a chord, while the fingers of her right hand rapidly pluck the strings in a set pattern. The audience recognizes the song and applauds.

These examples show some of the characteristics that distinguish humans from other animals—even from other closely

related animals, the primates. Humans, like many other primates, can grasp things with their hands and fingers. Primates such as gibbons, chimps, and spider monkeys also can grasp with their feet, a trait most humans do not share. However, the fine dexterity required to suture a vein or to play a complicated pattern of notes on the guitar appears to be unique to human hands. (The drawings in Figure E1.10 allow you to compare a series of primate hands.)

This precision is possible because humans have fully opposable thumbs that can move to touch the pad of any of the other fingers with precision. Not only is our grasp precise, it is strong. It is strong enough to grasp a baseball bat and hold on to it as we swing it with force, or to grasp a hammer and use it to pound a nail into a solid piece of wood.

Other primates share some degree of these various grips. A baboon that had been stung by a scorpion was able to grip the stinger and remove it. This action, however, does not require that the grip be strong. Human hands are shorter and broader than those of the baboon. Our thumbs are longer, stronger, and somewhat more flexible. The structure of the human hand allows room for additional muscle attachment, which results in a more flexible, more precise grip than that of the baboon.

Opposable thumbs are not the only characteristic that distinguishes humans from other primates and all other animals. Humans stand on two feet and walk fully upright with the body balanced directly over the feet. This **bipedal** method of moving is very different from other animals such as horses, spiders, or animals that fly. Although other primates sometimes walk upright, humans are the only ones that are *consistently* bipedal.

For any animal with a skeleton, the skeleton has features particularly suited to the animal's way of moving. Bird bones, for example, are mostly hollow and consequently are light—a property important for flying. Humans have large leg bones that support their weight. The bones of the spine form an S curve that is unlike the rounded arch of the gorilla's back (refer to Figure E1.11). Standing erect puts a lot of force and downward stress on the body. The S curve helps the human body tolerate that stress. In contrast, the gorilla usually uses all four limbs and walks on its feet and on the knuckles of its hands. For brief periods of time, the gorilla can walk upright, but the arch in its back is better suited to walking on all fours (see Figure E1.12).

Humans have other adaptations suited to bipedal walking. Look at your foot. The average human foot has rounded heels, an arch at mid-foot, and shorter toes than those

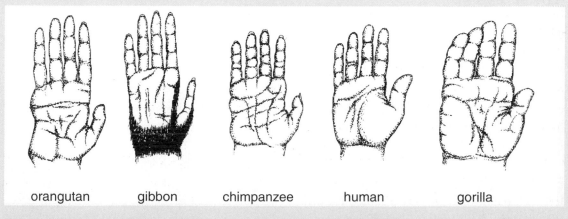

orangutan   gibbon   chimpanzee   human   gorilla

Figure E1.10   Primate hands.   Use these drawings to supplement your observations of primate hands. Which hands look capable of a power grip? Do you notice anything different about muscle development in the hands? Which hands do you think could use the precision grip? (See the essay *Do You Have a Grip on That?*)

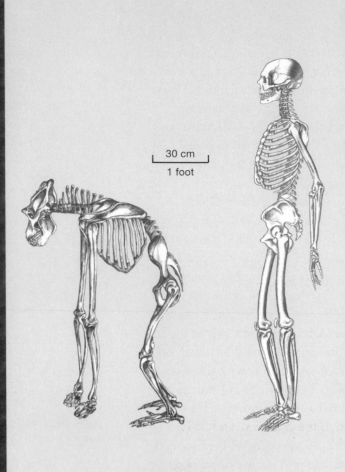

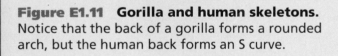

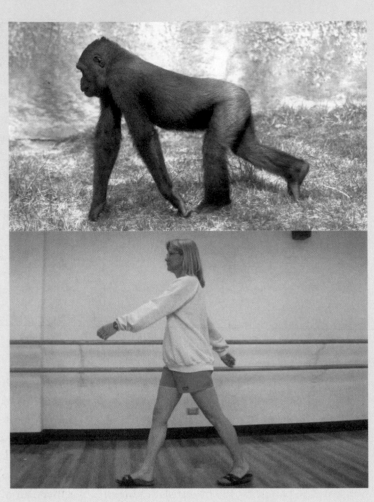

Figure E1.11 **Gorilla and human skeletons.** Notice that the back of a gorilla forms a rounded arch, but the human back forms an S curve.

Figure E1.12 **Methods of movement.** The gorilla is quadrupedal and walks on its hind feet and knuckles. Humans are completely bipedal, except as infants.

of other primates (see Figure E1.13). These features enable the foot to balance well and support the body weight even while walking on flat surfaces. Our legs are close together, allowing our weight to be balanced over each foot as we walk. A gorilla's foot certainly is more similar to a human foot than that of a cow or a lizard, but the gorilla's foot has longer toes and a big toe that looks and functions more like a thumb.

What are the advantages of upright posture? One important advantage is that it frees our hands and arms to do something other than to carry our bodies around. This way of moving about enables humans to gather and carry food or to carry and use tools.

Think back to the example of a surgeon (a tool user) repairing a damaged blood vessel. Even if a chimpanzee or gorilla could hold the surgical tools, would you want it to perform surgery on you? The human surgeon has a characteristic that makes such activities possible: humans have large and complex brains. It is important to remember, however, that the human brain is not the largest on earth—an elephant's brain and a whale's brain are larger. The brains of all animals control similar functions such as breathing, movement, and other body activities. But the part of the brain that controls abstract thinking and reasoning is very large and well developed in humans. In this function, the human brain appears to surpass all other animal brains—even those of relatively intelligent animals such as chimpanzees or dolphins. As a human, you have special abilities to find solutions to puzzles, to use complex language that is based on symbols, to use memories of the past to plan the future, and to reflect on all of these many abilities.

Although other animals may have some small degree of these characteristics, these abilities are very well developed in humans. As a collection, they distinguish humans from other organisms. Every animal and, indeed, every organism has a combination of characteristics that makes it distinctive; it also shares many characteristics with other living things. For example, human vision is better than that of a dog, but not nearly as acute as the vision of an eagle, which must spot prey on the ground from high up in the air. The dog, however, has an acute sense of smell to help it hunt. Humans are not nearly as fast as a cheetah, but humans are much faster than an armadillo or a slug. Each organism shares many basic life properties but each can be recognized by a collection of special traits.

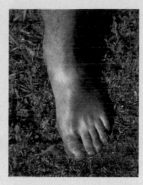

Figure E1.13 A gorilla foot and a human foot. Notice how the gorilla foot is similar to the gorilla hand (Figure E1.10). But the human foot, adapted for upright bipedal movement, is significantly different from the human hand.

In the huge and diverse group of animals, humans are most similar to mammals, which are animals that have hair, give birth to live young, and nurse their offspring. Within the group known as mammals, humans are most closely related to the primates. And now, having read this essay, you have accomplished something that as far as we know, no organism other than a human can do: you can read. ◆

Brains and a Lot of Nerve: A Complexity of Interactions

Look at the list of characteristics that you decided were unique to humans earlier in this chapter. How many of those qualities are possible only because of the way that the human brain works? What is it about the human brain that makes it able to think abstractly, remember complex information, and quickly process information from many sources at once?

Scientists who study the way the brain works use many methods to gather information about its functions. Some scientists use computer programs that model the abilities and processes of the human brain to aid their understanding. However,

it has been difficult to get computers to do things that are easy for humans to do. For example, think of how quickly you can recognize a familiar face. While computer scientists have been able to program computers to scan and recognize faces, they quickly lose their accuracy when there are simple changes, like the addition of dark glasses. Recognizing a person's face is likely to be something your brain does at the same time that you smell their cologne, remember past experiences, and speak a greeting. Imagine how hard it would be to build a computer and develop a program that models all of the human brain's abilities.

One reason it is so difficult for scientists to build a computer model of the human brain is that it contains many nerve cells, or **neurons**. The number of interconnections that these neurons form in the brain is astounding. Your brain contains about 10^{12} (1 trillion) neurons, and the many ways they can interconnect result in trillions of potential associations. Until someone develops computer technology that can form many more interconnections than are possible now, it will be difficult to model thinking that is similar to that of a human brain.

To understand how these interconnected neurons work, it is useful to look closely at the structure of a neuron. Figure E1.14 shows how unusual this cell is. At one end of a neuron are branched extensions, or **dendrites**, which act like antennae to receive incoming messages. At the other end of the neuron is an extension called an **axon**, which sends outgoing messages. Each neuron connects to hundreds or thousands of other neurons. This arrangement means that a single neuron can send or receive messages in many combinations with other neurons. For a message to travel to and from the brain, a sequence of interconnected neurons must receive and send the message. The neurons

form an organized network of neuron connections that extends throughout the brain and body. Biologists call the brain plus a body's network of neurons the **nervous system**. The nervous system provides communication between the brain and different regions *inside* the body, as well as linking the *outside* world and the *inner* world of the body.

Imagine what happens when you see a friend walk toward you smiling. You see the approaching person and it catches your attention. The sight of the person walking toward you is information that you receive from the outside world. A **stimulus** (plural: stimuli) is incoming information that causes the body to respond. The sound of footsteps is another form of stimulus. Your nervous system, like those of all animals, collects information from stimuli and signals the brain. The brain then processes the information and responds by sending back a signal to the appropriate part of the body. For example, the stimulus of seeing your friend's face allows your brain to recognize the person. Your brain responds to the stimulus and signals your face to smile back.

How is a message sent from one neuron to another? The message is actually a

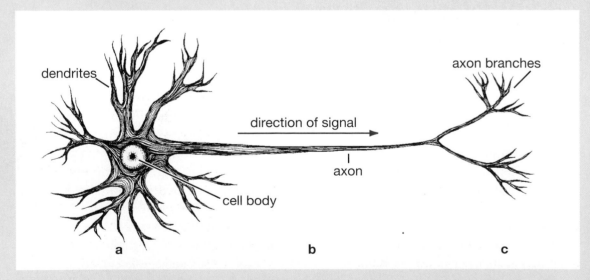

Figure E1.14 **A neuron is a nerve cell.** It has **(a)** extensions called dendrites, which receive nerve signals, **(b)** a long axon, which carries the nerve signals, and **(c)** axon branches, which transmit the nerve signals to the next neuron.

combination of an electrical signal that passes through a neuron and a chemical signal that passes between neurons. Changes in the electrical charge of the neuron cause the signal. An electrical impulse moves along an axon to the end of the neuron. Can you think of a time when an electrical charge built up on your body? For example, if you run around on a carpet in your socks, you sometimes feel a shock when you touch the television or another person. This example of an electrical charge is much greater than the charge found in your neurons. But the transfer of the charge from your body to another person's has some similarities to passing the signal between neurons. However, when an electrical signal passes from one neuron to another, it is translated into a chemical signal along the way.

A small space, or gap, separates neurons. This gap is called a **synapse**. When a message in one neuron (an electrical signal) reaches a synapse, it cannot jump the gap and continue sending the message electrically. Instead, the electrical impulse triggers the release of chemicals into the synapse. These chemicals are called **neurotransmitters** (*neuro* = nerve, *transmit* = to send). Neurotransmitters act as messengers that transmit the signal across the gap between neurons. When the neurotransmitters bind to specific proteins on the dendrites, or branching end, of the next neuron, the chemical signal is converted into an electrical signal. The electrical signal then travels along the length of the axon of the nerve cell. Once again, when the electrical signal reaches the next synapse, it will trigger the neuron to release neurotransmitters into the gap. This process is repeated to form paths of signals along the routes of various neuronal networks. These events happen very quickly, making it possible for you to have a thought and almost immediately signal your mouth to speak or your legs to run. This system of interconnected neurons and their ability to send and receive signals is generally found throughout different types of animals, not just humans.

Not all responses require processing through the thinking centers of the brain. If you touch a hot object, you will immediately withdraw your finger without having to think at all. Such a simple and quick response to a stimulus is called a **reflex**. The messages involved in this response travel from sensory detectors in your finger, through neurons in your arm, to the spinal cord. Then the messages go back to the muscles in your arm through other neurons, along a pathway called a **reflex arc** (see Figure E1.15). At the same time, messages are sent from the spinal cord to the brain. When your brain receives these messages, you interpret them as "that thing is *hot*!" By this time, however, you have already removed your finger from the hot object because of your reflex response. The advantage of a reflex over a signal that the brain must process is speed. In such a situation, you would need to move fast to prevent damage to your body. Reflex responses can save your life.

Newborn human babies turn their heads toward a touch on their cheek. This reflex encourages newborns to nurse in the first few hours of life, but they lose this reflex as time goes by. Most human activity, however, is processed through the brain, not carried out as reflexes. The human brain, with its trillions of interconnections between neurons, is well equipped to handle the everyday business of directing the activities of human life. Even simpler animals such as earthworms respond with reflexes to stimuli from their outside world. The ability to respond to heat, light, and moisture helps the worm to find food and keep from being dried out on a hot, sunny day.

The brain is responsible for so much complex human behavior. Responding quickly and appropriately to outside stimulus is just part of the human brain's job. It also must be able to store and retrieve information. For example, when you pick up a book and begin to read, you do not have to consciously think about how to read; you do it naturally. When you first were learning how to read, however, you needed to think about the sounds that the

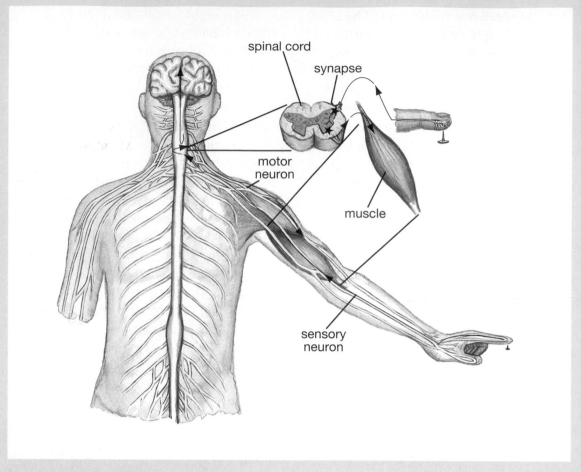

spinal cord

synapse

motor neuron

muscle

sensory neuron

Figure E1.15   Reflex arc. A reflex is an automatic response to a stimulus that occurs before the message reaches the brain. This type of response reduces the reaction time to a potentially life-threatening situation.

letters represented, how letters went together to form a word, and how the words went together to form a meaningful sentence. These processes seem natural to you now because your brain has learned and stored the patterns for thousands of words and the patterns for a variety of sentence structures.

Now that you are at the end of this essay, what do you think your eyes and brain have been doing while you were reading? ◆

The Importance of Being Children

"Will I be a grown-up tomorrow?"

This is a question that 4-year-olds all over the world ask in hundreds of different languages. The words may be different, but the question is the same—When will I know all that I need to know to be me?

Growing up and learning are intriguing and often puzzling processes. Even as adults, humans never stop learning. The complex interconnections in the human brain are one reason that humans have such a tremendous ability to learn. In fact, new connections between neurons are the biological basis of learning. That is, what and how much we learn is reflected in the physical structure of the brain. This plasticity, or ability to be molded, is particularly true of infants and young children because their brains (and bodies) are still growing at a rapid rate. Indeed, our longer period of childhood dependency may contribute significantly to making our capacity for learning greater than that of other animals.

Our long period of childhood dependency and our great ability to learn also give us time to acquire language. Language is one of the most important things that humans ever learn. Most languages have numerous intricate rules of grammar and thousands or tens of thousands of vocabulary words. As we learn language, we can communicate an infinite number of thoughts and ideas, and others who speak the same language can understand them. Even though the process of learning a language appears to be tremendously complex, it seems to occur quite naturally. While children learn to use language, they also learn about their culture from the adults in their lives. **Culture** is the set of shared, learned behaviors and beliefs that are passed from one generation to the next (see Figure E1.16).

Casual observations make it quite clear that it does not matter what culture or society a child is born into. A child naturally learns to speak the language that he or she hears at home. This capacity for learning languages is so great that children who grow up hearing one language exclusively at home and a different language exclusively at a relative's house can become fluent in both languages. Amazingly, children who learn two or more languages in this way do so with apparently little effort on their part. Language, like many cultural behaviors, is learned, or *acquired*, naturally as part of normal development. However, the opportunity for learning language in this most efficient and natural way is quite limited. After age 8 or 9, the capacity for learning a language diminishes. This

limitation explains why it is more difficult to learn a foreign language in high school or college.

Of course, humans are not the only animals that communicate with each other (see Figure E1.17). Many organisms communicate with each other through grunts, whistles, songs, and movements. But do we consider these activities language? Experiments show that trained dolphins can understand a simple series of signals, and chimpanzees can learn some elements of symbolic language. In fact, one chimp has been trained to understand more than 100 spoken English words. Other chimpanzees and gorillas have learned to communicate using American Sign Language and are thought to communicate about as well as a 4-year-old child would. Some of these chimps also have taken certain signs and created their own words. One chimpanzee put together the sign for *cold* and the sign for *food* to create a

Figure E1.16 During our long childhoods, we learn about ourselves and our societies.

Figure E1.17 Communication between wolves. Animals communicate in a variety of ways with different levels of complexity. Wolves communicate with each other through vocalizations such as howling, barking, and growling, as well as behaviors such as licking and submissive postures.

sign for *refrigerator*. Such studies indicate that these animals have the capacity for language-like behavior.

Similarly, a number of different animals appear to think and solve problems creatively. Simple tool use seems to be fairly common in the animal world. Sea otters carry rocks that they use as anvils to break open shellfish. Vultures drop stones on ostrich eggs to break them. Dr. Jane Goodall first discovered tool use in animals other than humans when she witnessed chimpanzees using modified leaves to fish for termites. It is not clear whether these activities really are learned. They may represent behaviors that individuals can modify quickly to fit changing circumstances.

Consider the activities of a termite colony. A termite family is called a **colony** because it is such a big family. In a termite family, the king and queen are actually the father and mother, and there are two types of "children." One type of termite child is destined to grow up and leave home. The other type of termite child is destined to stay home and help. The termite offspring (children) that are going to leave are called **nymphs**, and they start growing small wings very early. When they are mature, these nymphs will fly off to start new families. For the helper offspring who will stay home, there are three possibilities. Most become workers who dig tunnels, find food, feed and care for the young, and fix the nest. A small number of the helper offspring become soldiers. Finally, a very small percentage of helpers may undergo a reproductive change if their parents die.

The soldier termites develop a special head capsule. In some termite species, the soldiers have huge, muscle-filled heads and sharp jaws for fighting. Other termite species have soldiers with squirt-gun heads that shoot sticky goo at their enemies. Soldier termites are special because, along with their strange bodies, they also have *altruistic* behavior. In other words, soldier termites instinctually sacrifice their own lives to save their fellow nestmates from danger.

Termites maintain their relationships through a complex system of communication. However, they do not communicate with language. Termite communication is heavily dependent on the release of chemicals that other members of the society can sense. These chemicals are called **pheromones**. You saw how tracking pheromones can be used to communicate which path a termite should follow in the Engage Section at the beginning of this course.

Although termite behaviors are very complex, they are not learned. Instead, termite social behaviors are primarily passed on genetically. They are fairly rigid, instinct-driven responses. Each baby termite has the genetic potential to become any type of helper or reproductive. The time of year, diet, and pheromones all play a role in determining what the baby, or **larva**, will develop into. Family structure that is based on this type of behavior is often extremely successful as long as conditions are constant or change slowly. Termite families do not encourage individual action or promote much creative response to new situations.

One of the most important features of the termite family is that it is built on monogamy. This means that there is usually only one mother and one father, and they stay together their entire lives. They are probably the most monogamous group of animals on earth. Because of this commitment to monogamy, termites have evolved to have complex colonies that are made up of brothers and sisters. As far as biologists know, social insects like termites, ants, and honeybees are the most sophisticated families ever to evolve. Human families are not nearly as advanced. Humans, in contrast to termites, have the most advanced, nonfamily-based social system known.

In contrast to the social insects, such as termites, bees, and ants, the group interactions of other animals generally are more variable and less dependent on instinct-based behaviors. In primate societies, learning, flexibility, and individuality are important characteristics. For example, some research scientists set up a feeding station for macaque monkeys in Japan. When one macaque began washing her sweet potatoes in seawater before eating them (see Figure E1.18), the practice gradually spread to almost every member of the troop and to the next generation of macaques. Bipedal walking also became more common as the monkeys learned to carry the potatoes in their hands to the water. Later, the monkeys learned to separate sand from wheat that they had collected on the beach. They carried it to the sea and plunged it into the water; the sand sank and the wheat floated. They then quickly retrieved the wheat and ate it. These behaviors demonstrate creative responses to new situations.

This type of behavioral flexibility—the ability not only to learn how to perform established behaviors but to invent new behaviors—reaches its greatest expression in human societies. Humans and many other animals have incompletely formed nervous systems at birth. However, a human's nervous system continues to develop for a much longer time. Consequently, our life experiences influence us to a greater degree than other animals. Much of our tremendous behavioral

Figure E1.18 Behavioral flexibility. When a feeding station was established, one macaque learned to wash sweet potatoes in the water before eating them. This behavior was adopted by most of the macaques in the community and even was passed on to the next generation of macaques.

flexibility is put to use during this long period of childhood development. This gives us the opportunity to learn about our culture. Recall that culture is the accumulated knowledge that is passed from generation to generation by parenting and education.

For at least 100,000 years, humans lived in wild conditions. During the Stone Age, the lack of human ability to form complex societies limited the amount of information that could be passed down from one generation to the next. Much of what a person learned during a lifetime was lost when she or he died. The only way to pass along information was through crude language and direct observation. We have progressed a long way.

The progress that occurs in human societies is called **cultural evolution**, which is very different from biological evolution by natural selection. Cultural evolution has carried humankind from a Stone Age cave dweller to our current state of technological sophistication. Modern human social organization does not depend on genes for instinctive behavior as termite social organization does. Instead, it depends on the accumulation of information, and the organization of knowledge and its transmission through education.

Language, in turn, helps us to record and communicate our culture more efficiently than if we had to rely exclusively on experience, imitation, and other nonverbal forms of communication. Imagine what our world would be like if we eliminated just one of our cultural uses of language, the preservation of information in libraries. Each new generation would have to rediscover or reinvent all of the complex technologies of the previous generation because oral transmission of so much detailed information would be impossible. The use of libraries, on the other hand, means that when technological or social challenges arise, we have a vast resource of information that we can use. This interplay between language and culture helps to further distinguish humans from all other animals. ◆

Fossils: Traces of Life Gone By

Glancing around nervously, a whalelike creature waddles awkwardly on its very short legs down the sandy slope. Once it enters the water, however, it moves gracefully, swimming with its powerful tail.

Although this particular mammal is a *Rodhocetus*, one of the ancestors of modern whales, it has something very special in common with dinosaurs, bacteria, ferns, horses, and even Lucy. They all left fossil evidence behind when they died. In each case, a series of unusual events occurred that preserved their bodies in the form of fossils, which scientists sometimes find and use in their studies of biological change.

Fossils do not form easily. From your own experience, you know that scavengers often eat dead animals or microorganisms quickly consume them. A recently deceased organism can become a fossil only under rare but specific conditions. Layers of mud or silt must cover the dead organism quickly to protect it temporarily from decomposition (see Figure E2.1). Although the tissues of the organism are now protected, they are not yet fossilized. A fossil is created when minerals in the water replace the minerals in the organism's tissues. Bones and shells are the most common tissue for mineral replacement.

Fossils usually are found in sedimentary rocks, which form as particles of mud, sand, or small pebbles slowly filter through water and settle into layers. The particles in these layers harden into rock after they are cemented together by a chemical reaction or by evaporation. Igneous and metamorphic rocks rarely contain fossils, because these rocks form in the presence of great heat and pressure. If an organism were present during those processes, it probably would be destroyed. Occasionally, volcanic ash or molten lava that has begun to cool will encase an organism and form a fossil.

If a preserved fossil escapes destruction by geological forces, it may become exposed by erosion. Often, this is how fossils are discovered. For that reason, fossils usually are discovered near the earth's surface. Generally, only the hard parts of organisms, such as shells or bones, are fossilized. In rare instances, scientists have found soft parts of organisms, such as the extinct giant mammoths frozen in arctic ice and the prehistoric insects fossilized in hardened tree sap. In other cases, soft tissues or body parts such as skin, hair, or feathers have been preserved as imprints that are connected to fossilized bone. Even if a fossil survives geological change and becomes exposed at the earth's surface, it cannot serve as evidence of biological change unless someone discovers it and realizes its importance.

In most cases, fossils are evidence of an organism as it appeared at the time of its death. Other types of fossils allow scientists to make inferences about an organism's life and behavior. For example, footprints of dinosaurs that walked in soft sand or mud sometimes survive as recognizable tracks in solid rock. These trace fossils suggest how the animal walked, including the length of its stride and where it placed its feet.

The fossil record not only provides information about once-living organisms, it also provides an account of how the earth itself changed across very long periods of time. For instance, if we find fossils of marine animals on what now are mountaintops, we may infer that the rock in that area once was under a sea. This may be because mountain-building geological forces lifted an ancient seabed up. In this way, the earth in which fossils are found gives clues to physical changes in climate and land conditions. A combination of fossils and the physical structure of the earth can serve as a geological record of change.

The geological record also reveals that the energy of the earth itself drives large-scale geological changes. Deep within the earth, the temperature is very high. The rock is molten liquid rather than solid. As molten rock, or magma, rises, it can form new landmasses or move existing continents, which results in an ever-changing organization of land on earth. Of course, such changes occur only across the vast periods of time that typify geological change. For example, about 230 million years ago, all of the land on the planet was grouped together in one gigantic continent called Pangaea. Since that time, the land has broken apart and reformed into the current arrangement of continents, a process called **continental drift**. Continental drift is now understood as the theory of **plate tectonics**. The movements of the tectonic plates are closely tied to changes in the earth's biological makeup. This happens because changes in land connections allow some living organisms to migrate to new areas. Other tectonic changes cause connections to be lost, eventually leaving some populations isolated. The fossil record documents many such migrations.

a
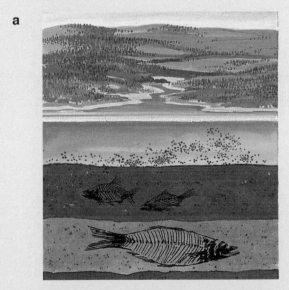

b

Figure E2.1 Fossil formation. (a) Dead organisms or their skeletons may remain intact in underwater sediments through long periods of time. Eventually, minerals circulating in underground water replace the bone of the skeletons, forming fossils. (b) Buried fossils may be brought to the surface by any of the forces that uplift segments of the earth's crust. Once near the surface, the fossil-containing rock layers are subject to erosion, which can expose the fossil from the rock.

Steller's sea cow The last confirmed sighting of a Steller's sea cow, a large marine mammal, was in 1768.

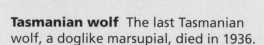

Ornitholestes This species of dinosaur became extinct about 150 million years ago. The mass extinction of many other dinosaur species, including *Tyrannosaurus rex*, occurred about 65 million years ago.

Dodo bird These large, flightless birds became extinct in the 17th and 18th centuries.

Tasmanian wolf The last Tasmanian wolf, a doglike marsupial, died in 1936.

Figure E2.2   Extinct animals.

A widescale analysis of fossil evidence reveals a fundamental feature of living organisms: throughout earth's history, the different types, or species, of organisms living on earth have changed. New species emerge and branch off from existing species, while many other species die off. The most dramatic change possible for a species—its complete disappearance—is called **extinction**. Figure E2.2 shows several examples of species that have become extinct. The fossil record chronicles many now extinct species. Of all the species that ever existed on earth, 99.9 percent are now extinct. Species continue to become extinct due to natural and humanmade changes in the environment. But new species continue to emerge as well. These new species arise from earlier ones through gradual biological change. The fossil record shows this change. ◆

Technologies That Strengthen Fossil Evidence

From sundials to atomic clocks, humans have invented many tools to measure time as it flows continuously from seconds to minutes to hours. Certain natural processes also measure time. For example, a cut through the trunk of a fallen tree reveals growth rings. Counting those rings is a way to measure the number of years the tree was alive and growing. The rings, however, do not tell how long it has been since the tree fell. Scientists often want to know when a rock was formed or how long ago an organism lived. This is difficult to measure, but often there are important clues that tell how long ago an organism lived.

Scientists who study the long-term history of life on earth are more concerned with measuring when an organism was alive than how long it lived. This task is difficult because these scientists must calculate the age of fossils that are thousands or millions of years old. The age of a fossil may be calculated two ways. First, it can be calculated indirectly, from the age of the surrounding rock layer in which it is found. Second, it can be calculated directly, from the age of the fossil itself. Indirect measurements are known as relative methods because these techniques allow a scientist to say only that a certain fossil is older or younger than another fossil.

Geologists use an indirect method called **stratigraphy** to help them determine the relative ages of fossils. In this method, geologists study the strata, or layers, of the earth (see Figure E2.3) to create a rough outline of the earth's geologic history. The relationship between layers of rock and the occurrence of certain fossils was noted nearly 200 years ago. Around 1800, William Smith, an English surveyor and civil engineer, became interested in rock strata because of its relationship to the structural success of the canals he was building. He noticed that certain layers contained fossils, and that throughout England there was a match between the type of rock layer, its placement between other layers, and the fossils it contained.

About the same time, two geologists, Georges Cuvier and Alexander Brogniart, were studying fossils in rock strata in France. When they compared the fossils they found with modern life-forms, they discovered that the modern forms were more similar to the fossils from the higher rock layers than those from the lower layers were. In fact, no modern species were found in the oldest and deepest layers. The reason for that is related to how fossils are formed. Sediment that settles on top of a dead organism is more recent than the sediment under the dead organism. Thus, scientists infer that any fossil that they find in a particular rock layer is older than any fossils found above that layer and younger than fossils found below that layer. Using this knowledge and other techniques, geologists can develop estimates of the time period for each layer of rock. They can then determine a rough idea of the age of a fossil. Direct dating

methods, however, can determine the age of fossils with much greater accuracy.

Direct dating methods depend on naturally occurring radioactive elements. These elements are unstable forms of matter that break down, or decay, at a steady rate into other chemical elements. When a radioactive element decays, it releases a pulse of energy. Different radioactive elements decay at different rates. For a particular element, however, decay occurs at a constant rate. Elements that undergo decay are called **radioactive isotopes**. For example, an isotope of uranium known as uranium-238 (^{238}U) decays into lead-206 (^{206}Pb). For a given amount of uranium, half of it is converted to lead in about 4.5 billion years. Another radioactive isotope, potassium-40 (^{40}K) decays into argon-40 (^{40}A), but at a much slower decay rate. It takes 1.3 billion years for half of a sample of potassium-40 to convert to argon-40. Because potassium-40 decays at such a slow rate, scientists can use the postassium-40 dating method to determine the age of both young and old volcanic rocks, meteorites, and rocks from the moon. Dating methods using uranium can be used to determine the age of rocks that are

Figure E2.3 Stratigraphy is a relative dating method. The stratification of rock in this cliff was exposed when a highway was built. Fossils of older organisms are found in the deepest layers. Organisms that lived more recently are found in the upper layers.

thousands of years old to rocks that are as old as the solar system, 4.6 billion years.

If scientists know the constant rate of decay for a radioactive element, they can measure how much of the radioactive element and its decay product are present in a material such as rock. The ratio of isotope to decay product shows how long the radioactive element has been decaying and thus how old the rock is. Likewise, if the scientist finds a fossil in this rock layer, he or she can infer that the fossil is approximately the same age as the rock that surrounds it. Potassium-argon dating is very useful for measuring the age of fossils because potassium is present in volcanic ash and lava. If fossils are found in between volcanic layers, scientists can determine the likely age of the fossils.

Another similar method is useful for organic material that is between 500 and 47,000 years old. This method is carbon-14 (^{14}C) dating. In the atmosphere, carbon-14 is produced when cosmic rays (neutrons) from the sun bombard nitrogen-14. Carbon-14 atoms then become part of a carbon dioxide molecule ($^{14}CO_2$) in the atmosphere. Carbon-14

becomes part of plants during photosynthesis. Animals take in carbon-14 when they eat plants. Carbon-14 decays to nitrogen-14. Most carbon in plants and animals is carbon-12, which is stable and does not decay. Scientists can determine the proportion of carbon-14 to carbon-12 to estimate the age of a fossil. Older fossils have a lower amount of carbon-14 compared to the amount of carbon-12. Fossils that are not as old have a higher proportion of carbon-14. In these fossils, there has been less decay of carbon-14. Figure E2.4 helps to illustrate this process.

Scientists often combine radioactive-isotope dating techniques with other methods for dating material, such as measuring magnetic properties. This improves the accuracy of their estimates of fossil ages. The increased reliability occurs because a combination of techniques allows them to check for the consistency of the estimates. These multiple lines of evidence, which support scientific reasoning, strengthen scientists' confidence in the conclusions. For example, varieties of dating techniques have strengthened our estimates of geological

Figure E2.4
Carbon-14 becomes part of plants and animals. Small amounts of carbon-14 exist in the atmosphere as carbon dioxide, which plants incorporate into their tissues. This carbon-14 enters animals when they eat plants. Scientists can measure the amount of carbon-14 in fossils. Because they know that the half-life of carbon-14 is 5,730 years, they can calculate the age of the organism.

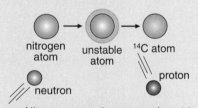

nitrogen atom   unstable atom ^{14}C atom

neutron   proton

a. Nitrogen atoms become carbon-14 atoms in the atmosphere.

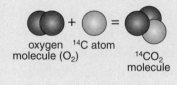

oxygen molecule (O_2) ^{14}C atom $^{14}CO_2$ molecule

b. Oxygen molecules combine with carbon-14 atoms to form carbon-14 dioxide.

c. Living organisms incorporate carbon-14.

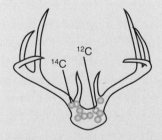

^{12}C
^{14}C

d. The proportion of carbon-14 to carbon-12 in an organism's remains indicates how long it has been dead.

time and have supported the theory of plate tectonics.

Using these techniques, scientists have determined that the oldest fossils ever found, primitive bacteria, lived about 3.5 billion years ago. Newer forms of bacteria are dated at about 2.5 billion years ago. Other microorganisms, ancestral plants, and animals without backbones (invertebrates) appeared later in the fossil record. They were followed by fish (500 million years ago); amphibians (360 million years ago); and reptiles (310 million years ago). Dinosaurs (215 million years ago); mammals (210 million years ago); birds (155 million years ago); and flowering plants (130 million years ago) appeared later. Lucy, one of the ancestors of modern humans, appeared relatively recently, at 3.4 million years ago. ◆

Modern Life: Evidence for Evolutionary Change

The fossil skeleton of Lucy has many of the same features as skeletons of modern humans. But modern human skeletons display some significant differences as well. Comparisons such as this, where fossils from long ago are compared with modern organisms, provide one line of evidence supporting the scientific view that living systems change. It is important to remember that the process of change is not only in the past, such as when Lucy lived. It is going on in all of the living systems alive on earth today.

On an isolated island in the Galápagos Archipelago, biologists observed two species of birds, the medium ground finch, and the cactus finch. During a 12-year period, the scientists recorded measurements of the size of the birds' bodies and the thickness of their beaks. During this time, there were two extreme dry spells, and many birds of each species died. At the end of the observation period, the scientists noticed that the average characteristics in the surviving populations of both species had changed slightly. The birds that survived, and their offspring, were a little larger and had beaks that were a little thicker than before. The scientists had witnessed a small but ongoing biological change that was influenced by natural circumstances and could be inherited. These results support the conclusion that species change gradually. They also suggest that across very long periods of time, small changes might add up to significant differences.

Additional evidence for biological change and the relatedness of different organisms comes from the study of comparative anatomy. This is the branch of biology that concentrates on the similarities and differences in anatomical features of different species. By comparing the anatomy of different organisms, scientists have noticed many structural similarities among organisms. A pattern of similar characteristics may suggest evolutionary relatedness. For example, compare the structure of the animal forelimbs shown in Figure E2.5. Although they have different functions, these limbs show consistent similarities among the organisms. In addition, the limbs have the same relationship to the body (they all are forelimbs), and they develop in the same way in the young. Because of these consistent similarities, biologists infer that the forelimb structure is a homology. A homology is a characteristic that is similar among different organisms because they evolved from a common ancestor.

In making anatomical comparisons, scientists also discover structures that are functional in some species, but seemingly useless in others. We refer to these dwarfed or apparently useless structures as vestigial, which comes from the word *vestige*, meaning "a remnant of." The "goose bumps" that you get when you are cold are an example of vestigial structures. Small erector muscles in the skin produce goose bumps. In other mammals and birds, the contraction of erector muscles causes the fur or feathers to fluff up. This mechanism helps the organism to warm up. Modern humans do not have very much hair, but we have retained the erector muscles. Figure E2.6 shows three more examples of vestigial structures.

Homologies and vestigial structures are examples of similar features shared by seemingly unrelated organisms. Is there additional evidence to suggest that the tremendous diversity of life arose from the gradual accumulation of small changes in related organisms? The answer is yes. This evidence is found by comparing modern species. You can study single-celled bacteria such as *Staphylococcus*, protoctists such as *Amoeba*, fungi such as mushrooms, or the more familiar plants and animals. In each case, you will find that each stores its genetic information in the same complex molecule, DNA (deoxyribonucleic acid). Genetic material in the form of DNA is the master plan for the diverse characteristics of each species. Yet the method of storing that information, including the code that is used to interpret the information, is essentially the same in any living organism.

Scientists have used this common basis for storing genetic information to determine just how closely two organisms are related. Molecular techniques now make it possible to compare the information encoded in DNA directly. Biologists have compared the DNA among modern species and even among modern and extinct species in the rare cases when the soft tissue of an extinct organism has been preserved. In fact, new laboratory techniques enable molecular biologists to transfer DNA from one species to another, where the DNA functions successfully. Through these techniques, the genetic information from one organism, such as a bacterium, can be interpreted by a completely different organism. Even cells from a human can receive and decode

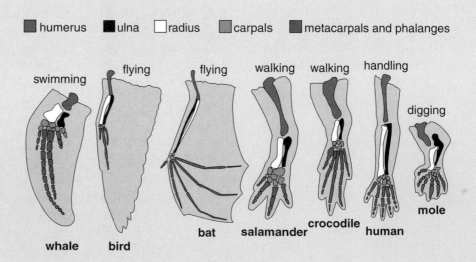

■ humerus ■ ulna □ radius ■ carpals ■ metacarpals and phalanges

Figure E2.5 Homologies are characteristics that suggest common ancestry. Although adapted for different functions, the bones of these forelimbs (not drawn to scale) show comparable structures. What similarities can you find?

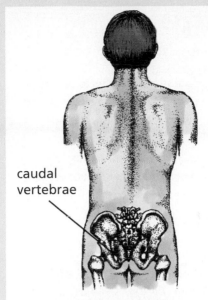

Blind salamanders. These salamanders from Arkansas and Missouri have become adapted to life in deep caves where sunlight never reaches. They possess eyes, but their eyes do not function. They are blind.

caudal vertebrae

Human tail structures. Most mammals have a well-developed tail, but this is lacking in apes and humans. Still, the tail is represented by the last three to five bones in the backbone of humans. Even though an external tail usually is not present, the muscles that move the tail in other mammals also are present in humans. On rare occasions, a fleshy tail in a human extends a few inches beyond the caudal vertebrae.

Snakes with legs. Notice the bony parts of the python's pelvic girdle to which tiny limb bones attach. The legs serve no function.

Figure E2.6   Examples of vestigial structures.

the DNA from a bacterium. Figure E2.7 shows a comparison among primates.

The probability that the primates listed in Figure E2.7 developed an identical DNA code without being related to one another is extremely small. A much more likely explanation for this close similarity is that they inherited the genetic code from the same ancestors. The similarity in genetic code across living organisms strongly suggests a common origin for all modern life. ◆

Animal	Percentage of DNA That Is the Same as Human DNA
Monkey (an old world primate)	93%
Gibbon (a lesser ape)	95%
Chimpanzee (a great ape)	98+%

Figure E2.7   Comparing DNA across primates.

Primates Show Change across Time

A carpenter walks up to a cabinet she is building and places a metal handle in a spot she has marked. Holding the handle with her left hand, she turns the screwdriver with her right hand to attach the handle to the wood. Somewhere, 5,000 years ago, a hunter steps quietly through a thin forest, keeping his sight fixed on a small deer a short distance away. As he walks, the hunter pulls an arrow from his quiver and sets it to the bow, ready for a shot that may win his family several good meals and a hide for clothing.

Walking upright has been advantageous for humans because it frees our fingers and hands to grasp and manipulate objects. This combination of abilities allows us to use tools even while we move about. While all primates have the ability to grasp objects with their opposable thumbs to some degree, humans have remarkably nimble fingers and hands. The biological changes that made the refined use of our hands possible took place over a very long period of time in human evolution.

The fossil record of primates supports the idea of biological changes at various rates in primate history. Today, the primate group includes such mammals as lemurs, chimpanzees, gorillas, orangutans, and humans. Millions of years ago, all primates shared a single common ancestor. Those

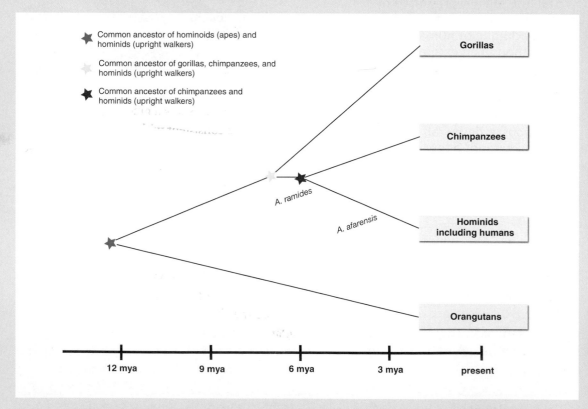

Figure E2.8   Gorillas, chimpanzees, orangutans, and humans share a common ancestry. This timeline shows a common interpretation of the general relationship between some present primates, including humans. Notice that humans are most closely related to chimpanzees, and that neither humans nor chimpanzees evolved from apes. Rather, modern apes and humans evolved from a common ancestor.

primates that are most closely related shared additional common ancestors (see Figure E2.8). Because of her pelvic and leg anatomy, scientists assigned Lucy to a group of primates called **hominids**. Hominids walked upright. Early hominids had brain cases more similar in size to apes than to humans. Still, hominid skulls indicate that their brains were larger for their body size than those of modern apes are. Lucy belongs to a group of hominids called *Australopithecus*. This group had more humanlike front teeth, which are considerably smaller than those in apes. In addition, the position of the opening that the spinal cord passes through into the skull indicated an erect, bipedal posture.

Likewise, Lucy's pelvis clearly indicates that she walked fully upright. By contrast, the shape of a chimpanzee's pelvis indicates that it is a knuckle-walker. Taken together, Lucy's skeletal remains suggest that her species was somewhere between apelike ancestors and modern humans. In 1995, a new species of hominid was uncovered in the Lake Turkana region of Kenya, in East Africa. It had many of the same features found in Lucy. In particular, its leg bones indicate that it stood upright and walked bipedally. It was named *Australopithecus anamensis*, and it was

scientifically determined to be approximately 4.1 million years old. This date makes *A. anamensis* more than half a million years older than Lucy's species. Combining this find with molecular evidence suggests that hominids split from the common ancestor shared with chimpanzees about 6 million years ago. The fossil *A. anamensis* moved science closer to that hypothetical common ancestor (see Figure E2.8).

Anthropologists discovered more hominid fossils in 2000 and 2002. These fossils were dated between 5.2 and 6.2 million years old. Until more of these fossils are found and further analysis is completed, scientists will not know if they represent hominids even closer to that common ancestor. There seems to be little doubt that we are getting very close to the root of the hominid family tree.

Other hominids that lived on earth more recently, such as *Homo habilis* and *Homo erectus*, show a more human appearance. They have a more vertical face, smaller front teeth, a smaller lower jaw, and a significantly larger brain case. These specimens show a gradual change in form that is consistent with the scientific explanation that hominids evolved and gave rise to humans. ◆

Darwin Proposes Descent with Modification

Charles Darwin, a 22-year-old English naturalist, was nervous and excited as he climbed up the gangplank to the scientific research ship, HMS *Beagle*, just after Christmas in 1831 (see Figure E2.9). Just imagine how much more excited he might have been if he had known what his voyage would mean to modern science. Although young Charles's journey would last only 5 years, the ideas born of that journey would change forever the way biologists understand the world.

The central mission of the *Beagle* was to chart sections of the coast of South America. While the ship's crew completed that work, Darwin spent his time on shore, collecting thousands of specimens and recording detailed observations of the interesting and exotic organisms he encountered. Darwin observed organisms in such diverse environments as the jungles of Brazil, the harsh plains of Tierra del Fuego (near Antarctica), the grasslands of Argentina, and the heights of the Andes mountains. Before it was over, the *Beagle's*

Figure E2.9 Charles Darwin. Born in 1809, Darwin studied medicine and theology to please his father, but his real interest was in natural history. Eventually, he left medical school to enroll at Cambridge University to study natural history, the term then used for biology. His mentor, the Reverend John Henslow, was a famous botanist who later recommended Darwin to the captain of the HMS *Beagle*.

voyage took Darwin to the coasts of Australia, New Zealand, Tasmania, and to several islands in the South Pacific and Atlantic oceans (see Figure E2.10).

One of the most important questions that Darwin pondered during his travels related to the geographical distribution of the organisms that he observed. Although similar to organisms in Europe, the plants and animals that lived in South America and the South Pacific were clearly distinct. That, perhaps, was not surprising. But what perplexed Darwin was the fact that organisms that lived in temperate (mild) areas of South America were more similar to organisms living in tropical areas of South America than to organisms living in temperate regions of Europe. Orchids, army ants, marine iguanas, penguins . . . each type of organism was well suited for the environment in which it lived.

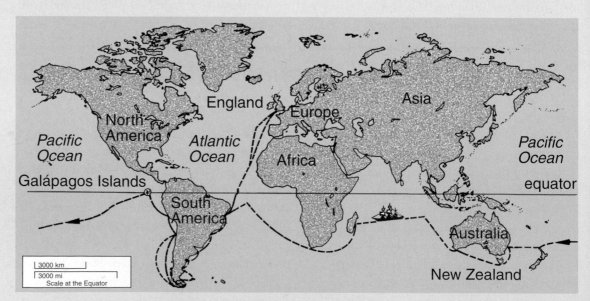

Figure E2.10 Voyage of the HMS *Beagle*. Darwin sailed around the world on the *Beagle*. The route included stops in South America and a stay in the Galápagos Islands. During the trip, Darwin collected evidence that he later used to support the theory of evolution.

Yet each seemed to be related to organisms living in other parts of that huge continent. How could one account for both the similarities and the differences among species. How could one account for their specific patterns of geographic distribution?

After he returned to England, Darwin spent nearly 20 years analyzing his observations and thinking about their implications before he published *On the Origin of Species*. Although this landmark book established Darwin as the author of the theory of evolution, Darwin did not use the word *evolution* in the first edition. Instead, he proposed the concept of *descent with modification*. This phrase expressed his view that all organisms on earth are related through descent from some unknown ancestral type that lived long ago. This idea helped Darwin develop an explanation for the diversity of organisms that he had encountered on his travels and also for the patterns in geographical distributions that he had observed. The concept of descent with modification is described in more detail in the next essay, *Evolution by Natural Selection*.

The publication of Darwin's book represents an interesting twist in the history of science. If Alfred Russel Wallace, a young scientist working in the East Indies, had not written to Darwin, Darwin might not have published the book when he did. In his letter to Darwin, Wallace enclosed a draft of a scientific paper that described a theory of evolution. His theory was less detailed than Darwin's theory, but almost identical in basic outline. Darwin was shocked to learn that other scientists not only were thinking about these ideas but also might be able to publish them before he did. Nevertheless, he behaved with integrity, acknowledging the excellence and importance of Wallace's work and forwarding Wallace's paper to another noted scientist for public presentation. Knowing of Darwin's nearly 20 years of study, the scientist decided to present Wallace's paper with an excerpt from an essay about evolution that

Figure E2.11   Alfred Russel Wallace. Although Wallace independently reached many of the same conclusions that Darwin reached, he seldom is acknowledged for his contributions to the theory of evolution.

Darwin wrote in 1844 but never published. This decision preserved Darwin's claim to these ideas, but Darwin still had to publish his full results. Motivated now by the concern that other scientists were about to reach the same conclusions that he had reached, Darwin worked feverishly for almost a year, finally completing *On the Origin of Species* in 1859.

Although Wallace published his paper first, Darwin's explanation of evolution was more detailed and contained more extensive supporting evidence than Wallace's paper. Darwin's journals also demonstrated that he had developed the central core of his ideas more than 15 years before reading Wallace's paper. Consequently, Darwin is known as the main author of the theory of evolution, and even Wallace thought that Darwin deserved the credit. (Wallace is pictured in Figure E2.11.) ◆

Evolution by Natural Selection

Even before Darwin's work, several individuals already had proposed the basic idea of evolution, the concept that differences among species are the result of changes across time. Unlike these earlier scientists, however, Darwin provided not only a logical argument to support evolution, but also clear evidence for his key points. Even more important, Darwin proposed a mechanism, that is, a way by which a new species could eventually appear from ancestral forms.

Although he was unable to explain the source of variation in organisms, Darwin observed that the individual members of any species show a great deal of variation in their characteristics. (Later, scientists found the source of variation to be genetics.) They may show differences in size, coloration, strength, behavior, and many other features. Some of these characteristics are passed on from parents to offspring. For centuries, in fact, plant and animal breeders have bred

organisms to emphasize or increase certain prized characteristics. Plant breeders, for example, try to improve disease resistance by selecting plants with high resistance and mating them together. They hope to obtain offspring with even higher resistance. Likewise, horse breeders may select mating pairs to try to increase speed, stamina, or both.

Sometimes these techniques can result in significant differences from one breeding group to another. Figure E2.12 illustrates six different types of vegetables that humans eat. All six plants are of the same species. Humans have bred them for different agricultural uses and to suit different human tastes.

If humans can bring about change in a population of organisms by this type of artificial selective breeding, Darwin reasoned that perhaps selection in nature also could bring about change. Such change eventually might result in the production of new species. A **species** is a group of organisms whose

Figure E2.12 Six types of kale. These kale plants differ primarily in the part of the plant that stores the most starch.

List of Mayr's points

Fact 1: All species have such great potential to produce large numbers of offspring that their population size would increase exponentially if all individuals that are born would reproduce successfully.

Fact 2: Except for seasonal fluctuations, most populations are normally stable in size.

Fact 3: Natural resources are limited, and in a stable environment, they remain relatively constant.

Inference 1: Because more individuals are produced than the available resources can support, and the population size remains stable, there must be a fierce struggle for existence among the individuals of a population. This results in the survival of only a part, often a very small part, of the offspring of each generation.

Fact 4: No two individuals in a population are exactly the same; rather, every population displays an enormous variety of characteristics.

Fact 5: Much of this variation can be inherited.

Inference 2: Survival in the struggle for existence is not random but depends in part on the characteristics that the surviving individuals inherited. This unequal survival is a process of natural selection that favors individuals with characteristics that fit them best in their environment.

Inference 3: Over the generations, this process of natural selection will lead to a continuing gradual change in populations, that is, to evolution and the production of new species.

Figure E2.13 The logic of the theory of natural selection.   Ernst Mayr has summarized the logic of Darwin's theory by extracting the major points of evidence and inference. (This list is adapted from E. Mayr, *The Growth of Biological Thought: Diversity, Evolution, and Inheritance,* Cambridge, MA: Harvard University Press, 1982.)

members very closely resemble each other because they share many key characteristics. Despite obvious differences in superficial appearance, all humans are one species because we share many fundamental characteristics. Organisms belonging to different species usually vary from one another in numerous key characteristics. For sexually reproducing organisms, one characteristic that separates species is the ability to mate and produce fertile offspring. A horse and a donkey, for instance, can mate and produce offspring called mules. But because horses and donkeys belong to two different (although very closely related) species, these offspring mules are sterile.

How would the process of natural selection take place? One way to trace

Darwin's thinking is to consider carefully the information displayed in Figure E2.13. This summary was proposed by Ernst Mayr, a noted biologist at Harvard University. He introduced a way to understand the mix of evidence and inference that underlies the theory of evolution. Let us follow the argument, point by point, and try to understand some of the thinking that led Darwin to his conclusions.

The first three facts in Figure E2.13 describe the situation that inevitably exists in any environment:

- In the absence of limits to population growth, organisms reproduce very rapidly.

- Nevertheless, our observations tell us that most populations in the wild are relatively constant in size.

- Our observations also tell us that the resources available in any natural environment are limited.

One important factor that influenced Darwin's views was an essay written in 1798 by Thomas Malthus, a member of the English clergy. Malthus argued that much of the human suffering that we see on earth is the inescapable result of the tendency of the human population to grow beyond the resources available to support it. This capacity for overpopulation seemed to Darwin to be a characteristic of every population. It led Darwin to infer that individual organisms within a population must face a struggle for survival, and that only a few individuals need to survive to pass on their characteristics from one generation to the next. The rest fail to develop; die of starvation, predation, or other causes before they reproduce; or do not reproduce for other reasons. The effect of this loss of reproductive individuals from one generation to the next is that wild populations tend to be relatively stable in size.

The remaining two facts suggested to Darwin how this struggle for survival is played out among the members of a natural population:

- Individual organisms within a population are different in particular characteristics from one another.

- Most, although not all, of this variation can be inherited from one organism to the next.

Figure E2.14 Examples of adaptations. (**a**) snake caterpillar (**b**) flicker (**c**) red Irish lord fish Can you identify the adaptations possessed by these organisms? How might each adaptation benefit the organism?

From these observations, Darwin inferred that the outcome of the struggle for existence depends, to a certain extent, on the characteristics that an organism inherits. There are individuals whose inherited characteristics best equip them to survive in a particular environment. These individuals will be most likely to reproduce and to leave behind offspring with the same beneficial traits. We call these beneficial traits **adaptations** (Figure E2.14). By contrast, those organisms with characteristics that make it more difficult to survive and reproduce in an environment would be less likely to survive and to reproduce. As a result, their particular characteristics would be less likely to be passed on to surviving offspring.

For example, suppose a population of rabbits lived in a moderately warm climate. Within that population, a small proportion of the individuals might have thick fur. If this thick fur resulted from a difference in their genetic material as compared with that of other rabbits living in the same area, then this difference might be passed on to their offspring. Imagine first that the thicker fur is a disadvantage to the rabbits in this environment because they overheat when they are chased by coyotes. As a consequence, these thick-furred rabbits do not survive and reproduce as well as the rabbits with thin fur. You probably can see, in this case, that thick fur would not be a very common trait in this population.

Now imagine that, through a period of several decades, the climate in this environment gets colder. In the colder climate, the rabbits with the thicker fur now would have an advantage. That is, the thick fur would be an adaptation that helps them survive the periods of cold weather. All other things being equal, the thick-furred rabbits would be more likely to survive long enough to reproduce and pass on their characteristics than the thin-furred rabbits. As Figure E2.15 shows, after many generations, the number of rabbits with thick fur might increase in the

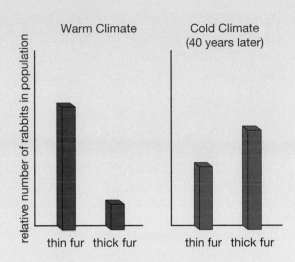

Figure E2.15 **Characteristics of a population change due to natural selection.**

population. This is the process of natural selection.

Although Darwin's understanding of selective breeding led him to propose his theory of natural selection, there is a key difference between selective breeding and natural selection. In selective breeding, humans choose how to allow organisms to reproduce in order to pass on desirable characteristics. In natural selection, however, each organism's ability to meet the challenges of survival and reproduction in a natural setting determines the mix of characteristics that will be transmitted to the next generation.

In such a setting, many pressures affect survival and reproduction. As you saw in the rabbit example, changes in the environment can alter the balance of life so that some characteristics are more beneficial than others. Sometimes these changes are catastrophic, like the effect a volcanic eruption might have on both local and very distant populations of organisms.

Competition among organisms for limited resources also acts as a selective pressure. For example, a plant needs sunlight to grow and sufficient soil to support its roots and provide water and minerals. The plant must cope with its environment to survive and

produce seeds for the next generation. The plant, however, is not alone. Nearby plants may grow faster than this plant and may block the sunlight, or they may have longer roots that drain off limited water. In that way, these other plants may compete with the first plant for survival. A difference in the ability of organisms to compete in an environment with limited resources is one of the selective pressures that can bring about evolution.

Predation is another pressure that many organisms face (see Figure E2.16). Living long enough to reproduce requires that the predator be successful in locating and catching prey. The prey, however, must escape predation until it is able to reproduce. In a predator/prey relationship, it may appear that the predator has all the advantages. Not so. Think of a lion whose jaw is broken by a well-aimed kick from a gazelle. The lion will die slowly of starvation because it can no longer eat. On the other hand, the gazelle that is not alert enough or strong enough to avoid the lion's jaws also will die, in this case, rather suddenly and dramatically.

What determines an organism's ability to survive and reproduce in the face of these pressures? Generally, it is not one characteristic or two, but a mix of characteristics that helps the organism adapt to a particular environment. Organisms, however, do not *acquire* these characteristics to *help* them survive. Rather, individuals inherit their set of characteristics

from their parents. Those individuals in a population who have the characteristics that make them best suited to their environment are most likely to survive and contribute their characteristics to the next generation.

It is important to realize that individual organisms do not evolve. Rather, populations evolve. Darwin's theory of evolution by natural selection proposes that sometimes the characteristics of a population can change so dramatically that eventually the population becomes recognized as a distinct species, different from the ancestral form. Here we return to Darwin's basic idea: descent by modification. *Descent* from a common ancestor provides a powerful explanation for the similarities that we see among related forms of life. *Modification* through variation and natural selection provides a powerful explanation for their differences.

We cannot overestimate the importance to modern biology of the theory of evolution by natural selection. Perhaps Darwin's greatest contribution was in giving biologists a way to understand the enormous diversity that we see in living systems. The theory of evolution explains the origin of this diversity and helps us to understand the relationships that exist among modern species and between modern species and their ancestral forms. As most biologists will tell you, these aspects of biology do not make much sense except in the context of evolution. ◆

Just a Theory?

What do we mean when we say that we have a theory about something? Usually we mean that we have an idea about how to explain something. We may suggest a theory about who killed the butler in the late-night thriller. Or we may have a theory about why Ms. Figueroa always looks so tired when she delivers the mail on Monday morning. Or we may have a theory about what the coach of the local baseball team said to his pitcher after they lost last night's big game.

These theories that we develop about things are often tentative. That is, when we say that we have a theory about something, we may mean that we don't have much evidence. If we don't have much evidence, other people don't usually agree with or share our theories. Nevertheless, it is fun to suggest clever ideas.

In contrast, scientists use the word *theory* in a very different way than we do. Scientific theories are explanations that are extremely well accepted by the scientific community because a variety of strong evidence supports them.

A good example of a scientific theory is the atomic theory, an explanation developed in 1803 by the British teacher and chemist John Dalton. You may already be familiar with one of the most important ideas of Dalton's atomic theory: *All matter (or things) in the universe is composed of tiny particles called atoms*. This idea was revolutionary at the time that Dalton first suggested it. But since then, physicists have accumulated an enormous body of evidence to support it. Part of that evidence is the result of our modern ability to detect, to manipulate, and even to subdivide atoms. Even though Dalton did not predict that atoms could be subdivided into smaller

Figure E2.17   The word *theory* often means different things to different people.

pieces such as electrons and protons, the general outline of his theory still stands.

Another example is the cell theory, which is the understanding that complex living organisms are comprised of small building blocks called cells. This is an example of a biological theory that is supported by an enormous body of evidence.

Despite the evidence that has accumulated in favor of the atomic and cellular theories, and despite the fact that no modern scientist questions most of these basic principles, we still refer to these ideas as *theories*. Clearly, scientists use the word *theory* very differently from the way most nonscientists do.

To understand how an explanation becomes known as a scientific theory, we have to consider first the meaning of the term **hypothesis**. You may have learned already that a hypothesis is a trial idea about something. During research, scientists develop hypotheses to explain the reasons underlying an event or a phenomenon. A hypothesis can also explain the relationships that scientists think they see among objects, events, or processes. As you will see in Unit 2, predictions made from such hypotheses are useful because they can be tested. Testing our hypotheses allows us to distinguish those trial ideas that adequately explain what we study from those that do not.

You probably can see, then, that the explanations we develop for things and events around us actually are *hypotheses*, not scientific theories. As hypotheses, these trial ideas or tentative explanations can be tested. In scientific terms, the police who investigate the death of the butler do so by systematically testing a whole set of hypotheses, not theories.

By contrast, a scientific **theory** is a hypothesis that already has been extensively tested and is supported by a large body of observations and evidence. A good theory explains data that we already know and relates and explains additional data as they become known. In fact, a good theory also predicts new data and suggests new relationships that we may not already have recognized.

Why do scientists call Darwin's explanation of descent with modification the *theory* of evolution instead of the *hypothesis* of evolution? First, it is considered a theory because of the enormous amount of evidence that suggests it is a correct explanation. As you already have seen, this evidence spans a wide range of different scientific fields, from anatomy to geology to embryology to physical anthropology. Second, it is considered a theory because it explains both the evidence that Darwin saw and recorded, as well as the new data that we continue to collect. It also successfully predicts new phenomena. That is, Darwin's explanation for biological change across time continues to be supported, even by evidence collected more than 100 years after his work. For those reasons and others, this explanation is almost universally accepted by scientists around the world.

OK, I guess my theory is wrong.

Actually, Sergeant, I think you mean your hypothesis is wrong. We'd better come up with a new hypothesis about who killed Mr. Smith.

Figure E2.18 When used by scientists, the word *theory* means an explanation that is supported by evidence and well accepted by other scientists.

Does this wide acceptance of Darwin's work mean that Darwin explained everything there was to explain about evolution or that every part of his explanation is correct? No, not necessarily. Darwin was not able to explain exactly *how* characteristics passed from one generation to the next. He did not include in his theory an explanation of the relationship between natural selection and genetic inheritance. However, this omission does not make Darwin's ideas incorrect. Since Darwin's time, biologists have added information on natural selection and genetic inheritance to the theory of evolution. In fact, the addition of information to Darwin's basic proposal illustrates the power of a sound scientific theory. As new information about inheritance became available, it supported, rather than contradicted, the original explanation.

So, when we talk about explanations for things in the world around us, we need to be careful. We need to decide whether are we talking about a theory (as we typically use the term) or are we talking about a *theory* (as scientists use the term). The difference between the two is quite large, indeed. ◆

Describing Life: An Impossible Challenge?

An alien spaceship orbiting a planet to make observations ejects a special robotic rover toward the planet's surface. Retrorockets fire to slow the robot's speed, and parachutes open to help it land gently. Now the robot settles down on the planet's surface, amid rocks and soil. Its mission: to determine whether life exists on the planet.

At first, the rover sits motionless, a foreign object on the bleak landscape. Then, slowly, it activates its electronic senses. It rotates its twin cameras to scan the horizon. It measures the local weather: temperature, barometric pressure, wind speed, and direction. It uses special equipment to sniff the air to determine its composition. The atmosphere is thin, but it

Figure E3.1 Technology to explore Mars. (a) In July 1997, the rover *Sojourner* landed on Mars. The white airbags that cushioned its landing are seen on either side of the photo. **(b)** In 2004, two rovers, *Spirit* and *Opportunity*, landed at different places on Mars and sent data back to scientists on Earth. In both pictures, you can see rocks on the surface and hills in the background.

does contain some water vapor, even a little more than observers had expected. This is a good sign . . .

Finding evidence for the potential of life on Mars has been very exciting, though difficult and inconclusive, so far. Scientists continue to design missions that will collect additional evidence. How should scientists involved in the effort look for life? The landing craft, though technologically very complex, is small. Its designers had to make careful decisions about the equipment that it carries and the activities that it is able to accomplish. Should they look for signs of evolution, of growth and development, of reproduction? All are fundamental characteristics of life, but all probably occur too slowly to be detected by a tiny, robotic craft. Instead, designers decided to test surface samples for more immediate, more easily recognizable signs of life. They will test for those signs that have to do with a living system's requirement to use matter and energy obtained from the environment to maintain its complex organization.

Suddenly, a mechanical arm extends from the strange craft and scoops up some of the Martian soil. At last, humans have collected a sample from another planet. It doesn't matter

Figure E3.2 Lichens are organisms that consist of a close association between a fungus and a photosynthetic organism such as an alga or a blue-green bacterium.

that the rover cannot return to Earth. It will send information about minerals, water, and the climate found on Mars back to scientists on Earth. Technology is extending our hands and eyes.

Slowly, the soil sample is deposited in a special chamber. A specially designed piece of equipment adds a mixture of radioactive gases. Some of the smallest forms of life on earth use light energy and certain gases in the environment around them to build more complex molecules that are necessary for them to live. Is there anything in the Martian soil that will use these gases as "molecular food"? Will these radioactively labeled molecules slowly begin to accumulate in the soil sample, as living things remove them from the air and use them to maintain and build their internal structures?

Recognizing life on an alien planet such as Mars is indeed a challenge. At minimum, such an endeavor requires that we start with a good idea of how to recognize life on Earth. But even this task is not simple. Living systems share many characteristics. But do any of these actually distinguish living things from nonliving things?

You already have an intuitive sense about life. If you were to ask your classmates to identify a tree, a dog, and a rock as living or nonliving, chances are great that all their answers would be the same. However, if you then asked your classmates precisely how they know what is living and what is not, their responses probably would vary. And suppose you asked them to categorize a less familiar object, such as the scaly, grayish green lichen on a boulder (like the one depicted in Figure E3.2)? This time, some of your classmates might say that this stuff is not alive.

How can we describe life so that we always can identify it when we see it? Perhaps the easiest way to begin thinking about life is to consider what happens when an organism dies. Think, for example, about a bird that has just died. The bird can no longer move, or eat,

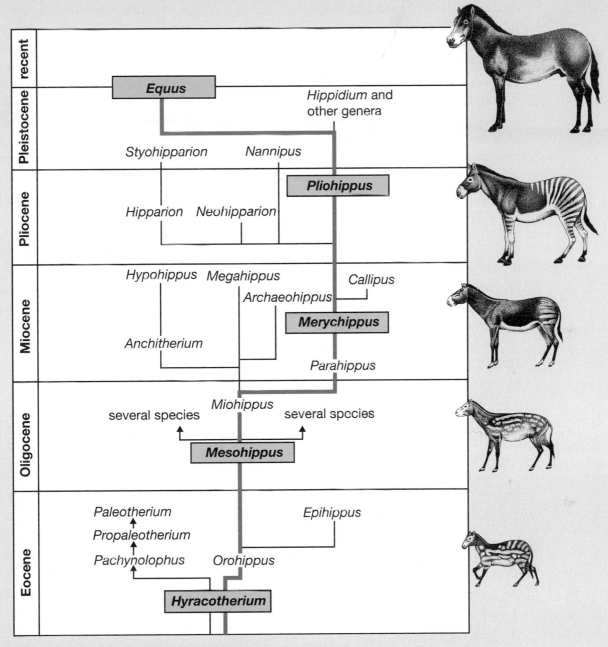

Figure E3.3 **A proposed evolutionary tree.** What evidence do you think scientists used to develop this explanation?

or keep itself warm. Even if you touch it, it does not respond. Eventually, the dead body will become decayed and disorganized. It will never recover its form or function, nor will it ever again produce offspring.

This simple example provides some clues to the nature of life by showing that certain properties of a living system are lost when death occurs. If, however, you try to write a simple description of life that absolutely

distinguishes it from nonliving substances, you may find it rather difficult. Rather than trying to describe life precisely, let us first examine the characteristics that we generally observe in living systems. Then, perhaps, we can consider how we might go about recognizing life, both on Earth and on another planet.

All forms of life, even vastly different forms such as humans, apple trees, spiders, and microscopic bacteria, share many basic characteristics. That should not surprise you. In fact, it is because living things share much in common that you can make some judgments about whether an unknown object is likely to be alive or not.

Understanding these common characteristics is fundamental to understanding biology. In fact, these characteristics are so important that we have summarized them as six unifying principles of biology, and we have organized the flow of topics in this course around them. You already have encountered evolution, one of these principles. As you begin to develop a deeper understanding of the remaining five principles, you will be developing a rich understanding of how all living systems, including humans, function.

Evolution: Patterns and Products of Change in Living Systems. As you already have seen in this unit, one significant characteristic of living systems is that they evolve, or change, across time. Through natural selection, some individuals have characteristics that make them best suited to their environment. These individuals are most likely to grow to maturity and reproduce. Those same individuals then pass their traits on to their offspring. As a result, those adaptive characteristics become more common in the population.

In some species, such as the horseshoe

Figure E3.4 This anole lizard can change color in response to its environment.

crab, characteristics remain unchanged for long periods of time. More often, however, natural selection results in gradual change in populations. These changes eventually lead to distinctly different populations of organisms that display an amazing range of diverse characteristics. Figure E3.3 illustrates how scientists think one type of organism may have evolved. *Evolution* represents the first unifying principle considered in this course. Although evolution is important in understanding life, living organisms, and their interactions, it is not particularly helpful in determining whether a particular object is living or not.

Homeostasis: Maintaining Dynamic Equilibrium in Living Systems. A second characteristic of life—and a second unifying principle of biology—has to do with a living system's ability to maintain an *internal balance*, referred to as homeostasis. All organisms regulate their internal systems in response to changes in their surroundings. When you are startled, your heart beats faster, sending blood through your body at a faster rate. This response ensures that your body will continue to have a good supply of oxygen and nutrients (which are carried in the blood) during a possibly stressful or dangerous time. In fact, all organisms show a similar type of internal regulation. Bacteria adjust their production of certain key products in response to changes in the nutrient levels in their environments. Plants respond to changes in humidity by opening or closing tiny holes in the underside of their leaves. And some animals can change their coloration in response to their environment (see Figure E3.4).

Energy, Matter, and Organization: Relationships in Living Systems. Another common characteristic of life is *organization*. All living systems are highly organized forms of *matter*. This matter is made from atoms held together in ways that form large, complex molecules. Scientists have identified more than 100 different types of atoms. One of the most remarkable similarities among all living things, however, is that they are made predominantly from only a few types of atoms. These are notably carbon, nitrogen, oxygen, hydrogen, phosphorous, and sulfur.

The molecules of living materials are organized into complex structures known as cells. Cells are the basic structural units of living matter. Because most cells are too small to see with the unaided eye, scientists did not see cells until 300 years ago, after the invention of the microscope. As Figure E3.5 illustrates, cells are baglike structures made of a membrane that encloses and protects the contents.

A related property of all living systems is that they require energy to build and maintain their highly organized structures and to carry out all of their activities. Recall that the bird, once dead, eventually will decay and disintegrate. It will lose its distinctive shape and appearance and become increasingly indistinguishable from the matter around it. The loss of the bird's characteristically high organization follows the more basic loss of its ability to obtain matter and energy from its environment and to use that matter and energy to keep its body (its matter) repaired and functional. Together, the ideas of matter, energy, and organization represent the third unifying principle of biology.

Continuity: Reproduction and Inheritance in Living Systems. The organization and the function of living systems depend on specific plans that are encoded in each organism's genetic material, or DNA. For example, maple trees display a characteristic structure and function because they possess DNA characteristic of maple trees. Humans grow and function in ways that we recognize as distinct from other life-forms because humans possess DNA characteristic of humans. DNA is a long and complex molecule that stores information (see Figure E3.6). One of the most significant characteristics that unifies living systems is the universal nature of this DNA. Although the

instructions that direct an organism's cellular activities and developmental events are specific for its species, all organisms, from bacteria to humans, use the same DNA to communicate those instructions. The ability to transfer those instructions—through DNA—to the next generation during reproduction represents a fourth important unifying principle of life, that of *continuity*.

Development: Growth and Differentiation in Living Systems. The *ability to grow and develop* represents the fifth unifying characteristic of living systems. Growth is an important activity in the early life of a human. Growing requires the body to assemble new tissue. As the organism's size increases, the way in which the organism's tissue is organized also changes. Human adults not only are larger than children are, but they also are shaped differently. And they can do a variety of things that human infants cannot do, such as walk and talk. Many

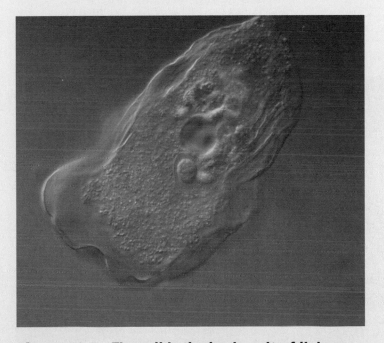

Figure E3.5   The cell is the basic unit of living matter. Most prokaryotic cells (cells without membrane-enclosed nuclei or organelles) are 1–10 μm in diameter. Most eukaryotic cells (cells with a membrane-enclosed nuclei and organelles) are 10–100 μm in diameter, but protoctists can be much larger. Notice the organization of the interior of this *Thecamoeba* cell, which is 10 μm.

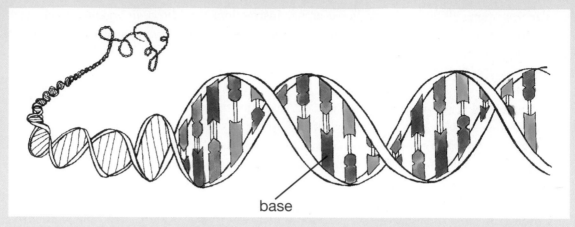

base

Figure E3.6 DNA is a complex molecule. It has a double helix (twisted ladder) shape.

plants, in a similar manner, begin life as small seedlings that push up through the soil and grow into mature plants that look quite different from the early seedlings. Plant growth also involves the addition of new tissue and the organization of new parts such as leaves and reproductive structures.

Ecology: Interaction and Interdependence in Living Systems.

Finally, all living systems on earth are part of an interactive and interdependent web of life.

Figure E3.7 Organisms along and in this stream interact and depend on each other.

Organisms do not exist in isolation, but rather live as one element in a complex community of life (refer to Figure E3.7). Imagine a wooded area alongside a stream on an early summer day. Plants provide shelter and food for a variety of birds. Perhaps a rabbit has dug a burrow nearby and now feeds on wild berries growing in the light shade close to the forest. Not far away a fox has just left her den in search of food for her young. This community of different, yet interdependent, living systems illustrates the sixth unifying principle of biology, the *interactive and interdependent nature of life*.

To the extent that these brief descriptions capture the essence of each of the unifying principles, we might say that in this short list of characteristics, we have described life—as it exists on earth. Can we say that any one of these principles *defines* life, in the sense that it alone is necessary for life and that it alone is an indicator of life? Probably not. Just as a *combination* of characteristics identifies you as a human, a *combination* of these principles indicates the presence of life.

To this day, curiosity about life on Mars remains high. Unfortunately, although two of the three tests described in Figure E3.8 yielded some interesting results, scientists failed to duplicate the results with subsequent samples. This was disappointing and suggested

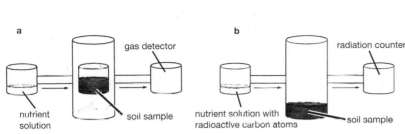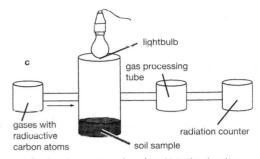

1. Soil sample is suspended in a porous cup.
2. Nutrient solution is added to the soil sample.
3. Changes in gas content are measured by a gas detector.

1. Soil sample is sprayed with radioactively labeled nutrient solution.
2. Any radioactive carbon dioxide that is produced by the soil and released into the air above the sample is detected and counted.

1. Radioactive gases are introduced into the chamber containing the soil.
2. The light is turned on as a source of energy.
3. The chamber is heated to release newly made substances into the air.
4. The air is processed to separate complex substances from the simple gases that had been introduced earlier.
5. Any radioactive carbon that is contained in these complex molecules is detected and counted.

Figure E3.8 **Three experiments to test Martian soil.** **(a)** A gas exchange experiment tested the Martian soil for evidence of organisms that took in gases from the Martian atmosphere and nutrients from the soil and gave off gases as wastes. This experiment is then performed using earth's soil. The experiment indicates the presence of microscopic organisms that take in oxygen and nutrients and give off carbon dioxide. **(b)** Scientists next search for the release of carbon dioxide. The experiment tests the Martian soil for evidence of organisms that could use simple nutrients and give off waste gases (CO_2). This experiment was similar to the gas exchange experiment. It served as an important check on its results. Again, this experiment gives strong, positive results when earth's soil is tested. **(c)** A third experiment tested the Martian soil for evidence of organisms that might build large, complex substances out of simple gases in the Martian atmosphere. This experiment is then performed on earth's soil. The experiment indicates the presence of microscopic organisms that use the energy of sunlight to help them build sugars and other large, complex molecules.

caution in interpreting even the changes that the distant instruments *did* detect. In fact, by 1979, most scientists involved with the project had agreed that although they could not rule out the possibility that life exists on Mars, all the data that they collected in the original experiments could be explained as resulting from purely chemical (not biological) causes. The rovers that landed on Mars in 2004 did not find life. But they did find evidence indicating that water, a necessity for life as we know it, existed on Mars in the past.

Describing life . . . a difficult, but not an *impossible* challenge. Looking for life, using earth's criteria, in a very different environment more than 40 million miles away . . . more difficult to be sure, but *impossible*?

What do you think? ◆

Five Kingdoms

In which of these pairs of illustrations are the organisms most closely related? Figure E3.9 shows two animals that bear little resemblance to each other. In contrast, Figure E3.10 shows two types of cells, each an individual organism and each looking quite like the other.

Surprisingly, from an evolutionary point of view, the two animals are much more closely related than are the two single-celled organisms. The animals are an African elephant and a close relative, a small mammal known as a hyrax. What you cannot see in Figure E3.9 is all of the ways in which these organisms are similar, from the basic structures of their cells to the structures of their feet and teeth.

Figure E3.9 **(a) African elephant (*Loxodonta africana*).** The average male African elephant is 350 cm high and weighs 5,000 kg. **(b) Rock hyrax (*Procavia capensis*).** A rock hyrax may be 30 cm high and weigh 4 kg.

On the other hand, the organisms in Figure E3.10 are very distant in their evolutionary connection, despite the fact that each is a single cell. If you look closely, you can find one of the characteristics that marks these two organisms as being very different. Notice that *Peranema* has an interior compartment that is missing in the other cell. That compartment is a nucleus, a membrane-enclosed structure in the cell that houses its DNA. The second cell is a bacterium called *Escherichia coli*. Like other types of bacteria, its DNA is not separated from the rest of the cell contents by a surrounding membrane. It lacks a nucleus.

These two cells illustrate the single largest dividing point that biologists recognize among all of the species on earth. The bacterial cell is a very simple type of cell known as a **prokaryote**. It has no nucleus, and the genetic material that it contains is a huge molecule of DNA, without any fancy packaging. In great contrast, the *Peranema* is a more complex type of cell called a **eukaryote**. Eukaryotes have cells with nuclei and DNA that is packaged with proteins to form structures known as chromosomes. Eukaryotic cells also may have other specialized, membrane-enclosed compartments that perform a variety of functions, such as energy transformation and protein storage and packaging. Although many similar processes go on in prokaryotic cells, these cells do not contain such compartments.

The structural differences and the evolutionary distance between prokaryotes

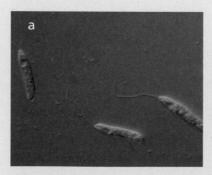

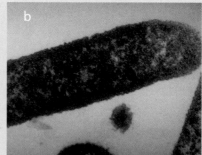

Figure E3.10 **(a)** This *Peranema* is about 40 μm. **(b)** This *Escherichia coli* is 3.5 μm in length (photographed at 35,000×).

and eukaryotes are so great that biologists categorize all organisms on earth on the basis of this distinction. Figure E3.11 illustrates the five major types of organisms recognized by most biologists today. Note that one of the kingdoms includes all of the prokaryotic organisms. In contrast, the organisms in each of the other four kingdoms are eukaryotes.

It would not be surprising if the classification scheme shown in the figure and used in this course seems a bit foreign to you. After all, most of us grow up thinking that the world contains only two basic categories of organisms, plants and animals.

We are not alone in this. From the days of Aristotle to the mid-1800s, almost everyone was content with this simple subdivision. We generally have little reason to question it, because we rarely encounter living systems that are so different in external appearance that they don't seem to fit.

By the middle of the 19th century, however, some scientists had started to question whether organisms such as fungi and bacteria really fit well into either the plant kingdom or the animal kingdom. Despite these questions, suggestions to increase the number of kingdoms were largely ignored. It was not until the 1960s that the prevailing attitude in the scientific community began to change. Scientists were discovering new forms of life and were using new microscopic and

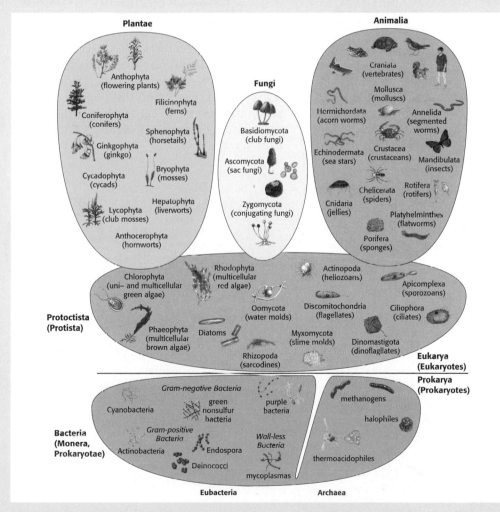

Figure E3.11   A five-kingdom scheme.   The Bacteria kingdom includes the organisms that do not have membrane-bound organelles. Plants, animals, fungi, and protoctists are all eukaryotes. What differences do you think separate the organisms in each kingdom?

biochemical techniques to examine cell structure and function in even well-known organisms. This led to an increasing amount of evidence that supported proposals to increase the number of basic categories that biologists recognize. Figure E3.12 illustrates some of these multikingdom schemes. These ideas will help you trace the changes that have occurred in scientists' thinking to bring us to the five-kingdom system that is most often used today.

As you read the following brief descriptions of the five kingdoms, look for patterns in the criteria that determine each group. Look as well for differences that distinguish one basic type of organism from the next. Do you see some of the reasons that biologists can no longer accept a two-kingdom view?

Kingdom Bacteria (Prokaryotae, Monera). The main criterion (or qualification) for membership in this kingdom is the presence of the prokaryotic type of cell (a cell that lacks membrane-enclosed compartments). The Bacteria kingdom includes the bacteria (or eubacteria)

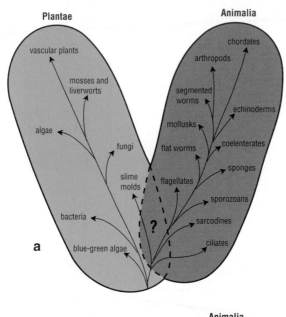

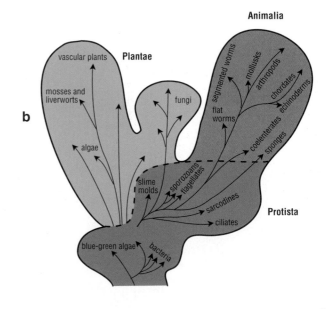

Figure E3.12   Scientific ideas change across time. (**a**) The first attempts to categorize life resulted in this two-kingdom division between plants and animals. (**b**) This model shows three kingdoms: plants, animals, and protists. (**c**) Scientists developed this four-kingdom scheme when they realized the great differences between eukaryotes and prokaryotes.

and the archaea. Bacteria usually are single cells, but they may occur in groups of cells. Bacteria come in a variety of shapes, as depicted in figure E3.13. Some swim by means of long, whiplike tails. Bacteria live in almost every environment, from the soil to inside the human mouth. Archaea often live in extreme environmental conditions. Some live at high temperatures or in highly acidic conditions; others live in high-salt conditions. Some archaea live in environments where there is very little oxygen, and they produce methane gas.

Bacteria show a great diversity in the processes that they use to obtain energy. Many bacteria can use the sun's energy directly to power the reactions required for making their own food through photosynthesis. Others use energy derived from the matter (food molecules) that they acquire from their environments. As a group, bacteria can digest almost anything—even petroleum. This ability is fortunate for us. Bacteria that can recycle matter through decomposition increasingly are being used to help with environmental cleanup efforts. All bacteria reproduce by dividing into two. But some also exchange small amounts of DNA—a form of sexual reproduction.

Kingdom Animalia. Among the four eukaryotic kingdoms is the kingdom in which humans are found, the kingdom Animalia. Animals are multicellular—they have a complex organization of many specialized cells. Animals also are characterized by their ability to bring food into their bodies and digest it. In addition, most animals reproduce sexually and have senses and nervous systems that enhance their ability to move.

Animals live in marine and freshwater environments, inhabit the soil, or live on land. In addition, animals come in a range of sizes, from microscopic worms that live in human blood to whales that can reach lengths of 27 meters (89 feet). Figure E3.14 shows a diversity of animals.

Kingdom Plantae. Another eukaryotic kingdom, the kingdom Plantae, includes organisms that acquire their energy not from eating, but from the sun. Plants carry out photosynthesis, a process by which cells use energy from sunlight to produce their own food. Photosynthesis takes place in membrane-enclosed structures within plant

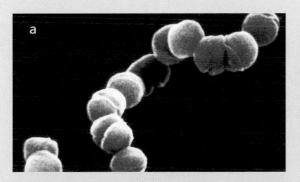

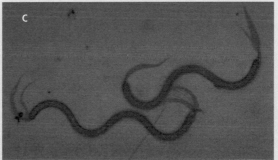

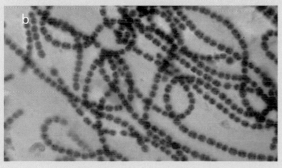

Figure E3.13 Examples of prokaryotes. (**a**) These *Streptococcus* bacteria (photographed at 40,000✕) can cause strep throat. (**b**) *Nostoc* (photographed at 400✕), a cyanobacterium, is common in freshwater lakes. (**c**) *Spirella voluntans* (photographed at 400✕) is part of a group of bacteria named for its characteristic spiral shape.

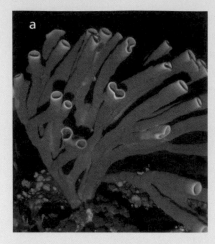

Figure E3.14 Examples of animals. (**a**) Tube sponges from the Red Sea (**b**) A click beetle in Arizona (**c**) A male hooded oriole from the southwestern region of the United States

cells called chloroplasts. Chloroplasts contain chlorophyll, the light-absorbing pigment that gives plants their characteristic green color.

Plants are multicellular, and their cell membranes are surrounded by a rigid cell wall that provides support. Most of them reproduce sexually. Plant forms are diverse and include mosses, liverworts, club mosses, ferns, conifers, and flowering plants, as shown in Figure E3.15. The bulk of the world's food and much of its oxygen are produced by plants.

Kingdom Fungi. Kingdom Fungi, also a eukaryotic kingdom, includes organisms that grow directly from reproductive cells called spores. Fungi, like plants, have cell walls, but they do not carry out photosynthesis. You probably are more familiar with the members of this kingdom than you realize. Fungi such as mushrooms become large, multicellular organisms, with tissues made of slender tubes of cells (hyphae) that may contain more than one nucleus. Other fungi, such as yeasts, live as single cells during their entire life cycle. Still others, such as molds and rusts, live as tiny multicellular structures on the surface of bread that has been sitting around too long or lettuce that is going bad.

Figure E3.15 Examples of plants. (**a**) This moss, *Lycopodium*, grows in moist areas. (**b**) A sword fern, *Polystichum munitium*, in Olympic National Park, Washington (**c**) An apple tree, *Malus* spp., in full bloom

Fungi do not digest food inside their bodies as humans do. Instead, they release molecules called enzymes into their surroundings. These enzymes break down (digest) biological material that other living systems have produced. The smaller food molecules then are absorbed into the cells. Thus fungi, along with many bacteria, play an important role as decomposers in many communities of organisms. The diversity of fungi includes yeasts, molds, morels, mushrooms, shelf fungi, puffballs, and plant diseases such as rusts and smuts (see Figure E3.16). Some fungi also interact closely with green algae or cyanobacteria to form the organisms known as lichens.

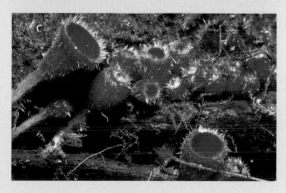

Figure E3.16 **Examples of fungi.**
(**a**) The mycelium of a wood-rotting fungus, *Stereum complicatum*
(**b**) A mushroom fungus, *Mycema lejiana*
(**c**) *Microstoma floccosa*, a small, cup-shaped fungus

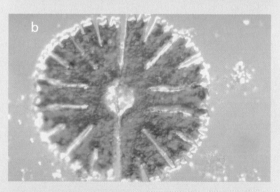

Figure E3.17 **Examples of protoctists.** (**a**) *Trichonympha* (photographed at 135×), a protoctist that lives in the gut of termites (**b**) *Micrasteria* (photographed at 100×), a type of green algae (**c**) *Fuligo septica*, a slime mold

Kingdom Protoctista (Protista). Finally, the kingdom Protoctista is a grab bag of all the remaining eukaryotes that do not belong to the animal, plant, or fungi kingdoms. Protoctists live in water and in moist habitats, such as in the soil, on trees, and in the bodies of other organisms.

Protoctists show a remarkable range of diversity in their methods of obtaining food, their methods of reproduction, their life cycles, and their lifestyles. Most protoctists are microscopic single cells and many grow as colonies—clusters of individual cells. Others, such as brown algae living in the ocean, may form multicellular structures up to 100 meters (328 feet) long. Some protoctists are brightly colored algae that produce their food through photosynthesis. Others are slime molds that obtain their food by decomposing the dead tissues of other organisms. Still other protoctists are parasites of animals, plants, or fungi. A single droplet of pond water viewed under the microscope reveals a world of protoctists in their myriad of shapes. Figure E3.17 depicts several protoctists.

Scientists may rethink the classification system once again as they continue to learn

Figure E3.18   Minerva Terrace, Mammoth Hot Springs, Yellowstone National Park.   Archaea live in environments like these hot springs.

more about the organisms that inhabit the earth. For example, evidence obtained during the last two decades suggests that the archaea, which are currently in the kingdom Bacteria, differ from other bacteria in that kingdom. The archaea include organisms that live in environments similar to those that probably existed early in earth's history, such as hot springs (like those in Figure E3.18), sulfur-containing muds at the bottom of ponds, salt ponds, and salt lakes. For that reason, biologists think that the archaea are among the very oldest organisms on earth. Because of their age and their differences from other bacteria, they perhaps merit a kingdom of their own. ◆

From Cell to Seed

Have you thanked a green plant today? Plants play a critical role in our existence on earth. They produce the oxygen that we breathe, the food that we eat, and the multitude of materials that we use, from rubber, to lumber, to medicines, to coffee. Perhaps we ought to ask, Have you thanked a 3.5 billion-year-old single-celled organism today? Such an

organism likely was the ancestor of all modern plants.

To understand how that could be, we need to trace the history of plant evolution. One of the ways we can begin to understand this history is to recognize that each of the major events of plant evolution that scientists think took place involved the appearance of a major adaptation. These events led to the emergence of the hundreds of thousands of different species of plants that currently inhabit every imaginable place on earth, from the frozen Arctic tundra to lush tropical rain forests.

The ancient seas. We begin our survey at a point about 3.5 billion years ago (see the timeline in Figure E3.19). Evidence indicates that plants, like all other modern species, evolved from single-celled organisms that first lived in ancient seas and resembled modern prokaryotes. The atmosphere above these seas is thought to have consisted of a mixture of gases, largely water vapor, carbon dioxide and carbon monoxide, nitrogen, hydrogen sulfide (the stuff that makes rotten eggs smell), and hydrogen. Because this mixture of gases probably contained little or no oxygen, animals and plants, as we know them today, could not have survived.

The first single-celled organisms that lived in these seas most probably used complex molecules in their environment as their source of energy. These molecules likely were formed as a result of chemical reactions that occurred among the various substances present in the seawater. At some point, however, the growing population of living cells probably started using these complex molecules faster than they were being formed. Scientists think that as these primitive food molecules became scarce, the limitation of resources favored the survival of occasional cells that were able to use sulfur compounds, carbon dioxide, and the energy in sunlight to build their own complex molecules. These cells possessed a chemical apparatus that was capable of building complex molecules from simple sources. Thus, they were largely independent of the dwindling supply of complex molecules that still floated free in the ancient seas.

The appearance of oxygen in the atmosphere. Scientists think that it was these first self-sufficient organisms that gave rise to modern plants. (Bacteria that use this same apparatus, such as those in Figure E3.20, still exist.) Even sulfur compounds, however, were not available in unlimited supply. A substance that was abundant was water. The appearance of cells that could use water instead of sulfur compounds to build complex molecules was a major evolutionary advance. This type of photosynthesis (a process in which water, carbon dioxide, and light energy are used to build complex molecules) releases oxygen

Era	Millions of years ago	
Cenozoic	7	Apelike ancestors of humans appear
	55	Primates appear
Mesozoic	66	Dinosaurs become extinct
	130	Flowering plants appear
	210	Mammals appear
Paleozoic	360	Amphibians appear
	430	Land plants appear
	500	First vertebrates appear (jawless fishes)
Precambrian	2100	Multicellular organisms (algae)
	2400	Free oxygen building up in the atmosphere
	3500	Prokaryotes (bacteria)
	4100	Oldest earth rocks
	4600	Origin of earth

Figure E3.19 Timeline of major evolutionary events. Why do you think each of these events is significant?

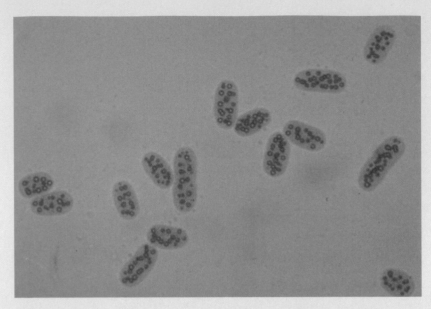

Figure E3.20 Modern phototrophic bacteria, *Chromatium okenii*, though only 15 µm long, are able to build complex molecules. The globules you see are sulfur particles.

Figure E3.21 **Photosynthetic bacteria.** Bacteria such as these *Gomphosphaeria*, which are each 1 µm in diameter, contributed to the production of oxygen in the earth's early atmosphere.

gas. This gas was a substance that probably had not been present in the atmosphere of the primitive earth. Today, photosynthesis is the major method of supplying energy either directly to living systems or indirectly to organisms that prey on others. Modern photosynthetic cells, such as the blue-green bacteria shown in Figure E3.21 and including those found in plants, contain a green pigment called chlorophyll that absorbs energy from sunlight.

By about 2.1 billion years ago, significant amounts of oxygen had collected in the atmosphere of the earth and formed a layer of ozone. (Ozone molecules are composed of three atoms of oxygen.) The ozone layer blocked out some of the dangerous ultraviolet light from the sun. Because ultraviolet light damages DNA, the establishment of an ozone layer made it possible for organisms to survive on land (water blocks ultraviolet light quite well).

The appearance of eukaryotic cells. The fossil record indicates that just about this time, another key evolutionary event occurred. By about 2.1 billion years ago, more complex cells—ancestral eukaryotes—had appeared in the fossil record. There is evidence that some of these early eukaryotes incorporated photosynthetic bacteria within their cells. As a result, they were able to carry out photosynthesis.

The appearance of multicellular organisms. At this point in evolutionary history, some of these eukaryotic organisms consisted of groups of cells rather than a single cell. A multicellular organism would have had a better chance of surviving on land than would a one-celled organism. The outer layer of cells might have protected the inner cells from drying out rapidly. The inner cells might have been efficient at photosynthesis. Other cells of the same organism might have become specialized in collecting water or nutrients from the environment. The specialized functions of different cells in one organism would have enabled the organism to exploit more of the resources in its new environment. The first plant may have been a specialized, multicellular organism, somewhat like the modern alga *Chara* in Figure E3.22. This first plant was able to live and reproduce on land if ocean spray or tides kept it moist.

Two plant groups apparently evolved from such relatively complex multicellular green algae. One group is represented today by mosses (refer to Figure E3.15a) and related plants. These organisms possess few adaptations to life on land and require a moist environment in order to live and reproduce. The other group, which includes fossils of the oldest land plants, has many adaptations to life on land.

Adaptations that enhanced survival on land. One adaptation to life on land was the development of a waxy material that reduced water loss by providing a protective covering over the outer plant cells. The development of vascular tissue was another important adaptation. This "plumbing system" carries water from the ground up through all the parts of the plant. Vascular tissue, depicted in Figure E3.23,

Figure E3.22 *Chara. Chara* is a modern multicellular alga. The orange and yellow globules are reproductive structures.

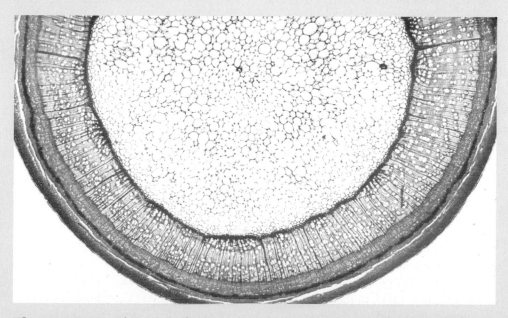

Figure E3.23 This magnified cross section of a young maple tree stem (photographed at 7×) shows the vascular tissues as rings around the outside.

 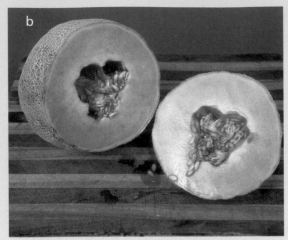

Figure E3.24 How are these seeds likely to be dispersed? **(a)** The female cone in this piñon pine will mature and have seeds on the inside of the scales. **(b)** A cantaloupe has seeds inside the fleshy fruit.

enables plants to grow to large sizes. The oldest common ancestor of modern vascular plants developed about 420 million years ago.

The earliest vascular plants, however, were limited by their means of sexual reproduction, which required them to live in a moist environment. In early land plants (and their present-day descendants), sperm cells could reach egg cells only if the plant was covered with a film of moisture in which the sperm could swim. As a consequence, these plants were more successful in environments that contained at least a moderate amount of moisture.

Eventually, however, new species evolved that carried out sexual reproduction internally, within specialized reproductive structures that eliminated the need for external moisture. These changes probably occurred about 400 million years ago and enabled these new species to inhabit drier areas. In the most advanced modern vascular plants, the reproductive structures are located in cones or flowers.

Another adaptation that evolved about 350 million years ago was the production of seeds. Seeds are products of sexual reproduction. They contain an inactive, tiny plant embryo packaged in material that provides food when the seed germinates and

begins to grow. This system allows wide dispersal of new organisms because the seeds are spread by various means (wind, animals, water) and begin to grow in new locations.

In cone-bearing plants such as pines and firs (refer to Figure E3.24a), seeds are dispersed from open structures. But in flowering plants, seeds develop inside a specialized structure that becomes the fruit of the plant (see Figure E3.24b). The flowering plants, products of millions of years of evolution, are the most successful type of living plants. They are represented by more than 250,000 species and have adapted to every habitat on earth except Antarctica. If you doubt their value and importance to us, try these simple tests:

- Ask a friend or a member of your family to name five types of plants quickly.

- Ask the same person to quickly name five important commercial products that come from plants.

Chances are that most, if not all, of the five plants or products that they name are, or come from, flowering plants. These are some of the modern-day descendants of simple, single-celled ancestors that lived in primitive seas about 3.5 billion years ago. ◆

Mutations Are a Source of Variation

Think about all of the organisms that you have observed. Despite their common ancestry and despite the common properties that they share as living systems, they really are quite different from one another. Even similar types of organisms—for example, the plants that you examined in the activity *Adaptation, Diversity, and Evolution*—have quite different characteristics. How can we explain the wide range of characteristics among the organisms on earth?

The key to that question is natural selection, the process by which evolutionary change occurs. You examined natural selection in the Chapter 2 activity *Modeling Natural Selection*. To understand the link between natural selection and diversity, consider briefly the sequence of events that might happen to a population of organisms living in a particular environment. A **population** is all of the organisms of one species living together in one area at the same time. As members of the same species, these organisms share certain characteristics. Nevertheless, within any population there also is some variability in characteristics (just look around you in your classroom). This variability results from the normal events of sexual reproduction as well as from random changes (mutations) that occur in an organism's DNA during reproduction.

What happens to this population if the environment does not change? Does this variability increase? On the other hand, do the members of the population continue to look very much like each other and like past generations?

Most likely, future generations of that population will continue to look very much the same. This continuity in adaptive characteristics from one generation to the next occurs because of natural selection.

Characteristics that are likely to be most widely represented in later generations are those of individuals that have the best ability to reproduce. Most of these characteristics likely have served as adaptations for that population for some time. On the other hand, new characteristics that may have appeared that *decrease* an organism's chance for survival at this time and in this environment are not likely to be passed on to offspring because the organism often dies before it reaches reproductive maturity.

Does this mean that the population never will change? Not at all. First, it is possible that a new variation might randomly occur that would increase an organism's ability to survive and to reproduce. In this case, natural selection would tend to perpetuate that new adaptation and the population might slowly begin to change. Second, it also is possible that the environment might change and that characteristics that were not adaptive in the earlier environment suddenly become beneficial. Remember as well, that characteristics that represent adaptations at one point in the history of a species may cease to do so as the environment changes. Adaptations relate to specific environments. If the environment changes, then a characteristic that had been an adaptation may no longer provide an advantage. Unless such a characteristic is *harmful* in the changed environment, it may not immediately disappear from the species because it will not be selected against. Gradually, the characteristic may become less prominent among individuals of the population in later generations because it no longer is advantageous.

The correlation between surroundings and adaptations is an explanation for the

Figure E3.25 Manatee.

rolling grasslands, and rocky coastlines. Each of these environments contains a variety of species, some unique to that environment. Each species has its own distinctive way of surviving and reproducing, which is somewhat dependent on its adaptations (see Figure E3.25). The enormous diversity of species in the five kingdoms is in part a result of the range of adaptations to the enormous variety of environments.

The adaptations that exist in an extreme environment, such as the desert, clearly show the relationship between adaptations and surroundings. Many desert plants have structures such as spines instead of leaves (see Figure E3.26). In addition, some are coated with a thick, waxy outer layer that reduces water loss. Most of the mammals are inactive during the day and often hide in the

shade or burrow into the sand to escape the drying heat. Life in a hot, dry climate challenges an organism's ability to maintain the body's balance of water, salts, and temperature. Many adaptive characteristics have arisen that respond to these environmental conditions.

As organisms compete for food and protection in a living environment, the characteristics that enable them to survive depend on the current physical conditions, such as amount of rainfall, temperature, and availability of light. They also depend on the presence of, and interaction with, other species. For example, a nighthawk has the beak structure, the eyesight, and the capability of maneuvering quickly in flight that enable it to catch flying insects. The nighthawk is in a good situation to compete for food, as long as there are flying insects to be had. In an unusually dry season, insects may not reproduce in large numbers, and the adaptive characteristics of the nighthawk would be less useful. If this climatic change persisted for many seasons, it would have long-lasting effects. The nighthawk population would decline.

Sometimes characteristics such as those of the nighthawk can be adaptive and yet somewhat misleading in terms of an evolutionary pattern. Insect-eating bats, for example, have some of the same characteristics as the nighthawk. They are well adapted for quick turns in flight and have a way to sense prey at night. (They rely mainly on sound-based sensory perception.) Both species have adapted to compete for the same food source at the same time of night. Yet the nighthawk is a bird and the bat is a mammal. To trace the true relatedness of these two species, we must consider a combination of traits rather than just one or two.

Through the long years of evolutionary history, new species have arisen as new adaptive traits appeared within some subgroup of a population. These adaptations must appear at a level sufficient to make this group distinct. Thus, a new species at first is related very closely to the remaining members of the species from which it was derived. As more time passes, generally more differences appear between the new and old species. Thus, classification criteria, which reflect the pattern of evolutionary change, often are characteristics that are, or once were, adaptations. ◆

Figure E3.26   Desert adaptations. The horned lizard (*Phryhosoma cornutum*) and the cactus (*Opuntia* spp.) show several adaptations to the desert environment. How many do you see?

Organizing Diversity

Whenever people collect information, they develop systems for organizing it. Think of the ways people organize the following: notes for research papers, computer files, recipes, or CD collections. Scientists organize information in specific ways for specific purposes. Health care professionals, for instance, organize information about blood types in a way that differs from how geologists organize information about soil types. Biologists, likewise, have developed their own systems for organizing the information that they accumulate about different types of living systems. One important way to categorize this information is by how long ago certain organisms shared a common ancestor. Thus, biologists have developed classification schemes that reflect our understanding of the evolutionary relationships that exist among the millions of different known species.

One of the criteria that biologists use to construct these schemes is structural similarities among organisms. A pattern of similar characteristics or homologies

Figure E3.27 **Giant panda (*Ailuropoda melanoleuca*).** The giant panda is closely related to bears.

(refer back to the essay *Modern Life: Evidence for Evolutionary Change* on page 107) may suggest evolutionary relatedness. Appearances alone, however, can be misleading when it comes to recognizing biological relatedness. For example, not all traits are significant when considering questions of relatedness. Some characteristics are acquired during an organism's lifetime, such as bigger muscles built up by weightlifting. Because these characteristics cannot be inherited, they cannot be used as clues to evolutionary relationships. The characteristics that represent biological relatedness are those that are heritable. These characteristics can be passed on from parents to offspring by way of DNA. True homologies always involve heritable characteristics.

Similarly, not all organisms that look different are necessarily unrelated. Think back to the elephant and the hyrax that you saw in the essay *Five Kingdoms* (page 127). Consider organisms that were commonplace some 150 million years ago—the dinosaurs. Long before computers and other special effects provided the technology for creative movie

re-enactments, films depicted dinosaurs by superimposing close-up images of lizards against a backdrop that suggested enormous size. These images were not very convincing to those who had visited a museum and seen fossilized skeletons of the extinct giants or reconstructions of them based on scientific data. Nevertheless, most people probably reacted more favorably to images of fearsome reptiles (dinosaurs) than they would have reacted to close-ups of fearsome songbirds. Yet, birds also are fairly close relatives of the dinosaurs. They are perhaps even closer than modern reptiles, despite the fact that birds look less like their prehistoric dinosaur ancestors.

Another type of evidence that biologists use to establish evolutionary relatedness and to organize meaningful classification schemes comes from biochemical examination of the proteins or DNA found in each organism. Biochemical homologies have become increasingly important in determining relationships. Sometimes comparisons of DNA sequences have changed our understanding of the relationship between organisms. The greater the similarities in DNA sequences, the more closely related two organisms are thought to be. (Refer to Figure E2.7, Comparing DNA across primates, on page 109.)

Biochemical techniques have helped to clarify some classification problems. For example, for many years experts could not agree on the classification of the giant panda (see Figure E3.27). Some experts grouped pandas with bears; others grouped them with raccoons. New techniques for studying the homologies in DNA have led to a greater understanding of the evolutionary relationships between bears, raccoons, and pandas. Now, the giant panda is classified with the bears. The evidence suggests that the raccoon and bear families diverged from a common ancestor between 35 and 40 million years ago.

As new information about organisms becomes available, scientists may alter their opinions about how they should group species to reflect these evolutionary relationships. Although evolutionary history does not change, the classification schemes that scientists use to reflect that history improve with new knowledge and may change a great deal.

Biological classification schemes. Modern biological classification schemes generally contain a number of categories. Each category represents a group of organisms with a particular degree, or level, of relatedness to each other. Organisms that have the greatest number of shared characteristics are grouped together in the category of **species**. You are a member of the species known as *Homo sapiens*, which is Latin for "knowing man." The first word, *Homo*, is the name of a group of species that share many homologies and as such form a larger category, known as a **genus**. The second name, *sapiens*, is the descriptive specific name within the genus group.

Although common names for a species may vary in different regions or different countries, scientific names do not vary. The use of scientific names is very important to accurate communication and efficient research. For instance, in California a gopher is a small, burrowing rodent with the scientific name *Thomomys bottae* (Figure E3.28a). Whereas in Florida a gopher is a type of tortoise whose scientific name is *Gopherus polyphemus* (Figure E3.28b). Imagine how difficult it would be for people who used the same common name for different organisms to communicate without confusion. Using scientific names avoids that problem.

As important as the concept of a species is, the category itself is sometimes hard to define. As a human, you share the physical characteristics of bipedalism, a precisely opposable thumb, and a relatively large, complex brain with other organisms in your species. Recall from Chapter 1, however, that these characteristics also are shared to some

degree by certain other primates. Decisions about which organisms are the same species and which organisms constitute a different species are not always easy to make. For some organisms that reproduce sexually, clues to where species boundaries occur can be gained from determining whether or not two organisms can, and do, interbreed to produce offspring that also will be able to reproduce. Production of fertile offspring is important if species characteristics are to be passed on to future generations (refer to Figure E3.29).

The criterion of interbreeding is not strict because many organisms that reproduce sexually do not, however, interbreed in natural conditions. For example, many plants, including dandelions and peas, reproduce sexually by self-fertilization. Other plants, such as strawberries, reproduce mainly by means of shoots or roots that grow into new plants, as shown in Figure E3.30a. Many organisms, such as bacteria and other microbes, rarely or never reproduce sexually. Instead, they divide into two cells or a new cell buds off (depicted in Figures E3.30b and E3.30c). In these cases, biologists must rely on shared characteristics to define the boundaries between species.

Humans are one species among 1.7 million that biologists have described so far. But scientists estimate that the earth's total number of species may be 30 to 40 million. How can such a huge number of species be organized according to their evolutionary relationships? Recall that biologists define different *levels* of relatedness. A species represents the closest level of relatedness in

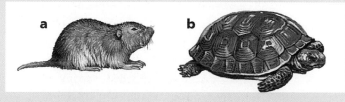

Figure E3.28 (a) *Thomomys bottae,* a burrowing animal called a gopher in California (b) *Gopherus polyphemus,* a tortoise called a gopher in Florida

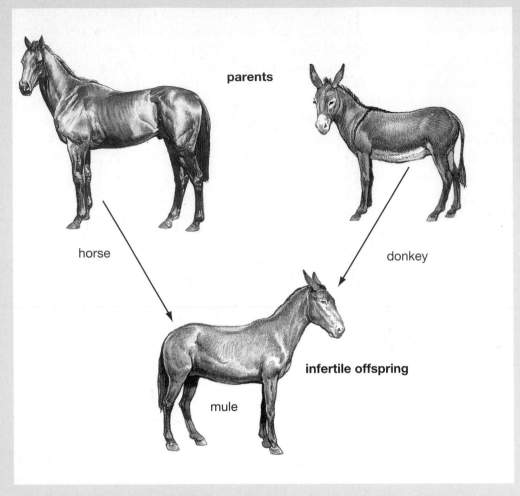

parents

horse

donkey

infertile offspring

mule

Figure E3.29 **Defining species.** Mating between a horse and a donkey results in a mule, which usually is infertile. The donkey and horse are considered to be separate species. All animals are shown about 1/45 of their actual size.

biological classification schemes. That is, members of the same species are considered to be the same type of organism. At the next level, the genus is a group of related species. Members of the same genus are very similar. (The genus Felis includes the domestic cat and several other species, such as the ocelot.) Groups of similar genera (plural of genus) form a **family**. (The family Felidae includes many genera, such as cats and panthers.) Families are organized in a large group known as an **order**. Orders are grouped together in a **class**. And classes form still larger categories known as **phyla** (singular, phylum) or, for plants, as **divisions**. Figure 3.6 in the activity *Using Unity to Organize*

Diversity shows the relationships of several organisms from the species level to the **kingdom** level. This category in biological classification systems includes the largest number of related organisms.

Biological classification offers a way to organize almost 2 million different species of organisms into categories based on their evolutionary relationships. In addition, it also provides a way to organize what we know about these species. Its power and usefulness in that regard are easily illustrated. What could you tell someone about the organism named *Gyrodon merulloides*? Not much, probably. If you were told, however, that this organism is classified in the same major category as a mushroom, an image of its general characteristics suddenly comes to mind.

The usefulness of the species-to-kingdom scheme also is illustrated by its enormous lasting power. This system developed gradually over about 100 years from the system of naming species that Swedish botanist Carolus Linnaeus established in 1753. With some changes, the scheme still is in use today. It has accommodated a tremendous volume of new knowledge that has been added in the past 200 years. And, if biologists are correct in their estimates of the number of species that remain to be discovered and described, we can expect it to accommodate the data yet to be examined and added. ◆

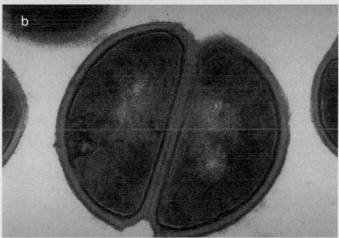

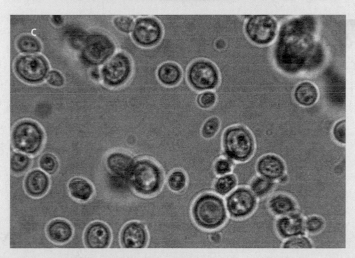

Figure E3.30 **Not all organisms reproduce sexually or interbreed.** (**a**) Strawberries develop new plants at the ends of runners. (**b**) Bacteria (*Staphylococcus*), photographed at 10,000×, divide into two new bacteria. (**c**) Yeast bud off new cells (photographed at 600×).

Homeostasis: Maintaining Dynamic Equilibrium in Living Systems

4 The Internal Environment of Organisms
5 Maintaining Balance in Organisms
6 Human Homeostasis: Health and Disease

Balance. Under normal conditions, it is an intricate, dynamic state that your body takes care of with little conscious effort. Think of a skater speeding across the ice. Not only does he balance on the edge of his blades, but his body also maintains a balance in other, less obvious ways. Although ice and frigid air surround him, his body temperature remains within a relatively narrow range. As he exerts energy to skate faster or to hold his position in a curve, his heart and breathing rates also adjust to keep oxygen levels within a specific range. In addition to temperature and oxygen levels, his body balances numerous intricate conditions to keep them all within healthy limits. His body is maintaining homeostasis.

In this unit, you will examine some of the processes involved in maintaining balance in the human body. You will consider the characteristics of the human life-form that allow for stable internal conditions. You also will apply what you have learned to study how the human body reacts when this balance is disrupted significantly.

By the end of Unit 2, you should understand that

◆ all organisms have an internal and external environment and are affected by interactions between these environments,

◆ the interactions of systems that adjust the internal environment result in a dynamic balance called *homeostasis*,

◆ stressors may overwhelm the ability of organisms to maintain a balance in their internal environment, and

◆ individual and collective behavior may influence an individual's ability to maintain homeostasis.

You also will continue to

◆ collect, analyze, and graph data;

◆ make and test predictions;

◆ construct and use models; and

◆ perform ethical analyses.

"My view of earth through the helmet visor was truly spectacular. At one point during a spacewalk as we were flying over the Gulf of Mexico, I could see both the east and west coasts of the United States, and at the same time I saw the aurora borealis over Canada. I wanted to breathe in the view so that it would become a part of me and I would never forget."

Dr. Kathryn C. Thornton (pictured below, servicing the Hubble Space Telescope) logged over 975 hours in space, including more than 21 hours spacewalking.

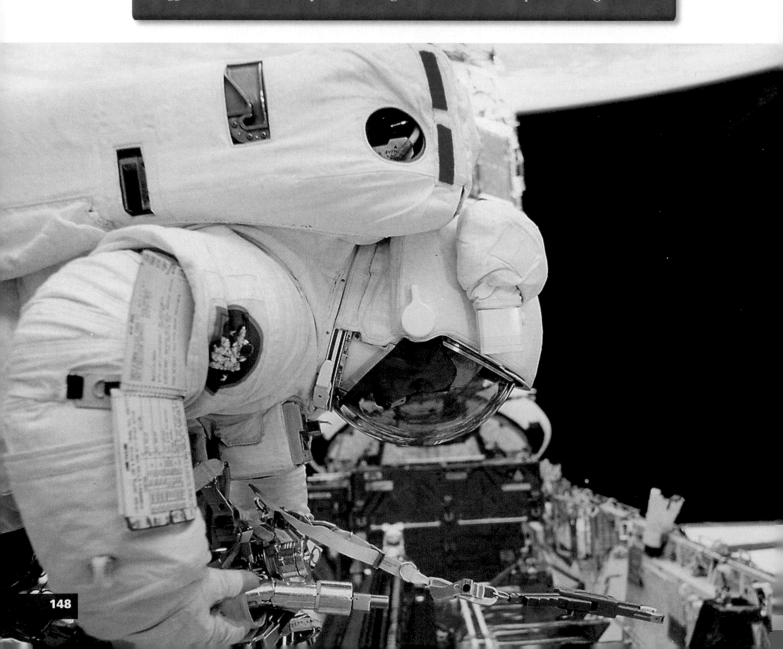

The Internal Environment of Organisms

Chapter 4

What NASA spent millions of dollars to develop, your body does for free!

Consider for a moment the importance of a space suit for astronauts who walk on the surface of the moon or venture into space to retrieve a satellite. In such circumstances, a space suit serves as an effective boundary between the external environment of space and the internal environment within the space suit. Without such a barrier between the external and internal environments, the men and women in space would die. Living organisms must maintain certain conditions within their bodies to stay alive.

Astronauts in space must consciously take care of the differences between their external and internal environments. The rest of us, however, usually pay little attention to these differences. As long as we eat and dress appropriately, intricate systems inside our bodies constantly monitor and adjust to maintain the balance of conditions necessary to stay alive. These processes occur in most organisms in a variety of ways. In this chapter, you will explore different systems in the human body—from the level of the cell, to the body as a whole—to learn the ways that it maintains an internal balance.

ACTIVITIES

Engage	Can You Stand the Heat?
Explore	Cells in Action
Explain	A Cell Model
Explain / Elaborate	Regulating the Internal Environment
Evaluate	Can You Stand the Heat—Again?

Can You Stand the Heat?

It's a scorching summer day. Getting out of the hot sun and into the shade seems like the natural thing to do. On a blustery winter day, seeking shelter in a warm house seems an obvious way to restore physical comfort. Even the family pets exhibit similar behaviors to minimize stressful external conditions. Behavioral responses such as these help to relieve stresses placed on the body by the external environment. Are there other ways your body works to maintain its internal environment in the face of external stresses? As you complete this activity, you will begin to answer this question. In the activities that follow, you will develop a more complete understanding of how the body maintains its internal environment.

PROCESS AND PROCEDURES

1. Read the story *A Pause That Refreshes?* to yourself (page 151).

2. After reading the scenario, work with your partner to develop an explanation for Josh's condition.

   Consider the evidence you have and what inferences you can make about how Josh's body responded to external stresses.

Analysis

1. As a class, develop answers to the following questions:

   a. What stresses from the external environment was Josh's body (internal environment) having to balance?

   b. How did the choices that Josh made affect the stresses placed on his body?

   c. What symptoms did Maggie show that were evidence that her body (her internal environment) was under stress from the conditions outdoors (her external environment)?

2. Work with your partner in a brainstorming session to develop a list of four terms and concepts that relate to homeostasis.

3. Contribute your list to a class concept map that shows what you currently understand about homeostasis.

Cells in Action

"A box without hinges, key, or lid, yet golden treasure inside is hid."*

Do you know the identity of the box in this riddle? Imagine the contents of boxes or containers that hold all sorts of treasures. While you might not think

---

*J.R.R. Tolkien, *The Hobbit*, 1966, Houghton Mifflin Co., Boston.

A Pause That Refreshes?

How much heat can you take? How does your body respond to the stress of a hot summer day, especially if you are involved in demanding physical activity? Perhaps you've experienced something like this and would not make the same mistake that Josh made. . . .

Josh had just graduated from college in Minnesota and was visiting his parents in central Texas. He was planning to surprise his parents, who would be gone all day, by clearing a large area of brush in preparation for a barn they wanted to build.

As his parents drove off, Josh loaded the pickup truck with the gear he needed for the job. Their dog, Maggie, wanted to come along, so Josh let her hop into the truck. This June day was already hot. The temperature climbed past 35°C (95°F) by late morning.

Josh began the job enthusiastically. He started clearing brush, digging up sharp-spined cacti, and raking debris. Even though he worked up a sweat, the small brush and cacti were no match for his muscles and tools. He thought that he could clear the entire area with 1 day of hard work, finishing before his parents returned.

After 2 hours had passed, Josh could see that the job might be bigger than he originally thought. This environment was about as hot as he had ever worked in. He was grateful for the ice-cold juice that he had brought. He drank often, although he kept reminding himself to conserve and make it last for the day. Maggie was obviously hot, too. She tried to find a spot of shade. She lay on the ground panting. Josh was sorry he hadn't thought to bring water along for the dog. He vowed that he and Maggie would get plenty to drink when they got back to the house. But first he wanted to finish the job he started.

By mid-afternoon, Josh was out of juice. He noticed that his mouth was extremely dry. He wanted to stay and finish the work but decided that he should drive back to the house and get something more to drink. As Josh opened the kitchen door, Maggie eagerly ran to her dog dish and lapped up all the water in it. Josh opened the refrigerator to look for a refreshing beverage. The first thing he spotted was a case of a popular energy drink. He read the can and saw that it contained caffeine, vitamins, and minerals. He helped himself to one can and then another. Josh sat for a while in the air-conditioned house to cool down; then he drank one more can of energy drink. He refilled Maggie's dish with water, made a bathroom stop, and then headed back out to the truck. That energy drink sure went through me fast, Josh thought as he drove back to the work site. Because he had less than an hour's work left, he didn't take anything along to drink.

Josh had been working again for only a few minutes when he experienced some dizziness and a faint touch of nausea. Nothing much, he decided. Besides, he would be quitting shortly. Soon he noticed a pounding in his head and some changes in his vision. Instead of seeing in sharp color, Josh began to feel as though his world was slowly becoming black and white. His muscles ached, and he suddenly felt very tired. His dizziness increased so that he had a difficult time driving the pickup back to the house.

Josh's parents returned at the same time that he pulled into the yard. Josh collapsed on the couch, and his father brought him a big glass of water and a cool washcloth. Later, when Josh explained what had happened, his parents were pleased to hear about the work he had done, but they were not surprised by his condition. . . .

(continued on page 167)

of an egg yolk as a "golden treasure," if you were a hungry hobbit, you might feel differently. Your body is another type of container that holds valuable contents. Think of the human body as a container with an inside environment that is different from the outside environment. This can help you understand what happened to Josh in the story *A Pause That Refreshes?*

Because the human body is a large and complicated container, it is difficult to study in detail. Let's begin to study it by examining cells, which are smaller containers within living systems. One way to study cells is to compare their contents to what is outside of them. In this activity, you will study several types of cells. Through scientific inquiry, you will begin to explore how cells (and the living systems that they compose) maintain an internal environment that is different from the external environment.

Materials

Part A   (per team of 4)

4 pairs of safety goggles	4 gloves
4 lab aprons	3 500-mL beakers
balance	bowls
plastic wrap	coffee filters
slotted spoon	paper towels
300 mL of corn syrup solution	300 mL of distilled water
3 shell-less eggs in a bowl of vinegar	

Part B   (per team of 2)

2 pairs of safety goggles	microscope slide and coverslip
dropping pipet	forceps
compound microscope	dissecting needle with a cork on the tip
scalpel	5% salt solution in dropping bottle
paper towels	onion wedge
distilled water	DVD and player (watch as a team)

PROCESS AND PROCEDURES

Part A   An Eggs-periment

How big is a cell? Most cells are so small that you need a microscope to see them. But there are exceptions. A chicken egg is actually a single cell, although it is an unusually large one. It is protected by a hard shell that surrounds several soft membranes that you can see when you peel a hard-boiled egg. Placing a chicken egg in an acetic acid (vinegar) solution for 3 days causes the calcium in the hard shell to dissolve. What remains is a fragile chicken egg surrounded by a soft membrane. This membrane separates the internal environment of the egg from its external environment. Even though the cell (the egg) that you will be working with is not alive, you can study how the membrane acts as a barrier, creating a compartment (the egg).

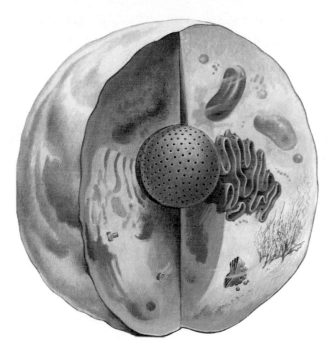

Figure 4.1 Generalized animal cell. A key feature of cells in multicellular organisms such as animals is their compartmentalization into smaller functional parts called **organelles**. The nucleus is one organelle. Do you recognize it? Can you name others?

You may already know that cells often contain a nucleus. Located inside the yolk, the nucleus of a chicken egg is barely visible. (Do not confuse the egg yolk with the nucleus.) Compare your egg to Figure 4.1, which shows an illustration of a generalized animal cell.

1. Start a new journal entry for your eggs-periment. Begin by working with your partner to describe the internal environment of an egg. How is it different from the external environment?

2. Write 3 questions about what might happen if you place the shell-less chicken egg in a different external environment. One way to change the egg's external environment is to place it in a beaker containing a solution.

   Your teacher will provide distilled water and corn syrup as solutions.

3. Choose the most interesting question that you wrote for your eggs-periment.

4. Work with your partner to develop a list of at least 3 results that you expect to observe. You will use these results to indicate whether the internal environment of the egg has changed after you conduct your experiment. Next to each result, record whether it will be a *quantitative* or *qualitative* observation.

   Quantitative observations involve results that can be measured with standard scales (mass in grams, or temperature in degrees Celsius, for example). Think of *quantity*—something that you measure—as part of quantitative.

   Qualitative observations involve verbal descriptions and results that can be measured with nonstandard scales (color, or temperature described as "warm" or "cold," for example). Think of *quality*—the nature of something that you observe—as part of qualitative.

5. Read the eggs-periment protocol. Use it as a guide for designing a controlled experiment to gather information that answers your question.

A **controlled experiment** is one in which you control all variables except one. See the need to know box on controlled experiments for more information.

Your experiment should include a control and a record of the results. Review the available materials and safety guidelines before you plan your experiment.

PROTOCOL

Eggs-periment Protocol

1. Per team, soak 3 eggs in vinegar for 3 days to remove the shells.

   a. Place the eggs in a bowl, and add enough vinegar to cover them. Cover the bowl loosely with plastic wrap. The acid in the vinegar will dissolve the calcium carbonate in the shells. The reaction will release bubbles of carbon dioxide.

   b. After 24 hours, carefully remove the eggs. Pour off the used vinegar, and replace with fresh. Repeat on the 3rd day.

   c. **Wash your hands thoroughly with soap and water after handling eggs.**

2. Shell-less eggs are delicate and must be handled carefully. Normally, both the shell and the membrane would act as barriers between the egg's internal and external environments. All of the shell must be removed to be certain that you are only testing how the membrane creates a compartment.

   a. Use the slotted spoon or gloves to remove each egg from the vinegar. **Avoid touching the eggs with your bare hands.**

   b. Remove any small patches of softened shell on your eggs. Gently hold the shell-less egg under warm, running water while you carefully rub the softened shell with your gloved finger.

   c. Shell-less eggs should appear almost transparent, with no areas of opaque white remaining.

3. One way to track a quantitative change in your egg is to measure its mass before and after you conduct your experiment.

   a. Before measuring and recording the mass of a shell-less egg, rinse it under running water. Then carefully blot the egg with a paper towel to dry it thoroughly.

   b. Use a coffee filter to hold each egg as you measure its mass.

4. Record other information as appropriate. This could include the amount of time the eggs were in the solution, the appearance of the eggs at different times, the volume of the solution, temperatures, or any other observations that you make.

5. Consider all of the variables involved in your experimental design. Keep all of them constant except the one that you are testing. (See Background on Controlled Experiments.)

6. **Wash your hands thoroughly with soap and water after working with eggs.**

Caution

External conditions for the egg	Predicted change	Explanation for prediction

Figure 4.2 Sample table. Record the observations you plan to make and your predictions in your journal.

6. Predict how you think the eggs will react to the condition that you will vary in your experiment. Create a table in your journal similar to the one in Figure 4.2 to record your predictions.

7. Have your teacher approve your design. Then conduct your experiment.

   Remember to record your experimental design and results in your journal.

SAFETY: Put on your safety goggles and lab apron.

Safety Goggles

Lab Apron

NEED TO KNOW

BACKGROUND ON CONTROLLED EXPERIMENTS

The process of science includes asking questions, gathering information, and proposing explanations. In Chapter 1, you learned about asking testable questions. In this chapter, you will focus on designing controlled experiments to gather information about testable questions.

Often scientists want to understand how some factor or event influences a living system. So they test that factor in an experiment that focuses on one measurable or observable aspect of their question. For this evidence to be meaningful, the scientists must control (keep constant) all factors—other than the one being tested—that could affect the results of the experiment. Only by controlling all other conditions can the scientists be certain that the effects they see are the result of the factor they are testing.

For example, imagine you want to find out what effect fertilizer has on houseplants. You could design a controlled experiment to answer that question. First, you would identify all the factors that might affect the plant's growth. These factors are called **variables**. Possible variables for houseplants include the location of the plants, amount of water they get, type of plants selected, type and amount of soil they are in, and type and amount of light they receive.

To test the effectiveness of the fertilizer, you would need to choose at least two plants of the same type, and control as many variables as possible. (You could pick two spider plants.) Place them in 250 grams of potting soil from a new bag, in identical clay pots, on the same windowsill. Then water each at the same time with the same amount of water. But add fertilizer to one plant only. If you maintained this setup, you would be conducting a controlled experiment.

Scientists systematically test each variable and the interactions among the variables. They repeat their controlled experiments, and they run the experiments with multiple subjects. This approach increases the scientists' confidence in the results and helps them develop more complete explanations.

Topic: scientific investigation
Go to: www.scilinks.org
Code: human3E155

Figure 4.3
(a) *Solutions* are uniform mixtures of two or more substances. (b) The dissolved substance is called the *solute*. (c) The substance that the solute is dissolved into is called the *solvent*.

SCLINKS
NSTA

Topic: solutions
Go to: www.scilinks.org
Code: human3E156

8. When your experiment is complete, enter your results in the class data table.

Report your actual results; resist the temptation to change your results if they do not match your classmates' data.

9. Discuss the following questions with your partner, and record your answers in your journal:

 a. Why is it useful to combine data from the entire class?

 b. What changes did you find, if any, in the internal environments of your eggs? Explain your answer by using specific evidence from your observations.

 c. How would you explain any differences that you noticed in the behavior of the 3 eggs under different external conditions?

 d. What controls did you use in your experimental design? Why?

Part B   Observing Cell Activity

In Part A of this activity, you explored the concept that cells are containers. You did that by putting the containers (eggs) in different solutions and observing the behavior of the cells (eggs). Scientists recognize the relationship between solutions and the internal environments of a cell. They use special terms to describe the similarities and differences between the contents of the external environment and the internal environment of a cell. Read and discuss the background information about solutions with your class.

NEED TO KNOW

BACKGROUND INFORMATION

Solutions are uniform mixtures of two or more substances. They may be solids, liquids, gases, or a combination of these. The substances in a solution are classified as a **solute** or a **solvent** (see Figure 4.3). The dissolved substance is called the *solute*. The substance that the solute is dissolved into is called the *solvent*. For example, when salt dissolves in water, salt is the solute and water is the solvent. In living systems, liquid water is frequently the solvent in a solution.

Scientists often use special terms to describe how a solution compares to the internal environment of a cell placed in that solution. You can use these terms to describe the solutions into which you placed your eggs.

An **isotonic** (*iso = equal*) solution provides an environment in which the concentration of solutes outside the cell equals the concentration of solutes inside.

A **hypertonic** (*hyper = over*) solution is one in which the concentration of solutes outside a cell is greater than the concentration inside.

A **hypotonic** (*hypo = under*) solution is one in which the concentration of solutes outside the cell is less than the concentration inside.

Can you think of other words that use the prefixes *iso, hyper,* and *hypo* to describe something as the same, more than, or less than something else?

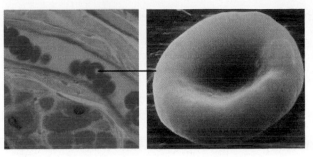

Figure 4.4 Red blood cells and oxygen transport. Red blood cells move single file through a capillary. Each red blood cell contains molecules that can bind to and transport oxygen. Most of the carbon dioxide that enters the blood from the body cells is carried in the blood **plasma**, the liquid portion of the blood.

In this part of the activity, you will observe microscopic cells (see Figure 4.4) responding to changes in their environment.

1. View the DVD segment "Blood Cells in Solution," which illustrates the behavior of animal cells in different solutions. Before you watch this segment, create 3 columns in your journal. Label them *isotonic*, *hypertonic*, and *hypotonic*. Use these columns to record your observations about changes in the cells.

2. To observe the responses of plant cells, prepare a wet mount of onion skin by following these steps:

   a. Remove 1 layer from your onion wedge.

   b. Snap the layer backward, as shown in Figure 4.5.

   > This should expose the edges of several smaller layers.

   c. Use forceps to separate a piece of the transparent, tissue-thin layer from the outside of the original layer.

   d. Lay the piece flat on a clean microscope slide.

   e. As necessary, use the scalpel to trim the piece so that it will fit under a coverslip.

   f. Use the dissecting needle to smooth out any bubbles or wrinkles.

 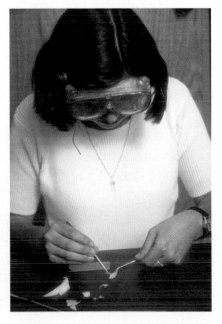

Figure 4.5 Preparing an onion skin specimen.

CAUTION: Scalpel blades and needles are sharp; handle with care. Replace cork on needle tip after use.

 g. Use the dropping pipet to add 1 or 2 drops of water to the slide. Then place a coverslip over the piece of onion skin.

3. Examine the onion skin under the low power of your microscope.

Take turns observing the cells.

4. Switch to high power, and focus sharply on a few cells. Make a sketch of the cells in your journal. Then place a small piece of paper towel at 1 edge of the coverslip (see Figure 4.6).

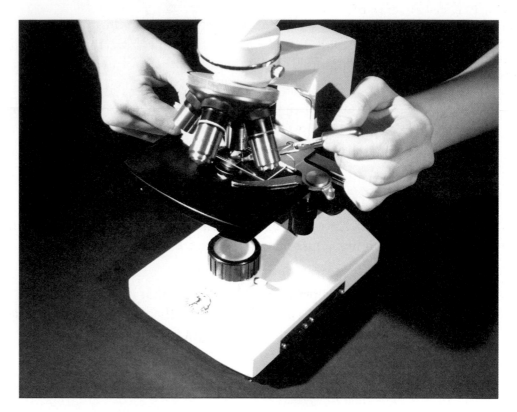

Figure 4.6 Adding solution to a wet mount.

5. Test the effects of changing the external environment of the cells you are viewing. To do this, place several drops of 5% salt solution against the edge of the coverslip opposite from the paper towel. Observe what happens, and record it in your journal.

Take turns observing the cells. Compare your onion cells to the generalized plant cell illustrated in Figure 4.7.

Figure 4.7
Generalized plant cell.
Plants also are multicellular organisms. Their cells contain many of the same functional compartments, or *organelles,* that animal cells contain. One difference between plant and animal cells is the presence of an outer cell wall in addition to the cell membrane. The **cell wall** makes plant cells rigid and gives them a distinct shape.

6. Add more salt solution, if necessary, until you see changes in the cells. Record your observations in your journal by sketching the cells both before and after adding the salt solution.

   Be sure to record how much salt solution you added.

7. Dilute the salt solution on the slide by adding distilled water. Continue to add water until the cells return to their original condition. Make observations while you do this, and record them in your journal.

   To add water, use the same technique that you used to add the salt solution. Remember to record how much water you added.

Analysis

Discuss the following questions with your teammates. Then record your responses in your journal.

The essay *Compartments* on page 218 will be a helpful resource for this Analysis and for the next activity.

PAGE 218

The essay *Compartments* on page 218 will be a helpful resource for this Analysis and for the next activity.

1. What evidence did you collect that indicates that the external environment affects the internal environment?

2. In this activity, how did the egg serve as a model of how cells function as containers in living organisms?

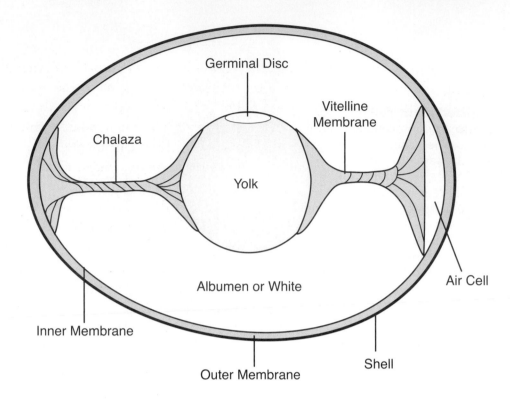

Figure 4.8 This illustration shows the membranes that are inside the eggshell.

3. What do eggs, animal cells, plant cells, and the human body have in common?

4. Based on your observations of cells, what might have been happening in Josh's body in the story *A Pause That Refreshes?* when he

   a. first became hot and started to sweat,

   b. became thirsty,

   c. went to the house for refreshments, and

   d. returned to work?

Further Challenges

To learn more about the way cells function as containers, examine a fresh wet mount of an onion cell. Look for internal structures. A stain, such as Lugol's iodine solution, may make such structures more Make sketches of what you observe, and label all the compartments and boundaries.

WARNING: Lugol's iodine solution is a poison if ingested. It is a strong irritant, and can stain clothing. Avoid skin/eye contact; do not ingest. If contact occurs, flush affected area with water for 15 minutes; rinse mouth with water. Call the teacher immediately.

A Cell Model

You have been studying examples of interactions between internal and external environments and the boundaries that separate these environments. These boundaries exist in every organism, from the smallest cell to large plants and animals. In the last activity, cells served as good examples of compartments with membrane boundaries. Although you experimented with different external environments for the cells, you were unable to manipulate the contents of the internal environments directly.

In this activity, you will use a membrane to construct your own cell model. The membrane will allow you to change both the internal and external environments. You will use dialysis tubing and several solutions to build your cell model. In addition, you will have indicators to help you detect what substances can and cannot pass through the membrane. **Indicators** are chemicals that show the presence of certain chemicals. Using this model, you will continue your study of how cell boundaries affect the internal cellular environment. Your job is to develop an explanation for how boundaries and compartments help living systems maintain and regulate the conditions necessary for life.

Materials   (per team of 2)

2 pairs of safety goggles   2 lab aprons
materials to carry out the experiment that you design

PROCESS AND PROCEDURES

1. Read steps 1–5, and review the protocol for making a cell model.

PROTOCOL

Protocol for Making a Cell Model

For your cell model to work, the membrane must be the only barrier between the internal and external environment.

1. Rinse all lab equipment with water. Handle the internal and external solutions for your experiment carefully to reduce the chance of contamination.

2. Obtain a section of dialysis tubing. Tie one end of the tubing securely so that nothing can leak out of the knot.

3. Measure and record the amount of solution you will add to each cell model in your investigation.

4. Carefully pour the internal solution into your cell. Tie the open end securely to prevent all leaking.

5. Rinse the outside of your cell model to be certain there is no internal solution present to contaminate the external environment.

6. Blot the cell model dry with a paper towel, and record its initial mass.

7. After conducting your experiment, rinse, dry, and record the cell model's final mass.

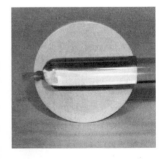

Figure 4.9 Cell model. Tie the ends of the dialysis tubing tightly so that nothing can leak in or out. Rinse off the outside of your cell after it is constructed. This will minimize the risk of contamination.

2. Generate at least 2 testable questions about how membranes affect the internal environment of the cell and that meet the criteria in step 4.

3. With your partner, choose the testable question that you would like to investigate. Have your teacher approve your question.

   Consider the results that you found interesting from the eggs-periment. Choose a question that builds on your experiences in that investigation.

4. Design an experiment to test the question you chose. Your design must be safe, and it must use dialysis tubing and

   ◆ starch suspension,

   ◆ glucose solution, or a teacher-approved solution designed to help you answer your question, and

   ◆ appropriate indicators.

   The background information in this need to know box may help you design your experiment.

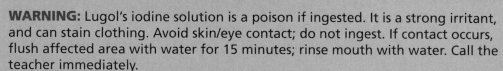

BACKGROUND INFORMATION

Dialysis tubing is a synthetic membrane, made of a thin, cellophane-like material. Microscopic pores in dialysis tubing allow molecules smaller than a certain size to pass through the membrane.

   Glucose is a simple sugar that dissolves readily in water.

   Glucose test strips indicate the presence of glucose in solution by changing color. (Your teacher will give you information on how to interpret the color change.)

   Lugol's iodine solution is an indicator that changes color in the presence of starch. Use one drop of Lugol's iodine solution for every 1 mL of starch suspension; a blue black color indicates the presence of starch.

WARNING: Lugol's iodine solution is a poison if ingested. It is a strong irritant, and can stain clothing. Avoid skin/eye contact; do not ingest. If contact occurs, flush affected area with water for 15 minutes; rinse mouth with water. Call the teacher immediately.

   Starch is a complex molecule that forms a suspension in water. Starch turns blue black in the presence of Lugol's iodine solution.

   The size of a molecule is an important characteristic that partially governs how the molecule behaves. Chemists have shown that all the molecules of a given substance are the same size. Molecules of different substances can vary significantly in size. In other words, all water molecules are the same size. But water molecules and glucose or starch molecules are not the same size.

Poison!

5. Create a data table in your journal to record a brief summary of your experimental design and your predictions. Use the table in Figure 4.10 as a model.

Cell model	Contents of internal environment	Contents of external environment	Predicted change	Explanation for prediction
A				
B				

Figure 4.10 Sample table. A table like this one will help you to record your plan and predictions.

6. Predict what will happen when you conduct the experiment. Record this information in your journal.

7. Have your teacher check and approve your design.

   Remember to identify the variables in your experiment, and plan to test only 1 variable at a time.

   Reread the testable question that you wrote. Be sure that your designed experiment will generate results that will help you answer your question.

SAFETY: Put on your safety goggles and lab apron.

Safety Goggles **Lab Apron**

8. Set up and conduct your experiment. Create another data table similar to the example in Figure 4.10 to record your observations and results.

   Make observations of your setup for as long as possible, and record all observations and results in your data table.

9. Wash your hands thoroughly before leaving the laboratory.

10. During the next class session, observe your setup again. Record your final observations and results in your data table.

11. Wash your hands thoroughly.

12. With your partner, develop possible explanations for your experimental results. Record your explanations in your journal.

   The essays *Membranes* on page 220 and *Molecular Movement* on page 222 provide useful information that may help with this step. Be certain that you pay attention to the concepts of *exchange, diffusion,* and *osmosis.*

PAGE 220 **PAGE 222**

Analysis

Work with your partner to make a lab report about your experiment. Your teacher will instruct you to make either a written report or an oral presentation. Your lab report should include the following:

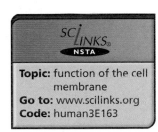
SCILINKS
NSTA
Topic: function of the cell membrane
Go to: www.scilinks.org
Code: human3E163

♦ A statement of the question you tested and the results you predicted

♦ A description of your methods (how you performed the experiment), including the materials that you used

♦ A description of the results that you obtained, presented in a well-organized table or diagram

♦ An explanation of your experimental results that clearly explains how a cell membrane behaves as a barrier and how the dialysis tubing setup serves as a model of a cell

Regulating the Internal Environment

Shrinking cells and exploding cells dramatically illustrate the internal response of cells to external conditions. In the previous activities, you studied the processes that allow substances to move between internal and external environments. In addition, you have seen that the membranes that form boundaries around the contents of cells influence the exchanges between compartments.

How are the same processes of exchange, diffusion, and osmosis important in large body systems? To begin to answer that question, consider two important compartments within the human body—the circulatory system and the urinary system. In this activity, you will see how these two systems help regulate the internal environment in humans.

Materials

poster board or large sheet of butcher paper (1 per student)
colored markers
DVD and player

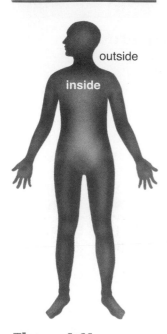

Figure 4.11
The body is a compartment. Conditions inside the body are different from those outside. All living things maintain an internal environment that is different from the external environment.

PROCESS AND PROCEDURES

Part A   Circulatory System

1. Watch the DVD segment "The Circulatory System" with your class. Take notes in your journal. Ask questions if you need clarification about the path your blood takes and the functions of structures in the circulatory system.

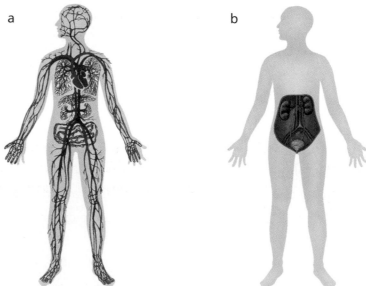

Figure 4.12   (a) The circulatory system. The heart and an extensive network of vessels make up the circulatory system. **(b) The urinary system.** The urinary system regulates water balance, the blood's ion levels, blood volume, and eliminates waste products from the body.

2. Imagine that you are a red blood cell. What would be the path you might follow through a human's body as you traveled from the left little toe, through the heart, and on into the right big toe?

a. Draw a large, simple outline of a human on your poster board or butcher paper.

b. Draw a heart (including all the chambers) and enough vessels to trace the path of a red blood cell from the left little toe to the right big toe.

c. Label your drawing, and create a legend next to your illustration that describes the path.

   You will know that you have described your journey adequately if you have included

   • capillaries,
   • veins,
   • arteries,
   • all four chambers of the heart, and
   • the lungs.

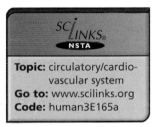

Topic: circulatory/cardio-vascular system
Go to: www.scilinks.org
Code: human3E165a

Part B   Making Exchanges

1. Create a table in your journal to describe how you, as a red blood cell, are involved in exchanges in each of the places listed in Figure 4.13.

   Leave room to add to your table as you learn more in this chapter and the next.

   The DVD segment "The Circulatory System" and the essay *Making Exchanges throughout the Body* on page 224 will help you with these tasks.

PAGE 224

	Tissues of the toe	Tissues of the kidneys	Tissues of the lungs	Tissues of the intestines	Tissues of the liver
Types of exchanges with blood					

Figure 4.13   Sample table. A table like this one will help you to record some of the types of exchanges that take place in the body.

2. To expand your understanding of how various systems help regulate the human body's internal environment, watch the DVD segment "Regulation in the Urinary System." Use this information and the essay *Disposing of Wastes* (page 227) as background resources.

PAGE 227

Analysis

Work with your team of four to complete the following task. Divide your team into two pairs. Decide which pair will develop a response to question 1 and which pair will develop a response to question 2. As you answer your question, refer to the information that you developed in Parts A and B of Process and Procedures.

Topic: urinary system
Go to: www.scilinks.org
Code: human3E165b

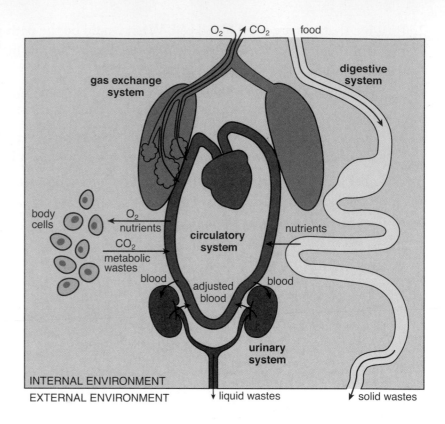

Figure 4.14 Exchanges. Major body systems work together to maintain homeostasis.

Include a supporting illustration in your response. You may wish to use an illustration similar to portions of Figure 4.14. When both pairs are finished, present your responses to each other.

1. How does the circulatory system help regulate the internal environment of the body? How does the urinary system influence the work of the circulatory system?

2. How does the urinary system help regulate the internal environment of the body? How does the circulatory system influence the work of the urinary system?

Evaluate

Can You Stand the Heat—Again?

In this activity, you will return to the opening story *A Pause That Refreshes?* and examine Josh's situation, and homeostasis. Your job is to evaluate your understanding of how internal balance is maintained when the external environment places significant stress on it.

PROCESS AND PROCEDURES

1. Look back at the class concept map that you and your classmates constructed at the start of this chapter. Consider all that you have studied throughout the chapter. Then make a new concept map that reflects your current understanding of homeostasis. Include the following concepts and any others that you have learned:

   - Diffusion
   - Gas exchange
   - Compartment
   - Waste removal
   - Environment
   - Homeostasis
   - Water
   - Osmosis
   - Concentration gradient
   - Cell membrane
   - Internal conditions

2. Read the following conclusion to Josh's story, *A Pause That Refreshes?*

SCENARIO

A Pause That Refreshes? (continued from page 151)

"You drank what?" his father exclaimed, when Josh reported that he had returned to the house and had a few energy drinks. "You were seriously dehydrated. What did you learn about dehydration when you took biology in high school and college? Didn't you learn that caffeine is a diuretic?"

"A *diuretic*! What is that? And how could I be seriously dehydrated?" Josh responded. "I drank three cans, and it was liquid that felt good to me! Plus, I needed the energy boost." Josh felt considerably better now that he had drunk water and cooled down a bit. But he was irritated that his father had questioned his thinking.

3. To learn more about Josh's condition, examine the data in Figures 4.15 and 4.16. Study the additional information in the need to know box.

	Before working (A.M.)	After completing work (P.M.)
Josh's body mass (kg)	77.25	73.55*

* This measurement of Josh's mass was taken before he drank more water at the end of the story.

Figure 4.15   Change in Josh's body mass.

Fluids	While working	During afternoon break	After completing work
In	.95 L juice and water	.95 L energy drink	.78 L water
Out	Constant perspiration	.91 L urine	

Figure 4.16   Tracking fluids.

NEED TO KNOW

ADDITIONAL INFORMATION

If athletes, or other people performing strenuous exercise or exposed to extreme heat, lose 3 to 8 percent of body mass in the form of fluids, they experience a condition called *dehydration*. Dehydration can be quite serious if the person is unable to replace the lost fluids within a short period of time.

A **diuretic** is a substance that causes the membranes in the kidney to remove more water from the body than is taken in. Common diuretics are alcohol and caffeine (found in coffee, tea, chocolate, energy drinks, and cola beverages). Diuretics increase the loss of water, resulting in an increased concentration of solutes, such as sodium ions and potassium ions, in the blood. These increases can seriously disrupt the body's internal balance. For example, a high concentration of sodium ions can result in high blood pressure. Diuretic drugs that physicians prescribe to adjust blood pressure increase both the loss of water and sodium, thus avoiding problems that result from altered solute concentrations.

Analysis

Answer the following questions to explain how Josh could be dehydrated. Record your responses in your journal.

1. What percentage of body mass did Josh lose in the form of fluids? Do you think this represents a serious condition? Explain your answer.

   Percentage body mass lost in fluids equals [(final mass − original mass) ÷ (original mass)] × 100.

2. In what ways was Josh's body attempting to maintain an internal balance in spite of the changing nature of his external environment?

3. How did Josh become dehydrated even though he drank 1.9 liters of liquid?

4. How could Josh's water loss have caused him to become dizzy?

5. Do you think that Josh would have been better off to replenish his fluids by drinking iced coffee or tea rather than the energy drink? Explain.

6. Use your knowledge of homeostasis to write a brief explanation about why a plant in the hot sun might wilt. Include the following terms in your answer, as well as any others that will show your level of understanding:

- Osmosis
- Balance
- Compartment
- Cell
- Water
- Permeability
- Membrane

> "If we remove the lowest card in a house of cards or topple the first domino in a line, the structure collapses."
>
> *Marjorie Elliott Bevlin,* **Design through Discovery,** *1977*

Maintaining Balance in Organisms

Chapter 5

What do swelling and shrinking eggs and a thirsty college student have in common? They are all able to communicate information about external conditions to an internal environment. Of course, in eggs, this interaction is simply a matter of chemistry. However, communication in thirsty college students and many other organisms is generally much more complicated. This is because complex living systems rely on a broad range of interactions to help them regulate internal conditions. These interactions include (1) chemical—like diffusion in response to a concentration gradient; (2) behavioral—like feeling thirsty in response to a dry environment and hard work; and (3) physiological—like the kidneys conserving water in response to dehydration.

Luckily, humans and other organisms do not have to consciously plan and carry out a response to every change in the environment. Most regulatory processes occur automatically. Well-coordinated and rapid changes in our organ systems mean that we usually can take the internal conditions of our bodies for granted. However, understanding and appreciating these conditions and the interactions that keep them within normal limits can contribute to a longer, healthier life. In this chapter, you will consider some of the ways that your body maintains its internal balance as you participate in everyday activities.

ACTIVITIES

Engage **Explore**	The Body Responds
Explore	What's Your Temperature Now?
Explain	Stepping Up the Pace
Elaborate	On a Scale of 0 to 14
Elaborate	How Do They Stay So Cool?
Evaluate	Homeostasis in Your Critter

The Body Responds

The bus is just starting to pull away as you turn the corner. You break into a sprint to try to catch it. After 10 or 12 seconds, the driver finally sees you in the side mirror and stops to wait. Out of breath and red-faced, you climb onto the bus and collapse in a seat while your friends cheer sarcastically. After a minute or so, your breathing returns to normal, and you are talking with your friend about the game last Friday night.

Figure 5.1
Hurry, hurry, hurry.
How can your body respond so quickly to changing conditions?

This brief sequence of events probably seems trivial because your body responds to environmental factors all the time. However, the changes you felt while running for the bus and recovering from the run actually required your body to coordinate a tremendous number of responses. Think for a moment about how your rapid breathing slowed to normal. For that matter, consider why it sped up in the first place.

Before you plunge into the details about how such regulation of a response can occur, let's examine a range of possible responses. In this activity, you will view a set of simple human activities and try to match them with their internal responses. When you think about the surprisingly complicated biological responses, you may be grateful that you can usually take your internal conditions for granted!

Materials

DVD and player

PROCESS AND PROCEDURES

1. As you watch the DVD segment "Just a Body Responding," think about similar experiences that you have had. Your teacher will show the segment, stopping the DVD briefly after each scene to allow you to think of a short descriptive title for that scene. Record your titles in your journal.

   These titles can be funny or serious, as you choose. Make sure that each title is descriptive enough to help you remember what happened in each scene.

2. Listen while your teacher reads 4 descriptive paragraphs aloud. Each paragraph describes a set of events that might have gone on inside someone's body in response to 1 of the external situations from the DVD segment. While you listen, record the number of the paragraph that you think best matches each scene next to the scene titles in your journal.

3. Discuss the following questions with your partner:

   a. Which DVD scene would you match to each description?

   b. What information from the description is most helpful to you in determining a match?

   c. How did the internal responses benefit the people involved?

4. Participate in a class discussion about the questions.

Analysis

Make a table in your journal. Identify three *behavioral* and three *physiological* types of responses from each of the four scenarios.

> The word *physiological* refers to internal biological and chemical functions, like the actions of internal organs.

What's Your Temperature Now?

Explore

Each character in the DVD segment "Just a Body Responding" experienced a different set of external demands and internal responses. Did each character's body respond randomly? No, each body responded in a way that was appropriate for each situation. For example, the body of the person who ate a big meal responded with dilated stomach blood vessels of the stomach. This increased the stomach's circulation, a response that speeds digestion. On the other hand, the blood vessels in the stomach of the frightened person constricted and reduced circulation. This response sent blood to other areas of the body—in this case, the muscles of the arms and legs. Understanding how the body responds to change requires an understanding of the automatic physiological processes that detect and respond to change.

In this activity, you will explore the relationship between core (or internal) and surface temperatures under different conditions. This exploration will help you understand how the body automatically accommodates specific external changes with specific internal responses.

Materials   (per team of 4)

3 thermistors and associated probe ware, or 3 thermometers
graph paper
materials to carry out the experiment that you design

PROCESS AND PROCEDURES

1. Together with your teammates, begin designing an experiment to test the following hypothesis:

> If the human body can regulate its internal temperature automatically, then cooling the skin will result in a change in the internal temperature of less than 2°C.

The Temperature Comparison Protocol will help you to design your experiment.

PROTOCOL

Temperature Comparison Protocol

1. To design an appropriate experiment, you and your teammates first must think about the following question:

   How can we measure and compare changes in internal body temperature, surface body temperature, and environmental temperature, all at the same time?

2. For this experiment, you will have 2 conditions that will facilitate the experiment. First, we will assume that the temperature of the inside of the elbow joint represents the internal (core) body temperature. In reality, it is a few degrees cooler than the actual core temperature (see Figure 5.2). Second, we will use the temperature of the index finger to measure the body's surface temperature.

3. With your teammates, develop an outline of your experimental design, and record it in your journal.

   You will know your experimental design is complete when you have included the following:

   • A method to measure the initial temperatures of the body core, body surface, and environment

   • A setup that cools the body surface temperature safely (For instance, you must not cool the body surface for more than 30 seconds at 1 time because excessive cold can damage the skin.)

   • A method for recording the color of the skin and the temperatures of the body core, the body surface, and the environment at regular intervals until the surface temperature warms to its initial temperature

   • A list of any of the materials that your teacher provides that you plan to use

   • Your teacher's approval of your experimental design before you conduct the experiment

4. To conduct a precise experiment, your group needs to share responsibilities. Assign the following roles and related jobs among your teammates:

   Test subject: Describes his or her feelings and sensations throughout the experiment.

   You will monitor this person's body temperature during the experiment.

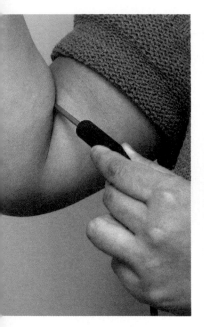

Figure 5.2 In this experiment, the temperature of the inside of the elbow joint represents the internal, or core, body temperature.

Timer: Keeps track of time as the experiment proceeds.

The timer also can operate the computer or probe ware if you are using it.

Observer: Records the time, observations of the test subject, and any comments the test subject makes.

Observations should include color of the skin at each interval or in the test subject's behavior.

Recorder: Records temperatures in his or her journal.

Recorders must enter temperature data in a data table at regular intervals.

Scientists often manage complex projects by dividing the duties among lab partners. Each scientist's individual role and responsibility, however, is crucial to the overall results. As you conduct this experiment, pay attention to your individual responsibilities as well as the work of the team.

2. In your journal, write your own prediction for how you think your test subject will respond to the environmental changes that you designed in your experiment.

   Mark your prediction clearly so that you and your teacher can easily refer to it when you analyze your results.

3. Conduct your experiment.

   When the experiment is completed, each team member should obtain a complete set of data from the recorder and the observer and then copy these results into a data table in his or her journal.

Figure 5.3   This team is sharing the responsibilities required to conduct its experiment.

4. Construct a line graph that shows how the test subject's core and surface temperatures changed throughout the experiment.

Plot the temperature on the *y*-axis and the time on the *x*-axis. Use dashed and solid lines or different-colored lines for the core and surface temperature data. If you need assistance with graphing techniques, refer to Appendix B, *Technique 2 Graphing*.

5. Analyze your team's graph. Use any patterns that you see in your graph along with your data and observations to answer the following questions with your teammates. Record your answers in your journal.

   a. How do the data from the temperature readings compare with observations made by the observer?

   b. What changes did you observe in the core and surface temperatures of the test subject?

   Calculate the changes (increase or decrease) in temperatures (°C) for body core, body surface, and environment by subtracting the starting temperature from the final temperature.

   c. Explain whether your experimental results support or disprove the hypothesis given at the start of the experiment and your own prediction for how the test subject would respond.

   Refer specifically to both the hypothesis stated in step 1 and the prediction that you wrote in your journal after you designed your experiment.

Analysis

Complete the following tasks on your own, and record your answers in your journal:

Read the essay *Homeostasis* on page 229 for information that will help with these tasks.

1. How might the changes that you observed in the core and surface temperatures benefit the test subject and help to maintain homeostasis?

2. Create a table like the one in Figure 5.4. Use it to identify stressors, behavioral responses, and physiological adjustments that help humans maintain homeostasis. In addition to temperature, name two other stressors that the human body might encounter and adjust to automatically. Give two examples each of the types of behavioral and physiological adjustments that the body makes in each case.

3. Explain whether regulation to maintain homeostasis is a random or specific activity of the body.

4. Describe four qualities that you would expect to see in a highly respected scientist.

External stressor	Behavioral response	Automatic physiological response
1. Low temperatures	1. 2.	1. 2.
2.	1. 2.	1. 2.
3.	1. 2.	1. 2.

Figure 5.4 Table for examples of stressors and some of the human body's typical responses.

Stepping Up the Pace

Explain

The average temperature of humans is 37°C (98.6°F). That temperature fluctuates over a small range, but in healthy people, it stays fairly constant and predictable. The automatic responses of the circulatory system help maintain this balance. The circulatory system responds specifically to certain changes in temperature. Perhaps you observed some of these responses during *What's Your Temperature Now?*

Did any of your observations suggest that organ systems other than the circulatory system might be involved in regulating temperature? The circulatory system is just one of several different systems that work together. Most of those other systems, however, are difficult to observe because their responses occur inside the body and are not visible externally. The role of these other systems is important because maintaining homeostasis involves the *interaction* of many systems. To understand homeostasis fully, you must gain an appreciation for how changes in one system affect the performance of another system.

One way to observe the interaction of systems is to consider systems for which internal changes have measurable external effects. As you have seen, you can detect change in the circulatory system by measuring temperature. Can you think of any other external methods of detecting change in circulation? External measures provide only an indirect view of the body's internal environment. Still, they are valuable in helping to illustrate the complex interactions of internal organ systems. In this activity, you will examine physical exercise as a way of helping you explain how organ systems in the human body interact to maintain homeostasis.

Materials   (per team of 5)

breathing rate sensor (optional)
stopwatch or clock with a second hand

heart rate sensor (optional)
graph paper

PROCESS AND PROCEDURES

PAGE 231

1. Read the essay *Careful Coordination* on page 231.

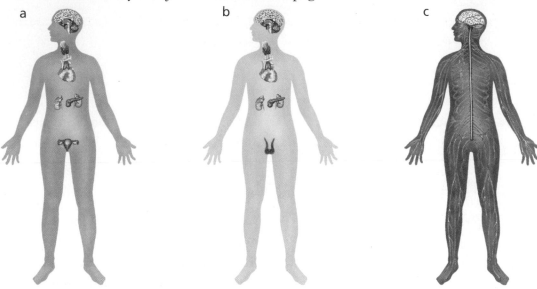

Figure 5.5 **(a) The female endocrine system. (b) Male endocrine system.** The endocrine system is a collection of glands, cells, and special neurons that secrete hormones into the bloodstream. **(c) The nervous system.** The nervous system controls and coordinates the body's responses and integrates the activities of other organ systems.

2. Complete the following in your journal as you work individually:

   a. Why can maintaining homeostasis be particularly challenging for multicellular organisms?

   b. How does the endocrine system compare to the nervous system in regulating homeostasis (see Figure 5.5)?

   c. Explain the role that sensors play in the maintenance of homeostasis in the human body.

   d. Describe a typical cycle that might take place as a body determines how to adjust internal conditions in response to change.

   The essay *Careful Coordination* (page 231) contains information that will help you understand and answer these questions.

3. Make a prediction about how heart rate, breathing rate, and exercise are related.

4. As a team, examine the predictions that each of your teammates made in step 3. Then develop 1 testable hypothesis that you think offers the best explanation of the relationships between heart rate, breathing rate, and exercise. You will conduct an experiment to evaluate your hypothesis.

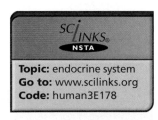
Topic: endocrine system
Go to: www.scilinks.org
Code: human3E178

Your hypothesis must be testable. In other words, your hypothesis will be an educated guess that provides a logical and possible answer to a testable question. Refer to the need to know box in Chapter 1 (page 22) to review the criteria for testable questions.

5. Rewrite your hypothesis as an if-then statement.

In some cases, you can test a hypothesis by making a prediction and then collecting data to determine whether the prediction was accurate. For this, it is useful to express the hypothesis as an if-then statement such as, "If milk gets hotter than 80°C, then it will boil."

6. As a team, read the Protocol for Conducting a Step Test. Discuss how you would use this exercise protocol to test your hypothesis.

PROTOCOL

Protocol for Conducting a Step Test

1. Work with your team to decide what data you will need to collect and analyze to test your hypothesis.

   Consider exercise rates and resting conditions, pulse rate, breathing rate, and any other conditions. The exercise rate is the speed at which the test subject steps (or performs some other repetitive exercise).

2. As a team, decide who will be the test subject, who will be the timer, who will count and record the test subject's breathing rate, and who will count and record the test subject's pulse.

   You will use a step test to measure pulse and breathing rates for the exercise rates that you determine in your experimental design. You might begin with 1 step every 5 seconds. This activity will succeed only with the cooperation and support of all team members.

3. With the test subject sitting quietly in a chair, count the test subject's resting pulse rate and breathing rate for 30 seconds. Record the resting pulse rate and breathing rate per minute in your data table.

   a. To record the pulse rate, do 1 of the following:

   ◆ Attach a heart rate sensor to the test subject's finger according to the sensor's directions. Time and record the pulse rate for 30 seconds. Then multiply this rate by 2 to obtain the *pulse rate per minute*.

   OR

   ◆ Locate the test subject's pulse by pressing on his or her wrist with the index and middle fingers, as shown in Figure 5.6. Time and record the pulse rate for 30 seconds. Then multiply this rate by 2 to obtain the *pulse rate per minute*.

   b. To record the breathing rate, do 1 of the following:

   ◆ Attach a breathing rate sensor to the test subject according to the sensor's directions. Time and record the breathing rate for 30 seconds. Then multiply this rate by 2 to obtain the *breathing rate per minute*.

   (continued)

Protocol for Conducting a Step Test (*continued*)

OR

◆ Instruct the test subject to count her or his number of breaths while a team member times and calls out 30 seconds. Count 1 complete breath—inhalation and exhalation—as 1 breath. Time and record the breathing rate for 30 seconds. Then multiply this rate by 2 to obtain the *breathing rate per minute.*

4. Assign jobs to your team so that you can measure both the pulse and breathing rate at the same time. You may want to measure other indicators of homeostatic changes as well. For example, you also could measure the test subject's temperature. What other observations may provide useful data?

Your team will need jobs such as the following (depending on your experimental design):

- Timer
- Test subject
- Computer operator (if using probe ware)
- Pulse counter
- Breathing counter

Figure 5.6   Checking pulse rate.

5. Control the rate of exercise in your experiment in order to make precise scientific comparisons. Do this by designing a method for timing your test subject's actions. For example, you could perform the step test by following this process. This example assumes an exercise rate of 1 step every 5 seconds.

Timer: Tell the test subject when to start. Then quietly call out "step" every
5 seconds for 1 minute.

Test subject: When the timer says "step," step up onto the platform with
1 foot, then with the other foot; next, step down with the first foot, then
with the other foot.

Timer: Say "stop" after 1 minute.

Computer operator (optional): Take the experiment off PAUSE or WAIT, and
MARK the graph.

Timer: Immediately begin timing for the pulse and breathing rate counter
for 30 seconds.

Pulse counter: Count the test subject's pulse for 30 seconds immediately
after exercise. Record the rate per minute. Record the beginning and
ending MARK numbers (if using a computer), or enter data into a table (if
no computer is being used).

Computer operator (optional): MARK the graph at the end of 30 seconds.

Breathing counter: Count the test subject's breathing rate using the sensor
or assist the test subject in counting his or her own breathing rate. Record
the rate per minute. Record the beginning and ending MARK numbers (if
using a computer), or enter data into a table (if no computer is being
used).

6. Repeat step 5 to measure the other rates according to your experimental
design.

Remember, the more data you collect, the better you will be able to draw
reasonable conclusions and test your hypothesis.

7. Construct a data table in your journal for the experiment.

Include columns for each of the exercise rates and resting conditions that you decide
to use. Make rows for pulse rate, breathing rate, and any other conditions. The
exercise rate is the speed at which the test subject steps (or performs some other
repetitive exercise).

8. Identify the variables in your experiment, and decide on an appropriate
control. Record the variables and the control in your journal.

Variables might include exercise rate, step height, and test subject's weight. Your
control should allow you to test 1 variable at a time. You also may want to compare
the responses of 2 or more test subjects.

9. Design an experiment to test your hypothesis. Your experiment needs to meet
all of the criteria listed below. Your experiment must

◆ be safe,

◆ be manageable in a classroom setting and appropriate for the length of the
class period,

◆ use the materials available, and

◆ allow each team member to handle materials and record data.

**Figure 5.7 The
respiratory system.**
The primary function
of the respiratory (or
gas exchange) system
is to provide a large
area within the body
for the exchange of
gases between the air
and the circulating
blood.

10. Have your teacher approve your design; then begin your test.

   As you proceed with your test, you may need to modify the design of your experiment. If that happens, record the changes in your journal.

11. When you have completed your experiment, construct a graph that shows how pulse and breathing rates changed from the resting state through increasing rates of exercise. Copy the graph into your own journal.

12. After you have finished your graph, analyze your experiment. Develop a conclusion that describes the interaction between the circulatory and gas exchange systems during exercise.

   For a strong conclusion, analyze the data that you collected, including the graph, and relate those data to the hypothesis that you tested.

Analysis

Complete the following tasks individually. Write your explanations in your journal.

PAGE 236

   Use the information in the essay *The Breath of Life* on page 236 to develop well-reasoned answers. Consider the role of the respiratory system in your experiment (see Figure 5.7).

1. Use the concept of interacting systems to explain how oxygen from the atmosphere can reach cells deep within the body.

2. Explain how the acidity of blood controls breathing rate.

Elaborate   # On a Scale of 0 to 14

   In *Stepping Up the Pace*, you learned that several organ systems could interact to maintain homeostasis. In addition, you began to explore a chemical mechanism—the amount of acid in the blood—that links the circulatory system to the gas exchange system. The amount of acid in the blood is related to the amount of carbon dioxide in the cells of the body. By sensing and responding to these levels, the body can maintain a proper balance of oxygen and carbon dioxide in its internal environment. In this case, the acidity level is a regulatory signal. The body responds to this signal when maintaining the balance between two large organ systems. The acidity level, as measured on the pH scale, must remain balanced in humans and other organisms.

   In this activity, you will elaborate on your understanding of physiological regulation. How do living systems maintain internal conditions of pH? Consider the significance of that question for your body. You put all sorts of foods and beverages into your body. Yet normally your body can keep its pH within a healthy range. How does your body balance the different pH levels that it encounters?

To study that question, you will compare how a variety of materials respond to the addition of an acid and a base. Among these materials are **homogenates** (mixtures that are uniform throughout) made from living cells. These homogenates act as models of the internal environment of living systems. They will allow you to investigate how the level of acidity inside cells can be maintained within certain limits.

Materials (per team of 3)

2 pairs of safety goggles
50-mL beaker
petri dish half
jar of tap water for storing pH probes
   (if using probe ware)
distilled water
dropping bottle of 0.1*M* NaOH (base)
materials that your teacher provides

2 lab aprons
50-mL graduated cylinder
pH probe or pH indicator strips
forceps
graph paper
dropping bottle of 0.1*M* HCl (acid)
50 mL of liver or potato homogenate

PROCESS AND PROCEDURES

Part A   pH Is Everywhere

1. If you compared 2 solutions, 1 with a pH of 6 and another with a pH of 5, what would be the difference? Read the background information about pH to find out.

NEED TO KNOW

Background Information

We use pH to measure how acidic or basic a solution is. A pH of 7 represents a neutral solution that is neither acidic nor basic. The pH scale ranges from 0 (very acidic) to 14 (very basic). The scale is logarithmic; each difference of 1 pH unit means a tenfold difference in acidity. For example, a solution with a pH of 8 is 10 times more acidic than a solution with a pH of 9. In other words, a pH of 8 is 10 times less basic than a pH of 9. Strongly acidic and basic solutions can be quite harmful to the external environment of living systems. Strong acids and bases can burn skin badly. Even minor imbalances in internal pH, however, can disrupt the normal regulation of cells.

2. Make a table in your journal. Include the name of each household solution that your teacher provides and 2 spaces. In the 1st space, you will make a prediction of what you think the pH will be. In the 2nd space, you will record the pH that you measure.

3. On your own, record your prediction for what you think the pH of the available solutions will be.

4. With your partner, determine the pH of the available solutions by using a pH probe or pH indicator strips. Record these pH readings in the data table in your journal.

5. Discuss the following questions with your class:

   a. Do any of the pH measurements differ from your predictions?

   b. Which of the solutions that you tested could be harmful to the pH balance of your organ systems? Why?

Figure 5.8   Household products.   Do you know which products in your home have a pH low enough or high enough to hurt you?

Safety Goggles   Lab Apron

Part B   Regulating pH

SAFETY: Put on your safety goggles and lab apron.

1. To investigate how living cells regulate pH, you and your partner will compare how water and 1 type of cell homogenate respond to the addition of acids and bases. Water is not living. The homogenate, made from cells that were recently living, will model the internal environment of a living organism. Your job is to collect data that will allow you to compare the responses of a nonliving and "living" substance to the addition of an acid and then a base.

2. Read the protocol for changing the acidity of a liquid.

PROTOCOL

Systematically Increasing and Decreasing the Acidity of a Liquid

1. Pour 25 mL of distilled water into a 50-mL beaker.
2. Determine the initial pH of the solution as you did in Part A, step 4.
3. Record the initial pH in your data table under the column labeled *0 Drops.*
4. Add 0.1*M* HCl to the beaker 1 drop at a time until you have added 5 drops.

    ◆ Gently swirl the mixture after each drop.
    ◆ You are making the water more acidic.

CAUTION: 0.1*M* HCl is a *mild irritant* (an acid). Avoid skin/eye contact; do not ingest. If contact occurs, flush affected area with water for 15 minutes; rinse mouth with water. Call the teacher.

Caution

5. Determine the pH of the solution. Record this reading in your data table.
6. Repeat steps 4 and 5. Record the pH after every additional 5 drops of acid until you have added a total of 30 drops of acid.
7. Discard the mixture, and rinse the beaker and pH probe (if you are using one) thoroughly.
8. Repeat steps 1 through 7, *but add 0.1M NaOH drop by drop instead of HCl.*

    ◆ Gently swirl.
    ◆ You are making the water more basic.

CAUTION: 0.1*M* NaOH is a *mild irritant* (a base). Avoid skin/eye contact; do not ingest. If contact occurs, flush affected area with water for 15 minutes; rinse mouth with water. Call the teacher.

Caution

9. Repeat steps 1 through 8. But instead of starting with distilled water in step 1, pour 25 mL of the homogenate into the beaker.

    You will be observing how the homogenate responds to the addition of an acid and then a base.

10. Wash your hands thoroughly with soap and water after the experiment.

---

3. Determine which homogenate your team will be using.

    You will use either liver homogenate or potato homogenate. Your teacher made these homogenates by blending pieces of liver or potato at high speed to break open the cells and release their contents. Remember, these homogenates will act as models of the internal environment of living systems.

4. On your own, draw a graph that represents your prediction for how you think pH will change for both water and your homogenate when you add acid. Also, graph how you predict the pH will change for both when you add a base. Draw your predictions on a graph with the axes labeled like those in Figure 5.9.

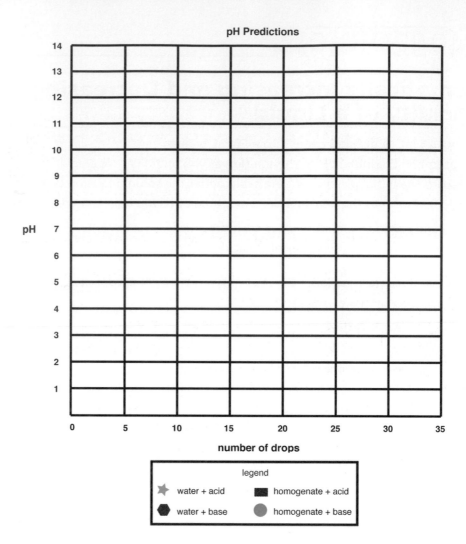

Figure 5.9   Sample graph for recording pH predictions.

5. Below your prediction graph, write a brief justification for your predictions.

6. Divide the data collection jobs fairly among your team members. You need someone who will perform the acid tests, someone who will perform the base tests, and someone who will record pH levels in a data table. Change jobs after testing the water so that every team member takes a turn measuring the pH of a solution.

   Use a table similar to the one labeled *pH Changes* in Figure 5.10 to record the data that you collect. After the experiment, all team members will copy the data from the experiment into their journals.

7. On graph paper or in your journal, draw a full-sized graph. Label the *x*- and *y*-axes the same as you did on the graph that you made for your predictions. Use the pH data that your team collected to make a line graph that shows 4 separate lines: 1 each for water plus acid, water plus base, homogenate plus acid, and homogenate plus base. Your graph should show the relationship between pH and the number of drops of acid or base.

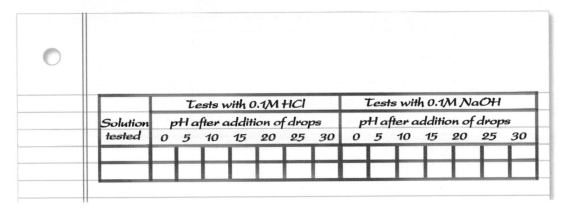

	Tests with 0.1M HCl							Tests with 0.1M NaOH						
Solution tested	pH after addition of drops							pH after addition of drops						
	0	5	10	15	20	25	30	0	5	10	15	20	25	30

Figure 5.10 pH changes. You will need a table like this one to record your test results.

Code your lines, using color or different line types. You will want to distinguish between the 4 conditions that you are graphing.

8. Discuss the following question with your partner. Record an explanation in your journal based on the information portrayed on your graphs.

   What similarities and differences do you see in the results of adding HCl or NaOH to water compared with a homogenate?

9. Join a team that tested the other homogenate. Compare data and explanations.

pH of Common Foods

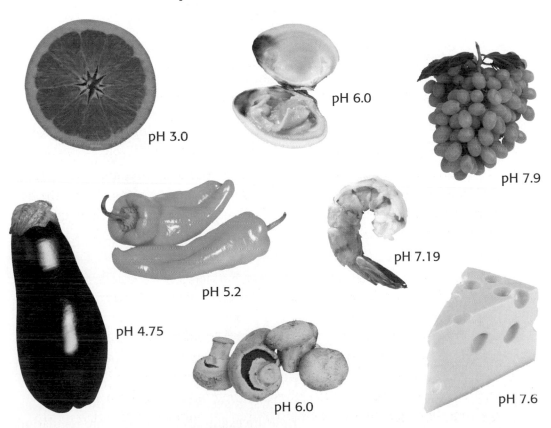

pH 3.0

pH 6.0

pH 7.9

pH 5.2

pH 7.19

pH 4.75

pH 6.0

pH 7.6

Figure 5.11 pH of common foods.

10. Discuss the following questions with your partner. Record the answers in your journal.

The information on buffers in the need to know box may help you with your answers.

   a. Based on your results and using water as a comparison, do you think potato and liver cells are buffered? Explain your answer.

   b. Is it likely that all living systems contain buffers? Why or why not?

   c. At what pH do you think living liver and potato cells function best? On what do you base this inference?

Analysis

Answer the following questions in your journal. Be prepared to contribute your ideas to a class discussion.

1. Based on your data from the experiment in Part B, how might a buffer help maintain homeostasis? Explain your answer.

2. Many manufacturers claim that their health care and hair care products are pH balanced or buffered. How would you test their claims?

NEED TO KNOW

BACKGROUND ON BUFFERS

Proper pH balance is important because different chemical and metabolic processes in living organisms work best under different pH conditions. In humans, for example, digestion in the stomach requires a low pH. But the functions of blood require a nearly neutral pH, not varying much from pH 7.2 to 7.4. In fact, each cell, tissue, and organ has a characteristic pH that is important for homeostasis.

Often, however, organisms are exposed to things that have a pH that is very different from their own. For example, much of the food that you eat has a pH that is different from that of your stomach. How do living systems maintain a relatively stable pH in their internal environment when changes occur in their external environment?

A **buffer** maintains the pH of a solution within a narrow range of values even when external conditions threaten to change pH. In effect, this means that small additions of acid or base to a buffered solution do not cause a change in pH. Cells have physiological buffers that help maintain its characteristic pH; this protects the internal environment. Different types of buffers are effective in maintaining pH within different ranges. One type of buffer might keep the internal pH in a slightly acidic range, and a different type might keep the internal pH of another cell in a neutral range.

SCI LINKS
NSTA

Topic: buffers
Go to: www.scilinks.org
Code: human3E188

Elaborate

How Do They Stay So Cool?

Animals regulate their internal conditions in a variety of ways. What methods of regulation have you experienced or observed so far in class or in the world around you? Do you have a dog that pants on hot days? Have you seen a bird fluff up its feathers when the temperature drops? Those are examples of temperature regulation through behavior.

Figure 5.12
The collared lizard.
This species of lizard has adapted to the extreme temperatures of a desert environment.

During the heat of summer in the New Mexico desert, a collared lizard, like the one in Figure 5.12, will wait beneath the cool shade of a rock. Other lizards dart about in the undergrowth. These reptiles survive in temperatures that would cause most humans to wilt in their tracks. (Temperatures at the surface of the soil can exceed 70°C, or 158°F.) Yet, the reptiles survive even though they have no sweat glands. What are the mechanisms that allow these reptiles to survive such high temperatures? In this activity, you will gather information to compare and contrast the mechanisms of temperature regulation in lizards and two other animals with those of the human body.

Materials

DVD and player

PROCESS AND PROCEDURES

In this activity, you will examine the question, How does the behavior of animals help them to maintain homeostasis? You will gather information to help you develop an explanation for this question.

1. Observe the DVD segment "Temperature Regulation in Animals." Record your observations in a data table that is similar to the one in Figure 5.13. Write your responses in your journal to the questions that the DVD segment poses.

Type of animal	Behavioral responses to changes in temperature
Give yourself room to observe 7 different types of animals.	

Figure 5.13 Use a table similar to this to record your observations.

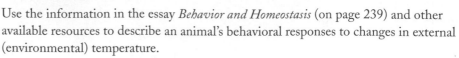

2. Add a column to your table, and record the behaviors of a living animal that you can observe directly.

   Focus your observations on the behaviors that the animal exhibits to regulate its temperature or to respond to changes in the external temperature.

   Use the information in the essay *Behavior and Homeostasis* (on page 239) and other available resources to describe an animal's behavioral responses to changes in external (environmental) temperature.

Analysis

Use your notes, observational data from the DVD, and the information in the essay *Behavior and Homeostasis* to answer the following questions. Write your responses in your journal.

Topic: poikilotherms
Go to: www.scilinks.org
Code: human3E190

1. What similarities and differences do you see between the behaviors that lizards and humans use to help regulate temperature?

2. What similarities and differences do you see between the way dogs and humans regulate temperature?

   Think about the physiology of a dog and of a human as each responds to temperature extremes.

3. Describe two homeostatic processes (aside from temperature regulation) that you or other animals regulate through behavior. For each process, identify the stimulus, feedback, and response. Record your responses in a table that is similar to Figure 5.14.

Condition that is maintained through homeostasis	Stimulus	Feedback	Behavioral response

Figure 5.14 Sample table for observations.

Evaluate

Homeostasis in Your Critter

Throughout Chapters 4 and 5, you have been exploring the concept of homeostasis. At this point, you should have a good understanding of the complex systems and processes that are involved. They help living systems maintain an internal condition of dynamic balance even while external conditions change dramatically.

In this evaluate activity, you will return to the description of the critter that you "discovered" in *First Encounter with the Critter* from Chapter 3. In doing so, you will evaluate what you have learned in this chapter. You will apply what you have learned about homeostasis to your critter. This will show your teacher what you have learned about how organisms maintain their internal environment when the external environment changes.

Materials   (per person)

descriptions and diagrams of your critter from Chapter 3

PROCESS AND PROCEDURES

1. Work individually to write a paragraph that answers each of the following questions. Include your paragraphs in your critter folder for evaluation.

    a. Based on what you have learned in this chapter and Chapter 4, how would you describe homeostasis?

    b. Why is it important for organisms to maintain homeostasis?

2. Recall your critter that you described in Chapter 3 and the environment in which it lives. List at least 5 specific environmental stress factors that your organism most likely would be subjected to in that environment. Include this list in your critter folder.

3. Use the medium of your choice to demonstrate a response to this question:

    In what ways does your critter maintain its internal environment considering the external stress factors that you listed in step 2?

    You will know that you have adequately addressed the question if your response includes an explanation, illustration, or demonstration of the following:

    ◆ How your critter regulates internal temperature in response to heat and cold

    ◆ How your critter regulates water balance

    ◆ How your critter deals with at least 2 other stresses caused by changes in the external environment that require a response by the internal environment

    ◆ How at least 2 key systems in your critter interact to adjust internal conditions

    A medium is the method or materials you use to convey your response. You could write a response, draw or paint a picture or diagram, develop a collage, or use some other method that your teacher approves.

Analysis

Evaluate your work according to the rubric that your teacher provides. Your teacher will use these guidelines to evaluate your work as well.

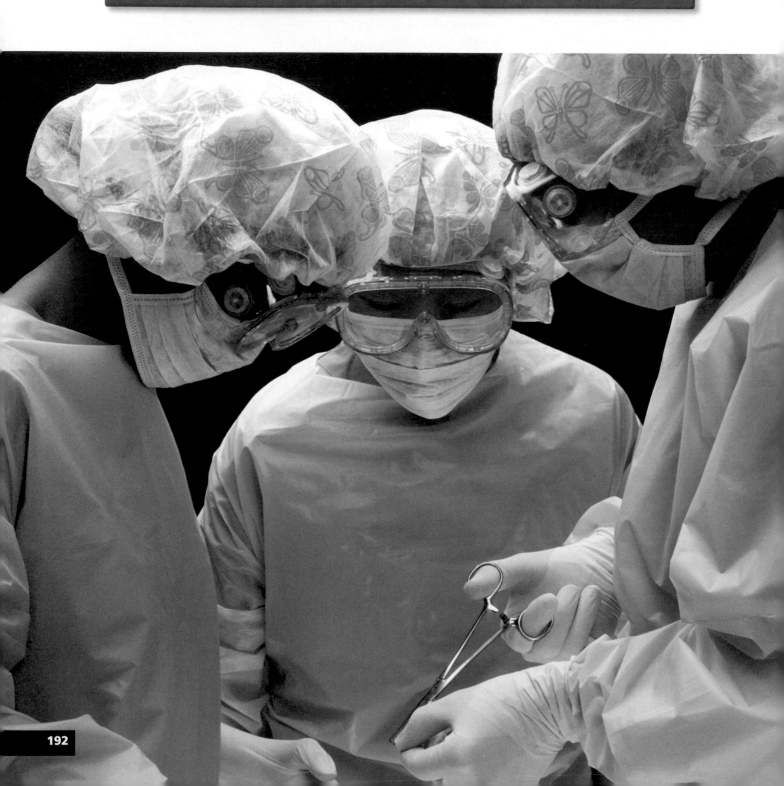

> "Here, we can only describe the faulty functioning of our body's machinery, or the role of external circumstances in overwhelming our body's machinery."
>
> *Bruce Wallace, Department of Biology, Virginia Polytechnic Institute and State University*

Human Homeostasis: Health and Disease

Chapter 6

The processes of homeostasis allow most people to enjoy relatively long and healthy lives. For these people, the common cold and other minor illnesses are only temporary disruptions. Their bodies are quite capable of recovering through normal regulatory processes. Occasionally, disruptions can affect our homeostasis. In turn, these disruptions affect our health in more serious and sometimes permanent ways. These cases often require medical care to help the body stay within the internal limits necessary for life.

In this chapter, you will examine what happens when homeostasis is disrupted in various ways. You will explore the effects of severe dehydration, allergic reactions, trauma, and a variety of other emergency health care situations. You also will consider how medical technology can help compensate for disruptions in the body's homeostasis. Then you will examine how certain personal behaviors can increase or reduce your risk of disrupting your body's homeostasis. After you have completed these activities, you will evaluate your understanding of disruption by developing a mock proposal that requests funds for a worthy health care initiative of your choice.

ACTIVITIES

Engage	Pushing the Limits
Explore **Explain**	Hospital Triage
Explain	Self-Defense!
Explain **Elaborate**	What's the Risk?
Evaluate	Health Care Proposal

Pushing the Limits

Just how much stress can the human body endure and still function? As you work through this activity, you will examine the limits of the human body. In the activities that follow, you will use your knowledge of the mechanisms for maintaining an internal balance to understand the limits of homeostasis further.

PROCESS AND PROCEDURES

1. Read the story *A Sweltering Experience*. As you read, use your journal to record details about the physical condition of the 2 hikers at the time of their rescue.

2. With your partner, complete the following tasks. Write your responses in your journal.

SCENARIO

A Sweltering Experience

The two hikers thought they had nothing to worry about. The day was beautiful: warm and clear, with a pleasant breeze sweeping off the high desert. The canyon trail offered great views. Monique and her father, Nelson, tromped enthusiastically downward. They stopped to enjoy the brilliant wildflowers and watched their steps as they skirted around a narrow switchback. Monique cried out in delight as she spotted an eagle soaring nearby, riding the warm air currents rising from the canyon depths.

They never thought about the distance, trekking downhill over nine miles of trail before they began to grow tired. They stopped to rest. Nelson removed his jacket, tying it around his waist, while Monique applied more sunscreen to her face. They remarked, with some surprise, that it was much warmer in the canyon than they had expected.

It was then that Nelson pointed out that they had finished most of the water from the single canteen they had brought. Neither of them was tired. But given the heat, and the distance remaining to the bottom, they decided they had better turn around and start back up toward the rim where they had left their car in the Forest Service parking lot.

Almost immediately, the effects of gravity became apparent. A trail that had been an easy stroll going down now became a daunting ramp rising steeply upward. Their progress was slow, and the canyon rim seemed impossibly high overhead. Monique started to feel concerned as, after an hour of climbing, they finally reached the switchback that had been just a few minutes away when they were going down.

a. List at least 4 human body systems that would be involved in restoring internal balance in the hikers.

> Think about your work in Chapters 4 and 5. Use your understanding of interacting body systems that work to maintain internal balance to complete your list.

b. List 4 situations not discussed in the story that could also severely disrupt homeostasis.

Analysis

Respond in your journal to the following:

> Use the information in the essay *Beyond the Limits* (page 242) as a resource.

PAGE 242

1. List two mild stressors and two severe stressors. Describe the effects that each stressor would have on the human body.

2. From your personal experience, describe two examples of disruptions of homeostasis in *nonhuman* organisms.

They were very thirsty but had to ration the last few mouthfuls of water carefully. Frequently, they stopped to mop the sweat from their faces, drawing deep, ragged breaths of dry air that didn't seem to refresh them much at all. They had no strength for conversation, merely plodded along slowly, kicking up clouds of dust with each footstep on the dry, gritty trail.

Suddenly, Monique cried out in pain and slapped at her leg, swatting away a bee—but not before the insect had driven its stinger through her skin. Grimly, she continued on. But within minutes, her leg began to swell around the sting. Limping in pain, she moved even slower than before, and soon she had to stop and rest.

Nelson was growing frantic. They still had three or four miles to go to reach the parking lot. They had seen no other hikers during the whole day. He found a small patch of shade near the trail and told Monique to stay there while he went for help. Leaving her the canteen, with its remaining sip or two of water, he started climbing as fast as he could. He hoped to find a ranger or call for help from the pay phone near where they had parked the car.

Climbing with all his strength and endurance, gasping for breath and sweating profusely, Nelson still took 2 hours to reach the rim. When he arrived at the car, he was badly dehydrated. His body could no longer cool itself adequately through perspiration. He was dizzy and nauseous, suffering from an excruciating headache, so confused that he couldn't think of what to do next.

It was only good fortune that a ranger who was a trained paramedic drove into the parking lot on a routine patrol. Immediately, he noticed that Nelson needed help. The hiker was breathing loudly and rapidly through his mouth, and the skin of his hand was hot and dry to the touch. Yet, his face was not very flushed. Even as he radioed for a backcountry rescue team to go after Monique, the ranger knew that Nelson himself was dangerously ill.

The rescuers reached Monique 3 hours after she had been stung. Her condition was alarming. They quickly loaded her onto a stretcher and carried her to the nearest clearing wide enough for a helicopter to land. Meanwhile, the ranger reported the patient's condition to the emergency room personnel.

"Her vision is blurred, and her breathing labored. Her leg is red and swollen near the bee sting, and she has a rash over her leg, spreading to her stomach. Her lips are cracked—she had trouble drinking when we gave her water."

The helicopter flight will not take long, but Nelson and Monique's fates both remain uncertain. It's up to you, the emergency room personnel, to save them!

Hospital Triage

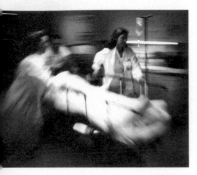

You and your partners are a team of physicians in the emergency room of Desert Metropolitan Hospital. It's about 8:30 P.M. on a Friday in July. You have been busy, as you usually are on summer weekends. Unfortunately, you are about to become even busier. You have just received a flurry of calls from local paramedics, and now you and your colleagues are preparing for an influx of patients suffering from a variety of illnesses and trauma injuries. This influx includes a flight-for-life helicopter carrying the two canyon hikers discussed in *A Sweltering Experience*.

Because there are many patients and only a handful of doctors, you cannot treat every patient at the same time. Your first task is to assess the severity of each patient's condition and establish a "priority for treatment," which is called **triage**. Triage is a process used in battlefields, disaster areas, and emergency rooms to assign the order for assisting patients and maximizing medical efficiency and success. You will need to use everything you know about the body's normal homeostatic mechanisms to complete this triage. Keep in mind that there are no "right" answers for your medical team. The most important measure of your success will be your team's ability to *explain* the treatment choices that you make.

PROCESS AND PROCEDURES

Part A   Triage in the Emergency Room

When you visit your doctor's office, a medical professional first measures and records your vital signs. Have you ever considered what your vital signs tell the doctor? Vital signs are body characteristics that can be measured quickly. They provide important information about major body systems. This information is particularly important to obtain and quickly interpret when patients are experiencing severe trauma.

Topic: vital signs
Go to: www.scilinks.org
Code: human3E196

1. Meet with your team of doctors, and read the Glossary of Vital Signs in preparation for interpreting your patients' conditions.

2. Review the *normal*, *serious*, and *critical* ranges for the vital signs in the need to know box. You will refer to this information to determine the level of trauma that your patients are experiencing.

3. Obtain the handout *Patients' Vital Signs—Preliminary Information* from your teacher. As a team, read about your patients.

   Pay particular attention to the description of each patient's injury or illness.

4. With your medical team, briefly discuss the possible outcomes for each patient.

5. Obtain 2 triage data sheets from your teacher. Divide your triage team to work in pairs to complete the following tasks. Work with your partner to evaluate the data for half of the patients. The rest of your triage team will evaluate the other half. When both teams have completed the initial patient evaluations, compare your findings and develop your treatment strategy.

Glossary of Vital Signs

Vital signs are body characteristics that can be measured quickly. They provide important information about major body systems.

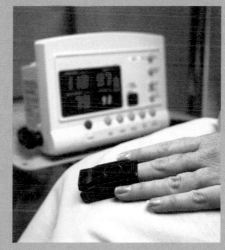

- **Pulse** is the rate (how fast or slow) at which the heart is beating. It provides clues to how well the heart is functioning. It also indicates how well the blood is carrying oxygen and other important substances to the tissues, including brain tissues.

- **Blood pressure** is another indicator of the heart's ability to pump blood throughout the body. It is measured at an artery and is usually represented as two numbers such as 125/85. The first number (**systolic**) is a measurement of the force of blood against the walls of the arteries, veins, and chambers of the heart as the heart contracts. The second number (**diastolic**) is a measurement of the lowest pressure reached as the heart relaxes.

- **Body temperature** indicates whether the body's thermal regulation is working. An elevated body temperature could indicate an infection. A low central body temperature, or core temperature, indicates a type of shock.

- **Rate of breathing** reflects how well oxygen is being delivered to the body. It also is associated with heart rate and circulation.

Taken together, vital signs give the physician a quick view of a patient's internal state, even if the patient is unconscious and cannot explain how he or she feels. These measurements vary over a relatively narrow range in healthy people, indicating that the body normally has precise control of internal conditions. When the vital signs are far outside these normal ranges, homeostasis usually is disrupted in the patient. Under these circumstances, the vital signs are direct indicators of problems with internal systems that are involved in maintaining homeostasis. Vital signs, however, usually do not indicate the cause of the disruption of homeostasis.

NEED TO KNOW

Range of vital signs	Normal	Serious	Critical
Blood pressure Systolic pressure (the top number) is the pressure created when the heart contracts and pumps blood. Diastolic pressure (the bottom number) is the pressure between contractions when the heart relaxes and fills.	110/70 to 140/90 mm Hg (systolic/diastolic)	90–100 mm Hg systolic	<90 mm Hg systolic
Resting pulse	60–100 beats/min	<60 or >100 beats/min	<50 or >120 beats/min
Temperature	37°C (98.6°F)	39°C–40°C (102.2°F–104°F)	>40°C (>104°F)
Breathing rate	10–20 resp./min	<10 or >20 resp./min	<10 or >30 resp./min

Key to units: mm Hg = millimeters of mercury, a measure of pressure; < is less than, > is greater than

Note: The figures quoted above are simplified guidelines. They are based on those used by medical personnel. *More precise ranges for different age-groups and sexes also are used.* Occasionally, healthy individuals have "normal" readings that are outside of these average ranges. For example, many young people have systolic blood pressure lower than 100 mm Hg.

In general, blood pressure must be evaluated in relation to the other vital signs and the patient's age and condition. For the purposes of this activity, assume that the normal state for each patient is within the normal ranges listed in the table.

Task 1: Compare the vital signs of each patient with the normal ranges.

Procedure: Use the information in the need to know box to decide whether each vital sign for every patient is within normal limits or not. Record the vital signs for each patient in the 2nd column on the data sheet. In the 3rd column, record a checkmark (✓) to indicate vital signs that are within normal limits. Use an X to indicate those outside normal limits.

Task 2: Identify the body systems most likely disrupted by each patient's injuries or illness.

Procedure: Work with your partner to develop a list of systems that are disrupted for each patient. Record your lists in the 4th column on your data sheet. Use your knowledge of interactions between internal body systems in maintaining homeostasis from Chapters 4 and 5 to make logical inferences from the vital signs.

Task 3: Join with your other team members to compare all of your patients and to assign treatment priorities.

Procedure: Use your best listening skills. Encourage all team members to contribute ideas about how your team should treat each patient.

Task 4: Suggest initial triage treatments, and explain your priority choice for each patient.

Procedure: **a.** Read General Triage Guidelines on page 200.

            b. Reread the description of each patient.

            c. In the 1st column of the data sheet next to each patient's name, write the number that corresponds to the order of treatment that your team agrees upon for this triage.

            d. In the 6th column, write a brief justification for the treatment priority that your team assigned each patient.

            e. For each of your patients, list 1 or 2 emergency medical treatments that might help each restore homeostasis. Record this list in the 6th column as well. Use the back of the data sheet if you need more space to record your responses.

a

b

Part B   Let's Get More Information

While you were performing your triage evaluation, medical technicians and laboratory staff conducted some additional tests. These include analyses of blood and urine samples. These new data may provide you with important information about each patient's condition that you were not able to discern from vital signs alone.

1. Obtain the Copymaster *First Priority* from your teacher. Discuss the importance of this new information with your teammates.

2. Working as a team, reevaluate the order you should treat each patient. Record your order of priority in the 7th column of your team's triage data table. (This may be different from the order given in task 4c.)

   Be prepared to share your ideas and your team's triage results in a class discussion.

3. Obtain the Copymaster *Additional Information* from your teacher. Read the information to learn the consequences of your secondary triage decisions.

4. In the 8th column, indicate any additional internal body systems (systems that were not identified as being disrupted in Part A) that your team thinks are disrupted. Base your decisions on the new information.

   The information in the Copymaster *Additional Information* may provide additional clues about your patients' body systems.

5. With your team, discuss any additional factors that may have contributed to each patient's condition and to your priority choices. Write a brief explanation for your patients' final ranking in the 8th column of the triage data sheet.

   These may include nonmedical factors, such as behavior and luck, which your team took into consideration.

c

Figure 6.1
Examples of technology in medicine. (a) MRI and monitor **(b)** CT scans **(c)** Intensive Care Monitoring Station

NEED TO KNOW

GENERAL TRIAGE GUIDELINES

1. All emergency care begins with the ABCs. Make sure there is an open *A*irway, that the patient is *B*reathing, and that the patient has adequate *C*irculation.

   a. Airway. Remove obstructions from the mouth, if necessary. Move the tongue if it is obstructing the airway. Close openings such as the nose or wounds that prevent the lungs from filling with air.

   b. Breathing. Restore breathing by artificial resuscitation. (This is a technique by which another person or device can temporarily provide air to a patient.) Or administer oxygen, if necessary.

   c. Circulation. Stop blood loss from serious wounds. Restore heartbeat by cardiopulmonary resuscitation (CPR), if necessary. CPR is a technique in which another person temporarily provides air and heart contractions for a patient whose heart has stopped beating or is not pumping blood effectively.

2. Look at the patient, and assess his or her injuries. Immobilize any injuries to the neck. The patient may become paralyzed if you initiate any movement. Always suspect neck injuries when there is extensive injury to the head or face.

3. **Shock** is extremely serious and life threatening. It occurs when blood pressure drops so low that it no longer delivers adequate supplies of oxygen and nutrients to the tissues. Shock can result from failure of the heart to pump vigorously enough. It can also result from serious blood loss or from a reduction of effective blood volume due to pooling in the capillaries or to dehydration.

   Shock due to reduced blood volume can be treated by elevating the feet, by using pressure suits that force blood from the extremities back into the body core, or by infusing blood or saline solution into the circulatory system. Shock due to weakness of the heart or damage to the circulatory system may require medications or mechanical devices that assist circulation.

4. The hypothalamus normally controls internal body temperature. If this control is lost, the core body temperature can rise to dangerously high levels, a condition known as **hyperthermia**. Extreme hyperthermia can kill cells, particularly brain cells. In these cases, external measures must be taken, such as rubbing the patient with ice to bring the body temperature back within normal limits.

   Conversely, the body can cool to dangerous levels. This is a condition known as **hypothermia**. Hypothermia can occur when people are cold and wet for a long period of time. Rapid evaporation of water can cool a person quite quickly, even if the air temperature is not extremely cold. In such cases, the body must be warmed slowly to bring it back within normal limits.

6. As a team, discuss what the prognosis, or long-term outlook, is for each patient. Prepare to present your reasoning in a class discussion.

For instance, you might think that some patients will recover completely, others will recover slowly and may suffer long-lasting effects, and others may never recover and even die because of their injury or illness.

Analysis

Work individually to respond to the following. Write your answers in your journal.

PAGE 244

The essay *Coping with Disruptions: The Role of Medicine in Homeostasis* (page 244) and the facts in the need to know boxes provide important background information for writing well-reasoned answers.

1. Why are vital signs so valuable in assessing a patient's condition quickly?

2. Explain how a head injury, such as the one Albert suffered when his motorcycle crashed, could affect so many internal body systems that are necessary to maintain homeostasis.

3. How did a bacterial infection cause a higher-than-normal temperature in Maria?

4. Monique and Nelson both had very high temperatures when they were brought into the emergency room. Why do you think Monique's heart rate was high and Nelson's heart rate was low?

5. Why was Monique likely to survive if she received treatment in time but Nelson died in spite of the priority he was given?

6. What, if any, nonmedical considerations did you use to rank the patients? Explain your response.

7. In one or two paragraphs, compare and contrast an illness or injury that the body can recover from on its own with one that requires medical intervention. Explain how the responses of internal body systems that are necessary to maintain homeostasis differ in the two situations.

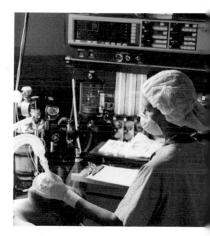

Looking Ahead

In the evaluate activity for this chapter, you will work with your teammates to develop a health care proposal. Because you will need extra time to collect information for your proposal, you need to start now.

With your team, turn to *Health Care Proposal* (page 209). Read the introduction to the activity, and complete steps 1 and 2. Then begin step 3. Developing your proposal will be more rewarding if you are well prepared.

Self-Defense!

You have seen how the body corrects minor disruptions in homeostasis and how medical technology can help when the disruptions are more serious. But would you believe that a battle is going on inside your body even when you are healthy? This battle is being fought by internal body systems that work together to protect your body against external conditions *before* they threaten to disrupt your body's normal balance.

As a living system, your body constantly fights against foreign chemicals and invading microorganisms and viruses. Where do these invaders come from? Recall the bee sting that Monique, the hiker, suffered. When a bee stings you, it injects venom into your body. This venom is made up of molecules that are foreign to your body, and your body reacts to them. Another source of invading particles is the air that you breathe. Air contains many unhealthy things. These include particles of pollutants, spores of fungi and bacteria, and virus particles. The number of potential invaders is even higher if you breathe the air near a person who has a cold and who sneezes.

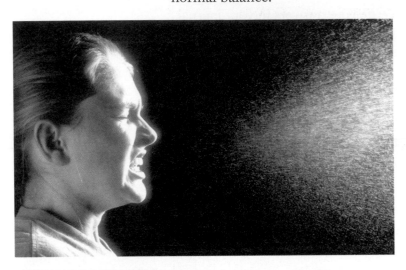

Figure 6.2 A single "kachoo" can release 10,000 to 100,000 virus particles.

It might seem impossible for living organisms to protect themselves against the disrupting influence of so many threats. Yet, all living systems have some means of protecting their internal environment against infection. As a human, you have a particularly elaborate system of natural defense, which is known as the immune system. Although it is not perfect, the immune system generally wins its battles. This activity will help you explain how your body defends itself.

Materials   (per team of 4)

test subject card   scenario card

PROCESS AND PROCEDURES

Part A   Natural Defenses

1. Respond to the following statements about how the immune system helps maintain homeostasis. Record your answers in your journal.

   Use the background information in the essays *Avoiding Disruptions: The Immune System* (page 246), *Self and Nonself* (page 250), and *Immune System Memory* (page 251) to help you with this task. The information in the Glossary of Immune System Components should also help.

PAGE 246   **PAGE 250**

PAGE 251

a. Why is it important for the body to distinguish material that is part of itself from nonself material? Explain what happens when the body fails to make that distinction.

b. Provide 2 examples of the immune system's nonspecific defense mechanisms. Explain how nonspecific immunity differs from specific immunity.

c. Explain why viruses are unaffected by antibiotics such as penicillin and tetracycline.

d. Describe how vaccination is a technological innovation that takes advantage of a basic property of the immune system.

2. Share your answers as part of a class discussion.

NEED TO KNOW

Glossary of Immune System Components

Antibodies are protein molecules that B-cells produce when they have been activated in response to foreign antigens, such as those present on pathogens. Antibodies have two identical binding sites, so they can bind two of the same pathogens. This forms clumps that inactivate the pathogens. Antibodies may be located on the cell surface of certain immune system cells. Or they may circulate freely in the bloodstream.

  Antigens (antibody generators) are specific molecules. They may be the proteins that are present on the surface of pathogens or foreign (nonself) molecules that are harmless. Antigens that the immune system recognizes as nonself, or foreign, can induce an immune response.

  B-cells are immune cells that are made and mature in the bone marrow. When B-cells are activated, they divide and produce two groups of cells—plasma B-cells and memory B-cells.

  Plasma B-cells produce free antibodies (identical to their surface antibodies). These antibodies circulate throughout the body to counter infections.

  Memory B-cells are long-lived cells. These cells ensure that future infections by the same pathogen will trigger a much more rapid immune response.

  Because of memory B-cells, it is less likely that a person will become ill a second time from the same pathogen. If a second illness does occur, it is usually less severe.

  B-cells can be activated in two ways. One way is by directly encountering an antigen that they bind to and process. The processed antigen presented on the B-cell surface can signal other immune cells. The second way B-cells are activated is through interaction with antigens presented on a macrophage or helper T-cell. B-cells require the presence of helper T-cells to mount a full immune response.

(continued)

SCLINKS
NSTA

Topic: immune system
Go to: www.scilinks.org
Code: human3E203

Glossary of Immune System Components (*continued*)

Complement is a group of proteins found in the blood that acts in a sequential manner, destroying pathogens. Antibody-antigen complexes can activate the first complement factors. These in turn activate other complement factors. After a series of step-wise activations, enough complement factors are activated to eliminate antigens in two ways. First, some of the activated complement proteins can attract macrophages, which engulf and destroy the antigen. Second, activated complement molecules can aggregate within the cell membrane of a pathogen. These molecules eventually form holes that cause the pathogen to burst.

Lymphocytes are the white blood cells involved in the specific immune response. They include the various types of B-cells and T-cells.

Lymphokines are molecules released by helper T-cells and other lymphocytes that help activate other cells of the immune system.

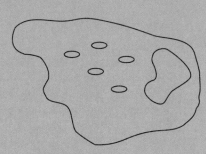

Macrophages are nonspecific scavenger cells of the immune system that are present throughout the body. They engulf the foreign material, including pathogens, that they encounter. Then they degrade it and present its antigens on their surface.

Macrophages move about in a manner similar to that of one-celled amoebas and are attracted to an infection site. If enough macrophages are present, the infection may be stopped at this stage.

Macrophages can interact with and activate other immune cells, including B-cells and helper T-cells.

Pathogens are organisms or particles such as a bacterium, fungus, or virus that have the potential to cause a disease.

T-cells are immune cells that are formed in the bone marrow but mature in the thymus. There are at least two types: helper T-cells and killer T-cells.

Helper T-cells are activated by interacting with macrophages or B-cells that have encountered foreign antigens. Activated helper T-cells secrete chemicals known as lymphokines, which activate B-cells and killer T-cells.

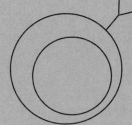

Killer T-cells carry out cell-to-cell combat. They destroy cells that are infected with a virus as well as cells that have become cancerous. These T-cells recognize virus-infected cells because the infected cells have viral antigens on their surface. These antigens are recognized as foreign. Killer T-cells must be activated by helper T-cells before they can multiply and attack virus-infected cells.

Part B Diagnosis: A Puzzle

Now you will use your knowledge about pathogens and the immune system to solve a puzzle. Use all available resources, including what you have learned in earlier activities. First, you will see how each test subject reacts to the *same, known* pathogen. Then you will use this information and similar strategies to try to determine the identity of an *unknown* pathogen.

1. Have 1 team member obtain a test subject card from the container that your teacher provides. Share the information on the card with the rest of the team.

2. Assume that your subject has just been exposed to the influenza virus. Complete the following tasks with your team. Record in your journal the evidence and inferences that support your conclusions.

   a. Generate a prognosis for your subject.

   > A *prognosis* is a prediction based on evidence and inference about whether a person will become ill, and if so, how soon he or she will recover.

   b. Discuss what effect penicillin would have if it were administered the 1st day that symptoms occur.

3. As your teacher directs, share your team's prognosis for your test subject with your classmates.

4. Try a different version of this exercise. Instead of knowing the *identity* of the pathogen and determining the prognosis, now you will know the *prognosis* of your test subject. Your job will be to identify this unknown pathogen.

   a. Assume that your test subject has been exposed to 1 of the pathogens from the list below:

      ◆ *Streptococcus* bacterium
      ◆ common cold virus
      ◆ rubella virus

   b. Obtain a scenario card that describes what happened after your test subject was exposed to the unidentified pathogen.

   c. Work with your teammates to analyze all available clues. Use this 1st level of analysis to determine the identity of your test subject's pathogen.

   > You might wish to organize your reasoning by filling in a table like the one shown in Figure 6.3. The available information may not help you determine with certainty the identity of your test subject's pathogen. However, you may be able to use this information to eliminate some pathogens from further consideration and to narrow the possibilities. Support your decision with reasons based on evidence. In your team, practice using the skill of consensus building.

5. Pick up the Copymaster *Complete Scenario Information* so that you can begin a 2nd level of analysis.

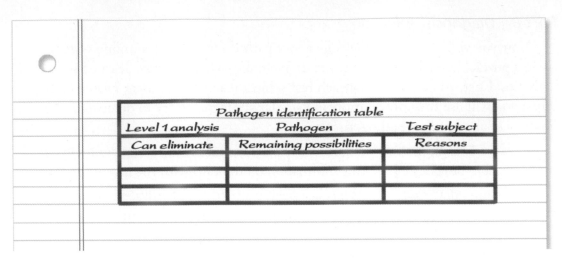

Figure 6.3 Pathogen identification table. Use a table like this to organize your thinking.

Topic: stress (management, body's response)
Go to: www.scilinks.org
Code: human3E206

6. Use this new information to try to determine your test subject's pathogen with greater certainty and to justify your refined answer. Include reasons and evidence that support your refined conclusions.

   The additional information should allow you to use a process of elimination to determine the unknown pathogen. For this 2nd level of analysis, you may wish to add rows to your table to organize your reasoning.

7. Use the table that you generated as a record of your thinking. Participate in a class discussion of the results of this exercise.

Analysis

Complete the following in your journal:

1. In Part B of this activity, you used the prognoses of different patients to determine the identity of an unknown pathogen. Explain how a combination of information from different scenarios was more helpful in identifying the pathogen than the information from a single scenario card.

2. What effect do risk factors such as fatigue, anxiety, and smoking have on a person's ability to defend himself or herself against infection and other homeostatic disruptions?

3. Assume that one healthy person had rubella as a child. A second healthy person was vaccinated against rubella as a child. And a third healthy person never encountered the rubella pathogen or vaccine as a child. If all of these people are exposed to rubella when they are 25 years old, how will their bodies respond to this pathogen?

Figure 6.4 **Humans are exposed to many risks.** Some risks are affected by behavior. Others are unavoidable despite an individual's behavior. Think about the risks involved in each of the images depicted and how those risks compare with each other.

What's the Risk?

Explain

Elaborate

Have you ever cut your finger while you were slicing vegetables or fallen and broken a bone? Your homeostasis can be disrupted at any time by accident or illness because you are exposed to many risks in your daily life (see Figure 6.4). You probably accept, consciously or subconsciously, some of these risks as unavoidable while you try to minimize other risks. In this activity, you will explore controllable and uncontrollable risks and explain what some of these risks mean in your life.

Materials   (per student)

1 prepared test tube in a rack
additional materials that your teacher supplies

Topic: AIDS
Go to: www.scilinks.org
Code: human3E207

PROCESS AND PROCEDURES

Part A   Fluid Exchange

1. Choose 1 test tube from those at the station your teacher has prepared.

2. Follow your teacher's instructions.

3. When you have completed the tests, return the test tubes to the station and wash your hands thoroughly.

4. Discuss the following questions with your classmates:

   a. What observations about the fluid exchange surprised you?

   b. Many illnesses, including the common cold, hepatitis, and AIDS, are spread by fluid transfer. What types of behaviors spread those illnesses, and what body fluids are involved?

   c. How can people completely eliminate their chances of contracting a sexually transmitted disease?

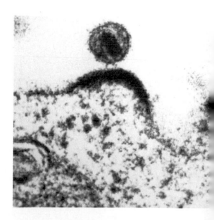

**Figure 6.5
Electron micrograph of the human immunodeficiency virus (HIV).**

PAGE 253   PAGE 255

Part B   Risk Assessment

1. Develop a list of at least 20 risks faced by humans.

   Use your personal experience and the essays *Avoiding Disruptions: Behavior, Choices, and Risk* (page 253) and *Individual Behavior Can Affect Larger Groups* (page 255) to make your list.

2. With your teammates, look through the headings on the Copymaster *Risk Assessment Data*. Decide who will be responsible for analyzing each of the following risk categories:

   - Smokeless Tobacco and Smoking
   - Alcohol
   - Cancer
   - Sex and Sexually Transmitted Diseases

3. Divide the remaining categories evenly. In your journal, record the categories you are responsible for.

4. Study the information in your risk categories.

   a. Highlight the statements in each category that provide information about whether that risk is a serious threat for teenagers only (t) or for the general population (g).

      Label each of these statements with a *t* or *g* to distinguish them.

   b. Use an asterisk (*) to mark the most shocking or surprising statistic in each of your categories.

   c. For each of your categories that are affected by behavior, record in your journal 1 or 2 behaviors that might reduce the risk.

5. Briefly discuss the results of your analysis by sharing some of the more relevant or surprising statistics with your teammates.

6. As a team, complete the following tasks in your journals:

   a. Make a list of 3 risks in our society that could be reduced if people would change their behavior.

      Select risks that would have a significant impact on the *entire population* if they were reduced.

   b. Make a list of 3 risks in our society that are unlikely to be reduced, either because the risk is not controllable or because people would be unwilling or unable to change their behavior.

   c. Next to each of the items on your lists, write a brief explanation for your choice.

7. Complete the Copymaster *Taking Risks: A Self-Evaluation* to determine your own personal risk level.

   Your teacher will collect these surveys and tally the responses for the entire class. *Your individual responses will remain anonymous.* You will use the summary data in the Analysis.

8. In your journal, write 2 paragraphs that analyze behaviors that you could change to reduce your own risk level.

Part C   Ethical Analysis

1. Draw a vertical line to divide a page of your journal in half. Use the left half to make a simplified list of the steps in ethical analysis.

   For example, you might list the 1st step as, Identify the question precisely. The essay *Ethical Analysis* (page 256) will help you with this task.

PAGE 256

2. On the right half of the page, next to the steps you have written, list the related steps in scientific inquiry as you have been learning about them in previous chapters.

3. With your team, discuss the following questions:

   a. How does the process of ethical analysis compare with the process of scientific inquiry?

   b. How similar or different are their uses?

Analysis

Respond to the following as part of a class discussion:

1. Identify several behaviors that are socially acceptable even though they have a negative impact on others. Explain why you think these behaviors are tolerated.

   Use the information in your journal and in the *Risk Assessment Data.*

2. Explain whether the behaviors you just identified in question 1 pose any ethical dilemmas. State how the behaviors pose an ethical dilemma and whether society has made any decisions that affect those behaviors.

3. Review the class data that your teacher has compiled from the survey *Taking Risks: A Self-Evaluation.*

   a. Compare the high-risk behaviors that are most common among students in your class to those of society.

      Use the list your team made in Part B, step 6.

   b. Which, if any, of the class risks match the risks that your team felt could be reduced if people changed their behavior?

   c. If any of these risks are the same, why do you think students in the class take these risks?

Health Care Proposal

Evaluate

In this activity, your team will develop a health care proposal and apply for some funds from the J. Nelson Jones Foundation. You will need to have a clear idea of what you want to do with the money and how your idea addresses society's needs. In addition, your job is to explain how your proposed program will affect the people involved. Specifically, you will need to explain what internal body systems will be

Entrepreneur to Fund Worthy Health Care Programs

Phoenix, Arizona—Samantha S. Jones, whose son, Nelson, died recently in a hiking mishap, announced Thursday that she will contribute a portion of her software company's profits to establish a health care endowment fund, the J. Nelson Jones Foundation. An annual award of $1 million, which may be split among as many as three different groups, will be given to worthy health care programs. The money will be distributed by a panel of health care experts who will evaluate proposals and choose the best. Groups interested in obtaining funds must demonstrate that their program is biologically sound, cost effective, beneficial to a significant number of people, and sensitive to ethical concerns in society and within the health care industry. When asked why she decided to fund this type of program, Jones replied, "I'd like to create a world with better health care, better education, and a better understanding of the limits of the human body so that this kind of tragedy can be prevented.

Samantha S. Jones creates health care endowment.

helped by your program. Remember, this assignment is an *evaluate*. Your proposal will be the evidence of what you have learned about homeostasis. To develop your proposal fully, gather information from different sources, such as this program, your journal, the Internet, and the library.

Your teacher will evaluate your proposal based on the criteria established by the private foundation. These are listed on a scoring rubric that your teacher will provide.

An exceptional proposal may be funded in its entirety, or as many as three proposals may be partially funded. However, if two or more proposals are submitted that deal with the same topic, only the strongest will be chosen.

PROCESS AND PROCEDURES

1. As a team, review the *Possible Health Care Options* (beginning on page 212). Choose an option that interests your team.

   Your teacher will keep track of which teams select which options.

2. As a team, develop a short description of your program. Then decide which team members will gather information for each of the following sections of the proposal:

- Homeostasis
- Risk Assessment
- Ethical Issues

Refer to the proposal guidelines in the need to know box to review the questions and issues that you must address in each of these sections. Regardless of which option your team chooses, you may use information from other options to support your position.

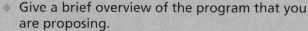

NEED TO KNOW

J. Nelson Jones Foundation Guidelines for Proposal Development

You must include each of the following sections in your proposal. Address each question or issue presented.

Short Description of Proposed Program

- Give a brief overview of the program that you are proposing.
- Is the treatment or program that you propose the only one available? (In other words, do the participants in your proposed program have any other choices?)

Homeostasis

- Which organs or regulatory system does your proposal most directly affect or influence? The biology of this system will be the focus of your proposal. What is the normal function of these organ systems in maintaining homeostasis? This should include a description of the anatomy involved, physiology, and the role of the immune system. (Many options involve several organ systems, but you need to choose only one system.)
- What is the nature of the homeostatic disruption that your proposal seeks to correct? How will this correction be accomplished?

Risk Assessment

- How common is the illness or injury that your proposal seeks to treat? For example, how many people will take advantage of your services?
- If your proposal targets a particular population, explain how this population's needs will be met.
- How does behavior affect a person's likelihood of experiencing the risks that your proposal addresses?
- Describe the controllability or uncontrollability of the risks involved. How can a person change his or her behavior to minimize the risks?

Ethical Issues

- Identify an ethical dilemma that is associated with your proposal. Describe the concerns surrounding this dilemma.
- Use the six steps of ethical analysis to analyze this dilemma. Explain your decision about what should be done.

3. Individually, gather all of the information that you will need to develop your part of the proposal. Analyze this information to identify the evidence that will support your arguments.

   Your teacher will suggest where you can find additional material. You will have about 1 week to complete this step.

4. Present the information that you have analyzed to your team. Explain how this information will strengthen the proposal.

   Practice the skill of advocating a position.

5. Work with your team. Discuss this information, and decide what specific data to include in your proposal.

   Focus on the most important and persuasive data because proposal space is limited.

6. As a team, use the steps presented in the essay *Ethical Analysis* (page 256) to conduct an ethical analysis of an issue that is involved in your chosen health care area.

   The team member who was responsible for gathering information on ethical issues should provide the team with several ethical issues to consider. Your team must choose 1 issue on which to focus the ethical analysis.

7. Write your proposal according to the proposal guidelines (page 211).

   Divide this task evenly among your teammates. Your work will be evaluated according to the criteria listed in the scoring rubric that your teacher distributed. Review those criteria carefully before you start writing.

8. Submit your proposal to your teacher.

Analysis

In your journal, write one paragraph in which you reflect on your experience of developing the proposal. Consider these questions as you write the paragraph:

 ◆ What section was hardest to write? Why do you think that was so?

 ◆ Why is ethical analysis a useful tool in science and in society?

 ◆ How can you positively or negatively influence the internal systems that are involved in maintaining homeostasis in your body?

Possible Health Care Options

Topic: alcohol and drug treatment
Go to: www.scilinks.org
Code: human3E212

❖ Option 1 Alcohol and Drug Treatment Program

 ◆ In the United States, 9 months of treatment for a drug-addicted mother costs approximately 1/6 what it costs to provide medical care for a drug-exposed baby for 20 days.

- Most people suffering from alcohol or drug abuse who cannot afford private treatment in hospitals receive their care as outpatients at clinics. Many receive no treatment at all. Because the addiction is so strong, many of these people eventually turn to crime to obtain the money that they need to pay for more alcohol or drugs.

- One federally funded treatment facility in a city of 300,000 serves 700 heroin addicts of all age-groups per month. A staff of 18 full-time counselors and 17 part-time employees implement a program designed to eliminate chemical dependency. This program provides heroin addicts with daily doses of methadone, a chemical narcotic that minimizes the craving for heroin and helps the addicts "stay clean." There is no limit to how long an addict can participate in this program. Approximately 25–40 percent of those on methadone stay on it for a year or more. Many find it extremely difficult to quit the drug habit completely. About 30 percent, however, are able to find work and at least partially support themselves. Methadone treatment dramatically reduces crime by addicts. (Statistics show that crime dropped from 237 crime days per person per year before treatment to 69 crime days per person per year after 4 months of treatment.) Methadone treatment also reduces HIV infection rates (from 39 percent among addicts not in treatment to 18 percent among addicts in treatment for 3 years).

Topic: heart disease
Go to: www.scilinks.org
Code: human3E213a

❖ **Option 2 Heart Disease Prevention and Treatment**

- The dietary habits of Americans are substantially different from those of other countries. This difference has contributed to the prevalence of heart disease in the United States. For instance, the typical diet in Japan contains far less cholesterol and saturated fat than the typical American diet. Consequently, a 50-year-old Japanese man has an average blood cholesterol level of 180 mg/dL. Compare that with an average of 245 mg/dL for a 50-year-old American man.

- Fifty-five percent of Americans in the United States are overweight or obese.

- After an individual has a heart attack, there is at least a 50 percent chance that the individual will die in less than 5 years unless the individual takes preventive measures.

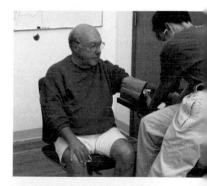

Topic: sexually transmitted diseases
Go to: www.scilinks.org
Code: human3E213b

❖ **Option 3 Education Programs Focusing on the Prevention of AIDS and Other Sexually Transmitted Diseases (STDs)**

- Twenty-three percent of all 14-year-olds and 30 percent of all 15-year-olds have engaged in sexual intercourse.

- Fifty-eight percent of 9–12th-grade students reported using a condom the *last time they had sexual intercourse.* Twenty-seven percent of 9–12th-grade students report that they are currently abstinent.

- Approximately 1 in 4 teenagers who are sexually active get an STD every year. However, 68 percent of sexually active teens do not consider themselves to be at risk.

- Antiretroviral drugs (sometimes called the "AIDS cocktail") given to HIV-positive individuals soon after infection helps to suppress the development of full-blown AIDS and the disabling effects of the illness.

- People without health insurance who are HIV-positive cannot receive payment for antiretroviral drugs through Medicaid (2001).

- Medicaid covers medical services for approximately 55 percent of all adults living with AIDS and up to 90 percent of all children living with AIDS. In 2003, federal and state Medicaid programs to treat HIV and AIDS were estimated to cost $8.5 billion.

- For individuals who qualify, Medicaid covers the costs for approved prescription drugs. These include drugs that help prevent opportunistic infections and those that treat AIDS, such as protease inhibitors.

- For every dollar spent notifying sex partners of HIV-positive patients, at least $11 is saved in annual medical care costs for each case of HIV that is prevented.

Topic: hospital equipment and procedures
Go to: www.scilinks.org
Code: human3E214

❖ **Option 4 Hospital Equipment and Procedures** (National Statistics)

- Dialysis, a procedure that substitutes for the normal functioning of the kidneys, costs $16,000–$18,000 for a typical 4- to 7-day hospital stay for kidney failure.

- A kidney transplant, which eliminates the need for dialysis, costs approximately $69,000.

- An electrocardiograph (ECG), an instrument used to monitor and diagnose heart problems, costs approximately $12,000.

- Pacemaker surgery, a procedure performed on patients who suffer from certain forms of heart disease, costs approximately $28,500.

- Angioplasty, a surgical procedure to open arteries in the heart that are blocked by cholesterol and plaque buildup, costs approximately $13,000.

- An appendectomy, the removal of a diseased appendix, typically requires a 3-day hospital stay and costs approximately $6,000.

- Alcohol and drug rehabilitation and detoxification costs approximately $5,000.

- A mastectomy, the removal of a cancerous breast, costs approximately $9,000.

- Arthroscopy, a surgical procedure to repair an injured joint, costs approximately $11,000.

- Magnetic Resonance Imaging, or MRI, is a technique in which strong magnetic fields generate a picture of the inside of the body (similar to an X-ray). Physicians use it to help them locate tumors in cancer patients (about $1,000 per use) or injuries and obstructions in people with difficult-to-diagnose illnesses ($950 per use).

- A tonsillectomy, the removal of tonsils and adenoids, costs approximately $6,000.

- Radiation therapy often is used to reduce the size and spread of malignant tumors. This therapy can be used in place of or in addition to surgery. It is frequently necessary if the patient is to have a chance of survival. Average cost for therapeutic radiology (to treat lung cancer, for example) is $13,000.

❖ **Option 5 Prenatal Care**   (National Averages)

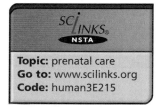

Topic: prenatal care
Go to: www.scilinks.org
Code: human3E215

- Prenatal care for a pregnant woman for 9 months (not including delivery) averages $750.

- For a very low-birthweight baby, each day in the intensive care unit costs from $1,000 to $2,500. Low birthweight is often due to prematurity, which may be a consequence of poor prenatal care. The lifetime medical costs for 1 premature baby average $500,000.

- The cost of a normal delivery is approximately $6,400.

- The cost for a complicated birth ranges from $20,000 to $400,000.

- Some public health care clinics have been established with good success for improving prenatal care. A public health care clinic can provide prenatal care for women, including education about nutrition, exercise, and avoidance of harmful behaviors. Such a clinic also could provide regular visits by nurses and handle uncomplicated deliveries. These programs are successful at producing full-term, normal-birthweight babies (greater than 5 lbs 8 oz). In fact, with a low birthrate incidence of only 7 percent, they produce a higher percentage of normal-birthweight babies than privately funded health care facilities that do not offer a prenatal care program.

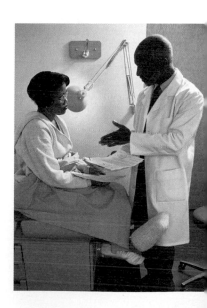

❖ Option 6 Quit Smoking Program

◆ Cigarettes kill more Americans than do AIDS, alcohol, car accidents, murders, suicides, drugs, and fires combined (about 430,000 people per year). This makes tobacco the number 1 cause of death and disease in the United States.

◆ Fourteen percent of all 10th-graders and 20 percent of all 12th-graders report smoking cigarettes daily in the year 2000.

◆ The Centers for Disease Control and Prevention estimate that nationwide, medical care costs attributable to smoking (or smoking-related disease) are more that $50 billion annually. They also estimate that the value of lost earnings and loss of productivity to be at least another $47 billion a year.

◆ Every dollar that is spent on smoking-cessation programs that are successful saves $21 during a working lifetime (defined as ages 20 to 64).

❖ Option 7 Vaccine Programs

◆ Nearly everyone in the United States got measles before measles immunization was available. At that time, there were approximately 3–4 million cases of measles each year. Between 1953 and 1962, an average of 450 people per year died from measles.

◆ In industrialized countries, up to 20 percent of people with measles are hospitalized. Seven to 9 percent suffer from complications such as pneumonia, diarrhea, or ear infections. It is estimated that as many as 1 of every 1,000 people with measles will die.

◆ Measles is one of the most infectious diseases in the world and is frequently imported into the United States. More than 90 percent of people who are not immune will get measles if they are exposed to the virus.

◆ The measles-mumps-rubella vaccine led to a tremendous decline in the occurrences of the diseases (see data below). According to the National Immunization Survey, approximately 78 percent of all children age 19–35 months had received 4 doses of the combined series vaccine. The target vaccination rate set by Health People 2000 is 90 percent.

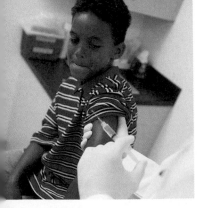

Disease	Cases in U.S. (year)	U.S. Cases (2001)	% Change
Measles	319,124 (1950)	116	−99.97
Mumps	104,953 (1970)	266	−99.75
Poliomyelitis	33,300 (1950)	0	−100.00

- Hepatitis B is an infection of the liver. It is caused by a virus found in the blood, semen, menstrual blood, and other body fluids of a person with hepatitis B. Five to 10 percent of adults who catch hepatitis B become "carriers" for the rest of their lives and can pass the virus on to others. About half of all adults who become infected with hepatitis B report never having felt sick at all. Symptoms, if present, are flulike.

- Hepatitis B infects more than 200,000 people each year and kills more than 5,000. The virus can be spread during sex, by sharing needles, or by being stuck with a dirty needle or tools used for tattooing or piercing. It can also be spread by getting blood or other infected fluids in the mouth, eyes, or onto broken skin. The virus also can be passed from mother to baby during birth.

- Carriers of hepatitis B are at risk of liver problems, like cancer or cirrhosis.

- Hepatitis B is 100 times easier to catch than the virus that causes AIDS. There is no cure for hepatitis B, but a vaccination can prevent it.

❖ Option 8 Programs for Women, Infants, and Children

Topic: women, infants, and children
Go to: www.scilinks.org
Code: human3E217

- Inadequate nutrition during childhood affects brain development and reduces a child's ability to learn.

- Many U.S. counties have programs that try to prevent malnutrition in pregnant or nursing women and children under age 5. These programs provide food vouchers that families can redeem for wholesome foods such as formula, baby food, milk, cheese, eggs, cereal, dry beans, peanut butter, and tuna fish.

- In 2002, an average of 19 million people received food stamps in the United States.

- Currently, the United States has medical costs of approximately $60 billion per year associated with osteoporosis. Teenage girls and adult women only consume 2/3 of the calcium that is recommended.

- Fifty percent of nutrition and health program participants adopt 1 or more habits that improve the development of healthy eating behaviors by their children.

Compartments

How do you feel on a very cold day? If it is wet and windy outside, you might notice a cold sensation on your face. Your fingers and toes may become chilled or even a little numb. Yet, if you pick up some snow and hold it in your bare hands, the snow melts. Your body is warmer than its snowy surroundings, even though your fingers and toes feel cold.

By contrast, what happens to your body on a very hot day? While you may feel hot and sweaty, your internal temperature does not vary much. In fact, if you compared your body's temperature under both the snowy and hot conditions, you would discover that your body maintains a fairly constant internal temperature.

How is it possible for your body to maintain an internal temperature that is very different from the external temperature? Part of the reason is that your body is a compartment with an internal environment that is kept separate from the external environment. You might think of all organisms as containers that hold specialized contents. Containers have walls, or external boundaries. These boundaries hold the contents and separate them from the surroundings. Think about how the wall of the Thermos bottle in Figure E4.1 helps to keep a hot beverage warm on a cold day.

Organisms, like containers, have external boundaries. In humans, the skin separates the inside of the body from the outside environment. In single-celled organisms, the cell membrane (and cell wall, if there is one) forms the boundary between the inside and outside environments. By forming a compartment, skin and cell membranes create conditions within the organism that may vary greatly from those on the outside.

Specific internal conditions must be met for life processes to take place in organisms. Temperature, water, minerals, nutrients, oxygen, pH levels, and other balances must be maintained. For example, marine fish are surrounded by water. Yet the water inside their bodies must be kept separate from the water that surrounds them. Why? Because seawater is much saltier than the fluids inside their bodies. The reverse is true of freshwater fish. As you might expect, it is partly a fish's waterproof skin that allows the difference in salt levels to exist and allows fish to live.

Figure E4.1 What do this sports fan and her Thermos bottle have in common? How are they different?

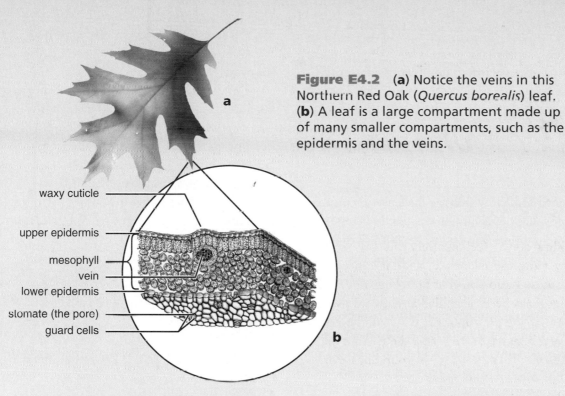

Figure E4.2 (a) Notice the veins in this Northern Red Oak (*Quercus borealis*) leaf. (b) A leaf is a large compartment made up of many smaller compartments, such as the epidermis and the veins.

a

waxy cuticle

upper epidermis

mesophyll

vein

lower epidermis

stomate (the pore)

guard cells

b

Complex organisms also may contain many smaller compartments, each with its own internal environment. Just as your skin separates the environment inside your body from the environment outside, the wall of your stomach separates the environment inside your stomach from the environment of the rest of your abdomen.

The same is true of plants. A waxy substance covers most leaves and protects the living tissue within (see Figure E4.2a). Another form of compartmentalization can be seen in the network of veins that is embedded within the leaf (see Figure E4.2b). These veins form separate compartments that connect to other tubular compartments in the stem. As Figure E4.2b shows, microscopic examination reveals even smaller compartments.

Like humans and plants, most other complex organisms also have several levels of compartments. At the microscopic level, the basic unit of life is the cell. A cell is a compartment whose boundary is formed by one or more membranes. **Prokaryotic** organisms consist of only one compartment, the cell itself. **Eukaryotic** organisms, even those whose bodies also consist of only one cell, contain smaller compartments. Many of these smaller compartments, as illustrated in Figure E4.3, can only be seen with the aid of an electron microscope. Foremost among such subcellular compartments is the **nucleus**, which contains **DNA**. DNA is the genetic code for the organism.

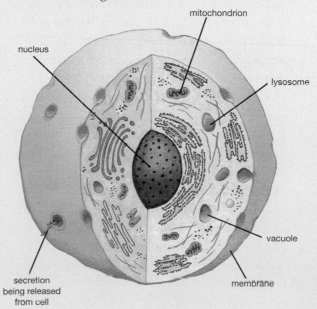

mitochondrion

nucleus

lysosome

vacuole

secretion being released from cell

membrane

Figure E4.3 The eukaryotic cell includes many internal compartments.

EXPLORING BIOLOGY

What is the advantage of having so many compartments in living systems? Remember that all organisms require specific internal conditions for life processes to occur. The presence of many compartments within one cell or one organism allows for the presence of many different internal environments. These environments provide the conditions that are required for specialized functions. The environment within the nucleus, for example, provides the conditions required for DNA to perform its functions. In contrast, the environment within the **lysosome** (see Figure E4.3) can kill invading bacteria and viruses. The environment in a human stomach is another example of a specialized environment. The pH of the stomach contents is much lower (more acidic) than the pH in the rest of the body. This difference allows digestion to occur.

What would happen if conditions within compartments were to undergo a significant, lasting change? As you will see in Chapter 6, changes beyond certain rather narrow limits can be dangerous to the organism. These changes disrupt the normal processes of life.

We call such disruptions injuries or illnesses. Sometimes, internal balance can be disrupted so severely that the organism dies.

Think back for a moment to the sports fan and her Thermos pictured in Figure E4.1. The caption asks how the woman and her Thermos are similar. Both the woman and her Thermos are containers, or compartments, with outside boundaries. These boundaries allow the contents (in this case, their temperatures) to be different from their environments.

The caption also asked how the woman and her Thermos are different. Consider what will happen to the temperature of the beverage in the Thermos over time? In contrast, what prediction can you make about the temperature of the woman's body? Clearly, there is more to maintaining internal conditions than just the presence of a boundary.

In this chapter and the next, you will examine in detail how living systems respond to this challenge. And the next time you melt a snowball by gripping it tightly in your bare hand, perhaps you will think about your body as a biological compartment. ◆

Membranes

In some ways, a cell is like a carton of milk. The membrane around a cell is like the walls of the carton. The membrane forms a boundary that separates the *inside* of the cell from the *outside*. Like a carton of milk, a cell contains a fluid substance with a variety of molecules in it.

The cell membrane is more complicated, however, than the walls of a milk carton. The cell membrane only lets *some* things pass through it. To act as an effective boundary, the membrane must prevent molecules from moving freely into or out of the cell. A membrane must be **impermeable** to most substances. In other words, the membrane must prevent most substances from being able to pass in or out of the compartment. Yet,

molecules that the cell needs for its activities must be able to enter through the membrane. Because cell membranes are only **permeable** to certain molecules, they are said to be **selectively permeable**. A membrane's selective permeability (its ability to regulate the passage of molecules) depends on the structure of the membrane.

As Figure E4.4 shows, a typical cell membrane is made up primarily of fat (lipid) molecules. The fat molecules are not locked rigidly in place. They drift randomly in the plane of the membrane. An important property of lipid molecules is that they do not mix well with water. In the cell membrane, the fat (lipid) molecules are arranged into two layers (called the **lipid bilayer**). The parts of the fat molecules that have the highest tendency to interact with water are oriented toward the outside and inside of the cell. The parts of the fat molecules with the lowest tendency to interact with water are oriented toward the interior of the membrane. The interior part of the membrane prevents molecules that are water soluble from passing easily through it. By contrast, fat-soluble molecules move through it with ease. Even though water molecules are not fat soluble, they can move through the membrane. This is because they are very small and their electrical charges are very slight.

Look at Figure E4.4. Notice that the membrane contains many protein molecules positioned among the fat molecules. **Proteins** are large molecules made up of many small molecules (called amino acids). These amino acids are linked together to form a long, folded chain. Some of these protein molecules, particularly those on the outer surface of the membrane, act as receptors. **Receptors** bind specifically to molecules such as hormones. The hormones act as chemical messengers. By binding to their receptors, hormones trigger the cell to respond to some body condition in an appropriate way.

In addition to receptor proteins, cell membranes contain many other proteins. These proteins allow specific molecules to move into and out of the cell. In other words, some cell membrane proteins allow the membrane to be *selectively permeable*. For example, some proteins form channels through which glucose and other sugars move. Molecules like these are too big to pass directly through the lipid bilayer part of the membrane. The only way that they can enter the cell is through a specific protein channel.

Other proteins form channels through which **ions** (molecules that have an electrical charge) may pass. For example, dissolve table salt, NaCl, in water. It forms the ions Na^+ and Cl^-. Ions like these are relatively small. So they cannot pass directly through the lipid bilayer because the fat molecules repel charged molecules. Cell membranes are selectively permeable. This is because the structure of the membrane determines the specific molecules that are able to cross into and out of the cell.

Thus, biological membranes are much more complex than the walls of an insulated beverage container. They also perform a far more complex and important role in regulating internal conditions. ◆

Figure E4.4 Diagram of a section of the lipid bilayer of a cell membrane. Lipids are oriented in such a way that the interior of the membrane repels water. Protein molecules may span the membrane or be exposed on the inner or outer surface. What structures facilitate selective permeability?

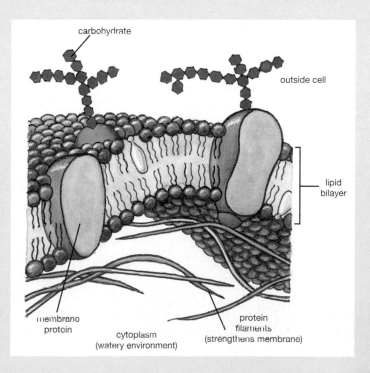

carbohydrate

outside cell

lipid bilayer

membrane protein

cytoplasm (watery environment)

protein filaments (strengthens membrane)

Molecular Movement

Someone in the next room opens the oven and takes out a pan of hot brownies. Almost immediately, your mouth starts to water as you smell the chocolate. How did the odor get to your nose? Molecules from the chocolate were released by heat and traveled through the air. The protein receptors on cells in your nose detected these chocolate molecules.

This is an example of molecular movement. Molecules disperse in random directions. But overall, they tend to spread from an area where they are more concentrated to an area where they are less concentrated. This dispersion continues until the concentration of molecules is the same everywhere (see Figure E4.5). This type of molecular movement is called **diffusion**.

Say you could sample the concentration at various points from the most concentrated area to the least concentrated area, You would find that the concentration decreases gradually. This gradual decrease forms a distribution known as the **concentration gradient**. Because molecules diffuse from areas of higher concentration to areas of lower concentration, they are said to move *down* the concentration gradient.

Diffusion occurs because the universe, and all the molecules in it, drifts into a less ordered state unless some energy input keeps it orderly. Think, for example, about your room. It takes your energy to maintain order—to keep your clothes off the floor, your CDs in one place, and your papers on the desk. Without a continual input of energy, the organization of your room soon disintegrates and begins to look like the room in Figure E4.6. Organisms use energy continuously to maintain their own order and unique internal environment.

The diffusion of molecules from higher to lower concentration occurs in solutions as well as in the air. For example, a solute, such as table salt (NaCl), is dissolved in a solvent, such as water. It undergoes diffusion until it is uniformly distributed. The movement of these salt molecules across a biological membrane depends in part on the relative concentration of the solute in the cell's internal and external environment. The movement also depends on special membrane proteins that act as carriers or channels.

Figure E4.6   Entropy, or the tendency toward disorder, in a system.   What evidence of entropy do you see in this drawing? What is needed to put this room into order?

One type of diffusion is called osmosis. **Osmosis** is the movement of water from an area of greater concentration to an area of lesser concentration. Osmosis can result in the buildup of significant pressure inside a membrane-enclosed compartment. For example, "pure" water has a high concentration of water (100 percent). A 10 percent salt solution contains only 90 percent water. Thus, water will move into a compartment containing a salt solution. When the initial concentration of water is greater outside a cell than inside,

water rushes into the cell. In that way, osmosis can result in such a buildup of pressure inside the cell that the cell swells and bursts. Conversely, if the concentration of water is greater inside than outside a cell, water leaks out and the cell shrinks. Figure E4.7 shows a range of cell responses in both animal and plant cells.

Osmotic pressure plays a special role in plant cells because of their rigid cell walls. Plant cells have an internal water-filled compartment known as a **vacuole**. The water in a vacuole exerts osmotic pressure on a cell's

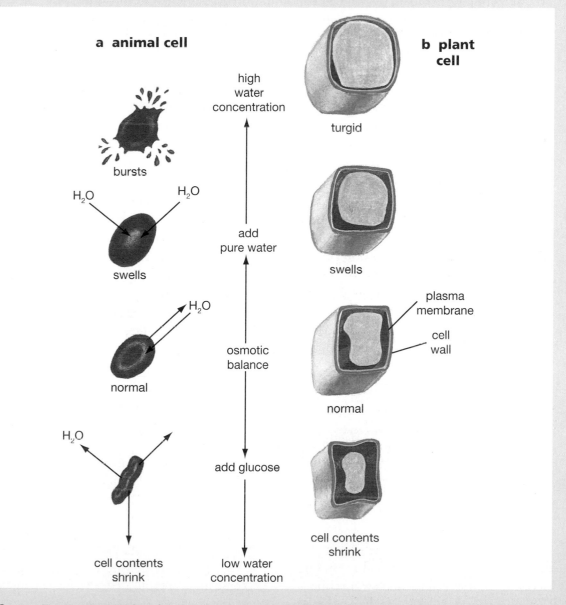

Figure E4.7 Osmosis. (a) An animal cell (red blood cell) in different solutions (b) A plant cell in different solutions What conditions make a cell shrink? What conditions make it burst?

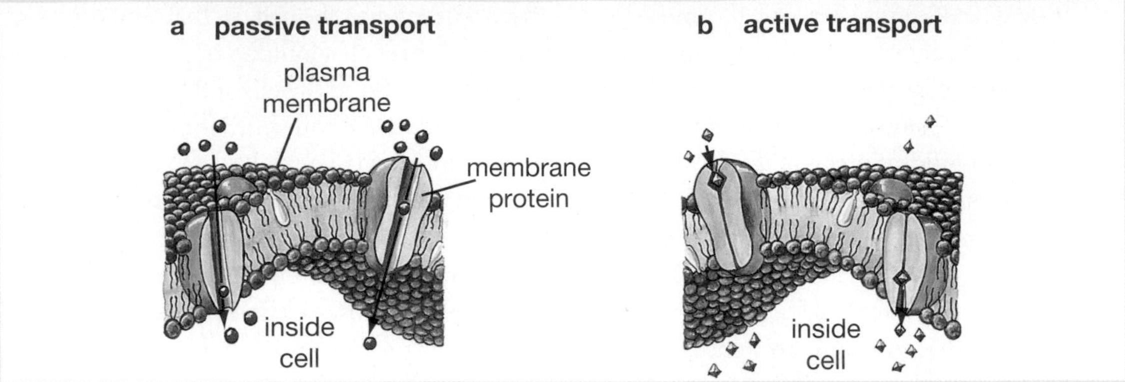

a   passive transport

plasma
membrane

membrane
protein

inside
cell

b   active transport

inside
cell

Figure E4.8   Passive and active transport. (**a**) In **passive transport**, substances move across membrane proteins, down their concentration gradient. (**b**) **Active transport** uses energy and membrane proteins to move substances against their concentration gradient. Active transport also can move substances with their concentration gradient.

contents. It presses the cell membrane tightly against the cell wall. This pressure gives plant structures, such as leaves, their firmness. What do you think is happening in a vacuole when a leaf wilts?

Diffusion, including osmosis, accounts for much of the exchange of materials between the internal and external environments of individual cells. But cell membranes are only *selectively* permeable. Only certain molecules can diffuse freely through them. Large molecules or molecules with electrical charges cannot cross lipid membranes efficiently by diffusion alone. However, as Figure E4.8 illustrates, membrane proteins have methods of transporting these molecules through membranes.

In **passive transport**, proteins move substances *down* their concentration gradient, either into or out of the cell. Cellular energy is not required. Each type of protein transports only specific substances. Cells use passive transport to move many essential ions.

In **active transport**, cells use energy to move substances with the help of transport proteins. Through active transport, substances move across a membrane against, or *up*, the concentration gradient. For example, the soil around a plant may contain low amounts of elements necessary for the plant's growth. Ordinary diffusion would not provide the plant with enough of these elements. By means of active transport, however, the plant's root cells accumulate these elements in relatively high amounts. This process is like collecting all of the clothes scattered about a room and placing them in a laundry basket. Once inside the plant, the elements are transported to all parts of the plant. ◆

Making Exchanges throughout the Body

Imagine you are spending the day in a one-room studio apartment. You have easy, direct access to all that you need. Now imagine spending the day in a 20-story office building. Your office is on the 15th floor, the restrooms are on the 10th floor, and the cafeteria is on the third floor. The same daily tasks that you perform in the studio apartment suddenly become more complicated because you do not have direct access to all that you need. You require more complex systems (for example, an elevator and hallways) to help you move from place to place and complete your daily tasks.

In a similar way, single-celled organisms such as bacteria have their entire living compartment directly in contact with the environment that surrounds them. For multicellular organisms, however, life is more complicated.

Most of the cells in humans and other multicellular organisms are buried deep inside their bodies. These cells are not in contact with the external environment from which they must obtain oxygen and food and into which they must release wastes. Despite this lack of contact with the external environment, cells must maintain levels of oxygen and nutrients continuously and remove waste products to survive. Survival depends on the body's ability to create an acceptable set of internal conditions in the face of an external environment that is constantly changing.

Maintaining these internal conditions requires the interaction of interconnected organ systems. An **organ system** is a group of organs that works together to perform a common function. Some are delivery systems. These carry vital materials to different parts of the body. Others are regulators of conditions. These respond to signals from various parts of the body.

Delivery systems include the gas exchange system, circulatory system, and urinary system. The gas exchange system is a delivery system that provides air to the lungs. Here oxygen is exchanged for carbon dioxide and delivered to the bloodstream. The circulatory system transports oxygen, nutrients, and other substances to cells throughout the body. It also carries waste products such as carbon dioxide from the cells. The urinary system eliminates excess water, salts, and wastes that contain nitrogen. The activity of all of these systems depends on the exchange of materials across boundaries. Many of these exchanges occur by the processes that move molecules—diffusion, osmosis, and passive and active transport. These processes depend on sensitive communication between tissues and organs, between the internal and external environments, and between the brain and the rest of the body.

Let's look closely at one delivery system. The circulatory system is essential for maintaining appropriate internal conditions. It is successful because it forms an extensive network that distributes materials throughout the body. At the center of this network is the heart. The heart is a muscular organ that pumps blood through the entire circulatory system. Branching out from the heart is a series of blood vessels. These blood vessels are interconnected tubes that carry blood and help control its flow. The blood itself is a complex mixture. It is made up of water, dissolved gases, nutrients, cells, large molecules, such as proteins, and a variety of other substances. Blood moves away from the heart through arteries. Blood returns to the heart through veins. Both types of vessels branch repeatedly to form hundreds of millions of smaller vessels. These are connected to each other by even smaller vessels called arterioles, capillaries, and venules. Arterioles branch out from arteries and carry blood to the capillaries. Capillaries are the smallest branches. In fact, the human body has more than 10 billion capillaries. These thin-walled vessels are barely as wide as the diameter of one cell. From the capillaries, blood flows into slightly larger venules. From the venules, blood flows into veins. Figure E4.9 illustrates the human circulatory system.

The network of capillaries in the body is extensive. Very few living cells lie farther than 0.01 millimeters (0.0005 inches) from a capillary. It is here, across the thin capillary walls, that the actual exchange of materials between the blood and the body's cells occurs. As blood passes through a typical capillary, oxygen, glucose, and other substances move out into the fluids that surround the cells. These substances then move from the fluids into the cells. Simultaneously, carbon dioxide and other wastes enter the blood.

The circulatory system is an example of an intricate system of exchange in the human body. ◆

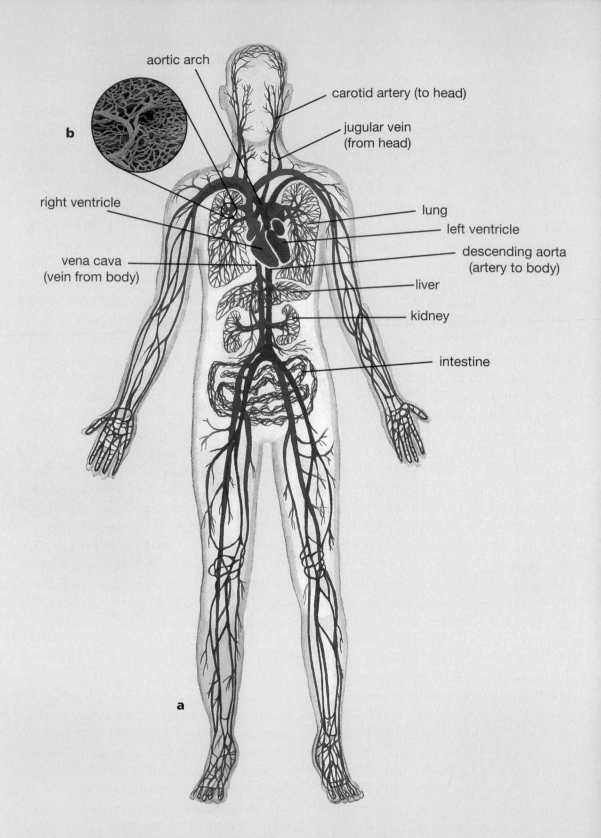

aortic arch

carotid artery (to head)

jugular vein
(from head)

b

right ventricle

lung

left ventricle

vena cava
(vein from body)

descending aorta
(artery to body)

liver

kidney

intestine

a

**Figure E4.9 Human circulatory system.   (a) Some of the components of the
human circulatory system** Blood vessels branch repeatedly to form smaller and smaller
vessels, eventually ending in capillaries. **(b) Colored electron micrograph of a capillary
bed** (photographed at 100×) Very fine capillaries (pink) branch off blood vessels (gray).

Disposing of Wastes

If you have ever taken out the trash, you have a good idea of how much waste people produce each day. The body produces waste also. For one thing, the body does not use all of the matter that it takes in. In addition, biological processes that are going on inside produce waste materials. These wastes become toxic if they build up in the body.

Wastes are disposed of in a variety of ways. As cells produce waste products, they deposit them in the bloodstream. The bloodstream carries away the wastes from cells. One waste product, carbon dioxide, is carried back to the lungs and eliminated by exhaling. Some excess salts and other waste products are eliminated through perspiration. Metabolic wastes—chemical wastes produced by biological processes—are eliminated primarily by the urinary system.

Have you ever smelled the pungent odor of a glass cleaner? This odor comes from ammonia. Ammonia is a toxic substance produced by cells as waste when proteins are broken down. If ammonia accumulates in the blood and tissues, it causes life-threatening illness. Humans, however, possess an organ system that efficiently removes ammonia and other toxins. As ammonia is formed, the liver immediately converts it to urea, a relatively nontoxic substance. The kidneys then remove urea by including it in the urine excreted from the body. The urinary system performs this essential function continuously. It also carries out other important roles, such as regulating blood pressure and adjusting fluid volumes.

The urinary system is one of the body's regulatory systems that operates automatically. The regulatory organs of the urinary system are the two kidneys, which are illustrated in Figure E4.10. The kidneys adjust the contents of the blood. First, the kidney filters the blood to remove urea and other waste substances. Then, the kidney restores the correct balance of water, salts, and other key compounds to the blood. Each kidney is connected to the bladder by tubes called **ureters**. The **bladder** is a sac that holds the waste-containing urine until it is released from the body.

The kidneys are complex, active organs. Each kidney consists of more than 1 million microscopic nephrons. **Nephrons** are long, coiled tubes that act as filtering units

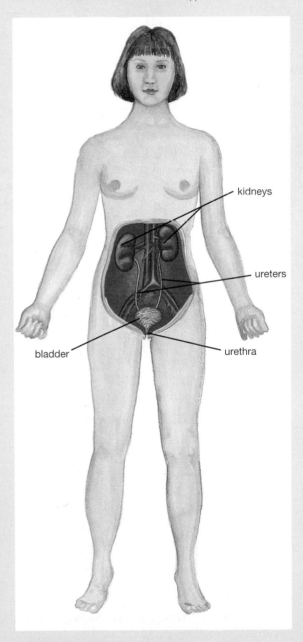

Figure E4.10 The human urinary system.

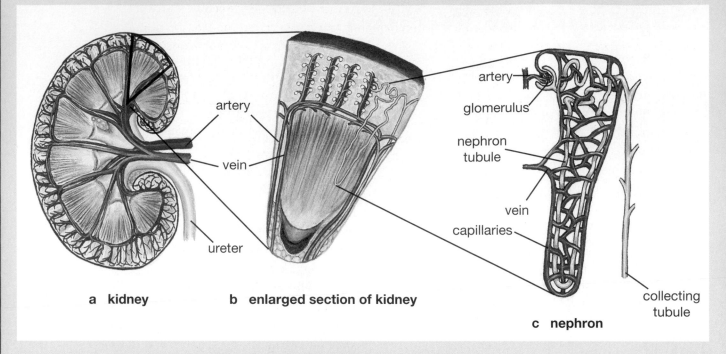

artery

vein

ureter

a kidney

b enlarged section of kidney

artery

glomerulus

nephron
tubule

vein

capillaries

collecting
tubule

c nephron

Figure E4.11 **(a) A section through the human kidney (b) An enlarged view of a section of a kidney (c) An enlarged view of one nephron with its surrounding capillaries.** The urine leaving the collecting tubule eventually enters the bladder, where it is stored temporarily.

(see Figure E4.11). One end of the nephron forms a capsule. This capsule surrounds a specialized capillary bed that is condensed into the shape of a knot. This capillary bed, called a **glomerulus**, is part of the blood vessel network. The glomerulus differs from other capillary beds because it is supplied by an arteriole and drained by another arteriole, rather than by a venule. The arteriole that drains the glomerulus transports the blood to a second capillary bed that surrounds the rest of the nephron. This second capillary bed returns the blood to the venous side of the body's circulatory system for its continued circuit back to the heart. It is in and around these two capillary beds and their nephrons that the kidney cleans and regulates the composition of the blood.

The kidneys are small compared with other organs. Together they weigh only about 300 grams, or 10 ounces. However, the kidneys and their supply of arteries normally carry almost 20 percent of the heart's output of blood at any time. This amount can vary,

depending on circumstances such as the amount of fluids being consumed. As it varies, so does the rate of urine production.

Look at Figure E4.11. As you read the description of how the kidney functions, try to trace what happens. Begin by finding the three major tubes of the kidney: the artery, vein, and ureter. Blood enters the kidney through the renal artery. The renal vein carries blood out of the kidney. Remember that smaller vessels called arterioles, capillaries, and venules connect arteries and veins to each other.

Not all of the substances in the blood entering the kidney leave through the renal vein, however. Some substances are removed from the blood and become urine. Urine collects in the nephrons in the kidney. The nephrons interact with the capillary beds to clean the blood and regulate its composition. The cleaning and regulation of blood composition occurs in three phases along the nephron. These phases are called filtration, reabsorption, and secretion.

Filtration takes place in the glomerulus. This specialized structure carries blood under much higher pressure than other capillary beds. Together the two kidneys filter as much as 125 milliliters (about one-half cup) of plasma *every minute*. If that entire amount were excreted, the results would be severe. To offset this fluid loss, you would have to drink 7.74 liters (2 gallons) of liquids *every hour*. That's 180 liters (48 gallons) *every day*! You would spend all your time drinking and urinating.

Shortly after the kidneys filter these fluids, however, 99 percent of the fluid is reabsorbed and returned to the blood. **Reabsorption** takes place between the nephron tubule and the second capillary bed. Reabsorption involves the active transport of sodium ions, sugar, vitamins, and other nutrients from the filtrate back into the capillary blood. The movement of ions creates an osmotic pressure that moves water in the same direction. The rate of water movement depends on internal conditions in the body. If blood volume is low (perhaps you just ran a few laps around the stadium), water is reabsorbed very efficiently back into the bloodstream. If, in contrast, blood volume is high (perhaps you just drank several glasses of water), then much of the extra water passes quickly into the nephron tubule to be excreted in urine.

In some cases, the kidneys' job of maintaining water balance is inhibited. Certain substances interfere with appropriate kidney responses. They cause the body to retain or dispose of too much water. A **diuretic** is a substance that causes the kidneys to respond by allowing excessive water loss. A diuretic increases urine production by increasing filtration and decreasing reabsorption. Caffeine is a common diuretic. For example, energy drinks contain large amounts of caffeine because it is also a stimulant. A stimulant increases alertness. However, the rate of urine production is directly related to water and chemical balance in the body. A diuretic artificially changes the chemical balance.

The third phase of kidney function is **secretion**. Secretion provides a way for the body to maintain pH balance. pH balance is achieved through the controlled secretion of positive ions and the reabsorption of negative ions by the cells that line the interior of the nephron tubule. These processes allow precise adjustments in the composition of blood and removal of waste products. Filtration, reabsorption, and secretion are of vital importance. Untreated kidney failure rapidly leads to death because it quickly results in severe disruption to water and waste product balance. ◆

Homeostasis

Have you ever wondered why you don't faint every time you stand up? Does it surprise you that even if you skip lunch you still can walk and talk? Explanations of those occurrences are quite complex. For instance, the cells in your brain all are exceedingly sensitive to tiny changes in the levels of oxygen and sugar. Even small decreases in those critical substances can cause fainting. Your blood pressure automatically rises when you stand up in order to maintain adequate oxygen flow to your brain. Likewise, you can skip lunch because a declining level of sugar in your bloodstream triggers your liver to release sugar held in storage.

Your body must continuously make adjustments to create and maintain an environment for your brain to function. These adjustments are made *automatically*. They assure that conditions within your body remain within rather narrowly defined limits. We call this condition of balance **homeostasis** (see Figure E5.1).

Humans are not the only organisms that maintain homeostasis. In fact, homeostasis is a fundamental characteristic of *all* living

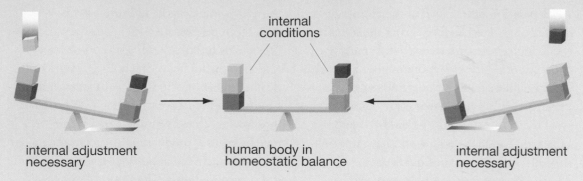

internal conditions

internal adjustment necessary

human body in homeostatic balance

internal adjustment necessary

Figure E5.1 Homeostasis. The human body is maintained in a state in which the internal conditions are balanced. When the balance is disturbed, the body adjusts its internal conditions to restore balance.

systems. In animals, internal organs that are similar in function to those in humans help to maintain homeostasis. In plants, specialized structures, such as those illustrated in Figure E5.2, enable plants to maintain balance.

In simpler organisms, such as the single-celled amoeba, simpler mechanisms maintain homeostasis. In amoebas, the removal of toxic waste happens without complicated internal organs and with few specialized structures. Instead, basic processes such as diffusion and osmosis remove waste. Although organisms

use different mechanisms to remove wastes and maintain balance, all organisms depend on maintaining homeostasis. Maintaining balance means life. Losing homeostatic balance for an extended period of time means death.

To maintain homeostasis, two things are required. First, an organism must be able to *sense* when changes have taken place in the external and internal environment. Second, it must be able to *respond* with appropriate adjustments. For example, humans can monitor **stimuli**, or external signals such as cold, because we have sensory neurons in our skin that allow us to feel the outside temperature. Once the message "cold" is received in the brain, our body can respond by changing blood flow. Our heart rate may increase. Certain blood vessels may constrict. This change is *involuntary*, or automatic. We do not consciously control this physiological process. In other words, we do not decide what the body should do. The body attempts to keep the brain, heart, and liver at a nearly constant temperature even if that means sacrificing fingers and toes.

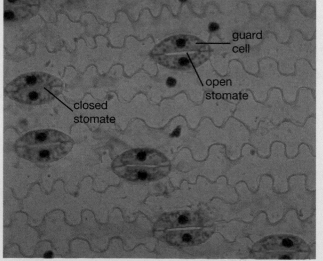

guard cell

open stomate

closed stomate

Figure E5.2 Guard cells control the rate of water loss in plants. Water loss is controlled by the condition of special cells, called guard cells. These cells regulate the size of microscopic pores in leaves. These pores are called **stomates**. When the plant has sufficient water, the guard cells swell and the stomates open. Water then evaporates through the stomates. When the plant is low on water, the guard cells shrink. The stomates remain closed, which preserves water. Based on the appearance of stomates in this leaf, how would you describe this plant's water balance?

The human body's response to change is quite specific as well as involuntary. For example, the body responds to cold temperature by diverting circulation to keep the most important internal organs warm. This type of response is appropriate for the external conditions. If the body becomes too hot, however, the circulatory system diverts blood flow away from the internal organs. This protects them from damage caused by excess heat.

These examples are rather dramatic. But the human body routinely senses and responds to thousands of small changes each day. It is through many small, specific, automatic changes that living organisms sense and react to an environment that is ever changing and sometimes hostile. Luckily, the mechanisms for maintaining balance are always on the job. ◆

Careful Coordination

Have you ever been so cold that you started shivering uncontrollably? Maybe your teeth even chattered. Perhaps you tried to stop the shivering, but your body continued to shake until you warmed up. The shivering that warms your body is an automatic response to the cold. The **nervous system** regulates this and many other automatic responses. For the most part, you cannot stop yourself from shivering.

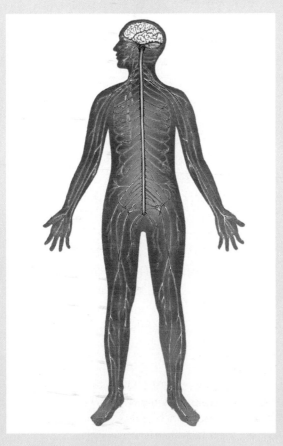

The nervous system is also responsible for all of the body's voluntary responses. For example, you can choose to put on a sweater in response to being cold because of the work your brain does in sensing and helping you respond to your environment. The nervous system is made up of all the nervous tissue, the brain, and spinal column (see Figure E5.3). It plays a key role in coordinating internal balance.

The nervous system contains two types of cells: **neurons** and **glial** cells. You read about neurons in the essay *Brains and a Lot of Nerve* when you studied the brain. Neurons produce and send nerve impulses. Glial cells protect, support, and insulate neurons. The rapid and accurate transmission of nerve impulses is responsible for every move that you make.

The command and control center for the nervous system is the brain. Recall from your earlier study of the brain that specific regions are responsible for receiving and transmitting different information. The brain stem directs the critical, automatic responses necessary to sustain life. The cerebellum is responsible for balance and posture. The cerebrum is responsible for conscious thought, language, and voluntary movement. Located below the

Figure E5.3 The nervous system is made up of the brain, spinal cord, and nerves throughout the body.

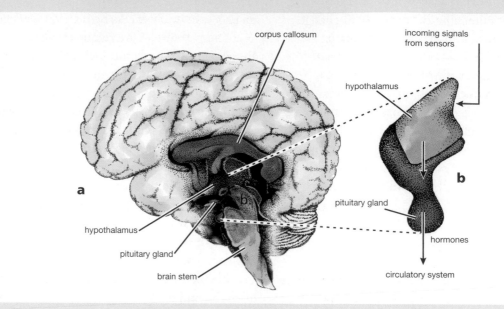

Figure E5.4 The hypothalamus. (a) The hypothalamus is a specialized part of the brain. It is part of both the endocrine system and the nervous system and is involved in detecting changes in internal conditions. (b) The hypothalamus responds to feedback by signaling other endocrine organs. In response to dehydration, the hypothalamus can release hormones that act on the pituitary gland. (The pituitary gland lies just underneath the hypothalamus in the brain.) The pituitary gland then releases hormones into the circulatory system.

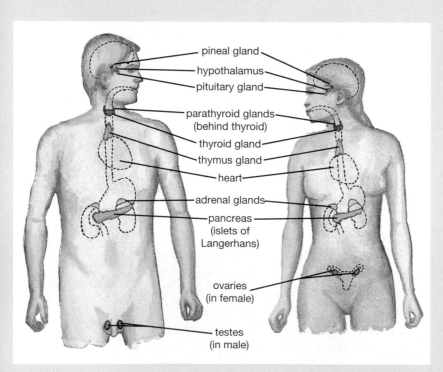

Figure E5.5 The endocrine system is a collection of glands, cells, and special neurons that produce and release hormones into the bloodstream.

cerebrum is a specialized part of the brain called the **hypothalamus**. The hypothalamus regulates a variety of **physiological processes**. These include water balance, body temperature, feeding, and sleep. It also helps to regulate several *endocrine* functions.

The **endocrine system** is made up of glands and cells that produce and release chemical messengers directly into the blood. These chemical messengers are called **hormones**. As a teenager, you probably have heard people refer to "raging hormones" in adolescents. There are indeed significant changes in hormone levels that regulate sexual maturity during puberty. But hormones play an important role in maintaining homeostasis for people of all ages. Many hormones function to regulate internal balances that are unrelated to reproduction, like water and blood sugar balance.

Hormones affect a variety of cells and organs throughout the body, stimulating processes that help maintain homeostasis. Although the blood transports hormones past every cell of the body, only certain "target" cells and organs can respond to a specific hormone. Whether a cell responds to a particular hormone depends on whether it has receptors for that hormone or not. **Receptors** are proteins that fit the shape of a specific hormone molecule. These receptors and their associated hormones work like a lock and key. When the receptor, or "lock," is exposed to the hormone, or "key," the hormone binds to the receptor. Once the key is bound to the lock, the hormone causes the cell with the receptor to respond.

Hormones control a variety of processes by binding to target cell receptors. For example, when you are dehydrated, sensors in the hypothalamus detect a shortage of water in your body. The hypothalamus detects that the body is short of water because the concentration of sodium increases when there is less water. Specialized neurons in the hypothalamus respond to the increase in sodium concentration by producing and releasing a hormone called **vasopressin**. The endings of these neurons are located in a part of the **pituitary**, an endocrine gland located in the brain. The release of vasopressin from the pituitary is a response to the signal of dehydration. Vasopressin, like other hormones, is a chemical messenger that is carried throughout the body in the blood. When the hormone reaches the appropriate cells of the body (in the kidney, for example), it reaches its target—cells that are involved in regulating water balance.

What organs and organ system would you expect to have target cells for hormones that help to regulate water balance? Recall that the urinary system regulates the body's water volume in addition to regulating the blood's solute and waste levels. In the urinary system, the kidney is the organ that regulates water balance. Cells in the kidney have receptors for the hormone vasopressin that the pituitary releases in response to dehydration. Vasopressin circulates in the blood. When it encounters the receptors in the kidneys' cells, it stimulates a response. Vasopressin causes the membranes of the kidneys' tubules to become more permeable to water. This means that more water can be reabsorbed and less water is added to the urine. Reabsorbing water and losing less of it in the urine prevents the body's dehydration from becoming more severe (see Figure E5.6).

At the same time that the endocrine system responds to dehydration, the nervous system also works to restore water balance. Parts of the nervous system sense the increased sodium concentration in the blood just like the hypothalamus does. The nervous system responds by triggering thirst to correct the imbalance in water levels. How many systems have we described so far that are involved in maintaining the body's water balance? The endocrine, circulatory, and nervous system responses are carefully coordinated to maintain homeostasis. Some of the body's responses are automatic, like the kidneys' response to vasopressin in the bloodstream. However, *you* decide whether to drink when you sense the thirst response. Homeostasis involves the coordination of many body systems and a combination of automatic responses and voluntary behaviors.

Maintaining internal conditions within a relatively small range is important for the body to function well. The body has mechanisms to detect changes and initiate the responses to bring conditions back to normal. What prevents the responses from changing internal conditions too far in the other direction or from overshooting the return to normal? For example, the body responds to dehydration by producing and releasing vasopressin. What controls the release of vasopressin so that the sodium balance is not allowed to get too low? The body uses **feedback systems** to maintain an internal balance and to regulate responses to changing conditions (see Figure E5.7).

Feedback can operate in one of two ways. Negative feedback systems work to shut off

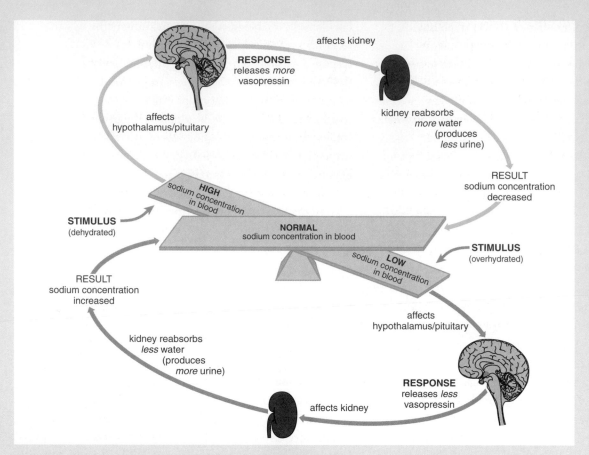

Figure E5.6 Regulation of water balance by vasopressin. (also known as an antidiuretic hormone, or ADH). When the sodium concentration in the blood rises, the hypothalamus and pituitary gland in the brain respond. This causes the release of vasopressin. Vasopressin stimulates the kidneys to reabsorb more water. As a result, the sodium concentration decreases, restoring water balance. What would happen if a person consumed a diuretic, such as caffeine or alcohol? Diuretics block the production of vasopressin.

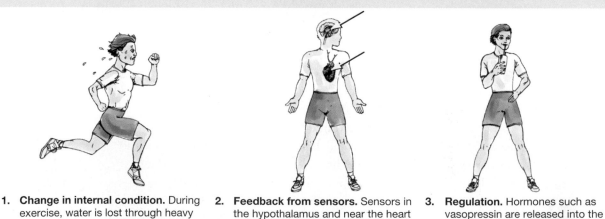

1. **Change in internal condition.** During exercise, water is lost through heavy breathing. This can lead to dehydration.

2. **Feedback from sensors.** Sensors in the hypothalamus and near the heart detect a loss of water. The concentration of certain components in the blood is an important signal.

3. **Regulation.** Hormones such as vasopressin are released into the circulatory system in response to the feedback signals. Vasopressin acts on the kidneys, causing them to retain water. You also feel thirsty.

Figure E5.7 Feedback and regulation work to reverse the effects of dehydration and restore balanced internal conditions.

the response that the body had to being out of balance. The previous example of the body responding to maintain water balance is one example of **negative feedback** (see Figure E5.6). When the body senses dehydration, it responds by producing more vasopressin and reabsorbing more water. When the body senses that the amount of water in the body is at the appropriate level, it signals the hypothalamus to reduce the amount of vasopressin that is released into the blood. In this way, the body continuously adjusts to produce the right amount of vasopressin so that the right

amount of water is reabsorbed in the kidney.

Another example of negative feedback is the body's regulation of blood pressure. **Blood pressure** is the pressure exerted by blood against the walls of arteries and veins. Like many other internal conditions, blood pressure must be maintained within defined limits. If the pressure is too low, sensors on large arteries in the chest and neck detect the change. The sensors send a signal through the nervous system to the brain. As Figure E5.8a shows, the brain responds by sending a signal to the heart that it needs to increase the rate

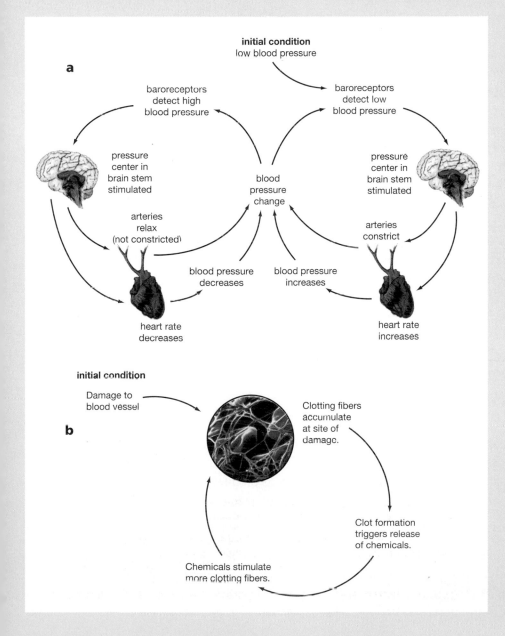

**Figure E5.8 Negative and positive feedback.
(a) Negative feedback** In response to a given set of initial conditions, the body responds by adjusting internal conditions. Negative feedback triggers changes that correct an abnormal situation. **(b) Positive feedback** In response to a given set of initial conditions, the body responds by adjusting internal conditions. Positive feedback occurs when some critical process must be completed quickly. In this case, positive feedback assures that a clot will form rapidly to minimize blood loss.

at which it beats. The increased heart rate causes an increase in blood pressure. The brain also signals arteries to *constrict*, or narrow. Constriction of blood vessels also increases blood pressure. If the blood pressure becomes too high, sensors detect this and signal the heart to beat more slowly and for the blood vessels to relax.

Figure E5.8b shows an example of **positive feedback.** Positive feedback adjusts internal conditions *toward* the initial condition. In the example shown, the initial condition is a small clot that begins to develop in response to a bleeding wound. Positive feedback triggers a regulatory response in which still more clotting fibers accumulate at the injury site. This has the effect of increasing the size of the clot, which helps to reduce blood loss. In this case, the initial condition was a high occurrence of clotting fibers at the wound. The response was to send even *more* clotting fibers.

Positive and negative adjustments are possible because most body systems are directed by the nervous and endocrine systems. These two organ systems reach every part of the human body. The nervous system is known for directing rapid, short-term, and very specific responses in the body. A reflex, such as jerking your hand back when you accidentally touch something hot, is an example of a rapid nervous system response. This reflex is a homeostatic response to a potentially dangerous rise in skin temperature. A reflex illustrates the interaction of sensory, nerve, and muscle systems. In this case, receptors in the skin send signals to nerve cells in the spinal cord. These, in turn, stimulate nerve cells leading to muscles in the arm. The muscle contracts and the hand withdraws from the hot surface.

Thus, the nervous system helps maintain homeostasis by regulating involuntary physiological activities. These include stimulating the hypothalamus and triggering automatic sensations such as thirst, cold, and pain. In addition, the nervous system assists in maintaining homeostasis by enabling the body to respond voluntarily to these sensations.

In contrast, the endocrine system usually directs slower and longer-lasting changes. For example, the secretion of vasopressin and the change in urine production that follows take longer to occur than the sensation of thirst brought about by the nervous system.

The combinations of fast and slow, automatic and voluntary, and physiological and behavioral responses are important for maintaining homeostasis. Coordinated by the nervous and endocrine systems, all of the body's systems work together to maintain balance within healthy limits. By delicately balancing positive and negative feedback mechanisms, the body can regulate the changing internal conditions that humans typically experience. ◆

The Breath of Life

Take a nice, deep breath. Let it out slowly. What do you think happens in your body with each breath that you take?

Each time you breathe in, you draw air into your lungs. This action is important for your survival because air contains oxygen. Oxygen, as you know, is a substance that every cell of your body needs to maintain normal conditions. Each time you breathe out, you expel air out of your lungs. This action is also important because it helps rid your body of carbon dioxide. Carbon dioxide is a substance that is produced in cells as a by-product of energy metabolism.

The process of breathing requires a finely regulated interaction of a number of organ systems. The organ system most directly involved in regulating your body's interaction with the atmosphere is the **gas exchange system.** The central organs of the gas exchange

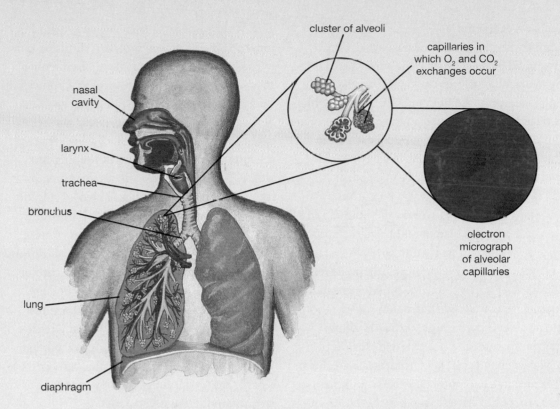

nasal
cavity

larynx

trachea

bronchus

lung

diaphragm

cluster of alveoli

capillaries in
which O_2 and CO_2
exchanges occur

electron
micrograph
of alveolar
capillaries

Figure E5.9   The human gas exchange system.   This lung has been cut away to expose the branching system of bronchial tubes. Part of the lung has been enlarged to show the air sacs and their relation to capillaries. Millions of air sacs in each lung give the tissue a spongelike appearance. If the surface of the human alveoli were spread flat, it would cover an area of 60 square meters (646 square feet). What is the advantage of such a large surface area?

system are the lungs. The lungs form two compartments that connect to the outside environment through your trachea (windpipe) and your nose. The air inside these lung compartments is not actually inside the internal environment of your body. Instead, the tissues of the lungs themselves separate this air from the rest of the cells of your body.

How does oxygen move from your lungs into the internal environment of your body? And how does carbon dioxide move from this internal environment back into your lungs and back into the external environment? The answers involve a combination of simple chemical processes and complex homeostatic regulation.

As you draw another deep breath, think about the path that the air must travel. The air passes through the nose where it is warmed, moistened, and cleaned. Sometimes

the air passes through the mouth instead. Then it enters the trachea, passes the vocal cords, and enters a branching system of bronchial tubes in each lung compartment. The surfaces of these breathing tubes are lined with mucus and cilia. Cilia are tiny hairlike structures that move in a wavelike manner. They sweep debris out of the passages. When the air finally reaches the ends of the passages in the lungs, it enters smaller compartments. These smaller compartments are made up of many tiny air sacs called alveoli. This pathway of air entering the lungs is shown in Figure E5.9.

Once the oxygen is in the alveoli, it is in the smallest lung compartment. However, it has not yet passed into the body's internal environment. To enter the internal environment of the body, the oxygen must diffuse across the alveoli's thin walls. These walls are called the alveolar membranes. The large number of alveoli increases the surface area of lung tissue. In fact, the surface area of these alveoli is 40 times greater than the entire outer surface of the human body. This very high surface area increases the amount of oxygen that can move into the body's internal environment. It also increases the amount of carbon dioxide that can enter the lungs to be exhaled.

The movement of oxygen across the alveolar membranes involves the interaction of the gas exchange system and the circulatory system. As shown in Figure E5.10, a system of capillaries filled with blood surrounds each small group of alveoli. This blood comes into such close contact with the thin membranes of the alveoli that simple diffusion allows oxygen to enter the body. The diffusion of oxygen depends on its concentration in the air sacs and in the blood inside the capillaries that surround them. If the concentration of oxygen is lower in the blood than in the air sacs, the oxygen diffuses from the air sacs into the blood. In the blood, the oxygen binds to the protein hemoglobin. Hemoglobin is found in the red blood cells. Through the flow of blood, oxygen is then carried to all parts of the body. In this way, these two systems work together to deliver oxygen to cells deep inside the body that have no direct contact with the outside environment.

At the same time that oxygen is diffusing into the blood, carbon dioxide is diffusing out of the blood and into the alveoli. Remember that carbon dioxide is a by-product of processes that take place in cells providing energy. The blood carries carbon dioxide away from cells all over the body. When carbon dioxide arrives at the lungs in the capillaries surrounding the alveoli, it diffuses across the alveolar membranes into the air inside the lungs. The concentration of carbon dioxide in the blood and in the air inside the alveoli determines the direction of diffusion. Because the concentration of carbon dioxide is usually higher in the blood, carbon dioxide usually diffuses out of the blood and into the air inside the lungs. The enormous surface area in the lungs speeds up the release of carbon dioxide from the blood into the lungs. When you exhale, you release this carbon dioxide from your lungs into the external environment around you.

Like many other homeostatic processes, breathing involves precise feedback systems. These feedback systems involve the gas exchange system, circulatory system, and nervous system. Consider, for example, what happens to your breathing rate during rapid exercise. As processes in the body speed up, the production of carbon dioxide also increases. Carbon dioxide causes the blood to become more acidic. Nerve cells in the aorta, brain,

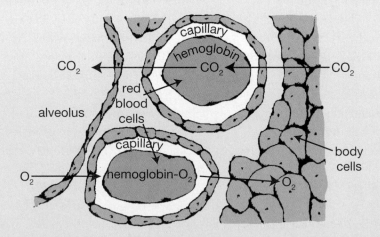

Figure E5.10   The gas exchange and circulatory systems work together.   Carbon dioxide produced in body cells is transported by red blood cells from body cells to the lungs. Oxygen from the lungs is transported by red blood cells to all body cells.

and arteries that lead to the head detect this increased acidity. These special cells send a signal to the respiratory centers in the brain. The respiratory centers respond by stimulating the diaphragm and rib muscles to contract more rapidly. Rapid contraction of these muscles increases the breathing rate. A faster breathing rate increases the rate at which oxygen is brought into the body. A faster breathing rate also increases the rate at which carbon dioxide is released from the body. When you stop exercising, the rate of carbon dioxide production declines. The blood, then, becomes less acidic. This change is detected by the sensory receptors in the blood vessels. The information is relayed to the respiratory centers in the brain. Finally, signals are sent to the diaphragm and rib muscles to contract more slowly.

This regulatory system works automatically. You do not have to control your breathing rate consciously. The signals involved are very powerful. Although you have some control over your breathing rate, you cannot hold your breath indefinitely. Once the carbon dioxide level in your blood reaches a critical level, the homeostatic signals override your efforts to hold your breath, and you are forced to exhale and take another breath.

Take one last deep breath. Can you describe what is happening in your lungs as you inhale and exhale? Can you remember how the rate of your breathing is normally controlled? Now consider this. Because of several complex homeostatic systems, many important adjustments that you never have to think about take place in your body.

What is the evidence that this is going on? Think of all the little breaths you took between those two nice deep breaths. ◆

Behavior and Homeostasis

Remember Josh, the character in *A Pause That Refreshes?* (Chapter 4)? What made Josh head to the refrigerator for a cool drink? Why does a lizard move toward a heated rock when its external environment cools off? What makes you reach for a sweatshirt when you enter an air-conditioned movie theater? Those questions all are focused on behaviors that seem to help maintain homeostasis. But what are the signals that prompt an organism to respond to changing conditions?

All those examples of behavior have a physiological basis. In other words, homeostasis is maintained by processes inside the body. Sometimes these internal processes result in behaviors we can see. But what is happening on the inside? Your body's internal conditions are controlled by a variety of monitoring and feedback systems that are connected. All organisms receive stimuli that prompt their monitoring and feedback systems. These stimuli arrive in many forms: light, temperature, sound, water, and chemicals.

Living systems vary greatly in the type of response they have for different stimuli. The feedback processes sometimes involve responses that include behaviors we can observe.

Internal conditions such as the level of carbon dioxide, body temperature, and salt concentration are examples of conditions that are controlled by physiological processes. You have learned that carbon dioxide plays an important role in regulating breathing rate. In general, the acid-base balance of the blood determines your breathing rate. Breathing fast is a typical behavioral response to increased exercise. This response restores carbon dioxide to acceptable levels. Under unusual conditions, such as fever, aspirin poisoning, or anxiety, the body responds with hyperventilation. In this potentially dangerous situation, the body "overbreathes." This overbreathing increases the breathing rate above the body's need to blow off carbon dioxide. Consequently, carbon dioxide is lost more rapidly than it is produced in the tissues. Your brain then does not get the

Figure E5.11 Violent shivering can increase the body's heat production by as much as 18 times normal.

feedback to signal breathing. Eventually, you might pass out from lack of oxygen. We can reduce the danger of this response by placing a paper bag over the victim's mouth and nose. This trick increases the level of carbon dioxide that the person breathes in. The body then receives the minimum carbon dioxide level that is associated with a normal breathing rate.

Scientists categorize the mechanism animals use to regulate body temperature into two major groups. Endothermic mechanisms are those that generate heat internally. Ectothermic mechanisms are mechanisms that collect heat from outside the body. Mammals and birds are endothermic. Animals such as fish, reptiles, and insects are ectothermic. Regardless of which type of animal an organism is, temperature regulation is a critical survival tool. Many fundamental cell processes depend on enzymes that function best in very narrow temperature ranges. This is why doctors are concerned when their patients run high fevers. A slight increase in temperature can help kill pathogens. However, a large or sustained increase will destroy vital cell functions. This situation can put the patient's life at risk.

Mammals and birds maintain relatively constant temperatures by balancing heat production with heat loss. For example, as you digest food, you generate heat. You can increase heat production by eating more, exercising, and shivering. You can decrease heat loss by adding insulation. You can put on a sweater. A bird, for example, fluffs up its feathers. On the other hand, you lose heat through the evaporation of water by sweating and breathing fast. You also lose heat through heat transfer. Taking your sweater off increases the loss of heat through transfer. These behaviors are all responses to changes in the external conditions. In each case, the organism used feedback to regulate a response that started in the body. Each response also included a behavior that we could see.

Across time, through evolution, a variety of interesting adaptations have arisen that help organisms maintain a constant temperature. Some of the most notable are the adaptations of mammals to extreme climates. For example, small desert mammals may live underground or be active at night to minimize the effect of the hot, dry days. Small mammals in very cold environments will live in tunnels under the snow. The temperature in these tunnels does not drop below −5°C (−23°F), even when outside air temperatures fall below −50°C (−58°F).

Ectotherms do not have internal processes that help regulate their internal temperature. Instead, they have internal receptors that trigger specific responses when their internal

Figure E5.12 Polar bear. Polar bears live only in the Northern Hemisphere, nearly always in association with sea ice. They maintain their internal temperatures in a very cold climate by hibernating in dens during the coldest months. What behaviors do you use to stay warm?

Figure E5.13   The lizard maintains a fairly constant body temperature by changing its body position relative to the position of the sun.

temperatures rise or fall out of a safe range. The behavioral responses of desert lizards have been studied extensively. Biologists have found that the lizards' responses are so finely tuned that they are able to maintain a body temperature between 36°C (97°F) and 39°C (102°F). How? Simply by moving in and out of the sunshine and by adjusting their orientation to the sun.

Reptiles, birds, fish, and humans show a variety of adaptations for regulating their salt concentration. Marine reptiles such as turtles have special salt glands above their eyes that excrete the excess salt they take in with their food. Birds have a similar adaptation, except that the salt solution drains out of their beaks. In humans and other mammals, excess sodium is removed by the kidneys and excreted in the urine. Some animals, such as the spider crab that lives in estuaries (a saltwater environment), can sense changes in the salt level. But they do not have a physiological mechanism for removing the salt. Instead, the spider crab moves to areas of lower or higher salt concentrations. In this way, the spider crab can maintain its internal balance.

Many animals have observable behaviors that are related to maintaining homeostasis. The ability of humans to think about their behavior, make choices about behaviors, and access technological solutions increases the range of responses that we have. We can cool and heat our external environment. We have developed sports drinks to restore our electrolyte balance after we sweat. We have

access to a wide range of foods, beverages, and drugs that can restore or destroy a homeostatic balance.

So, although Josh's body signaled him to restore the water balance in his body, his conscious behavior determined whether that balance would be restored. By choosing an energy drink, not a sports drink, Josh made his internal condition worse instead of improving it. Remember, an energy drink contains a high level of the diuretic caffeine. As you learned in Chapter 1, humans are distinguished from other animals by a set of characteristics, especially the capacity of our brain. That powerful brain gives us the capacity to choose to ignore certain signals or do something about them. ◆

Figure E5.14   Western gull (*Larus occidentalis*). Western gulls have a wingspan of 30–40 cm (12–16 inches). Note the drop of salt water at the tip of this bird's beak. Salt glands help sea birds eliminate excess sodium. How does your body control its salt concentration?

Beyond the Limits

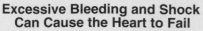

Excessive Bleeding and Shock Can Cause the Heart to Fail

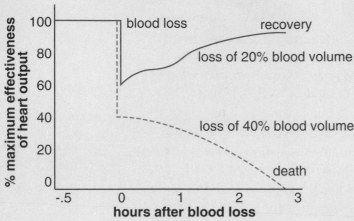

Figure E6.1 Blood loss. The body adjusts for blood loss by clotting the blood and increasing the heart rate. These responses slowly restore the effectiveness of heart output (see 20% blood loss curve). There is a limit to how much blood can be lost and still have homeostatic mechanisms restore function. In the event of a 40% blood volume loss, the effectiveness of heart output continues to drop. Eventually, the heart stops.

Figure E6.2 Chronic disruption of homeostasis. Diabetes mellitus is a chronic disease that can cause tissue damage throughout the body. The disorder is caused by inadequate amounts or functioning of the hormone insulin. Insulin regulates levels of glucose in blood, liver, and muscle cells. If this disease is not well controlled, diabetes can result in poor circulation. It can damage tissues such as **(a)** eye, **(b)** heart, **(c)** kidneys, and **(d)** peripheral tissue.

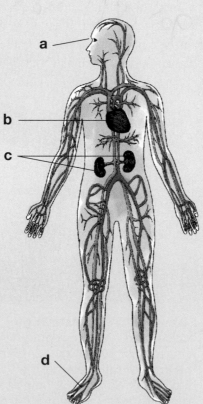

The human body has a remarkable ability to adjust to changes in the environment. The human body also has its limits. When people are in a harsh environment such as the desert, the body's challenge to maintain internal balance is even greater. In such situations, small errors in judgment, such as not drinking enough water, can have serious consequences. Even under pleasant conditions, homeostasis may be disrupted if one or more of the body's regulatory systems break down.

The factors that disturb homeostasis and stress the body are called **stressors.** Sunlight can be a stressor and so can a physical injury. You already are familiar with some of the disruptions that can take place on a hot day when you are dehydrated. If stress is mild or temporary, the problem may pass. The body may be able to recover normal balance. For example, a deep cut that bleeds heavily can temporarily disrupt the body's fluid balance. If the bleeding stops, the body may be able to return to a balanced state. With a more serious injury, a transfusion of blood may be necessary to restore balance. If the disruption is extreme, the body may be damaged permanently. In some of these cases, the body may not be able to reestablish balance. For instance, the rapid blood loss that occurs when someone cuts his or her leg badly may be faster than the body's ability to adjust to these conditions. If medical help is not immediate, serious illness or even death can result (Figure E6.1).

Even if a disruption in balance is less severe, the disruption still can be a serious threat if it lasts for a long time. Diseases such as diabetes (Figure E6.2) or heart disease are examples of this type of disruption. In these long-term disruptions, organ systems or tissues often are damaged slowly over time. In these cases, the body's attempt to regain the balanced conditions becomes progressively more difficult.

Other stressors that could overwhelm balance in the body include a lack of nourishment (starvation); a lack of oxygen (suffocation); or the presence of toxins in the air being breathed (air pollution). Other stressors might be a large dose of toxic compounds (such as a drug overdose), or a serious infection. One such infection, septicemia, is caused by a bacterium. Septicemia affects many aspects of the human body and can result in an extremely dangerous form of shock. In the early stages of the infection, toxins produced by the bacteria enter the bloodstream. Once the toxins are in the bloodstream, they cause symptoms such as fever, flushed skin, and rapid heartbeat. The patient develops local bleeding and tiny blood clots. The patient may go into irreversible shock and die. Possible sources of this type of infection include an untreated bladder infection, a skin infection caused by *Streptococcus* or *Staphylococcus* bacteria, a blockage in the intestine, or an unsanitary surgical procedure.

The examples of disruptions we just described are familiar because they are human injuries or illnesses. Homeostatic disruptions put all organisms at risk. Every species on earth is adapted for survival in a specific habitat and under specific conditions. If an organism is put in a very different environment, its ability to maintain internal balance may be pushed beyond its limits. Consider the very different situations faced by fish living in freshwater and those living in salt water (see Figure E6.3). Both types of fish must adjust their internal concentrations of water and solutes such as sodium chloride (salt) to maintain the proper balance. Mechanisms have evolved that are effective

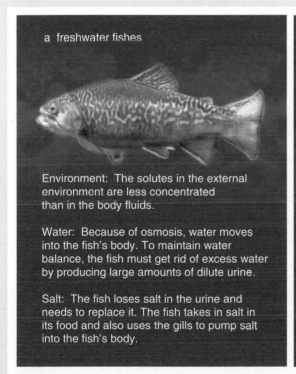

a freshwater fishes

Environment: The solutes in the external environment are less concentrated than in the body fluids.

Water: Because of osmosis, water moves into the fish's body. To maintain water balance, the fish must get rid of excess water by producing large amounts of dilute urine.

Salt: The fish loses salt in the urine and needs to replace it. The fish takes in salt in its food and also uses the gills to pump salt into the fish's body.

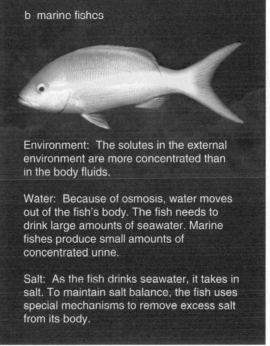

b marine fishes

Environment: The solutes in the external environment are more concentrated than in the body fluids.

Water: Because of osmosis, water moves out of the fish's body. The fish needs to drink large amounts of seawater. Marine fishes produce small amounts of concentrated urine.

Salt: As the fish drinks seawater, it takes in salt. To maintain salt balance, the fish uses special mechanisms to remove excess salt from its body.

Figure E6.3 **(a)** Freshwater fishes must continually remove large amounts of water so that the solutes in their internal environment are not diluted. **(b)** Marine fishes must drink water to maintain the water balance in their bodies. They must remove solutes such as sodium chloride via their gills. The kidneys remove other kinds of salts from the fish's body. What do you think would happen if each of these organisms were placed in each other's environmental setting?

at accomplishing this task for each type of fish. Kidneys help regulate these same conditions in humans. These mechanisms, however, are sufficient only for the usual variations in water and salt balance. That is why we define homeostasis as maintaining conditions *within certain limits*. If either type of fish were suddenly put in the other's external conditions, the fish would be beyond its limits. The fish most likely would die. Extreme stressors on any organism might leave the organism unable to restore normal internal conditions. Such a state of imbalance is often fatal. ◆

Coping with Disruptions: The Role of Medicine in Homeostasis

What happens if internal conditions go beyond our body's ability to recover? In societies with advanced technology, scientists and physicians have developed tools that

provide both temporary and long-term help. Some of these tools help correct internal conditions. Other tools may temporarily take over one of the body's regulatory systems. In some cases, this requires surgery. For example, sometimes surgeons can repair heart defects by replacing valves in the heart. In other cases, a surgeon may insert a permanent device in the body. For example, a pacemaker is an electronic device that can improve circulation. The pacemaker provides a regular heartbeat. This regular heartbeat then helps the heart muscle contract and pump blood.

Other medical procedures use technology in different ways to help restore balance. For instance, if a person's lungs have collapsed, physicians can use a mechanical ventilator. The ventilator makes certain that oxygen enters the bloodstream. It also makes certain that carbon dioxide leaves the patient's body. Dialysis machines filter blood and assist with fluid regulation in patients whose kidneys have failed.

Health care professionals also use technology to gather information about a person's injury or illness. They can collect important information by checking the vital signs of the patient. This is the first step in a diagnosis. Medical workers can make accurate measurements by using tools that extend their senses. These tools include X-rays, electrocardiographs, stethoscopes, blood

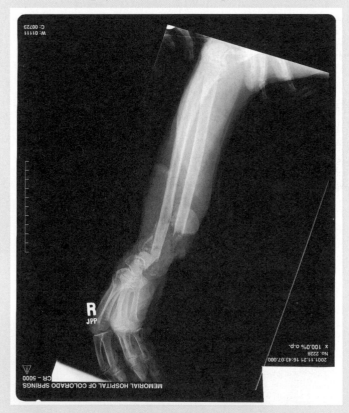

Figure E6.4 Imaging technology reveals internal structures.   Diagnosis of disruptions such as broken bones or tumors is made more efficient through analysis of X-rays and other images that allow physicians to view internal structures. Physicians used this X-ray of an arm to determine the extent of the injury.

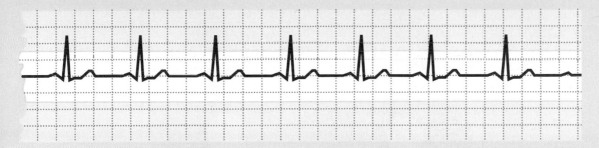

a   normal heart rhythm

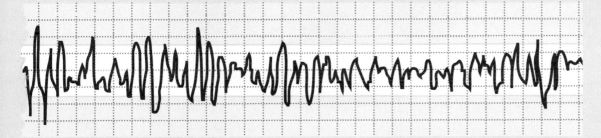

b   disrupted heartbeat

Figure E6.5   Electrocardiograms help physicians assess heart function.
Electrocardiograms reveal (**a**) normal and (**b**) disrupted heart function. This particular disruption in heart function is called ventricular fibrillation. This is when the muscles of a ventricle contract rapidly and continuously in an uncoordinated manner. How would a disrupted circulatory system affect gas exchange?

pressure cuffs, and thermometers. X-ray images provide experts with a way to assess internal structures. The bones of the arm are shown in an X-ray in Figure E6.4. An electrocardiograph maps the rate and rhythm of the beating heart. This instrument also prints out a record such as the ones shown in Figure E6.5. This record is called an electrocardiogram. It helps a heart specialist determine the health of a patient's heart and circulatory system.

Technological advances in the analysis of blood also have led to better diagnoses. The composition of blood often gives us important information about the health of internal organs. In one type of test, technicians count blood cells of many different types to evaluate whether the patient has a blood disorder. The ratios between different blood cell types and the total blood volume also are important indicators of health. In a healthy person's blood, red blood cells generally are present in a much higher concentration than white blood

cells. Generally, the ratio is about 700:1. An abundance of white blood cells usually indicates an infection. The components of blood plasma also may vary with certain types of imbalance. Plasma is the noncellular, liquid part of the blood. Plasma components include cholesterol, lipids, protein, glucose, and electrolytes. Electrolytes are solutes such as chloride, potassium, calcium, and sodium.

In cases where physicians find an internal imbalance, they sometimes use drug technologies to treat the disorder. They can use drug therapies to treat high blood pressure, heart problems, diabetes, psychological disorders, cancer, and many other potentially serious problems. For instance, the widespread use of antibiotics to treat bacterial infections has resulted in a dramatic decline in the number of deaths due to infections.

Antibiotics and many other drugs are recent developments. They provide an example of how technology has changed our cultural view of

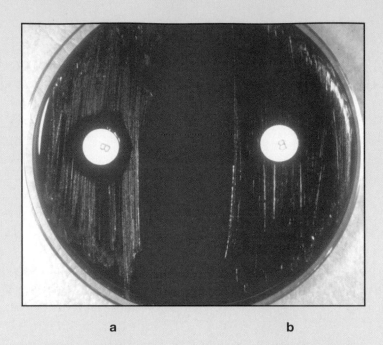

a   b

Figure E6.6   Bacterial resistance to antibiotics.   On this petri dish, two strains of bacteria were spread evenly across a nutrient material. Disks soaked in the antibiotic bacitracin were then added to the plates. The two bacterial strains were observed after further growth. The clear area in (**a**) indicates a lack of growth near the antibiotic disk. In (**b**), there is no clear area around the disk. This indicates that the bacteria grew there. What evidence do you see that indicates that bacteria can be resistant to the effects of antibiotics?

medicine during the past 70 years. Unfortunately, the widespread use of antibiotics has resulted in the evolution of some bacterial strains that are resistant to certain antibiotics. Bacterial infections once again are becoming more difficult to treat. Figure E6.6 shows an experiment that tested the resistance of two types of bacteria to an antibiotic.

The tremendous advances in medical technology have resulted in an increase in the quality of life for many people. Researchers are continuing to make further advances. However, some of these advances raise a number of

ethical questions. For instance, our increased use of life-support technology forces us to think about how we define quality of life. Health care professionals and the public struggle with using life-support systems for the long-term maintenance of terminally ill patients. New technology also raises financial concerns because the costs for many advanced medical treatments are extremely high. As our medical knowledge increases and as we develop more tools to assist medical professionals, society must learn how to balance the costs and benefits of the treatments. ◆

Avoiding Disruptions: The Immune System

Regulatory mechanisms in all organ systems are necessary to maintain homeostasis in living organisms. In humans, the immune system provides powerful protection against

disruptions that infections and foreign toxins cause. The body is a violent place. Like a fortress, your body's immune system offers many defenses to keep out or kill invaders.

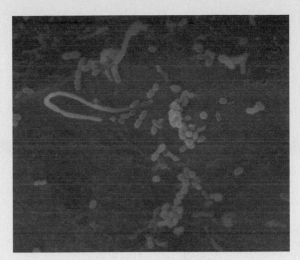

Figure E6.7 **Scanning electron micrograph of bacteria on skin, magnified 24,000×.**

The body's largest organ is the skin. The skin provides a *nonspecific* barrier or defense against invaders. A nonspecific barrier is one that does not have to recognize a specific invader. As the body's first line of defense, the skin helps to guard the body's internal environment from attack. The defensive role of the skin does not mean that it is a sterile environment on which nothing can live. In fact, millions of harmless bacteria live on the skin (refer to Figure E6.7). In most cases, these bacteria are beneficial. They compete effectively against disease-causing microorganisms. The term **pathogen** describes any disease-causing microorganism. Through time, humans and harmless bacteria have benefited from their interactions. Humans have benefited because these bacteria help to protect us from pathogens. Harmless bacteria have gained a resource-rich environment on which to live, the human skin.

Like the walls of a fortress, the skin helps to guard your internal environment from outside attack. This wall, however, is not perfectly secure. There are natural doors to the internal environment, such as the mouth, ears, eyes, nose, genital, urinary, and anal openings. These doors allow pathogenic invasion. Additional nonspecific defenses have evolved to help protect these natural openings. These include saliva, tears, mucus, and sweat. Some of these bodily secretions contain an antibacterial enzyme. Of course, cuts in the skin also provide avenues for infection. These openings give invading pathogens direct access to the tissues of the body's internal environment.

Protection against pathogens is not unique to humans. All organisms have some resistance to invasion by foreign material. Bacteria, for example, produce special enzymes that destroy foreign DNA, such as in viruses. Plants produce chemicals that kill areas of plant tissue infected by a fungus. The plant sacrifices the infected part. But this loss is less dangerous than an infection that spreads throughout the plant.

If pathogens pass through the skin successfully and reach the inside of an organism, other components of the immune system take over. In humans and other mammals, the invading pathogens face an army of cellular and molecular defenses. For example, there are nonspecific defense cells that recognize and scavenge many types of invading organisms and toxins. Among these scavenger cells are macrophages. Figure E6.8 shows a macrophage in action. In the lungs,

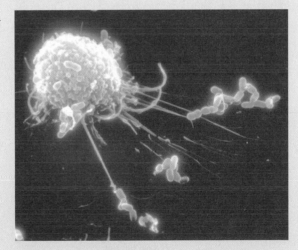

Figure E6.8 **Macrophage engulfing bacteria.** A macrophage is a nonspecific scavenger cell that helps protect the body against pathogens. In this photo, cellular extensions from a macrophage have captured several bacteria. Macrophages also play a role in the specific immune response.

macrophages help protect the body against pathogens that humans inhale.

Macrophages also act as generals in the immunity army. Macrophages activate, or signal, helper T-cells. In turn, helper T-cells recruit more immune cells to defend the body. They coordinate the immune system's specific barriers by directing groups of specialized cells to attack only *certain* invaders. (This response is very different from the nonspecific defenses provided by macrophages and the skin. They act to repel all invaders.) For instance, helper T-cells can activate killer T-cells. Killer T-cells kill specific infected cells. This line of specific defense is called the **cell-mediated response**. Figure E6.9 summarizes some of the interactions involved in the cell-mediated response.

Figure E6.9 Macrophages perform several functions as part of our immune system defenses. Macrophages scavenge pathogens nonspecifically. But they also play an important role in directing specific immune responses. During specific immune responses, macrophages interact with helper T-cells, which respond by producing signal molecules called lymphokines. These lymphokines can activate cell-mediated responses. These responses involve killer T-cells in a process that destroys pathogen-infected cells. Lymphokines can also activate antibody-mediated responses. These responses involve B-cells in a process that destroys circulating pathogens.

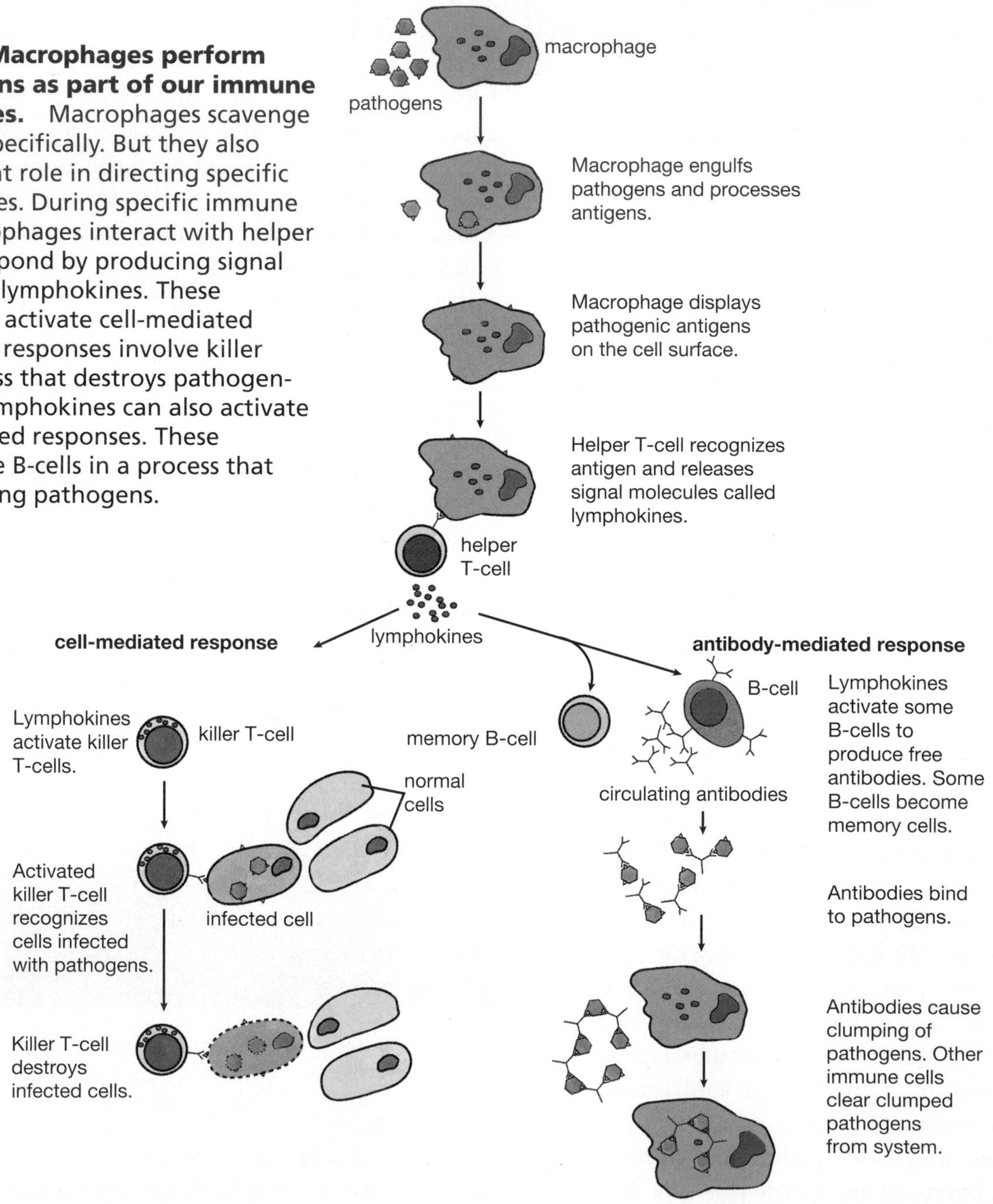

macrophage

pathogens

Macrophage engulfs pathogens and processes antigens.

Macrophage displays pathogenic antigens on the cell surface.

Helper T-cell recognizes antigen and releases signal molecules called lymphokines.

helper T-cell

lymphokines

cell-mediated response

Lymphokines activate killer T-cells.

killer T-cell

memory B-cell

normal cells

Activated killer T-cell recognizes cells infected with pathogens.

infected cell

Killer T-cell destroys infected cells.

antibody-mediated response

B-cell

Lymphokines activate some B-cells to produce free antibodies. Some B-cells become memory cells.

circulating antibodies

Antibodies bind to pathogens.

Antibodies cause clumping of pathogens. Other immune cells clear clumped pathogens from system.

Cell-mediated responses are an important part of the defense against viral infections. Once viruses enter the cells of their host, macrophages cannot find them. The viruses then use the host cell's own biochemical machinery to reproduce. With this effective adaptation, the virus uses the host cell as both a shield and a way to reproduce. Antibiotics kill bacteria that reproduce *outside* cells. Therefore, antibiotics are not effective against viral infections. Most chemicals that would kill a virus-infected cell also would kill healthy cells. Killer T-cells, on the other hand, *can* distinguish virus-infected cells from uninfected cells. Infected cells present unique molecular signals on their surface membranes. Killer T-cells attach to these molecular signals and destroy the infected cells. Uninfected cells are unharmed.

Macrophages also help activate B-cells. Activated B-cells produce molecular defenses known as **antibodies**. Antibodies enter the bloodstream and move throughout the body. Antibodies are protein molecules that recognize the protein molecules on pathogens. You may know these protein molecules as **antigens**. When circulating antibodies encounter the antigens to which they can bind, they attach to the pathogens. Pathogens that have antibodies attached to them become a target for destruction by macrophages. This line of specific defense is called the **antibody-mediated response**. It works together with the other components of the immune system to help protect the body against damage from invading pathogens or the toxins they produce. (Figure E6.9 illustrates this response.)

Sometimes the immune system works against the host. Antigens in insect venom, pollen, animal dander, or food protein are not necessarily serious threats to human homeostasis. In individuals with allergies, however, the body sees these substances as foreign invaders. Thus, exposure to these antigens can produce unpleasant hypersensitivities such as bee-sting reactions, hay fever, and asthma. Such responses occur because the antigens trigger the body's production of antibodies that bind to certain types of cells found in blood and tissues. These cells have granules that contain many substances, including chemicals called **histamines**. When the antibodies trigger the granule cells to release histamines, the result is usually sneezing, itchiness, and teary eyes. Histamines can sometimes cause smooth muscles to contract and blood vessels to swell. This, in turn, can cause the airways in the lungs to constrict, resulting in severe breathing problems. The **antihistamines** found in allergy medicines often are effective in reducing these symptoms. Antihistamines counteract the histamines that the granule-containing cells release.

As you have read, the defensive forces of the immune system destroy foreign material and infected cells. However, they also identify and destroy human cells that have changed into cancerous cells. Cancerous cells may arise when cells become faulty and no longer respond to normal homeostatic signals. One faulty response is for these abnormal cells to divide continuously. If enough abnormal cells accumulate, a cancerous tumor forms. If the cancer progresses, it may invade other areas of the body and eventually cause death. To prevent that, an active, healthy immune system is an essential protection. The relative rarity of cancer is a sign that the immune system usually attacks and destroys abnormal cells before a cancer develops.

With so many lines of defense, why does anyone ever get sick? The answer is that the immune system, like other systems that regulate homeostasis, has limits. There are limits to how many pathogens or abnormal cells the immune system can control. The body may not be able to protect itself if infections become too widespread or destroy too much tissue. Sometimes, the invader can escape detection.

People also become sick when their immune systems weaken. Many stressors, such as inadequate sleep, smoking, drug use, and anxiety, can weaken the immune system. With depleted natural defenses, pathogens can take over and cause disease. Acquired immunodeficiency syndrome, or AIDS, offers an extreme example of what can happen when the immune system is damaged. In AIDS, the human immunodeficiency virus, or HIV, directly attacks the helper T-cells. Without helper T-cells, most of the immune system's specific responses are disabled. As a result, the victim often is unable to fight off even minor infections. In addition, the victim is left vulnerable to many serious diseases, including pneumonia and cancer. Ironically, the tragic consequences of AIDS actually emphasize the impressive ability of the body to defend itself in most situations. The effectiveness of the immune system is based on complex interactions between various cells, organs, and systems within the body. ◆

Self and Nonself

The immune system is effective because it is able to distinguish between cells of the body (self) and foreign cells (nonself). The human immune system is so well adapted to making these distinctions that it can even distinguish between normal cells and cancerous cells. This important distinction usually keeps the immune system from attacking the body it is supposed to defend. Bacteria are protected in a similar way. They have protective enzymes that destroy foreign DNA, such as in viruses.

The considerations related to blood transfusions provide another example of the body's ability to distinguish self from nonself. The surface of red blood cells contains molecules that identify the blood group to which the cells belong. These molecules provide the basis for distinguishing blood as a certain *type*. They can vary among individuals, and as Figure E6.10 shows, are identified by the immune system as belonging to either self or nonself. The transfusion of one blood type into a person with another blood type causes the patient's immune system to attack the blood. The resulting blood clotting may make the patient so dangerously ill that death may occur.

When the human immune system cannot distinguish between self and nonself, it attacks and damages tissue in the body. In fact, many diseases are disruptions of immune function. These diseases are called **autoimmune diseases**. An autoimmune disease causes the body to damage itself. Autoimmune diseases include rheumatoid arthritis and multiple sclerosis (MS). In rheumatoid arthritis, the immune system causes inflammation and damage to joints. In multiple sclerosis, the

Blood type	Molecule on red blood cell	Antibody in plasma
O	None	Anti A, anti B
A	A	Anti B
B	B	Anti A
AB	A and B	None

Figure E6.10   ABO blood types.   Blood types are inherited. A patient with type A blood will have antibodies against type B molecules. That is, the antibodies will recognize type B blood as foreign, and the patient's immune system will attack the type B blood. People with blood type O can donate to people with other blood types without danger. This is because there are no blood-type molecules on type O cells to which antibodies can bind. The blood recipient's immune system will not attack type O blood. People with type O blood, however, can only accept blood transfusions from type O blood. Can you explain why?

immune system slowly destroys the nervous system. Intensive research into the causes of autoimmune diseases is currently underway. Scientists hope that a better understanding of how the body normally distinguishes between self and nonself will aid in developing new therapies, and perhaps, cures for autoimmune diseases. ◆

Immune System Memory

The human immune system is amazingly efficient at protecting against outside attacks. A powerful feature of the immune system is the ability of certain immune cells to retain a *memory of infection*. Due to this memory, your immune system can produce a faster and more powerful attack against pathogens the second time they enter your body. This response is possible because a few of the immune cells that fought a particular invader in the past remain in your body. They store a memory of the previous infection in their molecular structure. In other words, these immune cells are already programmed to respond quickly if the same pathogen tries to invade a second time. With this programmed response, your body may fight off the infection without ever having symptoms of illness.

The memory feature of the body's immune system explains how individuals become immune to particular illnesses. For example, if you have had measles, mumps, or chicken pox once, you generally do not contract that illness a second time, even if you are exposed to the pathogen that causes it.

Medical researchers have exploited immune memory by developing vaccines. Edward Jenner discovered the first vaccine in 1796 (see Figure E6.11). Vaccines trick the body's natural defenses into reacting against a

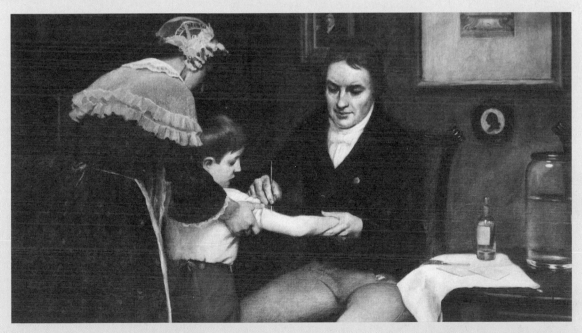

Figure E6.11 Edward Jenner discovered the first vaccine in 1796. At that time, smallpox was a deadly viral disease that had killed thousands of people throughout the world. Jenner gave patients doses of a virus that caused a much milder disease in humans, the cowpox virus. These patients developed antibodies that were effective against the smallpox virus. Then, when the patients were exposed to the smallpox virus, their immune systems could recognize the disease in time to mount an effective response and destroy the invading virus.

pathogen that is not attacking the body. Thus, the vaccinated individual can acquire immunity to a disease without ever having the disease. A common type of vaccine consists of inactivated pathogens, such as viral or bacterial particles, that are injected into the body. For example, the original vaccine for polio was made from a polio virus. This virus was treated with formaldehyde so that it could not reproduce inside the person who received the vaccine. The vaccine can activate a specific immune response because it includes antigens for a particular pathogen. The vaccine does not cause a primary infection and illness, however, because the pathogen is either dead or disabled. Some vaccines only introduce some of the pathogen's proteins. The newest approach to vaccines involves inserting the genetic material (DNA or RNA) of a virus into human cells to produce viral antigens. In all of the cases, the pathogen's antigens then trigger a minor immune response and produce memory cells.

As Figure E6.12 shows, vaccines can have a dramatic, positive impact on the spread of disease. There are vaccines for certain types of influenza, tetanus, rabies, measles, mumps, smallpox, chicken pox, hepatitis B, and many other diseases. Some diseases, however, lack effective vaccines because dozens of varieties of similar viruses can cause the same symptoms. For example, a vaccine developed against one variety of the virus that causes the common cold would not provide protection against all of the other varieties of cold viruses. Certain other diseases are difficult to prevent with vaccines because they mutate so rapidly. In the case of human immunodeficiency virus (HIV), a vaccine would protect the body against only one strain of the virus. HIV mutates so rapidly that different strains can appear in one individual. ◆

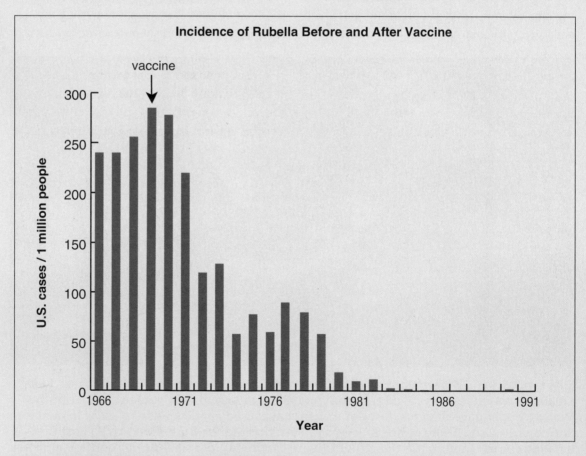

Figure E6.12 Vaccines and disease.   The widespread use of a vaccine has almost eliminated rubella, or German measles, in the United States.

Avoiding Disruptions: Behavior, Choices, and Risk

What human behaviors reduce the risk of disrupting homeostasis? Simple reflexes, such as closing the eyelids in response to a sudden, threatening movement or retracting the fingers quickly from a hot surface, are protective behaviors. In addition, humans have a tremendous capacity for complex thought. Therefore, humans have the option of reducing risks by choosing behaviors that prevent the disruption of bodily functions. For example, you can avoid being around someone who has the flu. You can choose always to buckle your seat belt while in a car. You can adopt the habits of getting adequate sleep and eating nutritious food. None of those behaviors will eliminate the risk of injury or illness. But they all represent some controllable factors that may greatly reduce the risk of either mild or major disruptions.

As we consider risk, it is important to distinguish controllable from uncontrollable factors. For instance, inheriting a genetic disease is not under your control. Would exposure to toxic substances in polluted outdoor air or in an unsafe workplace be under your control?

The onset of many types of cancer involves both controllable and uncontrollable factors. One of the most controllable factors related to lung cancer is cigarette smoking. Cigarette smoke damages the lungs' protective mechanisms and leaves a smoker more vulnerable than a nonsmoker to infection or to damage from other pollutants. Smoking does not guarantee that a smoker will get cancer, but it greatly increases the risk of lung cancer. It also increases the risk of heart disease from damaged blood vessels. A further consequence of smoking is that it damages the elasticity of lung tissue with each inhalation of smoke. This damage is progressive and results in the slow, and often painful, fatal disease known as emphysema. Figure E6.13 compares healthy lungs with diseased lungs.

Many smokers find it extremely difficult to quit smoking because the nicotine in tobacco is one of the most addictive chemicals known. What is more interesting is why

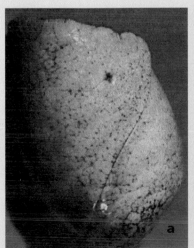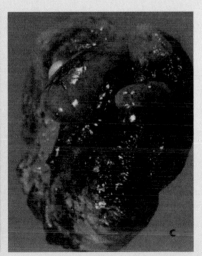

Figure E6.13 Smoking increases the risk for developing lung disease. A healthy lung (**a**) is light in color and has a consistent alveolar structure. Lungs damaged by cancer (**b**) or by emphysema (**c**) are dark in color and are unable to function as efficiently as healthy lungs.

people who have access to accurate data about the effects of smoking choose to start smoking. With smoking, as with other controllable and risky behaviors such as skiing, riding a bicycle or motorcycle without a helmet, drinking alcohol, or driving without a seat belt, an individual must weigh the risks against the benefits to make an informed decision.

A number of behaviors and risks, some controllable and some not, affect the efficiency of the immune system. It is not easy to test what effect each factor has on immune function because the immune system is so complex. However, the factors listed in Figure E6.14 do appear to have an effect on the immune system's efficiency.

Even if the immune system is strong, it may not successfully combat an infection if the number of pathogens is very large or if the pathogen damages too much tissue. Once again, there are ways to reduce the risks and give the immune system a good chance to work adequately. Avoiding exposure to polluted water, contaminated food, and animals or people with contagious diseases will reduce your risk to infection. Keep in mind that exposure may not mean simply being near the source of infection. Sitting in the same room with contaminated food will not make you ill, but eating it may do so. Can you catch a cold by shaking hands with a person who has a cold? Yes, if the person has just covered his or her mouth while sneezing, and then you touch your mouth or nose. Can you catch HIV by shaking hands with a person infected with HIV? No, you must share body fluids with a person infected with HIV. This could occur with direct blood contact or having sexual intercourse. Overall, the immune system, like the body itself, needs to function in a balanced manner, as indicated in Figure E6.15. ◆

Figure E6.14 Factors that influence immune function.

Enhances defense	Impairs defense
• Adequate rest	• Fatigue and lack of sleep
• Moderate exercise	• Extreme exercise (marathons, cross-country ski racing)
• Good nutrition	• Poor nutrition
• Positive mental attitude	• Anxiety or depression
	• Smoking
	• Excessive alcohol use
	• Excessive antibiotics use
	• Certain infections (such as mononucleosis or HIV)

Figure E6.15 Relationship between immune function and various stressors. Like other homeostatic systems, the immune system can become improperly regulated. This will result in disruptions caused by over- or underactivity.

Level of immune function	Response of immune system to stressor	
	Internal	External
Overactive	Autoimmune diseases	Allergies
Normal	Immune system Removal of abnormal cells	Immune system Removal of toxins and successful fighting of infection
Underactive	Cancerous cell growth	Susceptibility to infections

Individual Behavior Can Affect Larger Groups

You may be able to reduce some health risks, but members of your society must cooperate in order to reduce others. For example, you may make the choice never to drive a car recklessly or while under the influence of alcohol. Yet an accident caused by someone who does could injure you. In this case, the source of danger (drunk or reckless driving) is controllable, but not by you, the victim.

Your group of friends and your society also play a role in determining health risks. A society with laws restricting air pollution reduces everyone's risk of getting lung cancer. Is this a factor within your control? If you avoid excessive use of a car or vote to support pollution restrictions, then as an individual, you contribute to the reduction of risk. But your contribution alone will not have much effect. It takes many personal decisions to direct public policies that can affect a group or population.

Every organism is constantly at risk of disrupting its homeostasis through injury or illness. Yet, an enormous number of organisms populates our planet. How do they all survive? The answer is that they don't. Still, a sufficient number of organisms survive long enough to reproduce, thus continuing the existence of the species as they slowly evolve. Behavioral adaptations also help reduce the risks that individual organisms face and thus increase the species' chances for survival.

Through a combination of immunological and behavioral adaptations, all living organisms have evolved mechanisms that help them cope with homeostatic disruptions. Certain mammals such as rabbits have two primary behavioral responses to danger. One, they hold very still to reduce the chance of being spotted by a predator. If the danger is more imminent, they run away quickly. Many

Figure E6.16   Uncontrollable risks.   Even though the driver of this car was driving carefully and wearing a seat belt, she was severely injured by a reckless driver.

flowering plants protect themselves against freezing by losing their leaves in the winter. Even bacteria can detect toxic substances and respond by moving away. Humans, therefore, are not the only organisms that have behavioral and physical means to maintain homeostasis and survive. Humans, however, may be the only organisms with the ability to make *conscious decisions* about behaviors that can affect not only their own species, but also every other species on the planet. ◆

Ethical Analysis

Science can tell you about how things work. Science can help answer questions about whether something could happen in a given situation. Science, however, cannot tell you what you *should* do in a given situation. Questions that involve issues of "should" are ethical questions. In an ethical dilemma, your choices depend not only on facts about the world, which science may help explain, but also on values. Values are those ideas that are important to you, your family, or your society. The complex interactions between religion, philosophy, and culture shape our values.

The thinking and evidence-collection processes that scientists use to study questions about nature also are valuable for studying ethical questions. Just as scientists must gather data to support or disprove their hypotheses, ethicists must work hard to develop strong arguments that support their positions. Evidence is as crucial to the ethical process as it is to science. An opinion that lacks the weight of critical thinking and supporting information likely will not be persuasive. People who approach ethical choices in a careful way, using analysis and reasoning to make their decisions, are using the process of ethical analysis.

What are some steps in the process of ethical analysis?

First, *identify the question* of interest clearly and precisely. It is difficult to construct strong arguments unless you are clear about the question you wish to address. For example, you might ask: Is it ethical to have a law that requires car occupants to wear seat belts?

Second, *gather information* about the issue in question. This information might include expert opinions about the issue from various perspectives. Experts may include philosophers, historians, theologians, economists, and scientists. The information must be accurate so that you can use it effectively to support your arguments.

Third, *evaluate the information* to understand how it applies to the issue you are facing. It is important to evaluate the information as it pertains to the individuals and groups that may be affected. You must consider how the issue affects the *interests* of

Figure E6.17 **Complicated issues have no simple solutions.** The facts of such issues must be analyzed in light of the interests of everyone affected.

each individual, of particular groups of people, and of society as a whole. It also is important to consider these interests in light of both the *consequences* of any actions and any *rights*, or freedoms, which might be denied. For example, consider again the issue of requiring all people to wear seat belts while traveling in a vehicle. Such a law promotes the best interests of the individuals and of society because it reduces the chance of injury in a car accident. Some argue, however, that it infringes on the rights and freedom of individuals to make their own choices.

Fourth, use your data to *form well-reasoned arguments* that support one or more solutions to the ethical issue or conflict. For instance, evaluate the health care costs that society must pay when car occupants who don't use seat belts are injured in accidents. A cost might be an increase in insurance premiums for other car owners. You might reason that the rights of individuals not to wear seat belts are less important than the increased costs of health care and insurance to society.

Fifth, you and the people to whom you present your arguments and conclusions must critically *analyze your case* to determine its validity. For instance, an economist might challenge the assertion that car occupants without seat belts contribute significantly to overall health costs. In such a case, you could analyze the new cost data. (The economist is using these data to support the position that individuals' rights should not be denied.) Then you could determine whether it is more or less reliable than the data used to support the original argument. (Society's interest in reducing health costs is of greater importance.)

Sixth, *make a recommendation* about what *should* be done about the issue. Use these well-supported arguments to help decide how you or society as a whole plan to take action to address the issue. ◆

Energy, Matter, and Organization: Relationships in Living Systems

Energy. We all use it in varying amounts, 24 hours a day, 365 days a year. What exactly is energy, and where does it come from? How is energy related to the matter we take in each day as food? How do matter and energy help organisms like us perform? Think of a runner nearing the finish line. From where does the runner get the energy needed for that final burst of speed?

In this unit, you will explore matter, energy, and the relationship between them. You will investigate how matter and energy can explain levels of human performance that allow a runner to sprint to the finish line at the end of a long race. Then you will see how cellular processes in the body extract energy from the food consumed by this runner. You will learn where the energy present in food originates. Before beginning Chapter 9, you will construct experimental worm habitats and observe how the worms interact with their environment. You also will see how matter and energy link all of the organisms in a community.

By the end of Unit 3, you should understand how

- an individual's performance depends on diet and exercise,
- maintaining fitness involves matter and energy,
- energy is stored in the organization of matter,
- living organisms obtain and process matter and energy for activity as well as to build and maintain body structures, and
- communities of organisms depend on the cycling of matter and the flow of energy.

You also will continue to

- collect, organize, and analyze data;
- propose explanations; and
- test hypotheses.

> "Durability is part of what makes a great athlete."
>
> *Bill Russell*

Performance and Fitness

What do the people in these photos have in common? Each is engaged in a physical activity that requires a certain level of fitness. The people playing on the beach may not necessarily have the same degree of athletic fitness as a professional tennis player, but to live an active, healthy life, they still must meet a certain standard of fitness.

In this chapter, you will learn how matter and energy are related to human physical performance. You will explore your understanding of the term *fitness* and why being fit should be an important priority for all of us. You will investigate the biological explanations for how exercise and good eating habits promote fitness. By the end of this chapter, you should begin to see how the foods you eat provide the matter and energy necessary to build your body and keep it functioning.

ACTIVITIES

Engage	Thinking about Fitness
Explore	What Determines Fitness?
Explain	What Is in the Food You Eat?
Explain	You Are What You Eat
Elaborate	Structures and Functions
Evaluate	Marathon

Engage

Thinking about Fitness

What is required of the body during extreme levels of human performance? What is required to sustain even basic levels of nonathletic activities such as climbing stairs or playing catch with a friend? Let's begin our exploration of the biology behind human performance with a look at what it means to be *physically fit*. Fitness often means different things to different people. Physicians may view fitness as freedom from disease. Coaches may emphasize physical performance. In this activity, think about some possible meanings of the term *fitness*. How might this concept apply to you?

PROCESS AND PROCEDURES

1. Carefully consider your answers to the questions below. Record your responses in your journal.

   a. What is your personal definition of fitness?

   b. What factors most affect your level of fitness, as you defined it?

2. Copy the fitness scale diagrams shown in Figure 7.1 into your journal.

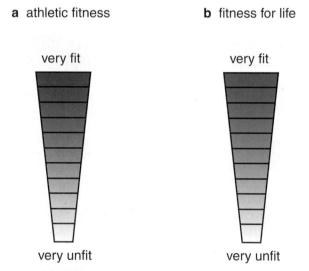

a athletic fitness   **b** fitness for life

very fit   very fit

very unfit   very unfit

Figure 7.1 Types of fitness. An individual's level of athletic fitness does not necessarily correspond to his or her level of fitness for life.

3. As you read the story *The Sky Awaits*, think about the fitness scales and what they mean.

SCENARIO

The Sky Awaits

It's 4 a.m. The sun has not come up yet on this day in early August, but there's work to be done. Captain Yates rolls out of bed, takes a shower, dons a flight suit and boots, and heads for the kitchen of the small apartment. Breakfast consists of a slice of grilled ham, two eggs over easy, wheat toast with strawberry jam, a glass of orange juice, and a cup of coffee.

Yates steers the bright-red sports car onto the highway and heads out to the air base. As the car approaches the main gate of the base, the sky begins to brighten in the east. It looks as though it will be a good day to fly. As an instructor pilot in the U.S. Air Force, Yates flies a T-38 Talon—a supersonic jet trainer capable of speeds up to 1,450 kilometers per hour (900 mph).

After parking the car, Yates checks the schedule and learns that the first student pilot today is Lieutenant Sullivan. Yates then checks the weather forecast—no ceiling, unlimited visibility, and calm winds until about 1100 hours, when clouds will begin to build. After the preflight briefing, in which Yates explains the objectives of the flight to Sullivan, the two pilots get into their G-suits and parachutes. At the airplane, they go through the preflight checklist, run up the engines, and check the equipment that will deliver 100 percent oxygen for them to breathe. They taxi onto the runway. Almost immediately, it's their turn to take off. Yates stands on the brakes and sets the throttles at full afterburner. The takeoff roll is smooth. Sullivan retracts the wheels as the jet soars into the brilliant sky.

This flight is an acrobatics mission in a practice area some 120 kilometers (75 miles) west of the air base. At an altitude of 7,925 meters (26,000 feet), the outside air temperature is –26.2°C (–14°F). Yates executes a roll to look in every direction, and then Sullivan takes over for the next phase of the mission.

U.S. Air Force T-38 supersonic jet fighter

The first maneuver is a "G-awareness turn" that prepares Yates and Sullivan for the rigors of the training mission. In the first half of the turn—a 70°–80° bank—the pilots strain against the nearly instantaneous pull of up to four times the force of gravity, or four Gs. Because of the acceleration forces that result from making sharp turns at high speeds, Yates and Sullivan weigh almost four times their normal weight. Their G-suits automatically inflate around the lower portion of their bodies so blood will not pool in their hips, legs, and feet. This could possibly cause them to black out from a decreased flow of blood and oxygen to their brains. Sullivan tightens the turn to a 90° bank. This produces almost six Gs, before the plane rolls back to a straight and level flight.

This warm-up is the beginning of a strenuous and physically exhausting routine that lasts almost 30 minutes. The routine consists of loops, rolls, stalls, and other similar high-G maneuvers. During this routine, the pilots' bodies strain against blacking out from the added force. Their heart rates soar, their muscles tense as hard as rock, and their breathing is labored.

When their maneuvers are complete, Yates and Sullivan begin to relax. The return flight is much less demanding. The approach to the base and the landing are uneventful. As they walk off the flight line and enter the squadron building, both pilots realize that they are now very hungry and a bit tired. It's no wonder. The physical demands of the morning's flight were similar to those required of highly trained, competitive athletes. The training and level of fitness necessary for this work are a way of life for Captain Jennifer Yates and Lieutenant John Sullivan.

4. Refer to the fitness scales as you discuss and complete the following with the members of your team:

   a. What does scale *a* represent? What physical and behavioral characteristics would you expect to find in an individual who scores very high on such a scale?

   b. What does scale *b* represent? What characteristics would you expect to find in an individual who scores very high on this scale?

   c. Where on each scale would you place Sullivan and Yates? In your journal, mark and label where you would place Sullivan and Yates on each scale. Below the diagrams, write a sentence explaining why you placed Sullivan and Yates at those positions.

   d. These separate scales represent athletic fitness and fitness for life. They suggest that it may be possible for a person to lack special athletic skills and still be very fit for life. Mark and label where you would place such an individual on each scale. What benefits do you think might be associated with a high level of fitness for life?

   e. Where would you place yourself on the fitness-for-life scale? List several ways that you and the other members of your team could modify your lifestyles to improve your positions on this scale.

Explore

What Determines Fitness?

At times in our evolutionary past, *Homo sapiens* depended on strength and endurance to survive. The physical ability to get food and stay safe determined one's physical fitness. Advances in technology, however, have helped shape a lifestyle in which most people in technological societies can obtain food and shelter without performing any *strenuous* work. Nevertheless, medical evidence suggests that a basic level of physical fitness is essential to withstand the stresses of life and maintain a sense of well-being.

A number of factors appear to determine fitness. In this activity, you will explore two factors, exercise and diet, that affect your level of fitness. Remember, your goal in this chapter is to understand the *biological basis* for how exercise and diet influence human fitness.

PROCESS AND PROCEDURES

Part A Looking at Physical Activity

1. Work individually to complete the *Physical Activity Analysis* that your teacher provides.

   Attach this analysis to your journal; you may need to refer to it during subsequent activities.

Figure 7.2 Comparing activities. Who is using more energy?

2. Answer the following questions individually. Record your answers in your journal. Base your responses on your activity level that you determined in step 1.

   a. How do you think your activity level compares with that of a typical student in your class?

   b. How do you think your activity level might compare with that of Yates and Sullivan from the story *The Sky Awaits*?

3. On the sheet that your teacher circulates, place a check mark (✓) next to your activity level, which you determined in step 1.

   Your teacher will use this information to create an activity level profile for the class.

4. Enter the activity level profile for the class in the appropriate spaces on the worksheet in the *Physical Activity Analysis*.

Part B Looking at Diet

1. Work individually to complete the *Dietary Analysis* that your teacher provides.

   Attach this analysis to your journal; you may need to refer to it in subsequent activities.

2. Answer the following questions individually. Record your answers in your journal. Base your responses on the *Dietary Analysis* that you completed in step 1.

   a. How do you think your diet compares with that of a typical student in your class?

   b. How do you think your diet might compare with that of Yates and Sullivan?

3. Work with your team to complete the following steps. The data you provide will help your teacher generate a dietary profile of a typical student in your class.

    a. Choose 1 of the food groups listed on the *Dietary Analysis*. Ask 4 students outside your team how many servings from that group they ate yesterday. Record their responses.

      Each member of your team should choose a different food group.

    b. Calculate the average number of daily servings (from the food group you chose) that you and the 4 students you polled ate yesterday.

      Average # of servings = (total # servings eaten in 1 day by you and 4 other students) ÷ 5.

      This will give you a rough approximation of how much a typical student in your class eats from that food group.

    c. Contribute your data to the dietary profile your teacher will compile on the chalkboard.

4. Enter the information for this typical student into the column titled Class Profile on the *Dietary Analysis* worksheet.

5. Participate in a class discussion of the following. Base your responses on the information that you collected in Parts A and B.

    a. Are you surprised at the activity profile or dietary profile of your class? Are you surprised at how your own profiles compare to the class profiles? Explain your answers.

    b. Identify ways in which the class profiles do not accurately represent typical activity levels and dietary patterns in society.

    c. Why do you think many people fail to sustain an adequate level of physical activity or fail to eat an appropriate number of servings from each food group?

Analysis

PAGE 326

1. Work individually, and use all of the information in this activity to help you answer the following questions. Record your responses in your journal.

    The essay *Human Performance: A Function of Fitness* (page 326) will be helpful.

    a. What resources does your body require during extreme levels of physical performance?

    b. What resources does your body require to sustain basic levels of nonathletic activity?

    c. Refine and rewrite your personal definition of fitness from step 1 of the engage activity. Incorporate any new ideas that you have learned.

2. Work with your partner to complete the following task. Then follow your teacher's instructions for posting your advertisement.

    Imagine that you are the owner of a new health club in your neighborhood. Create a one-page newspaper advertisement for your club that would draw a reader's attention to the most compelling reasons you know for maintaining or improving one's fitness for life.

What Is in the Food You Eat?

Do you ever read food labels or the nutrition panels on the boxes of the cereal that you eat for breakfast? These labels list the names of all the ingredients, some of which are probably familiar while others may be unfamiliar. Many of these ingredients include the nutrients that supply the matter that is essential for your body to function naturally. Consider the previous activity, *What Determines Fitness?* Perhaps it is now clear that the energy source required for fitness is also food. The nutrients in food supply both the matter and the energy that your body requires for performance. Are all of these nutrients equivalent? How do food scientists know what nutrients are present in particular types of food?

In this activity, you will determine the presence or absence of five specific nutrients in a set of foods that your teacher will provide. You will combine these test results with the dietary analysis that you completed in *What Determines Fitness?* to discover what you *really* ate last week.

Materials (per team of 4)

4 pairs of safety goggles
4 lab aprons
4 pairs of plastic gloves
dropping pipet
500-mL beaker
3 10-mL graduated cylinders
12 18 × 150-mm test tubes
test tube clamp
3 test tube racks
2 glass-marking pencils
hot plate
brown paper
Benedict's solution in dropping bottle
Biuret solution in dropping bottle
indophenol solution in dropping bottle
isopropyl alcohol (99%) in screw-cap jar
Lugol's iodine solution in dropping bottle
4 food samples

Positive Controls

5 100-mL beakers

5 10-mL graduated cylinders

50 mL of 1% ascorbic acid (vitamin C)

small tub of regular margarine or small bottle of vegetable oil

50 mL of a 6% suspension of gelatin

50 mL of a 10% solution of sucrose

50 mL of a 10% solution of glucose

50 mL of a 6% suspension of starch

PROCESS AND PROCEDURES

To begin developing your own explanation for what is in the food you eat, set up and complete the following tests:

1. Assemble in the teams of 4 that your teacher assigns. Obtain the 4 food samples that your team is to test.

2. In your journal, create a table for recording the foods that the class will test, your predictions about what nutrients each food contains, and the actual test results.

   Each team will test 4 foods. But your table should have space to record your predictions and the class results of 5 tests for each of 12 foods. Indicators are available to test for the following nutrients: starch, sugar (glucose and sucrose), vitamin C, fats and oils, and protein. *Indicators* are chemical or physical methods used to test for the presence of certain substances.

3. Begin to fill in your table. Enter your predictions about what nutrients you will find in each of the 12 foods that the class will test. Discuss your predictions with your other team members.

4. Review the protocol for nutrient testing. Each member of your team will test 1 food for each of the 5 nutrients.

   Be sure to use the correct indicator for each test. Follow the directions carefully for its use.

5. Read the information in the need to know box to help you understand the role of indicators in certain types of investigations.

6. As a team, make a complete set of positive and negative controls to be shared.

   Be sure to label each test tube clearly with the nutrient that the indicator tests for. Use a plus sign (+) if it is the positive control, or a minus sign (−) if it is the negative control.

7. Complete your tests. Follow the instructions in Protocol for Nutrient Tests. Record a plus sign (+) in the results column of your table if the food contains a given nutrient. Use a minus sign (−) in the same column if it does not contain the nutrient. Also, record your observations about the color. Indicate how sure you were about your interpretation of each test result for later reference.

NEED TO KNOW

The Role of Indicators

When scientists use indicators, they run positive and negative controls side by side with the unknowns. Positive controls show the expected results if a given substance is *present*. Negative controls show the expected results if a given substance is *absent*. For example, a known sample of glucose (a positive control) tested with a glucose indicator gives a positive result. If you see the same result after testing a food, you could conclude that glucose is part of that food. In contrast, water (a negative control) tested with a glucose indicator would give a negative test result (see Figure 7.3). Recall that all controls, except for the variable under study, should be handled in exactly the same manner as the experimental materials.

SAFETY: Put on your safety goggles, lab apron, and gloves. Tie back long hair.

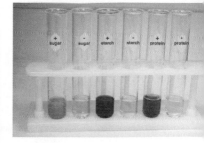

Figure 7.3 Make and label a set of positive and negative controls for each nutrient that your team will share.

Safety Goggles **Lab Apron**

Lab Gloves

Remember, compare the appropriate negative and positive controls each time you test your food for a nutrient.

Pay particular attention to the warning/caution statements for each of the indicators.

8. Wash your hands thoroughly with soap and water.

   Follow your teacher's instructions for disposing of all waste materials.

9. Share your results with the other members of your team. Then enter their test results in your data table.

   Be sure that you understand the results of each test.

PROTOCOL

Protocol for Nutrient Tests

Nutrient	Test
Fats and oils	Rub a drop of ground-up food on a piece of brown paper. Hold the paper up to a light after the water in the sample has evaporated. Fats and oils make a translucent greasy spot on paper. No translucent spot appears in the absence of fats and oils. *Note:* When food contains only a small amount of fats or oils, it may not be detected by this method. If no fats or oils are detected, do the following: a. Place the assigned food in 10 mL of a fat and oil solvent such as isopropyl alcohol (99%).

(continued)

Flammable! Poison!

Figure 7.4 Indicators are substances that show the presence or absence of another substance by changing characteristics, especially color.

Poison!

Irritant

Irritant

Irritant

Protocol for Nutrient Tests (*continued*)

WARNING: Alcohol is *flammable* and is a *poison*. Do not expose the liquid or its vapors to heat, sparks, open flame, or other ignition sources. Do not ingest; avoid skin/eye contact. If contact occurs, flush affected area with water for 15 minutes; rinse mouth with water. If a spill occurs, flood spill area with water; *then* call the teacher.

b. Allow the food to dissolve in the solvent for about 5 minutes.

c. Pour the solvent on brown paper. The spot should dry in about 10 minutes.

d. Check the paper for a translucent spot.

Protein

Place 5 mL of ground-up food in a test tube. Add 10 drops of Biuret solution. Biuret is an indicator (see Figure 7.4). The Biuret test gives a pink to purple reaction in the presence of protein. No color change occurs in the absence of protein.

WARNING: Biuret solution is a *strong irritant* and may damage clothing. Avoid skin/eye contact; do not ingest. If contact occurs, flush affected area with water for 15 minutes; rinse mouth with water. Call the teacher immediately.

Starch

Add 5 drops of Lugol's iodine solution to a 5-mL sample of ground-up food. Lugol's turns bluish black in the presence of starch. No color change occurs in the absence of starch.

WARNING: Lugol's iodine solution is a *poison* if ingested, a *strong irritant*, and can stain clothing. Avoid skin/eye contact; do not ingest. If contact occurs, flush affected area with water for 15 minutes; rinse mouth with water. Call the teacher immediately.

Sugar

Add 3 mL of Benedict's solution to a 5-mL sample of ground-up food. Place the test tube in a beaker of boiling water. Heat for 5 minutes. If the test tube contains glucose, the Benedict's solution will react and turn orange or brick red. If the test tube contains either sucrose or no sugar, no reaction will take place. The solution will remain pale blue.

CAUTION: Benedict's solution is an *irritant*. Avoid skin/eye contact; do not ingest. If contact occurs, flush affected area with water for 15 minutes; rinse mouth with water. Call the teacher.

WARNING: Use test tube clamps to hold hot test tubes. Always hold a hot tube in such a way that the mouth of the tube is pointed away from your face or anyone else's. Boiling water will scald, causing second-degree burns. Do not touch the beaker or allow boiling water to contact your skin. Avoid vigorous boiling. If a burn occurs, *immediately* place the burned area under cold running water; *then* call the teacher.

Vitamin C

Add 8 drops of indophenol solution to a 5-mL sample of ground-up food. Blue indophenol becomes colorless in the presence of vitamin C. (Disregard the intermediate pink stage.) No color change occurs in the absence of vitamin C.

CAUTION: Indophenol solution is an *irritant*. Avoid skin/eye contact; do not ingest. If contact occurs, flush affected area with water for 15 minutes; rinse mouth with water. Call the teacher.

10. In the class data table, list the foods that your team tested. Enter your test results.

11. Complete your data table by entering the class data.

Some foods may have been tested by more than 1 team. Enter all results in your table. Discuss any discrepancies in the results as a class.

12. Discuss the following questions with your teammates. Record your answers in your journal.

   a. How did the predictions that you made in step 3 compare with the test results? Which results were the most surprising? Why?

   b. How might the natural colors of the foods affect the results?

   c. Why was it important to test each indicator using water as the negative control substance?

   d. Why was it important to test each indicator with a substance known to contain the nutrient in question?

Analysis

Complete the following tasks. Record your responses in your journal.

Read the essays *Food: Our Body's Source of Energy and Structural Materials* (page 328), and *Pioneers: The Changing Face of the Food Guide Pyramid* (page 333).

PAGE 328

PAGE 333

1. Examine the *Dietary Analysis* that you completed in the activity *What Determines Fitness?* Notice that the foods you tested in the laboratory included one from each of the six food groups in this analysis. If you assume that foods from the same food group contain many of the same nutrients, then you can use your test results to determine the actual nutrients that were likely present in the foods you listed on your dietary analysis. Based on your tests alone, identify which foods you ate that your body could use as a source of

   a. protein,

   b. sugar,

   c. starch,

   d. vitamin C, and

   e. fats and oils.

2. Compare your test results with the information given in the essay *Food: Our Body's Source of Energy and Structural Materials*. What does the information in this essay suggest about the sensitivity and/or the accuracy of the tests you completed?

3. Which, if any, of the foods that you ate contained all of the nutrients for which you tested? What does this mean for eating a balanced diet?

Further Challenges

Study the two graphs in Figure 7.5. These graphs represent the results of an experiment in which a cracker was placed in a test tube along with saliva. Points on the graphs were determined by using the same indicator tests for starch and sugar that you used in this activity. Use the results displayed in these graphs to explain the changes that the saliva caused.

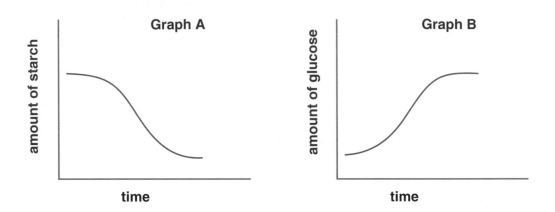

Figure 7.5 Changes in nutrient content across time. Graph A shows the changes in the amount of starch across time. Graph B shows the changes in the amount of glucose across time.

Explain

You Are What You Eat

In the previous activities, you investigated what is in the food that you eat. But once this food is inside you, how does it become useful to your body? What does your body do to this matter so that you can use the energy it contains for performance? How does your body prepare this matter so that you will have the building blocks necessary for growth and repair (*biosynthesis*)? In this activity, you will look at digestion to understand the role it plays in preparing to release the energy stored in food molecules and in providing a source of building blocks for biosynthesis.

Materials (per team of 4)

materials to carry out the experiment that you design
DVD and player

PROCESS AND PROCEDURES

Part A   Food for Energy

1. Read the background information in the need to know box to yourself.

NEED TO KNOW

Background Information

Starch is an energy-storage molecule in plants. It makes up a large part of the food that many organisms eat. Plants manufacture starch using energy from the sun. Energy from the sun is stored in the starch molecules. When plants break the starch into its component sugars, the energy that was stored in the starch molecules is released. In this way, plants use the energy from the starch, which originally came from the sun, to live.

Animals that eat plants can use starch in the same way that the plants that built the starch can. The energy from the sun that the plant used to build starch molecules is available to animals that eat the plant. Starch is too large to be absorbed into the bloodstream directly from the intestine. Many animals have enzymes that break down starch to small sugars. In humans, the enzyme amylase, which is present in saliva, breaks down starch.

Amylase is an enzyme found in human saliva. It also is available in pure form from commercial suppliers.

Benedict's solution is an indicator that shows an orange or brick red color in the presence of glucose and green in the presence of sucrose. No color change occurs in the absence of sugar. Add 3 mL of Benedict's solution to 5 mL of sample solution. Place the test tube in a beaker of boiling water. Heat for 5 minutes.

CAUTION: Benedict's solution is an *irritant*. Avoid skin/eye contact; do not ingest. If contact occurs, flush affected area with water for 15 minutes; rinse mouth with water. Call the teacher.

WARNING: Use test tube clamps to hold hot test tubes. Always hold a hot tube in such a way that the mouth of the tube is pointed away from your face or anyone else's. Boiling water will scald, causing second-degree burns. Do not touch the beaker or allow boiling water to contact your skin. Avoid vigorous boiling. If a burn occurs, *immediately* place the burned area under cold running water; *then* call the teacher.

Buffers can be added to a solution to control the pH.

Enzymes are proteins that speed up chemical reactions. A solution containing an enzyme must be added to a solution containing the appropriate substrates before the reaction can begin. Several factors can affect the activity, or behavior, of the enzyme. These include the temperature, the pH of the mixture, and the incubation time. (This is the time that the enzyme and the substrates are in contact with each other.)

Glucose test strips indicate the presence of simple sugars (such as maltose) in solution by changing color. (Your teacher will give you information about how to interpret the color change.)

Lugol's iodine solution is an indicator that changes color in the presence of starch. In a spot plate or test tube, use 1 drop of Lugol's iodine solution for 1 mL of sample solution that you are testing.

WARNING: Lugol's iodine solution is a *poison* if ingested, a *strong irritant,* and it can stain clothing. Avoid skin/eye contact; do not ingest. If contact occurs, flush affected area with water for 15 minutes; rinse mouth with water. Call the teacher immediately.

(continued)

Topic: proteins/enzymes
Go to: www.scilinks.org
Code: human3E273

Caution

Poison!

Background Information *(continued)*

Maltose is a sugar that results when starch is broken down by amylase. It can be obtained in pure form from commercial suppliers.

Starch is a macromolecule that can be obtained in pure form from commercial suppliers.

Substrates are molecules to which enzymes bind. Enzymes act to speed up reactions involving substrates.

PAGE 334

2. With your team, develop an outline of a controlled experiment to investigate the process whereby amylase breaks down starch to sugar.

   Use these resources to help you complete this task: the essay *What Happens to the Food You Eat?* (page 334), Background on Controlled Experiments (page 155), and the background information in the need to know box in this activity.

3. Choose a variable that might affect the amylase/starch reaction. Develop a hypothesis about its effect on the reaction. Variables that you might consider include

   ◆ presence of light,

   ◆ concentration of amylase,

   ◆ concentration of starch,

   ◆ temperature, and

   ◆ pH.

4. Have your teacher check that your outline demonstrates the appropriate reaction and that you have designed a controlled experiment.

5. Write a hypothesis for your experiment in your journal. Explain how you think your variable will affect the amylase and starch reaction, and why.

   You may want to write your hypothesis as an *if . . . then* statement combined with an explanation.

6. Have your teacher approve your hypothesis. Then write a detailed procedure for your experiment. Again, ask your teacher to approve it.

7. Carry out your experiment, and record all results in your journal.

Safety Goggles   **Lab Apron**

SAFETY: Put on your safety goggles and lab apron.

8. Wash your hands thoroughly when you are finished.

9. In your journal, prepare a lab report of your experiment. Each team will present its findings to the rest of the class.

   You need to report the following information clearly to your classmates:

   ◆   A statement of the question or hypothesis

   ◆   The procedure for conducting the experiment

- Your results
- An analysis of the data
- An explanation of the role of enzymes in digestion and the effect of different variables on enzyme reactions

10. Participate in a class presentation and discussion of each team's results.

Take notes on the effects of variables on enzyme reactions. Your classmates' results will be important for your final analysis.

11. Based on your class's data, add to your lab report a final summary and analysis of the effect of different variables on enzyme reactions.

Part B Food for the Body's Building Blocks

Food provides energy. But it also is the source of matter that animals use to produce new structures necessary for body maintenance and continued operation.

1. Take notes as you watch the DVD segment "Introduction to Biosynthesis."

2. Participate in a class discussion about this question: What happens when a foreign protein enters an animal?

3. The digestive system is a group of organs that breaks down food into small molecules. In this way, the molecules can be absorbed into the blood and transported by the circulatory system to all cells of the body (see Figure 7.6). In your journal, create a flowchart or diagram of the digestive system. Trace the path that the nutrients in a cheeseburger would take from being eaten to being absorbed into the bloodstream.

salivary glands
esophagus
liver
stomach
gall bladder
pancreas
small intestine
large intestine
rectum
anus

digestive system

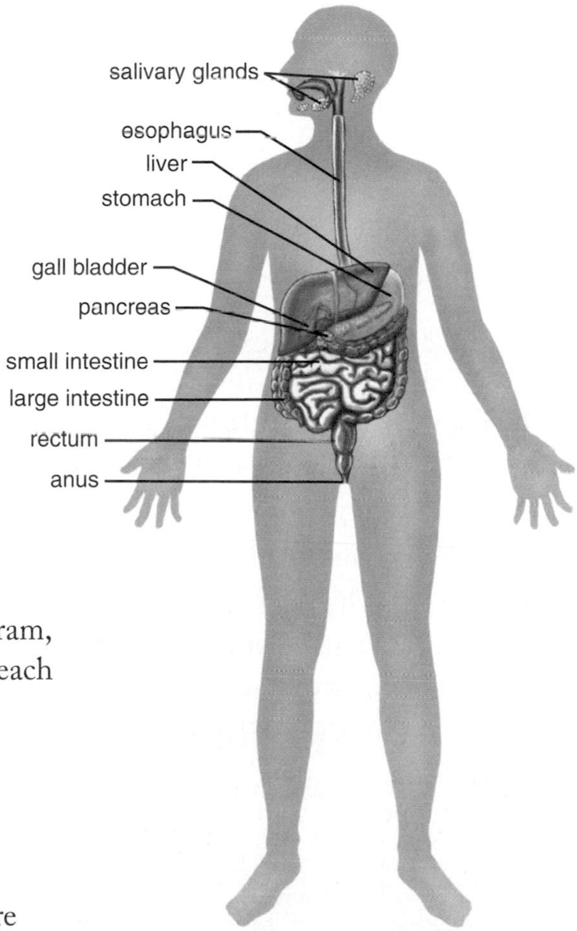

Figure 7.6 The digestive system is a group of organs that breaks down food into small molecules.

4. Alongside your flowchart or diagram, write *break down* or *absorption* at each step according to which process occurs at that stage of digestion.

5. Read the essay *Anorexia Nervosa: Dying to Be Thin* (page 337). In your journal, explain where the building blocks for biosynthesis are obtained for a person suffering from anorexia nervosa.

PAGE 337

Structures and Functions

Recall from the previous activity, *You Are What You Eat*, that the food you eat is broken down by the digestive system. The raw materials that result from digestion, materials such as amino acids, sugars, and fatty acids, may serve as building blocks in the synthesis of various body structures. Muscle tissue is a good example. For instance, amino acids are the building blocks your body requires for repairing and growing muscle tissue. Once these building blocks are synthesized into muscle protein, they become part of a larger structure: a muscle. The function of muscles is to provide mobility. But not all proteins—for example, enzymes—provide mobility. Amylase is an example. This protein provides an important function for the body, the breakdown of starch. What is special about how muscle proteins are arranged into structures that allow physical activity?

In this activity, you will think about how building blocks obtained from the matter of digested food become organized into larger structures that have very specific functions. You will also relate the relationship between structure and function to human fitness and performance.

Materials (per team of 2)

brass brad	25-cm piece of string
rubber bands	roll of tape
scissors	DVD and player
sheet of thin cardboard	

PROCESS AND PROCEDURES

1. View the DVD segment "Muscle Movement at the Molecular Level." With your partner, suggest an answer to the following questions:

   a. What type of movement does the structure of muscles permit?

   b. What are the advantages and disadvantages of this structural arrangement of muscle fibers?

2. Perform the following steps to explore the function of muscle fibers at a *higher* level of organization. This is a level at which matter is organized in a way that allows physical motion.

   a. Bend and straighten 1 arm while using your other hand to feel what happens to your biceps and triceps.

   PAGE 337

   Consult Figure E7.11 in the essay *The Structural Basis of Physical Mobility* (page 337) if you are not sure where the biceps and triceps are located.

   b. Develop an explanation of how your biceps and triceps generate these movements.

   c. Discuss your observations and understandings with your partner.

3. Working with your partner, use the materials provided and the information in Figure 7.7 to construct a working model of your thigh and lower leg. Be sure to show the attachment sites of the quadriceps muscles on the front of the thigh and the hamstring muscles on the back of the thigh.

You might use the cardboard for bone, the string or rubber bands for muscle, the tape for tendons, and the brad for the knee. You may use a different combination of parts to form your model. Try to make the model as realistic as possible.

4. Place your model on the table with the leg straight. Grasp the hamstring just below the upper attachment site. Gently pull the hamstring. What happens? Release the muscle, but do not reposition the lower leg. Record your observations in your journal.

5. Now grasp the quadriceps just below its upper attachment site and pull gently. What happens? How does this movement differ from that in step 4? Record your observations and explanation in your journal.

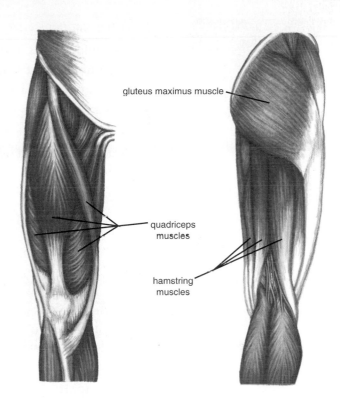

Figure 7.7 Muscles of the human leg. The quadriceps and hamstring muscles each extend across the knee to connect to the bones of the lower leg.

6. Discuss the following with your partner. Record your responses in your journal.

a. Explain the statement, Muscles work in pairs. Why is that important?

b. What is the role of the joint in producing movement?

c. Recall from the DVD segment that the molecular filaments in muscles can shorten muscles but cannot lengthen them. How do you think it is possible for us to push on anything?

You may wish to test your answer by pushing on a wall. Feel both your biceps and triceps muscles. How are they acting to stabilize your arm? Why is this important to your ability to exert force against the wall?

Analysis

Participate in a class discussion of the following. For important background information, read the essays *The Structural Basis of Physical Mobility* (page 337), *The Ant That Terrorized Milwaukee* (page 341), and *Energy's Role in Making Structures Functional* (page 342).

1. Explain the *basic* matter and energy requirements needed for a muscle to contract.

2. What happens *biologically* when muscle fatigue occurs?

3. We build models to mimic a structure or an event. Good models mimic the actual structure or event so closely that changes in the model predict what would happen in the real world. Describe the strengths and weaknesses of your leg model.

4. Vertebrate muscles contract against the resistance of an internal skeleton made of bone. Create a table in your journal. Compare two advantages and two disadvantages of a hydrostatic skeleton, an exoskeleton, and an endoskeleton (see Figure 7.8).

            a   b   c

Figure 7.8 **(a) Hydrostatic skeleton. (b) Exoskeleton. (c) Endoskeleton.**

5. How does increased physical activity promote fitness? Be specific. Include the effect of increased activity on the structure and function of an individual muscle.

6. Recall that your heart is a muscle. During vigorous activity, your heart pumps faster and harder. It delivers blood more rapidly to both the lungs and the exercising muscles. How would vigorous activity promote the increased fitness of the heart itself? How would it help muscles in other parts of your body to function more effectively?

Evaluate   # Marathon

Remember the last Summer Olympic Games? Many athletes broke world records. If you watched the games on television, you may have thought that those athletes made it look easy. Nevertheless, you were watching some of the highest levels of human performance ever recorded. A tremendous number of biological and behavioral factors had to be just right for such exceptional performances.

One of the most physically challenging of all events is the marathon. This race covers a distance of 42.2 kilometers (26 miles, 385 yards). Athletes usually train for many years to build up to the endurance level that is required to compete in this event. In this activity, you will follow the progress of four people who entered a marathon. You will propose explanations for the role that matter and energy played in their performance. Your analysis will provide evidence of your understanding of the biological relationship between matter and energy and human performance and fitness.

Materials

DVD and player

PROCESS AND PROCEDURES

1. As a class, watch the DVD segment "A Good Day for Running."
2. With your team of 4, read *The Race*. This story describes a marathon and the training and performance of 4 people who participated in it.

SCENARIO

The Race

The Scenario

It is a mid-August day in a high-altitude town in Colorado. Runners are gathering for an annual marathon that has been held at this site for many years. This race is interesting because several shorter races and a full marathon are held simultaneously. All of the runners start together. Each runner, either before or during the race, decides the exact distance he or she will run. The runners do so simply by stopping at certain measured increments. They may run 5K, 10K, 21K, or the full marathon distance of 42.2K. About 100 runners are lined up and ready to start.

Four of the Runners

Mel

Mel, a grandfather in his late 40s, is a college professor who began running in his early 30s. Mel decided to begin running to control his weight and discovered that he really enjoyed this activity. As his running program progressed, he went from recreational running to competitive running because of the many positive changes he saw in his body and his lifestyle.

Amy

Amy was a member of her cross-country team in college. Now, at age 33, she is an attorney and maintains a high level of competitive fitness. Amy continues her running program as part of her lifestyle. She trains regularly and enters several races each year.

Neal

Neal is an exercise physiologist. He is currently employed as a scientist in a government laboratory. At the lab, Neal manages a wellness program for employees. He puts together exercise prescriptions for people who want to attain various levels of fitness. Neal was a track star and a classmate of Amy's in college. He also decided to make competitive running a major part of his life. He and Amy have run together many times.

John

John is in his early 40s. He is an engineer who always had enjoyed watching runners and had wished that he could run. One evening after a very greasy supper, John announced to his wife that he was going to train for and complete a marathon. His wife laughed. In contrast to the other three runners listed, John was a smoker, slightly overweight, had done no running except for occasional short-distance jogging, and drank alcohol "slightly more than moderately" (as he explained it).

How the Runners Trained

Mel

This was Mel's first full marathon, but he had participated in many shorter-distance races and fun runs. The farthest he had run competitively was a half-marathon. He had a practice course that he especially liked. He ran the course 4 days a week, a distance of about 8K (5 miles). About 1 month before the

(continued)

The Race (continued)

marathon, he increased his commitment to 13K (8 miles), 4 days a week. Mel lived and trained at high altitude in Colorado. Leading up to the race, Mel ate regular meals with his family. These balanced meals included carbohydrates, proteins, low amounts of fats, and plenty of vegetables. He had a meal of French toast and juice the morning of the race.

Amy and Neal

Their approaches to training and their lifestyles were nearly identical. They worked out at a moderate pace, consistently drinking plenty of fluids, and eating diets that emphasized carbohydrates. They participated in a regular training program in which they ran a variety of distances at different speeds. About 6 weeks before the marathon, they finally settled on a steady workout regimen of running 16K (10 miles), 4 days a week. They included rest periods in their weekly schedules to allow recovery from mild stiffness, soreness, and tired muscles. For several days before the race, they ate large amounts of whole-grain bread, cereals, and pasta. On the morning of the race, their breakfast consisted of oatmeal with a little milk and several glasses of juice.

John

John described his first month of training as "terrible." He vowed to quit smoking for the year of training leading up to the marathon. But he struggled with shortness of breath during the early weeks. During the first month, his knees hurt enough to make him reconsider his decision to train and compete. Due to his increased activity, he lost 7 kilograms (15 pounds) in 2 months. He ran mostly at lunch and occasionally again after work. He limited his running to about 5K (3 miles) per workout, 5 days a week. After about 6 weeks, his knees stopped hurting. John was proud of his new energy level, which markedly increased his alertness at work. He also found that he required less sleep and that he slept well. In the 6 weeks before the race, John increased his training distance to 10K (6 miles), 4 days a week. He did not have time to work out more than this. On the day of the race, he thought, I feel ready! Like Mel, John ate meals during training that consisted of whatever his family was eating. About 2 hours before the race, he ate ham and eggs, grits, three pieces of toast, several glasses of juice, and one cup of coffee.

The Race

The race began at 8:00 a.m. sharp. The crisp air of the high-altitude summer morning was invigorating and added to the sense of excitement that all of the runners felt. Some of the participants had arrived nearly an hour before start time. They were slowly stretching both upper and lower body muscles, concentrating on their leg muscles to prevent pulling and cramping. Others were slowly jogging and drinking fluids. Friends and spectators were gathering for the start. Runners prominently displayed their numbers. The weather promised to stay clear and dry.

The runners lined up after some brief instructions and last-minute information about the condition of the course from the starter. How many would go the whole distance? The starter's pistol cracked loudly, and the mass of runners moved forward.

During the first 3K (1.9 miles), the line of runners gradually spread out. Five runners ran in a small pack a good distance out in front of the others and established a quick pace. Amy and Neal, running together for the moment, were in the front third of the main pack and running at a respectable but comfortable pace. John was slightly behind them. Mel was at the beginning of the final third of the pack. A few runners straggled well behind.

Because the first quarter of the race was a gentle downhill stretch, most of the runners felt good. Each established his or her desired pace and settled in for the long haul. At the 5K (3 mile) mark, about 10 runners decided to call it a race. It had been fun for them. At the 10K (6 mile) point, Amy, Neal, John, and Mel were in the same respective positions, all running steadily without tiredness, soreness, or fatigue. All felt that their training was serving them well. They watched as several more runners, including a couple of the front-runners, decided to stop.

The runners now were spread out over a 1.5K (1 mile) length. As the 21K (13 mile) marker came into view on an uphill segment, some runners were obviously struggling to continue. Having established a plodding gait, these runners were ready to call 21K their distance. Several of the front-runners stopped here as well. Amy and Neal were now about one-fourth back in the remaining pack and still were running together.

John was among the last 10 runners. Mel was in the middle, now 400 meters (438 yards) ahead of John. John was feeling a slight pulling sensation in his right calf muscle. He had altered his stride slightly to see whether he could "work it out."

The next 10K (6 mile) segment was quiet and uneventful. All four of our racers and their fellow runners settled into an automatic pace. Amy and Neal were running in relative comfort, pushing themselves slightly, but doing well overall and still maintaining their positions. Mel maintained his middle-of-the-pack position, but was beginning to experience some leg muscle fatigue. In fact, the race was becoming a serious effort. But he was still all right and willing to go the entire route. John noticed the beginning of a blister on his right foot as his shoe rubbed the same spot over and over. Both of his calf muscles were very tight and beginning to hurt, especially now that he was running on hard pavement. Like Mel, he was experiencing leg muscle fatigue, and he considered stopping where he was. Still he ran on. Several other runners were dropping out, some limping, and a few holding their tightened or pulled leg muscles. Some were holding their cramping abdominal muscles. Most just suffered severe fatigue.

The last 12K (7 miles) produced the greatest change in the positions and welfare of the remaining runners. About 30 of the original 100 were left. Neal was running sixth. Amy was about 500 meters (547 yards) back, but she still was running smoothly and steadily. Mel's stride was short, and he felt as though a brick was at the bottom of his chest. The race had become very hard work. His leg muscles were beginning to cramp.

The only way he could relieve these effects was to reduce his pace somewhat and to run with an exaggerated heel-toe gait. With 8K (5 miles) to go, John "hit the wall." His legs became so tired, heavy, and cramped that he could do little more than make slow and laborious forward progress. His pace was only slightly faster than a walk. His chest muscles ached severely, and he began to feel somewhat nauseated. He was in last place, hurting all over, but he still was determined to finish.

Neal was now in fourth place. As he entered the last 2K (1 mile), however, he experienced a "wall" effect. He was pushing himself hard, seeing not only the end of the race, but the possibility of improving his position as well. He crossed the finish line in third place at 3 hours, 5 minutes, 5 seconds, edging out the next male competitor by 50 meters (55 yards). His body went limp, and he had difficulty standing upright. Amy finished at 3 hours, 29 minutes, and was the fifth female competitor to cross the line. She experienced similar final effects as Neal. At 3 hours, 55 minutes, 10 seconds, Mel finished. His "wall" experience in the last 5K (3 miles) had been quite dramatic. He had no energy left for a final sprint to the finish.

At 4 hours, 22 minutes, 20 seconds, John completed his first marathon. His finishing pace was a slightly elongated walk. He held his middle. His legs would no longer support him. He went first to his knees, then over on his back in total collapse. His chest heaved with exaggerated breathing for several minutes before he was able to sit upright. As the runners were recovering from the race and congratulating one another, John's thought was, maybe one is enough!

3. Decide which person in your team will study each runner in depth.

4. Review the information in Figure 7.9, Physiologic Data Related to Physical Performance.

   Think about how each set of information might help you analyze your runner's training and performance. It might also help you suggest general strategies for a marathon runner.

5. Copy Figure 7.9A, Energy Expended in Training and Racing, into your journal. Use information in Figure 7.9C, Exercise and Energy Expenditure, as well as information in *The Race* to complete the table in your journal.

6. Use your understanding of biology, the data in Figure 7.9A–G, and the table that you just completed to analyze your runner's training and performance on

race day. Consider each of the points listed below. Record brief notes about any important information that may help you in the analysis.

Although each of you should analyze only your own runner, you may wish to remain in your teams as you do so. This strategy will allow you to share ideas and begin comparing the runners as you examine their training and performance.

a. Examine your runner's training schedule. In what ways did this schedule prepare him or her to finish the race? How did your runner's energy expenditure per week of race training compare with the amount of energy he or she expended during the marathon?

b. Examine the diet of your runner in the weeks preceding the race. Did your runner appear to be increasing or decreasing his or her intake of any particular class of nutrients during training?

c. Summarize the strategy that you think your runner was using during training.

d. Examine your runner's behavior on the race day before the race began. What strategies do you think he or she was using to prepare for the race?

e. Examine your runner's performance during the marathon. (For example, look at his or her pace, fluid intake, and apparent stamina and success.) What strategies did he or she seem to be using?

f. Propose reasons why your runner's body behaved as it did.

g. Propose ways your runner could have improved his or her performance.

7. Meet with members of other teams who studied the same runner, and compare your findings. Modify your conclusions based on the group input.

Figure 7.9A–G Physiologic data related to physical performance. The following collection of data provides various types of evidence related to diet and physical performance. Use the data to help you analyze your runner's preparation and performance and to help you suggest strategies for improving them.

Runner	Weight	Kcals used/week normal workout (assume 7 min/ mile pace)	Kcals used/week race training (assume 7 min/ mile pace)	Kcals used for marathon (see finish time)
Neal	68 kg (150 lbs)	N/A		
Amy	50 kg (110 lbs)	N/A		
Mel	82 kg (181 lbs)			
John	75 kg (165 lbs)			

Source: From Wilmore, J. H. and D. L. Costill. *Physiology of Sport and Exercise*, (1994). by Human Kinetics.

Figure 7.9A Energy expended in training and racing.

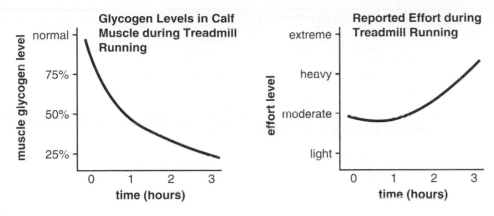

Source: FromWilmore, J. H. and D. L. Costill. *Physiology of Sport and Exercise* (1994). by Human Kinetics.

Figure 7.9B   Muscle glycogen levels in relation to perceived effort during 3 hours of treadmill training.

Exercise	Kcals used/pound every 10 minutes	Exercise	Kcals used/pound every 10 minutes
Bicycling		Skiing	
slow 8 km/h (5 mph)	0.25	downhill	0.59
moderate 16 km/h (10mph)	0.50	cross-country	0.78
fast 21 km/h (13 mph)	0.72	(noncompetitive)	
	0.29		
Golf		Soccer	0.63
Hiking	0.42	Stationary Running	0.78
		(70 80 counts/min)	
Running			
9.6 km/h (10 min/mile)	0.79	Swimming (crawl)	
10.7 km/h (9 min/mile)	0.84	20 m/min	0.32
12 km/h (7 min/mile)	0.89	50 m/min	0.71
13.6 km/h (7 min/mile)	0.95		
16 km/h (6 min/mile)	1.00	Walking	
		3 km/h (2 mph)	0.22
Racquetball	0.63	8 km/h (5 mph)	0.64

Figure 7.9C   Exercise and energy expenditure.

Food	Percentage of fat	Percentage of protein	Percentage of carbohydrate	Kcals (food value) per 100 g
Apples	0.4	0.3	14.9	64
Bacon, fat	76.0	6.2	0.7	712
broiled	55.0	25.0	1.0	599
Beef, medium lean	22.0	17.5	1.0	268
Bread, white	3.6	9.0	49.8	268
Butter	81.0	0.6	0.4	733
Cabbage	0.2	1.4	5.3	29
Carrots	0.3	1.2	9.3	45
Cheese, cheddar	32.3	23.9	1.7	393
Chicken	2.7	21.6	1.0	111
Corn (maize)	4.3	10.0	73.4	372
Haddock (fish)	0.3	17.2	0.5	72
Lamb, leg	17.5	18.0	1.0	230
Milk, whole	3.9	3.5	4.9	69
Oatmeal, dry (uncooked)	7.4	14.2	68.2	396
Oranges	0.2	0.9	11.2	50
Peanuts	44.2	26.9	23.6	600
Peas, fresh	0.4	6.7	17.7	101
Pork, ham	31.0	15.2	1.0	340
Potatoes	0.1	2.0	19.1	85
Spinach		2.3	3.2	25
Strawberries		0.8	8.1	41
Tomatoes	0.3	1.0	4.0	23

Figure 7.9D   Energy and nutrients.

Diet	Amount of glycogen in muscles (g/kg)	Average endurance running at speeds characteristic of a marathon (min to exhaustion)
High carbohydrate diet	40	240
Mixed carbohydrate and fat diet	20	120
High fat diet	6	85

Source: Guyton, A. C. (1991). *Textbook of Medical Physiology*, 8th edition, by W.B. Saunders Co.

Figure 7.9E   Effect of diet on muscle glycogen and muscle endurance.

1. Mild to moderate increase in number of muscle fibers.
2. Increased capacity to transport oxygen from the blood to the mitochondria.*
3. Increased number of mitochondria.
4. Increased growth of capillaries serving the muscle.

* Mitochondria are the cell parts that are primarily responsible for the oxygen-requiring release of energy from glucose.

Source: Guyton, A. C. (1991). *Textbook of Medical Physiology*, 8th edition, by W.B. Saunders Co.

Figure 7.9F   Effect of exercise on muscle structure.

	Stroke volume* (mL)	Heart rate (beats/min)
Marathoner		
resting	105	50
maximum	162	185
Nonathlete		
resting	75	75
maximum	110	195
* Volume of blood moved in one heartbeat		

Source: Guyton, A. C. (1991). *Textbook of Medical Physiology*, 8th edition, by W.B. Saunders Co.

Figure 7.9G   Comparing cardiac outputs of marathoner and nonathlete.

Analysis

Work individually to answer the following questions. Record your responses in your journal.

PAGE 343

Refer to the essay *Factors Influencing Performance* (page 343) to provide greater depth to your understanding of fitness and performance.

Remember, your answers should involve evidence of everything you learned in Chapter 7 about the biological basis of human performance and fitness. Draw from the data in Tables 7.9A–G to give specific evidence to support your analysis.

1. Which runner expended the most energy during training? Which runner expended the most energy during the marathon? Explain the relationship between the energy expended during training and the energy used on race day.

2. Compare the training schedules and diets of the four runners before the race. Complete the following tasks:

   a. List at least two training and dietary strategies that you think would be valuable for a person to consider if he or she were preparing for the same race next year.

   b. Explain the physiologic change(s) that you would expect to occur as a result of each strategy.

   c. Describe why such changes would be important to finishing the marathon. Support your answer with specific data from Tables 7.9A–G.

3. Explain how humans obtain energy.

4. Explain how the process of energy release from matter is more efficient in highly trained athletes than in most other people.

5. Write a two- or three-paragraph explanation for how digestion, breakdown, and biosynthesis relate to the repair of a torn muscle in a marathon racer.

> "Life's splendor forever lies in wait about each one of us in all its fullness, but veiled from view, deep down, invisible, far off."
>
> *Franz Kafka*

The Cellular Basis of Activity

Chapter 8

Gasoline, nuclear power, and electricity. All are obvious forms of energy. But do you also think of energy when you see sunlight or green plants? In fact, energy is found wherever matter is organized, from the molecules of rocks, to cells, to entire living organisms. Most people are unaware of the complex role that energy plays in living systems. Without energy, life would not be possible.

In this chapter, you will begin to investigate the important relationship between matter and energy. You will consider examples of where and how energy is stored and released. In Chapter 7, you studied the concept that food contains energy that humans and other organisms require for daily activities and demanding physical performances. Eating and digestion, however, do not explain exactly how food molecules become useful as energy. How is energy in food converted to fuel the chemical reactions that keep cells, tissues, and organisms alive? What is the original source of the energy in food? Once you understand the basic connections between energy and matter, you will explore some of the specific cellular reactions that require energy. You will study the reactions that result in new molecules and maintain the organization that is characteristic of living systems.

ACTIVITIES

Engage	Releasing Energy
Explore **Explain**	Energy in Matter
Explain	Keep on Running!
Explain **Elaborate**	Using Light Energy to Build Matter
Elaborate	Building Living Systems
Evaluate	Tracing Matter and Energy

Releasing Energy

A runner in a marathon is pushing hard several miles before the finish line. But then she suddenly slows to a walk, clutches her side, and sways dizzily, about to fall. This athlete is said to have "hit the wall." She did not actually slam into a brick barrier, but she may feel as if she has done so. In this case, "hitting the wall" means that the runner has exhausted the energy supplies necessary to keep running.

After eating food and resting, those energy supplies will be replenished. Yet, how does this additional food become the energy needed for physical activity? In this activity, you will begin to examine the relationship between matter and energy. In this example, the matter is grain (see Figure 8.1). What is the energy?

PROCESS AND PROCEDURES

1. Read the story *A Matter of Explosions*, and think about the following questions:

   ◆ Where did the energy for the grain explosion come from?

   ◆ How can energy be stored in grain?

   ◆ What started the explosion that released the energy?

   ◆ How do you explain the fact that you do not explode when you eat grain products such as cereal or bread?

   ◆ What would you do to decrease the danger of explosion and better protect a grain storage facility and its employees?

2. Contribute your thoughts about the questions in step 1 to a class discussion.

SCENARIO

A Matter of Explosions

Brad celebrated his 20th birthday by starting a new job at the town's grain storage facility. He was eager to make a good impression. Washington County Grain Cooperative was the largest employer in town. The company offered good wages, great benefits, and opportunities for advancement. The facility consisted of three huge grain elevators that stored wheat. Each storage elevator was shaped like a giant cylinder that rose 30 meters (about

Figure 8.2 **Grain storage elevators.**

Figure 8.1 Grain handling facilities are required by the Occupational Safety and Health Administration (OSHA) to meet certain standards that reduce the risk of associated safety and health hazards.

100 feet) aboveground and descended 6 meters (20 feet) underground. A series of tunnels connected the underground portions of the cylinders. The tunnels contained machinery that dropped the grain onto concave conveyer belts and moved the grain from one storage tower to another. In the storage cylinders, giant elevating platforms lifted the grain to the top of the tower.

Brad was in a small underground storage room next to one of the towers. He was waiting for his supervisor to arrive and give him instructions. The floor was covered with several inches of dust from the grain, and he was making a mess as he paced impatiently. Noticing a metal snow shovel by the door, Brad decided to get busy and clean up the place a bit. He was scraping the shovel along the cement floor when his boss and another worker appeared at the door. In an instant, they jumped at him, one grabbing his arms while the other grabbed the shovel. Brad was dumbfounded.

"Sorry to startle you," the boss said. "I know you haven't completed your orientation yet, but you've got to learn some critical rules. First and most important, don't do anything that could cause sparks!"

"But there's no gasoline around, just wheat. What difference would a few sparks make?" Brad responded, feeling embarrassed.

"Here, read this," the boss stated grimly as he removed a worn letter that had been posted on a bulletin board. This is what Brad read:

---

10 August

Dear Sarah,

I am amazed to be alive and able to write this letter to you— or actually to dictate it; my hands are burned too badly to write it myself.

As you heard on the news, the worst happened: an explosion in elevator number two. We all had been warned, but I never imagined anything like this could actually happen. The whole terrible thing took only seconds. First, there was an odd "whoosh" noise, and my right side was seared with heat. Before I could think about what was happening, there was a deafening noise. I still have ringing in my ears.

I was lucky not to be at the center of the explosion. Four guys in there didn't make it. It's hard to believe that the whole thing probably started with a tiny spark from the conveyer belt gears while we were shifting grain—we'll never know for sure. The explosion was like dynamite. It blew the top right off the number two elevator, and then the fire took over.

I know your facility is similar to ours. Whatever you do, don't let this happen there.

Yours truly,

Mike

Brad looked silently at the others in the room. He had no idea that the flourlike dust from simple wheat could produce such an explosion and fire. He certainly couldn't explain *why* such a thing could happen or *how*.

Energy in Matter

Explore

Explain

Explosions are dramatic examples of the release of a tremendous amount of energy. But what is the source of all that energy? In the case of the grain elevator explosion, the energy came from grain dust and air. These are two simple forms of matter that few people think of as energy sources. Grain and air, however, are not exceptional forms of matter; all matter contains energy. Not all matter contains the same *amount* of energy,

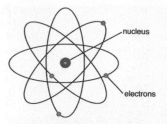

nucleus

electrons

Figure 8.3 This is a graphic model of an atom. What do you already know about atoms?

however. The particular organization of **atoms**—the building blocks of matter—in a substance determines its precise amount of energy (see Figure 8.3). In this activity, you will investigate some of the links among matter, energy, and organization and attempt to describe the close relationship among them.

Materials (per team of 2)

2 pairs of safety goggles	Pyrex test tube
125-mL flask	2 microscope slides
graduated cylinder	dropping pipet
test tube rack	materials for molecular model
spatula or spoon	2-cm piece of magnesium ribbon
hand lens or microscope (optional)	ammonium nitrate
	saturated urea solution
hydrochloric acid solution	DVD and player (watch as a team)
2 lab aprons	

Safety Goggles **Lab Apron**

Warning

Figure 8.4 This team is noting the temperature as magnesium dissolves in hydrochloric acid.

PROCESS AND PROCEDURES

Part A   Energy in Reactions

SAFETY: Put on your safety goggles and lab apron.

1. Discuss with your partner how you would define *matter*. In your journal, write your definition and 3 examples of matter.

2. Discuss with your partner how you would define *energy*. In your journal, write your definition and 3 examples of energy.

3. Explain how matter and energy are related. Record your explanation in your journal. Include 1 or 2 examples to illustrate your ideas.

4. Try this exercise:

   a. Use a graduated cylinder to measure 5 mL of 0.7M hydrochloric acid. Pour this into a test tube that is firmly seated in a test tube rack. Do not remove the test tube from the rack.

   WARNING: 0.7M HCl is a *strong irritant*. Avoid skin/eye contact; do not ingest. If contact occurs, flush affected area with water for 15 minutes; rinse mouth with water. Call the teacher.

   b. Feel the outside of the test tube to note the relative temperature (Figure 8.4).

   c. Place 2 cm of magnesium ribbon into the acid in the test tube. Observe what happens as the solid dissolves. In your journal, record your observations.

   d. Feel the test tube, and record your observations.

   e. Discuss the energy changes that you observed. Compare these changes with the events in the opening story.

   Perhaps you or your partner recall the terms that describe the types of chemical reactions that release and absorb energy from their surroundings (see Figure 8.5).

5. Now, try another exercise:

a. Put approximately 40 mL of room-temperature tap water in a flask.

b. Feel the flask to note the relative temperature.

c. Put about 2 spatulas of dry ammonium nitrate into the water in the flask. Swirl it gently to dissolve the powder.

CAUTION: Ammonium nitrate is an *irritant*. Avoid creating dust; avoid skin/eye contact; do not ingest. If contact occurs, flush affected area with water for 15 minutes; rinse mouth with water. Call the teacher.

Warning

d. Feel the flask. Record your observations in your journal.

e. Discuss the energy changes that you observed.

6. Finally, try this exercise:

a. Use a dropping pipet to place 1 drop of saturated urea solution on a microscope slide.

CAUTION: Urea solution is an *irritant*. Avoid skin/eye contact; do not ingest. If contact occurs, flush affected area with water for 15 minutes; rinse mouth with water. Call the teacher.

Warning

b. Use the edge of the 2nd slide to spread the drop in a thin layer across the surface of the 1st slide.

c. Watch the layer closely for changes. This may take several minutes to develop. Use hand lenses or microscopes, if available. In your journal, record your observations.

Include drawings to record the changes that you see.

d. Read the following information. Then answer the question in your journal.

In the urea solution that you used, water was the solvent and urea was the solute. The solute molecules in a solution move about freely, according to the forces of diffusion. In other words, these molecules have a great deal of entropy. Explain what appears to happen to the organization of urea molecules as the water in the urea solution evaporates. What do you think happened to the level of entropy?

7. Wash your hands thoroughly with soap and water.

8. Complete the following tasks in your journal. Be prepared to participate in a class discussion about the relationship between energy and the organization of matter.

a. Is the reaction in step 4 exothermic or endothermic? What about the reaction in step 5? State your evidence in each case.

b. Describe where the energy needed for the endothermic reaction came from. Describe where the energy produced by the exothermic reaction went.

c. What do you think happened to the organization of the solid ammonium nitrate molecules when they dissolved in water? How did that differ from what happened to urea?

Answer these questions thoroughly, because you will refer to your notes throughout this chapter.

Read the essay *Matter and Energy Are Related* (page 348) for helpful background information.

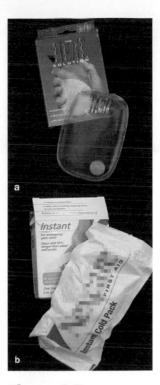

Figure 8.5
(a) Exothermic reactions. These reactions release energy to their surroundings. What form of energy does the hand warmer's chemical reaction give off? **(b) Endothermic reactions.** These reactions absorb energy from the surroundings. The reaction that takes place inside this cold pack is an endothermic reaction. What form of energy is absorbed? How could you slow each of these reactions?

Topic: matter and energy
Go to: www.scilinks.org
Code: human3E291

PAGE 348

CH₄

a chemical formula   **b** structural formula   **c** ball-and-stick model   **d** space-filling model

Figure 8.6 **Four different representations of the molecule methane.**

Figure 8.7 Why are bird droppings white? In mammals, ammonia is the primary waste product. It is produced when proteins are broken down into amino acids for use in biosynthesis. This ammonia can be toxic if left untreated. Mammals convert this ammonia into urea in the liver. The urea is excreted in urine by the kidneys. Birds, insects, lizards, and snakes convert the waste products from protein breakdown into uric acid. Uric acid does not dissolve easily in water. So it is excreted as a white paste with very little liquid.

Topic: atoms/molecules
Go to: www.scilinks.org
Code: human3E292

Part B   Molecular Models

Complete Part B individually.

1. Figure 8.6 shows several ways that molecules can be represented. Which representation would you use to demonstrate molecular structure (atoms bonded together) to a 6th-grade student who did not understand that matter is organized? Explain your choice.

2. Watch the DVD segment "Molecular Models." Be prepared to answer the following question.

   How do the atoms of simple molecules serve as building blocks for much larger and more complex molecules?

3. Use the materials that your teacher provides to construct a model of a urea molecule. Base your model on information from the DVD, the essays, the rule of molecular bonding, and the typical number of molecular bonds that the atoms in urea form (see the information below).

   The number of bonds that an atom usually forms is based on the number of electrons in its outer shell.

   ◆ Urea is represented by the chemical formula $CO(NH_2)_2$.

   ◆ Carbon usually has 4 bonds.

   ◆ Oxygen usually has 2 bonds.

   ◆ Nitrogen usually has 3 bonds.

   ◆ Hydrogen usually has 1 bond.

Analysis

Respond to the following tasks in your journal. Be prepared to share your responses in a class discussion.

Read the essay *Energy Is Converted and Conserved* (page 351) for additional information.

PAGE 351

1. If an exothermic reaction releases heat, why is it inaccurate to say that an endothermic reaction releases cold?

2. What is the difference between kinetic energy and potential energy? Provide at least two examples of each to help with your explanation.

Figure 8.8 Examples of energy conversion.

3. Explain why the energy that is stored in the chemical bonds of a molecule is not destroyed when that molecule is broken down into smaller molecules.

4. Define ATP's role as a link between matter and energy.

5. Refine your definitions of matter, energy, and their relationship from those that you developed in steps 1–3 of Part A. It may be helpful to use diagrams or other visual aids with captions to explain your definitions.

6. Read the essay *Historical Connections between Matter and Energy* (page 357). Write one or two paragraphs to Joseph Priestley if you had the chance to correct his explanation that phlogiston killed the mouse in his experiment.

PAGE 357

    Be sure to include descriptions of both the energy and matter involved in that experiment.

Further Challenges

1. In your journal, draw a diagram to show that starch is a macromolecule made up of many glucose molecules. Then explain how the arrangement of matter determines its energy content.

2. A saturated solution is a solution in which the concentration of solute is so high that no more solute can dissolve. With that knowledge, explain what happened during the crystallization of urea in step 6, Part A.

    Do you think a dilute solution of urea (one in which the concentration of solute is very low), if left uncovered for a long time, would eventually form crystals as well? Explain your answer.

Keep on Running!

The connections among food, energy, and exercise were so interesting to one of your classmates that he decided to investigate the career opportunities for nutritionists and dietitians. He began by subscribing to several health and nutrition magazines. In last month's issue of *Athlete's World*, he ran across this interesting ad:

NEED TO KNOW

Tudor Valley Marathon Snack Contest

Enter the Tudor Valley Marathon Snack Contest to develop the best possible marathon snack. At the next Tudor Valley Marathon, we want to offer a new healthful snack. The snack must meet the following criteria:

- Provide approximately 200 kilocalories (commonly abbreviated as Calories on food labels) per 30 grams.
- Be considered tasty by 8 out of 10 runners.
- Keep well for long periods of time, and survive the abuses of traveling in a runner's fanny pack.
- Include a snack label or brochure that explains how the body converts this snack into fuel that can power muscles.

This activity provides the tools for you and your teammates to compete in the Tudor Valley Marathon Snack Contest. Your teacher will award a prize.

Materials (per team of 2)

2 pairs of safety goggles
100-mL graduated cylinder
thermistor or thermometer
forceps
cork with sample holder (paper clip)
20 × 30-cm piece of extra
   heavy aluminum foil
materials to design a food label

2 lab aprons
250-mL Erlenmeyer flask
balance
tin can with cutout air and viewing holes
kitchen matches
2 pot holders
food samples
small container of water

PROCESS AND PROCEDURES

1. Your challenge is to select 3 different foods from the available choices. You will measure the calories in each according to the calorimetry protocol. You will then use at least 2 of these foods and up to 3 additional ingredients (plus your understanding of energy, matter, and nutrition) in a recipe that has the best chance of winning the Tudor Valley Marathon Snack Contest. Discuss and

develop your strategy with your partner. Record it in your journal. A good strategy will include the following:

- A brief, written explanation about why you would like to test the 3 foods you have chosen

  You might look back at Chapter 7 to remind yourself about the role of the different components of food.

- The use of the Calorimetry Protocol

- Predictions for the results

- Plans to average multiple calorimetry tests for each chosen food sample

- A data table for recording your results

  Divide the responsibilities of the calorimetry protocol evenly between team partners. Be sure to follow the correct safety procedures.

2. Have your teacher approve your strategy.

3. Conduct your tests.

4. Discuss the calorimetry results with your partner. Modify your recipe for the marathon food if your predictions were not supported by the results.

5. Compare the kcals per gram that you measured with the Calories per gram given on labels for the same foods. Explain any discrepancies that you find.

  Some of the foods that you tested may be listed in Figure 7.9D, Chapter 7. Note that these values are given in kcal/100 g.

  Remember to follow the required safety cautions.

SAFETY: Put on your safety goggles and lab apron. Tie back long hair, and roll up long, loose sleeves.

Caution

Safety Goggles

Lab Apron

PROTOCOL

Calorimetry Protocol

A calorimeter is an instrument that measures in calories the amount of energy in foods. A **calorie** is the amount of heat required to raise the temperature of 1 g (1 mL) of water 1°C. Notice that the caloric values of foods in diet charts and food labels are given in **kilocalories** (1,000 calories), or kcals. Instead of writing kcals on food labels, it is written as *Calories*, with a capital C (see Figure 8.9).

Using a simple calorimeter (Figure 8.10) and a thermistor or thermometer, you can measure the change in temperature of a known volume of water. The water absorbs

(continued)

Figure 8.9
On food labels, kcals are written as *Calories*, with a capital C.

Topic: calories
Go to: www.scilinks.org
Code: human3E295

Calorimetry Protocol (continued)

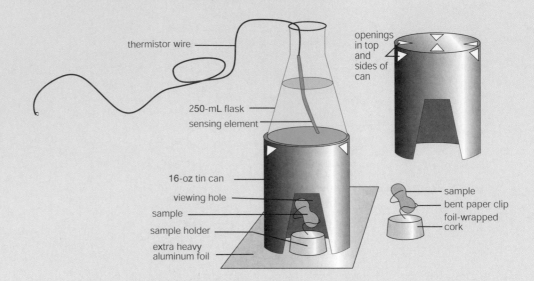

Figure 8.10   The calorimeter setup.

the heat given off by burning a known mass of food. Based on the change in temperature, you can calculate the amount of energy in the food.

> Calories generated per gram of food = (change in temperature × mass of water heated) ÷ (mass of food burned).

1. Select samples of the foods that your team chose to test.

2. Obtain a 250-mL Erlenmeyer flask, a tin can, a cork with sample holder, and a piece of extra heavy aluminum foil.

3. Assemble a calorimeter like the one shown in Figure 8.10. Practice assembling and disassembling the equipment.

4. With the calorimeter disassembled, measure 100 mL of tap wate. Pour it into the flask.

5. If you are using thermistors, start the computer application or set up the handheld device to measure temperatures between 15°C and 45°C.

6. Suspend your thermistor or thermometer in the water as follows. Use a loosely fitting cork or other apparatus to support the thermistor or thermometer in the flask. Make sure that the sensing element or bulb is submerged in the water without touching the glass.

7. When the reading has stabilized, record the current temperature of the water as the *starting water temperature*. Prepare a data table to record your test results.

    Begin each new food trial with fresh, cool water.

8. Place a food sample in the wire holder (paper clip) anchored in the cork. Then place the cork on the piece of aluminum foil.

    For runny foods, you may need to use extra heavy aluminum foil to construct a holder shaped like a boat or platform.

9. Using the balance, determine the mass to the nearest 0.1 g of the food sample, wire holder, and cork together. In the data table in your journal, record this as the *starting mass*.

10. Carefully set fire to the food sample. This may require several matches. Discard burned matches in the container of water.

WARNING: Matches are flammable solids. In case of burns, place burned area under cold running water. Call your teacher immediately.

Warning

11. Place the tin can over the burning sample with the viewing hole facing you. Place the flask of water on top of the tin can.

12. Continue recording the water temperature, even when the sample has burned completely. Record the water temperature until it begins to decrease.

    The temperature will continue to rise after the sample has burned completely as the water absorbs heat from the tin can.

13. Record the maximum water temperature reached.

14. Allow the calorimeter to cool for at least 2 minutes before disassembling.

CAUTION: The flask and tin can will be hot. Use pot holders to handle these items, and place them only on the aluminum foil. The sample holder also will be hot. Use forceps to remove the burned sample. In case of burns, place burned area under cold running water. Call your teacher immediately.

Caution

15. Using the balance, determine the mass to the nearest 0.1 g of the burned food sample, wire holder, and cork together. In the data table in your journal, record this mass as the *final mass*.

16. Repeat the procedure until you have data for 3 samples of each food. Change the water in the flask each time.

17. Wash your hands thoroughly with soap and water before leaving the laboratory.

18. Analyze your data using the following steps:

    a. Determine the average change in temperature for each of your 3 foods.

       Change in temperature = highest temperature reached − starting temperature.
       Average change in temperature = (sum of change in temperature for all trials of same food) ÷ number of trials.

    b. Calculate the average number of calories produced for each of your 3 foods. To do this, multiply the average increase in water temperature by 100 (the number of grams of water used).

       Average calories produced = average change in temperature × 100.

    c. Convert the average number of calories to kcals by dividing by 1,000.

       Average kcal produced = average calories produced ÷ 1,000.

    d. Calculate the kcals produced per gram of food. To do this, divide the number of kcals produced by the number of grams of food burned.

       Average kcal produced per gram = average kcal produced ÷ average grams of food burned.
       Average grams of food burned = (sum of grams burned for all trials of same food) ÷ number of trials.

    e. Enter all data in your table.

Analysis

Read the essays *Controlling the Release of Energy from Matter: An Overview of Cellular Respiration* (page 358) and *Cellular Respiration: A Closer Look at Converting Food Energy into Cell Energy* (page 359). These readings provide important background information that will be helpful in completing this task.

1. Develop a package label or brochure that is informative and is an effective marketing tool for your Tudor Valley Marathon Snack. Your package label or brochure should answer the following questions:

   ◆ What combination of foods did you decide to use in your snack?

   ◆ How did your calorimetry data and your understandings of nutrition influence your decision to make your snack using these particular foods?

   ◆ What are the qualities that make the matter in your foods particularly good as a snack for marathon runners?

   ◆ How does the matter in the food become usable energy for the body? In particular, how does it help a marathon runner keep on running?

   Your explanations should include information about nutrients, digestion, breakdown, synthesis, absorption, macromolecules, building blocks the runner will need, and how energy is obtained at the cellular level.

2. Submit your package label or brochure to the snack contest judges, and wait for a decision on the winner.

Further Challenges

Living organisms have evolved complex processes for extracting energy from matter and using it to fuel cellular reactions. As a result, when a cheetah accelerates toward a gazelle, it can produce enough ATP in its muscles to fuel the rapid contractions necessary for an explosive sprint. The same is true for an escaping gazelle. If the cheetah had too little energy, it would not catch its prey. Think back to the work that you did learning about homeostasis. Is it necessary for organisms to maintain a balance of energy to stay alive? Regulating the appropriate energy levels is another aspect of maintaining homeostasis. How do organisms balance their energy needs with their energy supplies? Read the essay *Regulation and Energy Production* (page 363). Draw a feedback loop that demonstrates how energy is regulated.

Figure 8.11 Adenosine triphosphate, ATP, stores potential energy in the chemical bond that binds the third phosphate group to the molecule. When that bond is broken, ATP becomes adenosine diphosphate, ADP. The energy released from breaking the chemical bond becomes available for cells to use.

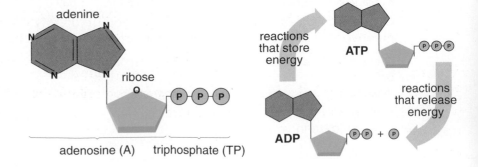

Using Light Energy to Build Matter

In the last activity, you studied cellular respiration. Cellular respiration is a method for obtaining energy from matter in a form that is useful for cell activity. This process depends on glucose molecules, which can be obtained from glycogen, starch, fats, and other macromolecules. In humans, this glucose, and indeed all of the carbon in human macromolecules, originally came from molecules produced by other organisms. Many of these molecules come from the plants we eat. The rest come from animals or other organisms that depend on plants.

Humans, and all organisms that depend on previously assembled molecules for their carbon and energy, are called **heterotrophs** (*hetero* = other, *troph* = to feed). This dependence on other sources raises interesting questions about the *original* source of energy and matter. For instance, how did energy first come to be stored in these molecules that are essential for life? The laws of nature tell us that energy cannot be created or destroyed, it can only be transferred. Since energy cannot be created, what was the original source of energy that became stored in the macromolecules that built the bodies of heterotrophs?

The answer is that the energy came from green plants, which are quite different from heterotrophs. They are called **autotrophs** (*auto* = self, *troph* = to feed). This means that they do not have to rely on other organisms for the complex molecules necessary for life. Autotrophs can make all of their own macromolecules. To grow, plants need only light, water, air, and a few essential elements that are available from the soil. In other words, plants can make their own food. They can make the carbon-containing molecules such as simple sugars and starch that are used to support their cellular activities. The process of making these carbon-containing molecules is called **photosynthesis** (*photo* = light, *synthesis* = to make).

A number of variables can influence the efficiency, or rate, of photosynthesis. In this activity, you will identify a range of variables and test one. This process will help you put together the entire cycle of energy, matter, and organization. You will do this by examining the processes that capture energy and trap it in matter.

Figure 8.12 This bee obtains matter from the nectar it drinks. Which is the heterotroph, the bee or the plant with the nectar-bearing flower?

Materials (per team of 4)

2-L beaker	2 pH probes *or* pH strips sensitive to pH 1–2 and narrow range pH strips (pH 4–11)	glass-marking pencil
100-mL beaker or small jar		distilled water
2 250-mL flasks		tap water at 25°C
2 25 × 200-mm test tubes	1-mL pipet	ice water (10°C)
test tube rack	1 thermistor *or* 1 thermometer	jar of tap water for storing pH probes (if used)
250-mL graduated cylinder	red, blue, and green cellophane	
wrapped drinking straw	aluminum foil	2 15-cm sprigs of young, healthy *Anacharis* (elodea)
fluorescent lamp	tape	
bromothymol blue	ruler	

1. With your teammates, develop a list of at least 3 variables that could affect the rate of photosynthesis.

   To help you generate your list, read the essay *Whose Discovery Is This?* (page 365) and the introduction to the essay *Getting Energy and Matter into Biological Systems* (page 367).

2. Compare your list with another team's list. Add any new ideas to your list.

3. Participate in a class discussion to identify at least 2 variables that you could test easily in your classroom.

4. Use the Photosynthesis Protocol and the materials available to you to outline an experiment that tests the influence of 1 of these variables on the rate of photosynthesis. Your experiment should

   ◆ answer some variation of the question, What affects the rate of photosynthesis?, and

   ◆ include an if-then statement that relates your question to your experiment.

Figure 8.13 To generate a list of factors that may affect the rate of photosynthesis, consider what the environmental conditions are like when plants outside are thriving.

PROTOCOL

Photosynthesis Protocol

There are several ways to measure the rate of photosynthesis. This protocol outlines a model system that allows you to determine how quickly photosynthetic reactions use carbon dioxide (CO_2). You will do this by measuring the decrease in CO_2 concentration in the surroundings of a photosynthetic system. You can indirectly measure CO_2 concentration in a water environment by measuring pH. When carbon dioxide gas dissolves in water, it produces carbonic acid (H_2CO_3). Removing CO_2 from the water decreases the carbonic acid, which increases the pH.

If carbon dioxide is added to the water, more of the reaction that produces carbonic acid takes place:

$$CO_2 + H_2O \rightarrow H_2CO_3 \rightarrow HCO_3^- + H^+$$

The increase in carbonic acid causes pH levels to drop. If carbon dioxide is removed from the water, some of the carbonic acid breaks bonds to form more carbon dioxide and water:

$$HCO_3^- + H^+ \rightarrow H_2CO_3 \rightarrow CO_2 + H_2O$$

The decrease in carbonic acid causes pH levels to rise.

A solution containing CO_2 reaches a specific balance between the amount of dissolved carbon dioxide and carbonic acid. When the addition or removal of carbon dioxide disrupts that balance, the solution must readjust the amount of dissolved carbonic acid. Consider what natural process plants carry out that would change this balance by producing carbon dioxide? What plant process would use carbon dioxide?

This model system uses 2 sprigs of *Anacharis* (a common aquatic plant called elodea) as the photosynthetic organism. A complete system for monitoring photosynthesis also should include a light source to provide energy for the plants, a thermistor or thermometer to monitor the temperature, and 2 pH probes or pH strips and bromothymol blue to measure pH changes associated with carbon dioxide use.

The following variables are among those that can be tested with the equipment you have available:

Light intensity: Moving the light source can change the intensity of light reaching the chloroplasts of *Anacharis*. Place the light source at a distance not greater than 50 cm (20 in) from the *Anacharis*.

Wavelength: The wavelength (or color) of light reaching the chloroplasts of the *Anacharis* can be changed by using red, blue, or green cellophane. For example, red cellophane isolates red light. Because light intensity drops as it passes through colored cellophane, place the light source at a distance not greater than 10 cm (4 in) from the *Anacharis*.

> Do *not* attach the cellophane to the light source. The heat from the light source may cause the cellophane to melt.

1. Put 125 mL of distilled water in a flask.

2. Put the straw in the flask. Blow gently through the straw into the water for 3 min. This adds CO_2 to the water.

   > Be careful not to suck any liquid into your mouth. Discard the straw after use.

3. Add 2.5 mL of bromothymol blue to the water. Swirl the flask to mix. In a 2nd flask, add 2.5 mL of bromothymol blue to 125 mL of distilled water that you have not exhaled into. Record color observations for both flasks. Explain what bromothymol blue must indicate to explain the differences that you see. Predict how the color of the solution is likely to change if the *Anacharis* carries out photosynthesis. In your journal, record your prediction.

4. Place 2 sprigs of *Anacharis*, cut end up, into 1 of the test tubes.

   > This is your experimental tube. Mark it as such.

5. Mark a 2nd test tube as a control. Then fill both test tubes ¾ full with the water that you blew into.

6. Use a pH probe or pH test strips to test the initial pH of the water. If you are using pH test strips, use the 1-mL pipet to transfer a drop of water from halfway down each test tube to a piece of narrow-range pH paper. Read the pH from the comparison chart on the strip. Record this starting pH.

7. Perform the following steps:

   a. Place the 2 test tubes in a test tube rack so that both are the same distance from the light source.

   > Maximize the amount of light reaching the *Anacharis* (unless that is your variable). Light passing through glass, water, and cellophane reduces its intensity. Position the light source so that it illuminates the entire *Anacharis* sprigs.

   > You might find that the light source causes the temperatures of your experimental test tubes to rise significantly. If this happens, it will add a variable to your experiment. You may have to place your experimental test tubes in a 2-L beaker containing 25°C tap water as shown in Figure 8.14 if this is the case. This setup will help to regulate temperature.

   (continued)

Photosynthesis Protocol (*continued*)

b. If you are using pH probes, calibrate them to a pH 4–11 range. Choose appropriate settings to monitor 2 pH probes. Save your data, and graph your results.

c. If you are using pH test strips (sensitive to pH in the 4–11 range), create a data table to record the pH readings at 5-min intervals.

d. Insert a thermistor or thermometer into each test tube. (Insert into the water in the 2-L beaker, if you are using one.)

e. If you are using pH probes, carefully position 1 probe in each test tube. Make sure that it extends into the water without damaging the *Anacharis*.

f. Adjust the pH probe (if used) and thermistor or thermometer. Secure in place by crimping a small piece of aluminum foil around the top of the test tubes.

If you use pH test strips, position the thermistor or thermometer so that you can slide a pipette into the test tube easily to withdraw a water sample.

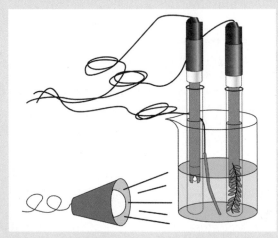

Figure 8.14 **Setup for measuring rates of photosynthesis with probes.**

8. Arrange your setup to test your experimental question.

9. Take pH and temperature readings for at least 30 min. (Check with your teacher for specific timing.) In your journal, record the current readings every 5 min.

10. In your journal, monitor and record color changes. Note the times when they occur.

11. When all data have been collected, do the following:

a. Generate a line graph showing temperature and pH for both test tubes over the time tested.

Color-code your graph. Create a legend so that anyone reading the graph can interpret your results.

b. Remove the pH probes, if used, and rinse them with tap water. Replace the probes in the storage jar of tap water.

c. Clean up and return the other equipment to storage.

12. Wash your hands thoroughly with soap and water before leaving the laboratory.

5. Write a plan for your experiment, and have your teacher approve it.

6. In your journal, write your prediction for how your chosen variable will affect the rate of photosynthesis. Explain your prediction.

7. Conduct your experiment.

   Record your data in your journal.

8. Draw a graph for the variable that your team tested. Plot the rate of photosynthesis, as indicated by pH, on the *y*-axis (vertical) against elapsed time on the *x* axis (horizontal).

   Remember, include a line that represents your control.

9. Record your team's data in a class data table, and present your team's conclusions to the class.

   Note the variables that the class tested and the range of values recorded.

10. Review the graphs from each team. You and your team can discuss your conclusions about the effects of each variable tested on the rate of photosynthesis.

Analysis

Complete the following tasks and questions individually:

1. Write three questions (with answers) for a quiz designed to assess your understanding of the experimental results and the concepts in the essay *Getting Energy and Matter into Biological Systems* (page 367). Your teacher will collect these questions from the class and develop a quiz.

2. The earth's early atmosphere had no oxygen. Use your understanding of plant photosynthesis to explain how photosynthetic organisms made the evolution of aerobic organisms possible.

3. Do plants carry out cellular respiration? Explain your response.

4. How does the trapping of light energy provide energy for carbon fixation?

Topic: photosynthesis
Go to: www.scilinks.org
Code: human3E303

Building Living Systems

Elaborate

The cells of your body must receive a constant supply of usable energy and matter if you are to grow into an adult. Even after growth has stopped, your body must be able to make new cells to replace damaged or infected ones. This process occurs wherever healing is necessary, such as the site of a skin cut. Cells use small, simple molecules (such as amino acids and simple sugars) to build more complex biological molecules (such as proteins and glycogen). These molecules are important for your daily activities. This building process is called **biosynthesis**.

At the same time that biosynthesis is taking place, many breakdown activities also are occurring, including digestion. Food and macromolecules are broken down into the building blocks that your body needs. Then these molecules of matter are

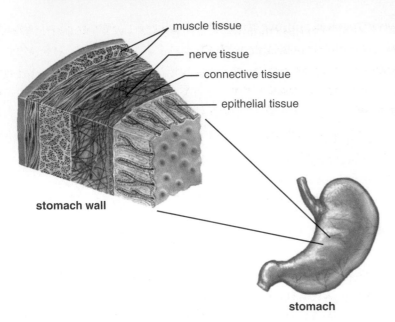

muscle tissue
nerve tissue
connective tissue
epithelial tissue

stomach wall

stomach

Figure 8.15 The stomach is an organ of the digestive system. An *organ* is a group of tissues that are organized together to perform a particular function. The stomach performs both mechanical and chemical breakdown processes during digestion. Where does absorption take place?

absorbed into the bloodstream and taken to all cells. Breakdown and absorption processes occur in the digestive system (see Figure 8.15).

Food molecules can come from a variety of sources: plants, animals, or fungi. Not surprisingly, the molecules that make up these other organisms are not always the same molecules that your body needs. In this activity, you will see how your body can take matter from an outside source, convert it into usable energy and matter, and rearrange the molecular structure of that matter to provide building materials for new molecules, cells, and tissues.

Materials (per person)

descriptions and diagrams of your critter from Chapter 5

PROCESS AND PROCEDURES

Part A   Metabolism

1. Read the following short story. Use the story and your understanding of energy, matter, and cellular respiration to answer this question: How can my body take in materials from a cow and make it a part of me?

SCENARIO

Hamburger or Beefburger?

Your high school women's basketball team won a hard-fought game against a rival team and qualified for the state basketball tournament. To celebrate, you and two friends go to your favorite fast-food restaurant and order the usual burger, fries, and soft drink. You notice that a new menu is on display. You see that the word *hamburger* was replaced by the word *beefburger*. After a brief discussion with your friends, you see the logic of the change. Your burger *is* a beefburger. This term accurately describes what you are about to eat. That realization leads to another discussion. The burger you are about to eat is rich in protein; with luck, it is not too rich in fat. Your body will use this cow protein and fat as a source of energy and as building material for biosynthesis. The discussion focuses on the question of how your body can take in materials from a cow and make it a part of you.

Figure 8.16   Beefburger.

2. With your partner, list 3 biological processes involving biosynthesis and/or breakdown that you think are necessary for maintaining the human body.

3. Choose 1 of the processes your team identified in step 2. Write an explanation in your journal of how energy and matter are organized during this process. Consider the following questions as you write your explanation:

   ◆ Why is this process necessary for survival?
   ◆ What is a source of energy for this process?
   ◆ What is a source of matter for this process?

   The essay *Metabolism Includes Synthesis and Breakdown* (page 372) will help you with your explanation.

PAGE 372

Part B   Energy and Matter for Your Critter

1. How does your critter use matter and energy to maintain its organization? Respond with an explanation, diagram, model, or demonstration of your choice. You will know that you have adequately addressed the preceding question if your response meets the following criteria:

   ◆ It indicates the critter's source of energy and matter and how these are obtained from its surroundings.
   ◆ It demonstrates how energy is stored and made available for the critter's activities.
   ◆ It distinguishes the macromolecules that your critter can synthesize from those that it must obtain from its external environment (through diet or other means).
   ◆ It uses specific examples from your work in Chapters 7 and 8 as evidence of what you have learned.

2. Obtain a rubric for this "critter" assignment from your teacher.

   Your teacher will use these criteria to evaluate your project.

Tracing Matter and Energy

Biologists can investigate the steps in metabolic processes (synthesis and breakdown) by feeding extremely small (or trace) amounts of radioactively labeled matter to laboratory organisms. This labeled matter undergoes changes in molecular structure during chemical reactions within the organism that consumed it. But the label remains detectable. The labeled matter continues to be traceable through transfers between the organisms. As these changes and transfers occur, the scientists can collect samples. In this way, they can trace the course of events by following the radioactivity.

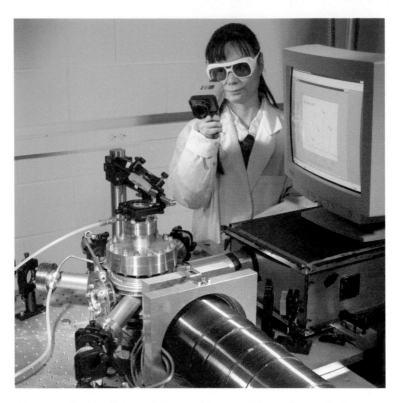

Figure 8.17 Scientist working with radioactivity.

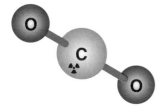

Figure 8.18 You will trace the path of an imaginary, radioactively labeled *carbon atom.* The atom begins its journey as part of an atmospheric carbon dioxide molecule (shown here). It ends up as part of a muscle protein in a human arm.

In this activity, you will trace the path of an imaginary, radioactively labeled *carbon atom* through the various molecules in which it is organized. The atom begins its journey as part of a carbon dioxide molecule. It ends up as part of a muscle protein in a human arm. Your task is to use the knowledge that you gained in this chapter to draw a diagram of what happens to the atom during its journey. Then you will explain the source of energy for these events.

Materials   (per person)

materials needed to complete your project, such as poster board and markers

PROCESS AND PROCEDURES

1. Construct a diagram or other visual aid to show a plausible set of events that could explain how a labeled carbon atom in a molecule of atmospheric carbon dioxide ends up in a human muscle protein.

   There is more than 1 possible scenario. But you must show a sequence that actually occurs in nature. You must be able to justify and explain the sequence that you choose.

2. Label your diagram so that it explains the sequence of events that you have illustrated. Clearly state the following:

   ◆ The type of metabolic process in each step (breakdown or biosynthesis)

   ◆ The energy source for each step

   ◆ The matter source for each step

   ◆ The names of metabolic processes that occur in the sequence

Analysis

1. Join the class in answering the discussion questions that your teacher raises.

2. After participating in the discussion, note in your journal any appropriate changes to steps in your sequence from Process and Procedures, step 2.

"Climb the mountains and get their good tidings. Nature's peace will flow into you as sunshine flows into trees. The winds will blow their own freshness into you, and the storms their energy, while cares will drop off like autumn leaves."

John Muir

The Cycling of Matter and the Flow of Energy in Communities

Chapter 9

Think about your school as a community. Picture the organization and interaction of people, books, paper, furniture, and food. People move through the hallways in repeated patterns throughout the day. Books and papers are moved from lockers, to class, and back to lockers. Desks are rearranged to accommodate various activities and events. Food is moved from the kitchen, to lunch trays, to hungry students.

These things move through the organized community of your school. In much the same way, energy and matter move through organized communities of living organisms of all sizes. In biology, we speak of a **community** as the group of living organisms that inhabit and interact with each other in a specific area. An **ecosystem** is a community of organisms interacting with its environment. Consider a bird living in the sandstone rocks in this photograph. Now think about the insects on which it feeds and the many other organisms that inhabit this piñon-juniper woodland. Together these organisms make up a community. Matter and energy move through this community in different ways. In this chapter, you will use your experiences from a variety of activities and related essays to develop an understanding of how matter and energy are organized within communities.

ACTIVITIES

Engage	A Matter of Trash
Explore	
Explore	Exploring the Cycling of Matter in Communities
Explain	Spinning the Web of Life
Elaborate	Generating Some Heat
Evaluate	What Have I Learned about Energy and Matter in Communities?

A Matter of Trash

What are your chores around your home? Do you wash dishes, mow the lawn, feed pets, babysit for a younger brother or sister, or take out the trash? Think about the last time you took out the trash. Did you look at what you were about to throw away? Where did the trash go after you put it out on the curb or tossed it into a trash container? What happened to the matter in the material you just discarded? Was any energy stored in that matter? Where did that energy go? Throughout this activity, think about the various forms of matter that you may consider to be waste and what happens to this matter after you throw it out.

Figure 9.1 Trash. Where will the matter and energy in this trash end up?

PROCESS AND PROCEDURES

1. Examine the discarded items in the trash demonstration that your teacher presents. Create a table or other visual diagram that includes the following information:

   ◆ A list of the trash in the demonstration

   ◆ A list of the trash's origin (for example, newspaper originated from trees, wood, and pulp)

   ◆ An indication of which trash items match your household trash (yes or no)

   ◆ A list of at least 2 possible fates for each trash item (for example, in a landfill, recycling plant, food for another animal, reused, etc.)

2. In your journal, write a short description of what you think might happen to the matter and energy in this trash after it is thrown out.

Analysis

PAGE 374

Working individually, answer these questions in your journal. Be prepared to share your responses in a class discussion. The essay *Garbage among Us—From Then until Now!* (page 374) will provide you with information about how matter cycles in other communities.

1. In what ways might the waste of one organism be useful to another organism? Give examples to support your answer.

2. How does your answer to question 1 support the idea that organisms in communities depend on one another for matter and energy?

3. As you compare how matter cycles in different communities, what do you notice about the type of matter and the length of the cycle? What problems have these differences caused for modern human societies?

Further Challenges

On a separate piece of paper, write 10–15 things you have thrown away in the past week. Exchange lists with your partner. Write four or five things that you might infer about your partner from his or her trash. Support your inferences.

Figure 9.2 When plastics and paper are recycled, what becomes of the matter they are made from?

Exploring the Cycling of Matter in Communities

Explore

Have you ever watched ants in an ant farm? They always appear to be busy modifying their environment in some way. In this activity, you will complete the observations of the earthworm habitats that you set up some weeks ago. Think about what your observations tell you about how these organisms interact with their environment. You also will reflect on your experiment's design. You will use this understanding to design another experiment to explore how other organisms interact with each other and with their environment.

Materials   (per team of 4)

Part A

6 slides	stereomicroscope	2 paper towels	earthworm habitat
hand lens	2 spoons	small tray	control habitat

Part B

250-mL flask

test tube rack

light source

2.5 mL of bromothymol blue (optional)

1 thermistor *or* 1 thermometer

straw

1- to 1½-cm freshwater snails

distilled water

4 25 × 200-mm test tubes

aluminum foil

2 pH probes *or* pH strips sensitive to
   pH 1–12 and pH strips sensitive to
   narrow ranges

1-mL pipet

jar of tap water for storing pH probes
   (if used)

15-cm sprigs of *Anacharis* (elodea)

PROCESS AND PROCEDURES

Part A   Reflections on the Earthworm Habitats

1. With your teammates, look at the earthworm habitats that you set up several weeks ago. Study the observations that you have recorded in your journal.

   Remember that the purpose of these habitats was to provide evidence of interactions between living systems and the physical environment, as well as evidence about the nature of these interactions.

Figure 9.3
In what ways do you think earthworms interact with their environment?

2. Discuss the following with your teammates. Record your ideas in your journal.

   a. What evidence did you collect that supports the idea that earthworms modify (interact with) their environment?

   b. Describe this interaction. What do you think happened in the earthworm containers?

   c. What was the specific purpose of each container in helping you identify and describe the interaction of earthworms and their environment?

Compare the containers that had earthworms with each other. (One contained soil and organic matter, and one only soil.) Why was it important to observe both types of containers? What did your comparisons tell you about the interactions of earthworms with their environment?

3. Read the essays *Matter in Nature Is Going Around in Cycles . . . What Next?* (page 377) and *Worms, Insects, Bacteria, and Fungi—Who Needs Them?* (page 381). The information in these essays will help generate a context for your observations. It will also prepare you to design your own experiment that explores the transformation of matter.

Check to see that your teammates understand the concepts in the readings and how they relate to your findings.

Part B   Snails and Anacharis: What Can I Learn from Them?

1. Devise an experiment to provide evidence of the cyclical movement of matter in a community. See the Materials section for the materials and equipment that are available.

   a. What have you learned about photosynthesis and respiration? Think back to previous chapters. In addition, read this need to know box for important background information.

PAGE 377   PAGE 381

Figure 9.4   Snails and *Anacharis*. How do these organisms interact to cycle matter in their environment?

NEED TO KNOW

Observing the Carbon Cycle in a Closed System

Plants and animals interact in a variety of ways. To limit the interactions that are possible in an experiment, you can conduct a study in a closed system. A **closed system** exchanges energy with its environment, but not matter. By setting up closed systems with an aquatic plant and an aquatic animal, you can study an interaction that is related to the carbon cycle. The **carbon cycle** is one of the chemical cycles in which matter (in this case, carbon) moves from the environment to organisms and back to the environment in different chemical forms.

Recall from Chapter 8 that carbon dioxide dissolves in water and forms a weak acid, which lowers the water's pH. A decrease in pH indicates an increase in the concentration of carbon dioxide. Conversely, an increase in pH indicates a decrease in the concentration of carbon dioxide.

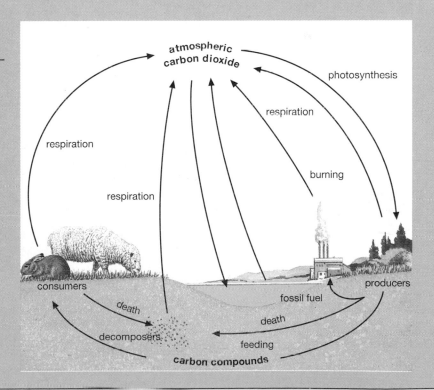

b. Develop a hypothesis about the cyclical movement of matter in an aquatic community. Record your hypothesis in your journal.

You must be able to test the hypothesis using the materials and information listed above.

c. Design an experiment to test your hypothesis. Outline your experiment in your journal.

Look at the design of the earthworm habitats. Apply your understanding of that design to the one you develop here.

Also, consider the experiment that you designed to investigate factors that influenced the rate of photosynthesis in Chapter 8. You may use a similar experimental procedure.

d. Have your teacher approve your design.

2. Use the Protocol for Monitoring Change in pH to conduct your experiment during the next 2 hours.

PROTOCOL

Protocol for Monitoring Change in pH

1. Put 125 mL of distilled water in the flask.

   You may wish to add 2.5 mL of bromothymol blue to the water as an additional pH indicator. If you use bromothymol blue, add it to the water at this point. Swirl the flask to mix. Record color observations.

2. Use a pH probe or pH test strips to test the initial pH of the water. Record this starting pH.

3. Set up your experiment.

4. Coordinate your data collection method with your teacher and classmates.

   Allow your experimental setups to run for at least 2 hours.

5. Perform the following steps:

   a. If you are using pH probes, calibrate them to a pH 4–11 range. Choose appropriate settings to monitor 2 pH probes. Save your data, and graph your results.

   b. If you are using pH paper (sensitive to pH in the 4–11 range), create a data table to record pH readings at 5-min intervals.

   c. If you are using pH probes, carefully position them in each test tube so that they do not interfere with your closed system.

   d. Adjust the pH probe (if used) and thermistor or thermometer (if used). Secure in place by crimping a small piece of aluminum foil around the top of the test tubes.

   This foil also can serve to stop the exchange of matter between your closed system and its environment.

   If you will be using pH paper, you will need to be able to slide a pipet into the test tube easily to withdraw a water sample.

Topic: pH
Go to: www.scilinks.org
Code: human3E314

6. Arrange your setup to test your experimental question.

7. Take pH readings for at least 2 hours. (Check with your teacher for specific timing.) In your journal, record the current readings every 5 min.

8. In your journal, monitor and record any changes in appearance. Note the times when they occur.

9. When all data have been collected, do the following:

   a. Generate a line graph showing how pH changed over the time tested.

      Color-code your graph. Create a legend so that anyone reading the graph can interpret your results.

   b. Remove the pH probes, if used, and rinse them with tap water. Replace the probes in the storage jar of tap water.

   c. Clean up and return the other equipment to storage.

10. Wash your hands thoroughly with soap and water before leaving the laboratory.

3. Prepare a lab report of your findings.

   You may want to refer to the guidelines in Part A, step 9, of the activity *You Are What You Eat*, in Chapter 7. Be sure to answer the following questions as part of your report:

   a. What was the specific purpose of each test tube that you set up? That is, what evidence did each test tube provide? What did you learn from each test tube?

   b. How was each test tube important in helping you develop your conclusion?

   c. Do your data support your hypothesis? Explain.

   d. Based on what you have learned from this experiment, what question would you like to ask and answer next?

Analysis

1. Take turns presenting your team's experimental design and results to the rest of the class. Also, share ideas from your lab report.

2. Participate in a class discussion of the various experiments conducted and the results that emerged.

3. With your teammates, create a visual diagram, such as a concept map, that represents your current understanding of the cycling of matter through a community. Base your diagram on the two populations that you studied in this activity.

Spinning the Web of Life

The next time you eat a hamburger, think about what it takes to make a pound of beef.

SCENARIO

Recipe for One Pound of Beef

Begin with 1 calf. Add the following ingredients over a period of about 2 years:

43 square yards of grazing land

8 square yards of farmland

13 pounds of forage

3 pounds of grain

6.4 ounces of soybeans

18 ounces of petroleum products

3 ounces of nitrogen

0.8 ounces of phosphorous

1.6 ounces of potassium

antibiotics

hormones

pesticides

herbicides

1,300 gallons of water, added regularly

You have already explored how matter cycles through various communities, and you should be aware that energy is stored in matter. When you eat various forms of matter, some of that energy is transformed. This transformed energy becomes available to you. It allows you to carry out the daily activities of life and the distinctive activities that make you who you are. Not all foods contain the same amount of energy. Not all organisms require the same amount of energy to live. So why does it take so much energy to make one pound of beef? In terms of energy and matter, what is the difference between eating plants and eating animals?

Let's examine the larger picture of matter and energy in your world. By relating one day's food intake to the plants and animals it came from, you can explore how the energy that is stored in matter flows through your community and fuels the activities of its organisms.

Materials   (per person)

set of colored pens or pencils, 3 colors

PROCESS AND PROCEDURES

1. Following the steps outlined below, generate a food web. A **food web** is a visual diagram of the interactions of matter and the consequent flow of energy.

   a. In your journal, create your ideal menu for 1 day. Include snacks as well as meals.

   > Choose your favorite foods and snacks.

   b. Make a 3-column chart in your journal. List the foods from your ideal menu in the 1st column and the ingredients in each menu item in the 2nd column.

   > Remember, many foods are combinations of different plants, animals, fungi, or bacteria. Record the ingredients of each food separately. For example, if you have a piece of cake for dessert, you should list oil, flour, sugar, butter, eggs, and milk.

   c. In the 3rd column of your chart, list the sources for the ingredients of each menu item.

   > For example, write *wheat* next to *flour*, *sugar cane* or *sugar beet* next to *sugar*, and *chicken* next to *egg*.

Figure 9.5 Think of the many steps involved in putting bread or tortillas on your plate.

   d. Create another 3-column chart in your journal. In the 2nd (center) column, list all of the animals that appeared in your 1st chart.

   e. For every animal that you have listed, do the following:

   ◆ In the 3rd column, list several foods that it eats.

   > For example, next to cow you would list the grass and corn that cattle eat.

Figure 9.6 Consider the sources of matter and energy that go into raising the eggs and chicken that may be part of your diet.

a

b

c

d

Figure 9.7 Classify the organisms in your lists by their diets. For example: (**a**) Herbivores primarily eat plants. (**b**) Carnivores primarily eat animals. (**c**) Omnivores eat both plants and animals. (**d**) Detritivores primarily feed off of dead organisms and the wastes or cast-off fragments of living organisms.

♦ In the 1st column, next to the animals that you listed in step d, record 2 animals that might eat each animal.

> For example, next to cow you might list wolf, bear, mountain lion, or human. Next to fish, you might list raccoon, otter, or sea gull, depending on the type of fish it is.

f. Create a food web from the information that you generated in your journal as follows. Use 1 different-colored pen or pencil for each step.

♦ Obtain a large sheet of paper from your teacher. Fold it like an accordion to create 5 equal-sized sections.

♦ List all the names of the plants in the bottom section.

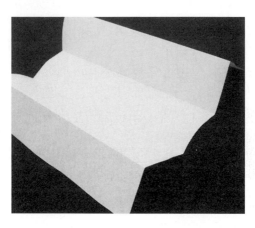

Figure 9.8 Obtain a large sheet of paper. Fold it to create five equal-sized sections. You will start your food web diagram by listing all the names of the plants in the bottom section.

♦ Write the names of all the herbivores (plant eaters) in the next section, above the plants.

♦ Write all the names of the omnivores (animals that eat plants and animals) in the next section, above the herbivores. Write your name at the end of this row.

♦ Write all the names of the carnivores (animals that eat only meat) in the section above the omnivore row.

g. After you have all the names of the plants and animals organized, draw arrows from the organisms that provide energy to the organisms that receive energy.

> Pay particular attention to the direction that you draw your arrows. They should show the direction of energy flow, *not* who will be eaten. Say, for example, your plant row includes grass and your herbivore row includes cattle. You would draw an arrow from grass to cattle with the point of the arrow aimed at the cattle.

2. Expand your food web in the following manner:

a. Think of other organisms that might compete with you for your food. In your journal, make a list of organisms that eat some of the same foods that you eat.

b. Using a pen or pencil of a different color, add the organisms that you listed in step 2a to the appropriate level of your food web. Add the appropriate arrows.

3. Work with a classmate to discuss briefly the following questions:

This strategy provides you with an opportunity to develop the skill of using your classmates as a resource.

Topic: food chain/
food web
Go to: www.scilinks.org
Code: human3E319

   a. What is the key difference between the way that producers and consumers accomplish biosynthesis?

   b. What sorts of matter do you think archaeologists might uncover years from now from the suburban family in Maineville, Ohio? How would this compare to what archaeologists have uncovered from the Ancestral Puebloans?

   You read about how matter cycles in other communities in the essay *Garbage among Us—From Then until Now!*

   c. Why is there no predator in Africa that lives by eating only lions and leopards?

   d. What effect are cattle and other domesticated livestock having on certain ecosystems?

   To help you with this task, read the letters in *Let's Ask Drs. Ricardo and Rita* (page 383) and the essay *Losing Heat* (page 388).

PAGE 383

PAGE 388

4. To demonstrate your more complete understanding of food webs, use a pen or pencil of a 3rd color to add detritivores to the top section of your food web. Detritivores feed off dead organisms and the wastes or cast-off fragments of living organisms. If you had mushrooms in your list of foods, they belong in this section. Use arrows to indicate the relationship of these decomposers to the other organisms present.

Analysis

Participate in a class discussion of the following. Record your ideas in your journal.

1. Describe how energy flows through the community, as shown in your food web.

2. Where is the most energy available in your food web? Explain your answer.

3. Compare the food web of a vegetarian in your class with the food web of someone who is not a vegetarian.

   ◆ What differences are evident?

   ◆ What do you think is significant about those differences?

   ◆ How does this relate to the recipe for one pound of beef?

4. How have we made our task of acquiring food easier than it was for the Ancestral Puebloans?

Generating Some Heat

Let's first read about a surprising source of heat in the story *Saturday Chores*. From your experiences in this chapter, you might guess that microorganisms were beginning to break down the grass clippings, especially those next to the soil. The microorganisms' life processes generated heat. This is an example of detritivores at work. This type of detritivore is called a **decomposer** because it makes organic nutrients available again to producers.

In this activity, you will elaborate on your knowledge of the cycling of matter and the flow of energy in communities. You will look, primarily, at the role of decomposers. You and your teammates are about to participate in a compost design competition. Your goal is to design a compost system that generates the most change in temperature.

SCENARIO

Saturday Chores

It's Saturday. You have a soccer game at noon. You promised your friends that you'll be there a half hour early to practice. But you know you have to finish your Saturday chores before you leave. This is your week to cut the grass, so you get up early to begin the task. Because the morning is cool, you find yourself making quick progress. But time is passing, and practice is about to begin. In an effort to shave some time off the job, you pile all of the clippings on some newly turned soil in a corner of the yard. You think, I'll bag the clippings later. Saturday and Sunday come and go.

School begins again on Monday. The clippings still are sitting there on the soil in the yard. Another Saturday rolls around and you have another game. It's your sister's turn to cut the grass. Good! No grass today! Your game is early in the morning. On the way out of the house, your dad reminds you that last week's clippings are still sitting in the yard and that it's your responsibility to bag them before you head out. You run to the yard with some lawn bags and begin scooping up grass clippings. Again, the morning is very

Figure 9.9 Fresh-cut grass that is piled shortly after mowing quickly gets hot.

cool. As you dig into the pile, you notice something interesting. Steam is rising from the clippings. In fact, the center of the clippings pile is hot, especially down near the soil. You wonder why the inside of the pile is so warm on such a cool morning.

Materials (per team of 4)

4 pairs of plastic gloves
pan balance
230–250 mL measuring cup
masking tape
sheet of plain newsprint
foam insulation material
bag of potting soil
bag of shredded leaf mulch or bark mulch

thermistor or nonmercury thermometer
1-gal plastic milk container with 4 cm
   of top cut off
4-gal plastic trash bag
trowel or spatula for mixing compost
packet of compost starter inoculum
bag of grass clippings
water

PROCESS AND PROCEDURES

1. As a class, make the following decisions about your compost designs:

   ◆ How much compost starter inoculum all teams will use

   ◆ How much water all teams will use

   ◆ How much total organic matter (the mass) all teams will use

   Why is it important that all teams keep certain features constant?

2. With your team, consider some recipes that you might use for your composting system. Discuss the following questions with your team to help you decide on a recipe. Record your answers and your recipe in your journal. Be sure to justify your decisions.

   a. What organic matter should you use?

   b. Should you use 1 source of organic matter or a combination of sources?

   c. If you use a combination, what proportions should you use?

   Composting is not an exact science. Gardeners frequently have their own personal compost recipes. Now it's your turn to create a compost recipe. You have all of the materials necessary for decomposers to work effectively. The grass clippings, shredded leaf mulch, and shredded bark mulch provide excellent carbon sources (organic matter to be consumed as food) for the microorganisms (starter inoculum). Check with your teacher if you wish to bring in and use any other matter in your recipe. Be prepared to explain why. Because these microorganisms thrive in soil, the potting soil should provide a suitable environment for initial growth. Remember, your entire compost needs to fit in the plastic milk container.

   As you develop your recipe, practice the working relationship skill of reaching consensus.

3. Carefully, create your composting system.

SAFETY: Put on your plastic gloves.

   a. Use the recipe that your team agreed on. Measure your soil and your food sources 1 at a time from materials you have available. Pour them into the plastic bag.

Figure 9.10
Organic materials can be composted. This causes the matter to be cycled more quickly than if it were left to decompose on its own. Where does the energy from the composted matter go?

Lab Gloves

b. Mix the ingredients thoroughly with a trowel.

c. Add the amount of compost starter inoculum that your class decided to include.

d. Add the amount of water that your class decided to include.

e. Again, use the trowel to mix the compost ingredients thoroughly. Then place your mixed compost into the plastic milk container.

f. Insulate your container of compost.

Cut enough insulation material to surround the container. Tape the insulation in place. Cut a small piece of insulation for the top. For the composting inoculum to work most efficiently, the system must retain the heat that the microorganisms generate. If they are not insulated, the compost systems will lose this heat to the environment.

4. Keep your system going for 2 more days. Record the temperature in the center of the compost twice a day. If you are using a thermistor, you may be able to set your data-collection device to save and record temperatures at regular intervals over the time of the experiment.

Create a data table in your journal in which to record the temperature of your compost.

5. Graph the temperature changes that you observed in your composting system.

Analysis

SCI LINKS.
NSTA

Topic: compost
Go to: www.scilinks.org
Code: human3E322

Complete the following tasks as a team:

1. Present your team's compost recipe and results to the class. Be sure to share the graph of your results.

2. Based on all of the teams' reports, determine which compost recipes generated the most change in temperature.

You and your classmates will judge the effectiveness of each composting recipe by examining each team's data.

a. Why do you think the most effective recipes worked better than others did?

b. What do your results tell you about the cycling of matter and the flow of energy?

c. What role did the microorganisms play?

3. The heat that you noticed is a form of energy. What form did this energy take before it was released as heat? What happens to this energy after it is released as heat?

4. What does your answer to question 3 reveal about the flow of energy in a community?

What Have I Learned about Energy and Matter in Communities?

By now you should be aware of how closely connected the flow of energy is to the cycling of matter in communities. In this activity, you and your teacher will evaluate what you have learned about these concepts. You will work individually to think about the impact that a natural disaster would have on various communities on earth. Then you will respond to some questions about survival in different communities.

PROCESS AND PROCEDURES

Part A   A Natural Disaster

1. Read about the following catastrophe:

   The earth is entering a phase of instability that no one had predicted. Throughout both hemispheres, hundreds of volcanoes are erupting with great force. The earth's atmosphere is thick with minute volcanic debris and dust. As much as 75 percent of the sunlight is now blocked from reaching the earth's surface. This period of eruptions is expected to continue indefinitely. It is likely that soon virtually all sunlight will be blocked from reaching the earth's surface.

Figure 9.11 The community around this volcano was drastically changed after the eruption.

2. Obtain a scoring rubric from your teacher. Read the following questions, and record your answers in your journal. Be sure to answer each part of each question. Your teacher will collect your journal and use the criteria listed in the scoring rubric to assess your understanding.

   a. What might be the effect if, instead, 80–85 percent of the sunlight were blocked from the earth? What might be the effect on the following organisms: an earthworm, a shark, a maple tree, a saguaro cactus, and a teenager?

   b. Imagine that all sunlight is blocked from reaching the earth's surface.

      ◆ What might be the effect on the following organisms: the producers, the consumers, and the decomposers?

      ◆ Describe how the cycling of matter through a community would be affected.

Part B   Strategies for Survival

Work with a partner to discuss the following questions. Then record your responses in your journal.

1. From the thousands that sprout, why will only 1 or 2 healthy trees grow into the available space between other existing trees?

2. Are the fish that live 2 km (1.2 mi) deep in the ocean likely to be herbivores or predators? Explain.

3. There were many years when DDT (a pesticide) was widely used in the United States. During this period, the populations of birds of prey, such as bald eagles, peregrine falcons, and ospreys, declined more than the populations of small songbirds. Why do you think that was so?

4. Human societies that live by hunting and gathering usually have much smaller populations than groups in a similar setting that live primarily by growing crops. Why do you think that is so?

5. Suppose you found yourself snowed in for the winter in a remote mountain cabin with no way of contacting the outside world. You must survive for several months with only what is on hand to eat. Aside from a small supply of canned peaches, your only resources are 2 100-lb sacks of wheat and a flock of 8 hens. Discuss the relative merits of the following strategies:

   a. Feed the grain to the hens and eat their eggs until the wheat is gone. Then eat the hens.

   b. Kill the hens at once, and freeze their carcasses in the snow. Live on a diet of wheat porridge and chicken.

   c. Eat a mixture of wheat porridge, eggs, and 1 hen a week. Feed the hens well to keep the eggs coming until all of the hens are killed.

6. Every breeding pair of bullfrogs produces hundreds of eggs each spring. During the time they are growing up in the pond, the small tadpoles feed entirely on microscopic water plants. Predators living in the pond eat a large fraction of the tadpoles before they transform into frogs. As adults, however, bullfrogs themselves are predators. Discuss why this strategy is more advantageous than one in which the tadpoles would be predators and the adults would be herbivores.

Figure 9.12
Bullfrog. Although adult bullfrogs are predators, the tadpoles are prey. Many are eaten before they reach adulthood.

Further Challenges

1. There are several hypotheses about how dinosaurs became extinct. One of these hypotheses involves a climatic catastrophe that has some similarities to the one presented in Part A. See what you can find out about this hypothesis. Report your findings to the class.

2. Write and perform a skit that depicts organisms defending their role in a community. In it, describe the advantages, the disadvantages, and the importance to the community of a producer, a predator, and a decomposer.

UNIT 3 ESSAYS

Energy, Matter, and Organization: Relationships in Living Systems

Human Performance: A Function of Fitness

For Yates and Sullivan, the characters in the story *The Sky Awaits*, being fit means being able to perform a demanding physical task successfully. To be fit, however, do you really need to have the strength required to put a supersonic jet into a 90° bank at six Gs? Do you need to have the speed and endurance necessary to place in the top 10 percent of a marathon? Is the level of fitness required to be an athlete the same as the level of fitness required for good health?

Figure E7.1 Human performance.
Consider the different levels of performance in this variety of complex human activities. Some activities are a part of daily life. Others are highly specialized. Each has its own special requirements, although general fitness for life helps in all cases.

If exceptional athletic performance were the standard, then very few of us could consider ourselves fit. Even Yates and Sullivan, prepared as they are for their type of work, would not necessarily be prepared for all types of athletic activity. The two individuals must be able to withstand sudden, strong forces without blacking out or losing concentration. This does not necessarily mean that they would be great sprinters or weightlifters. Likewise, the special qualities required of a sprinter may not be suited for the tasks required of high-performance pilots. What are some of the special abilities that sprinters must have?

Clearly, an athlete's body must be prepared for the demands of a specific activity. But fitness requirements vary depending on the nature of the activity. Outstanding performance in one sport does not guarantee outstanding performance in another.

Is it possible for a person who lacks the special skills required for any form of athletics to be fit for life itself? To function normally, our bodies must be capable of performing certain basic physical activities. We walk, talk, gesture, and sometimes even run. Even when we sit still, our bodies maintain a basic level of internal function. Fit-for-life individuals usually are in good physical condition and health. These individuals find that they can perform the routine activities of life easily, as illustrated in Figure E7.1.

What, then, is a useful definition of *fitness*? Some authorities define fitness as the ability to perform routine physical activities—such as walking, talking, lifting, and carrying—with enough energy in reserve to meet an unexpected challenge. A fit individual can run up three flights of stairs carrying a heavy book bag and immediately answer the question, "Why are you late?" upon reaching class. A less fit person may have to stop to catch her breath at the top of the second flight. She may have to collapse into a chair and breathe heavily for a while before answering that question.

Largely, your level of fitness determines the physical activities that you can perform. If your body can perform the basic functions of life, then clearly you possess a basic fitness for life. If you can race up three flights of steps quickly enough to beat the school bell, then you also possess a level of athletic fitness.

Whether flying jets, swimming, running to catch a plane, or just walking to school, the body requires two basic resources: matter and energy. In fact, all biological activity requires regular and sufficient amounts of matter and energy.

Consider the common factors in these activities: a ballet dancer executing a complex spin, a cheetah racing to attack a gazelle, and a lily bud opening its petals. Each of those activities relies on the organization of matter into specific structures. For the human and the cheetah, the muscles of the body act against the skeleton to produce coordinated movement. For the lily, the petals open precisely to produce a beautiful flower. In each case, a highly coordinated interaction of structural systems must take place.

Biological activity also requires energy. The bodies of organisms need energy to organize matter and provide the power to perform work. It takes energy, for example, to build the proteins needed for muscles or flower petals. It also takes energy for the

Figure E7.2 What structural systems must interact for this activity to take place?

muscles to contract or the petals to open. In fact, the bodies of all organisms require energy for all cellular processes as well as for obvious functions such as walking, running, or dancing (Figure E7.2).

If all human performance requires matter and energy, what is the difference between a person capable of winning a grueling 160-kilometers (99-mile) bike race and another capable only of watching the race on TV? One way to understand the difference is to think in terms of an ability to apply matter and energy to a specific task. The racer's matter is organized more effectively for biking

Figure E7.3 **Typical diet and exercise profile for a "couch potato."** Weight: 70 kilograms (154 pounds) (much fat, little muscle); exercise level: low; diet: high in fats and sugars

EXPLORING BIOLOGY

than that of a less fit person. Although the two individuals may weigh the same, the racer's muscles are larger and stronger. As a result, he or she is better able to apply force to the pedals. Likewise, the racer's body supplies energy more effectively than that of a less fit person. Although the two individuals both have circulatory and gas exchange systems, the racer's heart pumps blood more efficiently. The racer's body has a more extensive capillary system. This system efficiently delivers oxygen and nutrients to muscles and removes carbon dioxide and other waste products from them. Therefore, the racer's legs can pedal and the brain can function all the way to the finish line. ◆

Food: Our Body's Source of Energy and Structural Materials

They sat in the cold mess-hall, most of them with their hats on, eating slowly, picking out putrid little fish from under the leaves of boiled black cabbage and spitting the bones out on the table. . . . The only good thing about skilly was that it was hot, but Shukhov's portion had grown quite cold. However, he ate it with his usual slow concentration. . . . Sleep apart, the only time a prisoner lives for himself is ten minutes in the morning at breakfast, five minutes over dinner and five at supper.

The skilly was the same every day. Its composition depended on the kind of vegetable provided that winter. Nothing but salted carrots last year, which meant that from September to June the skilly was plain carrot. This year it was black cabbage. The most nourishing time of the year was June: then all vegetables came to an end and were replaced by groats.[1] The worst time was July: then they shredded nettles[2] into the pot.

The little fish were more bone than flesh; the flesh had been boiled off the bone and had disintegrated, leaving a few remnants on head and tail. Without neglecting a single fish-scale or particle of flesh on the brittle skeleton, Shukhov went on chomping his teeth and sucking the bones. He ate everything—the gills, the tail, the eyes when they were still in their sockets. . . .

A spoonful of granulated sugar lay in a small mound on top of [his bread-ration] . . . he sucked the sugar from the bread with his lips . . . and took a look at his ration, weighing it in his hand and hastily calculating whether it reached the regulation fifty-five grammes. He had drawn many a thousand of these rations in prisons and camps, and though he never had an opportunity to weigh them on scales . . . he, like every other prisoner, had discovered long ago that honest weight was never to be found in the bread-cutting. There was short weight in every ration. The only point was how short. So every day you took a look to soothe your soul—today, maybe, they won't have snitched any.

Source: From *One Day in the Life of Ivan Denisovich,* by Alexander Solzhenitsyn, translated by Ralph Parker, Translation © 1963 by E.P. Dutton and Victor Gollancz, Ltd. Copyright renewed © 1991 by Penguin USA and Victor Gollancz, Ltd. Used by permission of Dutton Signet, a division of Penguin Books USA Inc.

In its most basic sense, **food** is any substance that your body can use as a raw material to sustain its growth, repair it, and provide energy. In extreme situations such as Shukhov's, food is whatever will keep you alive.

Most of the substances we call food consist largely of water. A tomato, for example, is about 95 percent water. Water is

[1]Groats are hulled and crushed oats or wheat.
[2]Nettles are a coarse herb with stinging hairs.

an important nutrient that we often take for granted. However, our bodies need enormous amounts of it in comparison to other nutrients. An average American diet includes about 2 liters, or 2,000 grams, of water each day. In contrast, most of us eat only about 50 grams of protein in a day and only milligrams of many vitamins and essential elements.

The bulk of our food is made up of three major classes of nutrients: carbohydrates, proteins, and fats. The tiny remainder consists of vitamins and essential elements. An important function of the digestive system is to break down large nutrient molecules into small molecules. The molecules must be small enough to pass through the lining of the digestive tract into the circulatory system. For example, a complex carbohydrate such as starch is broken down into molecules of a simple sugar such as glucose. Proteins are broken down into amino acids. Fats are broken into an array of simpler molecules.

If food technically can be anything that keeps you alive, what constitutes good nutrition? The phrase *good nutrition* means ensuring that your body receives what it requires to remain healthy and functional. It also means avoiding those things that may cause it harm. Exactly what constitutes *good* may vary somewhat with the circumstances. For example, although not consistent with the general guidelines for a healthy diet, Jennifer Yates's breakfast was appropriate for her unusual type of physical activity. With its relatively high-fat foods, her breakfast contained stored energy and low bulk. A high-bulk breakfast such as pancakes and cereal would have put considerable physical strain on her digestive system. G forces in flight multiply the mass of stomach and intestinal contents.

Determining what constitutes a level of good general nutrition is the job of biochemists, nutritionists, and other health professionals. Their understanding of how the body uses energy and matter is critical to their work. As their understanding improves

through research, the nutritional guidelines that professionals suggest often change. Figure E7.4 outlines some nutritional guidelines for general fitness. (Note that the "calories" listed on food labels are actually kilocalories; 1,000 calories equals 1 kcal. Nutritionists often represent 1 kcal by *Calorie*, with a capital C. A calorie is a measure of the energy contained in food.)

There are many ways to achieve the balance of nutrients outlined in Figure E7.4. An individual's *diet*—the types of food that he or she eats on a regular basis—is a reflection of many influences. Your cultural background, your personal preferences, and the varieties of foods available all influence what you eat. Shukhov's diet  must have provided *some* nutrients. The "putrid little fish," for example, probably provided the prisoners with a critical source of protein. Protein is essential for repairing and maintaining body tissues.

Humans obtain needed protein from a variety of sources. This variety is necessary to provide all of the essential amino acids required for good health. The human body can synthesize most of the 20 amino acids needed in proteins. However, the body cannot make eight of the amino acids. These eight must be obtained from food. High-protein food from animal sources (meat, milk, eggs) has the proper balance of amino acids for the human diet, as does the plant source soybeans. Other plant-derived foods, such as grains, nuts, and seeds, are good sources of protein as well.  But most plant-derived foods lack one or more of the essential amino acids. It is

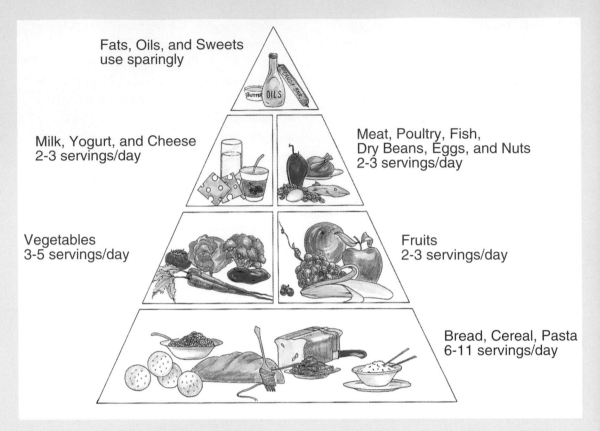

Figure E7.4 USDA food guide pyramid. Foods provide fuel for energy and matter for body structures. People in different cultures select and prepare foods in a variety of ways. What foods would you choose to meet the USDA recommended guidelines?

possible, however, to obtain completely balanced amino acids by combining these plant-derived foods in the diet. The combination of legumes (beans, peas, and peanuts) with grains or nuts can provide balanced protein diets. This is why peanut butter sandwiches are good for us. The amino acids in the peanuts complement the amino acids in the bread grains to provide the right balance for our bodies.

The fish probably also served as Shukhov's only significant source of fat. In this regard, the prisoners' diets might have been healthier than our own. Fats are important nutritionally for making hormones and cell membranes, and for storing energy. However, most Americans consume too many fats, and many of these fats are the wrong type. Of particular concern are saturated fats.

These fats, or lipids, are present in certain animal products such as meat, cheese, and butter. Because of the apparent link between the intake of lipids and cardiovascular disease, physicians now recommend that fats should make up less than 30 percent of the daily kcals. Fish oils, however, contain fatty acids that are good for the heart. These fatty acids also are required for normal development of the nervous and reproductive systems.

The carrots, cabbage, and groats in Shukhov's diet provided carbohydrates, fiber, vitamins, and essential elements. Carbohydrates provide the fuel a body can use most readily. What does fiber provide? Fiber comes mainly from cellulose in plants. Humans cannot digest cellulose. However, cellulose absorbs water and toxins, and helps ensure regular elimination of waste.

IMPORTANT VITAMINS FOR HUMAN HEALTH

Vitamin *fat-soluble*	Sources	Functions	Deficiency symptoms
A (retinol)	Liver, green and yellow vegetables, fruits, egg yolks, butter	Forms eye pigments; helps cell growth, especially of epithelial cells	Night blindness, flaky skin lowered resistance to infection, growth retardation
D (calciferol)	Fish oils, liver, action of sunlight on lipids in skin, fortified milk, butter, eggs	Increases calcium absorption from gut; is important in bone and tooth formation	Rickets (defective bone growth)
E (tocopherol)	Oils, whole grains, liver, mayonnaise, margarine	Protects red blood cells, cell membranes, and vitamin A from destruction; helps maintain muscles; synthesizes DNA and RNA	Fragility of red blood cells, muscle wasting, sterility
K (menadione)	Synthesis by intestinal bacteria; green and yellow vegetables	Assists liver in synthesis of clotting factors	Internal hemorrhaging (deficiency can be caused by oral antibiotics, which kill intestinal bacteria)

Vitamin *water-soluble*	Sources	Functions	Deficiency symptoms
B_1 (thiamine)	Whole grains, legumes, nuts, liver, heart, kidney, pork, macaroni, wheat germ	Facilitates carbohydrate metabolism, nerve transmission, and RNA synthesis	Beriberi, loss of appetite, indigestion, fatigue, nerve irritability, heart failure, depression, poor coordination
B_2 (riboflavin)	Liver, kidney, heart, yeast, milk, eggs, whole grains, broccoli, almonds, cottage cheese, yogurt, macaroni	Forms part of electron carrier in electron transport system; aids production of FAD; activates B_6 and folic acid	Sore mouth and tongue, cracks at corners of mouth, eye irritation, scaly skin, growth retardation
Pantothenic acid	Yeast, liver, eggs, wheat germ, bran, peanuts, peas, fish, whole grain cereals	Facilitates energy release and biosynthesis; stimulates antibodies and intestinal absorption	Fatigue, headaches, sleep disturbances, nausea, muscle cramps, loss of antibody production, irritability, vomiting
B_3 (niacin)	Yeast, liver, kidney, heart, meat, fish, poultry, legumes, nuts, whole grains, eggs, milk	Serves as coenzyme in energy metabolism; is part of NAD^+ and NADP	Pellagra, skin lesions, digestive problems, nerve disorders, diarrhea, headaches, fatigue

Vitamin	Sources	Functions	Deficiency symptoms
B_6 (pyridoxine)	Whole grains, potatoes, fish, poultry, red meats, legumes, seeds	Serves as coenzyme in amino acid and fatty acid metabolism and in the synthesis of brain chemicals, antibodies, red blood cells, and DNA; is essential to glucose tolerance	Skin disorders, sore mouth and tongue, nerve disorders, anemia, weight loss, impaired antibody response, convulsive seizures
Biotin	Cauliflower, liver, kidney, yeast, egg yolks, whole grains, fish, legumes, nuts, meats, dairy products; synthesis by intestinal bacteria	Serves as coenzyme in fatty acid, amino acid, and protein synthesis; promotes energy release from glucose; facilitates insulin activity	Skin disorders, loss of appetite, depression, sleeplessness, muscle pain, elevated blood cholesterol and glucose levels
Folate (folic acid)	Liver, yeast, leafy vegetables, asparagus, salmon	Serves as a coenzyme in nucleic acid synthesis and amino acid metabolism; is essential for new cell growth	Failure of red blood cells to mature, anemia, intestinal disturbances, diarrhea
B_{12} (cobalamin)	Liver, organ meats, meat, fish, eggs, shellfish, milk; synthesis by intestinal bacteria	Serves as coenzyme in nucleic acid synthesis; helps maintain nervous tissues; tissue; plays a role in glucose metabolism	Pernicious anemia, fatigue, irritability, loss of appetite, headaches
C (ascorbic acid)	Citrus fruits, tomatoes, green leafy vegetables, peppers, broccoli, cauliflower	Is essential to formation of collagen, an intercellular substance that holds cells together; protects against infection; maintains strength of blood vessels; increases iron absorption from gut; plays important role in muscle maintenance and stress tolerance	Scurvy, failure to form connective tissue, bleeding, anemia, slow wound healing, joint pain, irritability, premature wrinkling and aging

Figure E7.5 Important vitamins for human health.

What do vitamins do? Usually, humans need only very small amounts of vitamins. Partnered with enzymes, vitamins regulate cellular activities. Vitamins, therefore, are necessary for normal growth and maintenance of life. Thiamine and riboflavin, for example, are B-complex vitamins. B-complex vitamins help release energy from food. Thiamine deficiencies can lead to muscle atrophy, paralysis, mental confusion, and even heart failure. Figure E7.5 describes the sources, functions, and deficiency symptoms of vitamins.

Elements are the basic components of matter. Essential elements such as sodium and calcium are important to maintaining homeostasis. Figure E7.6 describes the sources, functions, and deficiency (and excess) symptoms of the major essential elements. ◆

IMPORTANT ELEMENTS FOR HUMAN HEALTH

Name	Food	Function	Deficiency symptoms	Excess symptoms
Calcium (Ca)	Dairy products, green vegetables (broccoli, greens), legumes, tofu (bean curd), small fish (with bones)	Helps in bone and tooth development; facilitates muscle contraction, blood clotting, nerve impulse transmission, and enzyme activation	Osteoporosis, stunted growth, poor quality bones and teeth, rickets, convulsions	Excess blood calcium (rare), loss of appetite, muscle weakness, fever
Chlorine (Cl)	Table salt, soy sauce, processed foods	Helps maintain acid/base balance; assists hydrochloric acid formation in stomach; promotes bone and connective tissue growth	Metabolic alkalosis (rare), constipation, failure to gain weight (in infants)	Vomiting
Magnesium (Mg)	Whole grains, liver, kidneys, milk, nuts, dark green leafy vegetables, seafood	Serves as a component of chlorophyll, bones, and teeth, and as a coenzyme in carbohydrate and protein metabolism	Infertility, menstrual disorders	Loss of reflexes, drowsiness, coma, death
Phosphorous (P)	Soybeans, dairy foods, egg yolks, meat, whole grains, shrimp, peas, leafy green vegetables	Serves as component of bones, teeth, nucleic acids, phospholipids, proteins, and ATP	Bone fractures (rare), disorders of red blood cells, metabolic problems, irritability, weakness	Decreased levels of calcium, muscle spasms, jaw erosion
Potassium (K)	Whole grains, meats, fruits, vegetables, milk, peanut butter	Helps maintain body water and pH balance; plays important role in nerve and muscle activity, insulin release, glycogen and protein synthesis	Muscle and nerve weakness, poor digestion	Abnormalities in heartbeat or heart stoppage, muscle weakness, mental confusion, cold and pale skin (all are rare)
Sodium (Na)	Table salt, soy sauce, processed foods, baking soda, baking powder, meat, vegetables	Helps maintain body water and pH balance; plays role in nerve and muscle activity and glucose absorption	Weakness, muscle cramps, diarrhea, dehydration, nausea	High blood pressure, edema, kidney disease
Sulfur (S)	Dairy products, nuts, legumes, garlic, onions, egg yolks	Serves as component of some amino acids; plays role in enzyme activation and in blood clotting	None known; protein deficiency would occur first	Excess sulfur-containing amino acid intake leads to poor growth

Figure E7.6 **Important elements for human health.**

Pioneers: The Changing Face of the Food Guide Pyramid

This chapter has introduced you to ways your body uses the foods you eat. How do you choose those foods? Have you ever seen a food guide pyramid? The standard food guide pyramid was originally designed to help people meet nutritional and dietary needs. Do you think this guide is appropriate for all people? Alternate food guides suggest ways that people with different dietary preferences may also get the nutrition necessary for a healthy lifestyle.

What are some ways you might use a food guide pyramid in your life? A good place to begin is knowing the difference between a serving and a helping. A *serving* is the amount of a food item that has been analyzed for nutritional value. A *helping* is the amount you choose to eat. Some food guides may tell you exactly how much of a food you should eat. Many newer versions merely suggest foods to choose from on a daily or weekly basis.

Does the guide consider foods that you enjoy with your family or friends? The standard food guide does not reflect cultural differences among families. Also, a great variety of food is available across the United States. Compare the standard guide and the Mexican native foods guide. The vegetarian food guide is for people who do not eat meat.

Does the guide recommend foods that every person can eat and digest? Many African Americans, Hispanics, Asian Americans, and Native Americans are lactose intolerant (cannot digest dairy products). These people might benefit from the Asian food guide, which suggests other foods. The few examples shown here demonstrate how the concept of a food guide is changing to meet the needs of our culturally diverse society. ◆

Figure E7.7 Alternate food guide pyramids.
(**a**) Standard: USDA and DHHS (**b**) Asian: ©2000 Oldways Preservation & Exchange Trust (**c**) Mexican native foods: adapted from American Dietetic Association (**d**) Vegetarian ©2000 Oldways Preservation & Exchange Trust

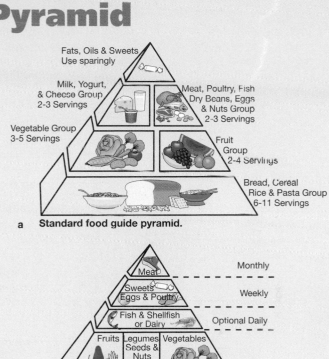

a   Standard food guide pyramid.

b   Asian food guide pyramid.

c   Mexican native foods guide pyramid.

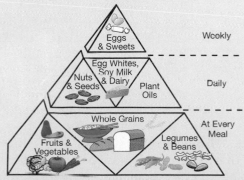

d   Vegetarian food guide pyramid.

What Happens to the Food You Eat?

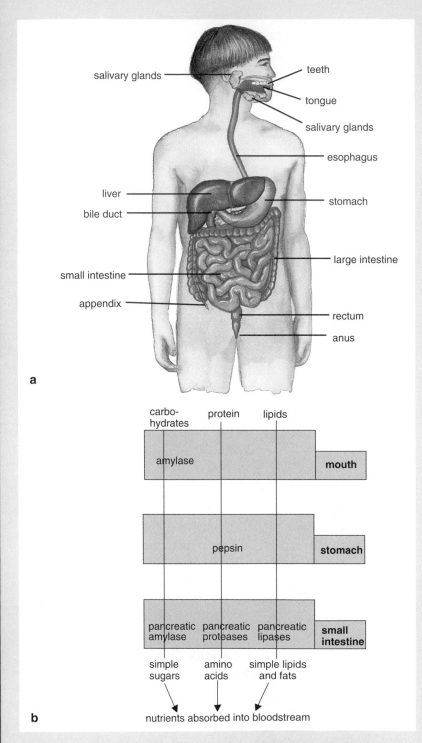

Figure E7.8 **The digestive system of the human body.**
(a) Location of organs and tissues involved in digestion
(b) Examples of enzyme action in breaking down food. Notice the compartments in which the enzymes for specific substrates act.

Have you ever watched a pizza commercial on television and heard your stomach growl as the actor pulls up a warm slice with stringy cheese trailing behind? When you feel hungry—whether in response to your body's actual need for nutrients or just over thoughts of a tasty slice of pizza—hormonal signals begin to prepare the digestive system for action. How does this work when your body truly needs nutrients? A decrease in nutrient levels in your blood sends a signal to the hunger center in your brain's hypothalamus. The hypothalamus responds by triggering the release of digestive juices into the stomach. A feeling of hunger then motivates you to find food.

Why do humans often eat when their bodies are not really in need of nutrients? Areas of the brain in addition to the hypothalamus are involved in controlling eating. Signals from sensory organs about the smell, taste, and sight of food may trigger the perception of hunger. Memories and attitudes that you have developed about food also affect your eating behavior.

Regardless of how your feelings of hunger began, the initial responses to hunger stimulate the secretion of hormones such as gastrin. Those hormones, in turn, stimulate further secretion of digestive juices in the stomach. Thus, a feedback system alerts your body that it needs (or wants) food. You respond by changing your behavior to locate the desired food.

Humans and most other animals must bring food inside their bodies to provide proper conditions for digestion. (Sponges and parasitic worms are examples of two exceptions.) Figure E7.8 shows the components of the human digestive system. The first steps are familiar: obtain food, chew it, and then swallow it.

Chewing performs an important digestive function. As you chew, the surface area of your food increases greatly. Increased surface area means that the chemical reactions involved in digestion can take place more quickly. In addition, chewing moistens the food with saliva. Salivary glands located under your tongue secrete saliva.

The mechanical breakdown of food is not enough. No matter how finely you chew bits of steak, the proteins remain intact. If your body is to use the proteins, it must break them down into subunit parts: amino acids. Similarly, chewed bread still has its carbohydrates intact, mainly in the form of long starch molecules. Your body must break starch down into sugars to use it. Starch is a molecule manufactured in plants. As shown in Figure E7.9, a starch molecule consists of many sugar molecules bonded together in a branching pattern.

How are large molecules broken down into small ones? The chemical action of special proteins known as **enzymes** helps make this happen. Enzymes catalyze, or speed up, specific molecular reactions that otherwise would take place very slowly. Enzymes act on molecules called **substrates**. Substrates bind to specific places on enzymes. Carbohydrate and protein molecules are substrates of many enzyme-catalyzed reactions, particularly those that take place during digestion. The reaction catalyzed by an enzyme changes the substrate into a different molecule. Enzymes that help break down food are present in your mouth, your stomach, and your small intestines.

Do you remember the discussion earlier about saliva? Saliva contains the enzyme amylase. Amylase breaks down starch into maltose molecules. (Maltose consists of two glucose molecules joined together.) In your stomach, the enzyme pepsin binds to protein molecules. Combined with the action of other digestive enzymes in the small intestines, pepsin breaks down protein into amino acids. This is illustrated in Figure E7.8b.

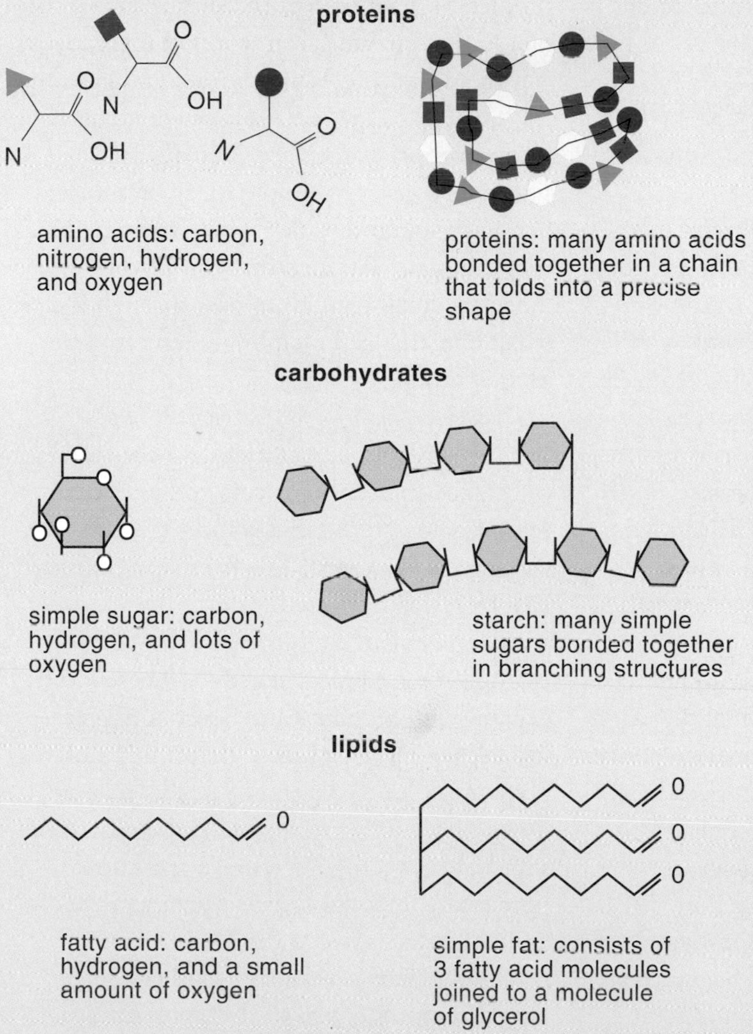

proteins

amino acids: carbon, nitrogen, hydrogen, and oxygen

proteins: many amino acids bonded together in a chain that folds into a precise shape

carbohydrates

simple sugar: carbon, hydrogen, and lots of oxygen

starch: many simple sugars bonded together in branching structures

lipids

fatty acid: carbon, hydrogen, and a small amount of oxygen

simple fat: consists of 3 fatty acid molecules joined to a molecule of glycerol

Figure E7.9 Examples of macromolecules and their components.   Macromolecules, such as proteins, carbohydrates, and lipids, are chains of smaller molecules. For example, proteins are made up of long chains of many different amino acids. Complex carbohydrates, such as starch and glycogen, are made up of long chains of simple sugars. (Starch and glycogen are storage molecules in plants and animals, respectively.) The lipids known as simple fats are made up of three long chains of fatty acids combined with glycerol, a small alcohol.

ROLE OF SOME DIGESTIVE ENZYMES

Type of enzyme	General reaction	Optimal pH
amylase	starch → double sugars (maltose)	pH 6.9 – 7.0
proteases	protein → amino acids	pH 2.0 (pepsin) pH 7.0 – 8.0 (most others)
lipases	fats → fatty acids + glycerol	pH 8.0

Figure E7.10 Role of some digestive enzymes.

In general, digestive enzymes break down complex molecules into their simple components. Figure E7.10 lists some examples of digestive enzymes, the reactions they carry out, and the pH conditions under which they function.

After you swallow, it takes less than 10 seconds for the chewed and moistened food to pass through the esophagus into the stomach. Smooth muscles encircle the digestive tract. These muscles contract in a coordinated fashion, called *peristalsis*, to move food through the digestive tract. In the stomach, food churns and mixes with digestive fluids for 3 or 4 hours. The stomach stretches during this process and makes you feel full. This sensation reduces your motivation to continue eating. (Unless, of course, the food tastes so good that you ignore these signals and continue eating anyway.) This is another example of feedback, which you studied in Chapter 5.

From the stomach, partially digested food passes into the small intestine. Final digestion of the complex food molecules, breaking down into their simple components, happens here. The cells that line the small intestine contribute fluids that contain digestive enzymes. Other organs, including the pancreas and liver, also deliver digestive enzymes to the small intestine. The pancreas is an organ in the abdomen that produces 1.4 liters (3 pints) of fluid per day. The fluid contains enzymes that contribute to the final digestion of the remaining macromolecules in the small intestine. The liver produces 0.8-1.0 liter (1.7–2 pints) of bile per day.

Bile is stored in the gall bladder. It is released into the small intestine after a meal. Bile contains bile salts, which act in a manner similar to detergents. Bile breaks fat into tiny droplets. This increases the surface area of the fats so that enzymes can work on them easily.

In addition to being the site of digestion, the small intestine is the organ where nearly all absorption takes place. The digested nutrients consist of simple sugar, amino acid, and fatty acid molecules. These building block molecules are obtained through digestion. They are small enough to pass through the small intestine cell membranes and into the bloodstream.

Liver cells monitor nutrient levels in the blood and adjust them as necessary. Substances present in excess amounts are removed and stored. Substances that are lacking are increased. The liver accomplishes that by releasing stored forms or by stimulating synthesis processes. Say, for example, you exercise heavily. Glucose levels drop in your bloodstream. Sensors trigger the liver to release glucose that it had stored as glycogen. The glycogen is quickly broken down into glucose to replenish the exhausted supply. Liver cells also remove and correct potentially toxic substances (such as alcohol and other drugs) from the blood.

Undigested remains of food cannot pass through the wall of the small intestine. Instead, this part of the food enters the large intestine. The large intestine absorbs water and returns it to the blood. The body then eliminates the compacted solid wastes. ◆

Anorexia Nervosa: Dying to Be Thin

She's been getting increasingly moody, she hasn't menstruated in 3 months, and the circles under her eyes suggest to others that she hasn't been sleeping well. The cold she caught 2 weeks ago has lingered, despite her efforts to shake it. Though she denies feeling tired, she seems to have less energy each day. Yesterday, her father noticed her swaying a bit—dizzy, perhaps?—when she jumped up to answer the phone. Yet, after dinner (an unhappy meal in which her parents pushed her to eat and Christine insisted she was not hungry), she went out to run her customary 3 kilometers (1.9 miles).

Although Christine doesn't know it and probably wouldn't admit it, she has anorexia nervosa. Anorexia nervosa is an eating disorder that affects an estimated 1 million people, mostly teenage girls, in the United States. Christine doesn't see that she is undernourished. In fact, she will insist against all evidence to the contrary that she is fat and needs to lose weight. Her self-discipline is the envy of all her friends. She denies her hunger and exercises relentlessly until she is convinced that she has burned off any "excess" calories she might have consumed.

Left untreated, Christine likely will continue starving herself—possibly to death. As her nutritional base deteriorates, she will experience profound physical changes. Her hormone levels will continue to drop. Her heart muscle will become weak and thin. Her digestive system will begin to function less and less efficiently. Electrical activity in her brain may become abnormal. Electrolyte imbalances in her body will put her at risk for sudden heart failure.

Because the underlying causes of anorexia nervosa are complex and involve self-image and mental attitudes, treatment of the disorder also is complex. Successful treatment must take into account the whole person: the physical self, the cultural self, and the psychological self. Not surprisingly, treatment is most successful when the entire family is involved and participates honestly in the process. ◆

The Structural Basis of Physical Mobility

Mary, James, Lolita, Madonna, Rodriguez . . . Writing your name seems simple enough, doesn't it? To do even this simple task, however, requires a highly coordinated series of muscle movements in your arm, hand, and fingers. Energy is necessary for all of these movements. Indeed, energy is required even to transmit nerve impulses.

All physical activities require some type of structure that can translate the energy of food into useful biological work. The muscles and skeleton of your arm, hand, and fingers, as well as the neurons that transmit nerve impulses, are biological structures. The functions of these structures are quite specific. A neuron alone cannot move your fingers, nor can a muscle carry nerve impulses. These examples illustrate that there is a close relationship between a physical structure and its function.

Consider, for example, the organization and function of skeletal muscle. Skeletal muscle produces the movements of your limbs. To generate most types of movement, muscles must work in opposing groups against the

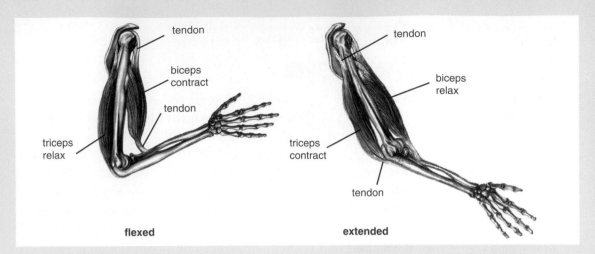

Figure E7.11
The human arm functions like a lever. The biceps and triceps muscles act on a fulcrum point, the elbow. Although these muscles are attached to the bones in the upper and lower arms, muscle contraction causes only the lower bone to move.

tendon

biceps contract

tendon

triceps relax

flexed

tendon

biceps relax

triceps contract

tendon

extended

skeleton. Figure E7.11 illustrates the organization of muscles in your arm. Notice that the biceps and triceps attach to the bones of the upper and lower arm by tendons. Tendons are flexible cords of connective tissue. The biceps' tendon attaches to the bone of the lower arm on the *inside* of the elbow joint. When you contract the biceps, your arm bends. By contrast, the triceps' tendon attaches to the bone of the lower arm on the *outer side* of the elbow. When you contract the triceps, your arm straightens.

Muscles in a vertebrate limb work on the bone just as a force works on a lever. A

relatively small amount of shortening of either produces a large movement. Even though this is the case in a wide variety of organisms, the details can vary greatly. These differences mean that different organisms are capable of different types of movements.

This variation is especially evident in organisms that have the same overall body plan but have adapted to different situations. Compare, for example, the forelimb of the cheetah to that of the mole in Figure E7.12. Both are vertebrates. Their limbs work according to the same principles (and even use the same muscles) as the human arm.

Figure E7.12
Structure and function in moles and cheetahs. The type of movement possible in an organism depends on the precise arrangements of skeleton and muscle. **(a)** Short, heavy bones, like those of the mole, are typical of animal skeletons that require power. **(b)** Thin, light bones, like those of the cheetah, favor speed. Think about the effect of applying forces to the two muscle attachment sites.

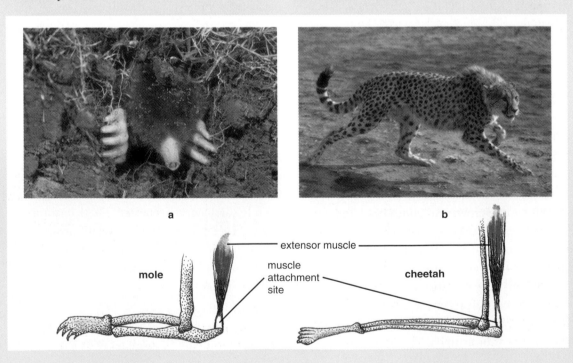

a

b

extensor muscle

muscle attachment site

mole

cheetah

The primary functions of these limbs differ greatly, however. The cheetah's limbs are adapted for running after fleet-footed prey. The mole's limbs are adapted for burrowing in the ground. What structural details underlie these adaptations?

The mole's digging forelimbs must generate power rather than speed. As the diagram in Figure E7.12a shows, the bones of such limbs are short and thick. In addition, look at the projection at the elbow to which the extensor muscles attach. It is quite long in proportion to the lower limb bone. Because of this structural arrangement, the extensor muscles generate great power in the lower limb when they contract. Now look at the limb of a running animal such as the cheetah. (Figure E7.12b) The extension at the elbow to which the extensor muscles attach is very short in proportion to the long lower limb bone. As a result, the same amount of contraction by the extensor muscles moves a cheetah's foot much farther than a mole's foot. Therefore, a cheetah can run at great speeds.

The importance of structure to the function of muscles is certainly apparent in the size and shape of the limbs. However, it also is apparent at the microscopic level. Examine the internal organization of skeletal muscle in Figure E7.13. As you can see, a muscle consists of many bundles of muscle fibers (Figure E7.13a). The thin and thick lines visible in Figure E7.13c are filaments. Filaments are specialized structures within muscle fibers. They consist of two types of long, thin protein molecules. When you contract a muscle, energy enables the filaments within each fiber to slide past each other. Think about how your interlocked fingers can slide past each other when you move your hands together. The sliding of the individual filaments shortens the larger muscle fiber. Together, the shortening of many muscle fibers shortens the whole muscle. When you relax your muscle, these filaments return to

their original positions. The muscle then regains its initial appearance and shape.

Studying muscle fibers at a subcellular level explains why it is important that muscles work together. While the movement of the molecular filaments past each other can shorten the muscle, it cannot lengthen the muscle again. That is, when a muscle relaxes, it cannot return to its normal length by itself. Because a muscle cannot lengthen, a muscle cannot push on anything. It can only pull. For every set of muscles that pulls a limb bone in one direction, another set pulls it back the other way. Were that not the case, many movements would not be possible.

The advantages of different structures also are evident in organisms that have body plans different from ours. In vertebrates, groups of muscles work in opposing pairs against an internal support system, the bony skeleton. Invertebrates have different types of support

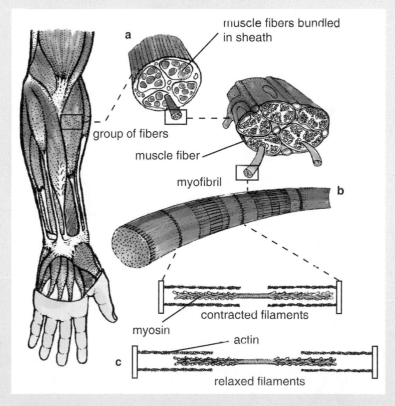

Figure E7.13 (a) A muscle is composed of many muscle fibers bundled in a sheath. (b) Each muscle fiber is made up of many parallel myofibrils. (c) Each myofibril is made up of protein molecules organized into thick and thin filaments.

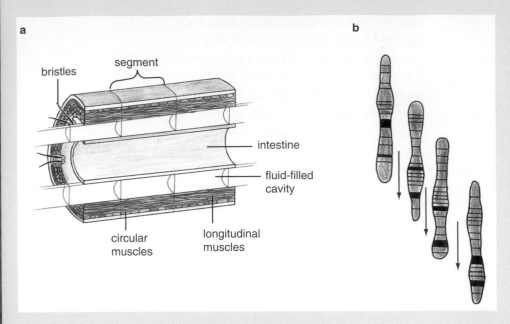

Figure E7.14 The earthworm has a hydrostatic skeleton. Each segment of the skeleton contains a fluid-filled cavity. **(a)** When the circular muscles around the segments of the worm's body contract, the fluid in those segments is squeezed. As a result, the segments become longer and thinner. **(b)** When the longitudinal muscles contract, the segments become shorter and thicker. The earthworm moves by anchoring one part of its body with its bristles while it extends another part.

systems. For example, many soft-bodied invertebrates have a support system composed of a surprising substance: water. A water-based support system, or hydrostatic skeleton, is not as odd as it might sound. Water, like other liquids, is not compressible. This characteristic means that although a flexible container filled with water may change shape in response to pressure, its volume remains constant.

Look at Figure E7.14. The contraction of the circular muscles around the segments of a worm's body squeezes on the watery fluid in those segments. This causes them to become longer and thinner. Contraction of the opposing longitudinal muscles, on the other hand, causes the segments to become shorter and thicker. When the worm crawls along, it alternately extends and contracts different parts of its body in this way. The worm uses stiff bristles on each segment to anchor some sections while extending others. Many soft-bodied animals such as slugs and jellyfish have variations on this system. They all have an internal hydrostatic skeleton surrounded by opposing groups of muscles.

Another common type of invertebrate support system is the **exoskeleton**. An exoskeleton is a hard skeleton on the outside of the body. (An **endoskeleton** is a hard internal skeleton such as in vertebrates.) The grasshopper shown in Figure E7.15a is a good

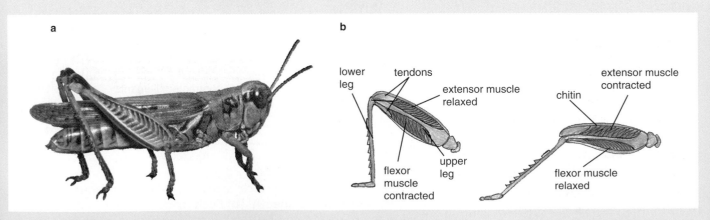

Figure E7.15 Exoskeletons have muscles attached to the inside of the skeleton. These muscles, however, still work in opposing pairs.

example of an animal that has an exoskeleton. Figure E7.15b shows diagrams of a grasshopper's leg. Note the opposing set of muscles. When a grasshopper draws up its leg, the lower muscle contracts while the upper muscle remains relaxed. What happens when a grasshopper needs to hop? The upper muscle contracts while the lower muscle remains relaxed. Although these muscles attach to the inside of an external skeleton, the mechanical aspects of the system are similar to those of the human arm. In addition to being quite strong for its mass, an exoskeleton also provides a layer of armor that protects the soft parts of the animal's body. The essay *The Ant That Terrorized Milwaukee* considers what happens if an animal with an exoskeleton gets too big. ◆

The Ant That Terrorized Milwaukee

The huge, black thorax towered over Damien, blocking the light. The enormous insect was rearing up on its back two pairs of legs. Its front legs pawed at the air like a huge stallion, or more accurately, like a menacing and hideous monster. Its antennae quivered and twisted in the air, searching for anything that might challenge it. The air was heavy with the animal's stench.

Now that he was this close, Damien could understand why his pitiful attempts to bring down the beast had failed so miserably. The animal's body was encased in a shiny, hard, black substance. The armor seemed impenetrable to any weapon Damien could get his hands on. Through his fear he vaguely remembered something important he knew about insects. . . yes, that was it! A hard outer skeleton— what did Mrs. Baxter call it? But no, too late. . . . As the moving mouth parts drew nearer, Damien's last thought was, but she *insisted* they couldn't get this big. . . .

You may have heard the following statements. "An ant can carry 10 times its own weight. So an ant the size of a person could lift a car." "A grasshopper the size of a horse could jump the length of a football field." An overused plot in horror films has insects or other tiny creatures become gigantic. You have seen that multicellular organisms exhibit a wide range of body plans that work by the same basic principles. Is there any limit to how big, how fast, or how strong an organism might be?

For physical reasons, giant creatures usually are not possible. This is because basic structural and mechanical considerations limit the sizes for which particular body plans are suitable. For example, growth is one limitation to animals with exoskeletons. The exoskeleton encases the whole body in armor. Thus, it must be shed completely every time there is significant growth. The animal is relatively

helpless and vulnerable while the new exoskeleton hardens.

Another major limitation of such a body is due to the material that makes up exoskeletons. The material is a complex carbohydrate called *chitin*. Hollow tubes of chitin are very strong for their mass. In larger sizes, however, the mass of the chitin needed would increase to impossible levels for sufficient body support and bracing against muscle contractions. An ant the size of a person probably couldn't even pick itself up, let alone wreak havoc on Milwaukee. ◆

Energy's Role in Making Structures Functional

The structure of muscle fibers explains how a muscle contracts. But where do muscles get the energy needed for contraction? Scattered among muscle fibers are many mitochondria. **Mitochondria** are oblong-shaped compartments, or organelles. They are located within cells, as shown in Figure E7.16. Chemical reactions that involve oxygen, water, and food take place within the mitochondria and result in the release of energy. This process is called **cellular respiration**. You can think of it as aerobic production of molecules such as ATP that the body uses for energy. **Aerobic** means "occurring in the presence of oxygen." Aerobic energy production fuels most of our physical activity most of the time.

When you need a sudden burst of energy—for example, to catch a bus pulling away from its stop—the supply of oxygen to your muscles may not be enough for aerobic energy production. When that happens, your muscles can shift to another energy-producing process.

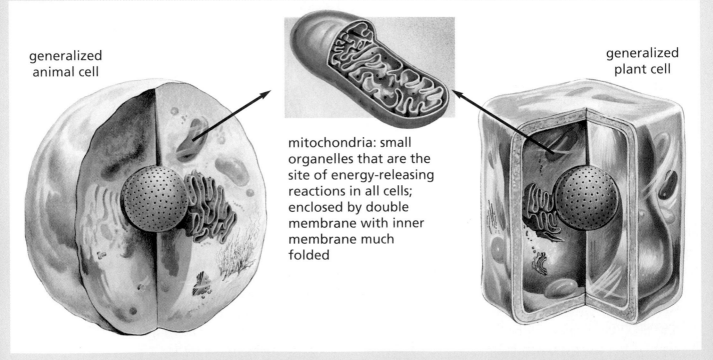

generalized animal cell

generalized plant cell

mitochondria: small organelles that are the site of energy-releasing reactions in all cells; enclosed by double membrane with inner membrane much folded

Figure E7.16 Multicellular organisms, such as plants, animals, and other eukaryotes, have mitochondria in their cells. These organelles are the site of an aerobic breakdown process called cellular respiration. This process converts energy stored in matter to a more useable form in the chemical bonds of ATP.

The alternate process, **fermentation**, or **anaerobic** energy production, does not require oxygen. In comparison to cellular respiration, fermentation provides much less energy per glucose molecule. Still, it can allow your muscles to continue working for a minute or two. A disadvantage of fermentation is that it creates a by-product called *lactic acid*. The buildup of lactic acid rapidly causes muscle fatigue. At one time, physiologists believed that the buildup of lactic acid was the reason for the sore muscles that people often have after participating in strenuous exercise. These scientists now recognize, however, that lactic acid is rapidly transported to the liver. In the liver, it is converted back into glucose and energy storage molecules. Physiologists who studied muscle tissue samples from marathon runners before and after races found microscopic evidence of tears and other damage to muscle fibers. They believe this damage is a primary reason for delayed muscle soreness. Full recovery from extreme anaerobic exercise may require several days of rest, with adequate oxygen delivery and nutrient intake.

Because contracting muscles demand more oxygen to produce energy, vigorous exercise requires a large increase in circulation. The blood flow to exercising muscles may reach 15 times the normal levels. The increased blood flow delivers enough oxygen for aerobic exercise and also removes waste products. Regardless, vigorous exercise eventually results in muscle fatigue. Muscle fatigue is a condition in which the muscles' glycogen supplies are so depleted that energy can no longer be released. (Glycogen is a form of stored sugar.) The only solution for extreme fatigue is rest. With sufficient time and proper food, glycogen is replenished and normal functioning can resume. ◆

Factors Influencing Performance

Genetic and Gender Differences. Are great athletes or great dancers *born* or *made*? They are probably a combination of both inheritance and training. On the one hand, as humans, we are born with a certain basic set of physical capabilities. As individuals, we may have special abilities in a particular area. On the other hand, many things that we do and don't do affect how well we can use our inborn capabilities.

First, we are humans. We are not cheetahs, ants, or any other type of creature. As humans, we are capable of performing certain functions because our bodies can acquire and use energy in particular ways. As individuals, we inherit traits that may enhance or limit our capacity to perform particular activities.

For example, inheritance largely determines our height. A person's height may affect whether or not he or she is likely to become a professional basketball player. Inheritance also appears to be important for skills required for gymnastics. Most successful gymnasts have small, compact bodies. Our gender and genetic makeup also influence other physical factors. These include skeletal and muscle mass, lung capacity, and the rate at which our bodies use energy. All of those factors may influence the types of physical activity that we can perform best.

Gender clearly has an effect on the body's physical development. Testosterone levels typically increase in young men during puberty. Rising testosterone levels cause an increase in muscle mass. Increased muscle mass, in turn, results in increased muscle strength. Therefore, males at puberty and older tend to be stronger than females of the same age and height. Anabolic steroids are popular among some athletes because they mimic some of the effects of testosterone (testosterone is a type of steroid). Although steroids may improve athletic performance, such substances have a number of serious and sometimes irreversible effects. These effects include high blood pressure, alterations in heart muscle, and reduced fertility. For those reasons and others, the National Collegiate Athletic Association (NCAA) and the International Olympic Committee (IOC) have banned steroid use as a performance-enhancing technique.

Metabolism is the approximate rate at which your body uses food for energy. This rate differs among individuals as well. In general, females tend to have a lower metabolic rate than males. The combination of your metabolic rate, diet, and level of exercise determines your body mass. If your food intake is balanced with your body's nutritional demands, metabolic rate, and activity level, then your body mass will remain about the same. If you take in excess food, your body will store it as fat. A slight excess in food intake is necessary for proper development during adolescence and the teen years. This is because the bodies of these individuals are growing. The body is producing more body tissues such as muscles, fat, and blood.

Remember the increase in muscle mass during puberty in boys? Girls also experience an increase in body fat during adolescence in response to the release of estrogen. Estrogen and other hormones, along with the increase in body fat, are necessary for ovulation to occur. All of this growth, as boys and girls become men and women, requires additional energy.

In moderate, controlled dieting, food intake is slightly less than your body's needs. Your body will then use stored fat for the matter and energy it needs. Long-term fasting or starving depletes the body's stored fat supplies. In such a case, the body breaks down

its own structural components, such as muscle, to keep itself alive. That is why conditions like anorexia nervosa may cause muscles, including the heart, to become thin and weak.

Conditioning. Despite gender and genetic differences, human performance also is based in large part on general physical fitness. Consider what happens, for example, with a group of hikers. Those who normally engage in an exercise program soon take the lead, while others lag behind. The slower ones may breathe heavily and later suffer from aching muscles. One basis for these differences is the way the body changes during a regular exercise program. A regular exercise program is called *conditioning*.

Conditioning can improve both general and athletic fitness in several ways. The major effect of regular exercise is to bring about changes in the structure and function of the body. Muscles enlarge and become stronger. The number and size of mitochondria in the muscle cells increase. The muscles' capacity for glycogen storage and blood supply increases. The net effect is a greater ability to convert fuel into useful energy.

What is a reasonable amount of exercise for staying fit? As little as 20–30 minutes of moderate exercise two to three times a week can help your circulatory and respiratory systems work more effectively. Conditioning lowers your resting heart rate and increases heart output. Conditioning builds muscle mass and tone (firmness). It strengthens the skeleton by maintaining, or increasing, bone mass. It improves the communication between nerves and muscle. Better strength, coordination, and endurance are the rewards. Aerobic activities such as jogging, brisk walking, bicycling, or swimming can accomplish these goals.

Behavior. The lifestyle that an individual adopts also influences fitness. In addition to exercise, you decide what and how much you eat and drink. For example, individuals who wish to stay at a constant weight must keep the number of kcals they consume equal to the number they expend over the long term. On the other hand, people who are interested in losing weight must take in fewer kcals than they expend. Athletes who are training for a marathon may want to increase the amount of carbohydrates that they consume. Carbohydrate loading increases the amount of glycogen available to muscles. Figure E7.17 describes diets in each of these categories so that you may compare the relative amounts of servings in each food group.

A good mental attitude can lead to behaviors that promote good general fitness. In contrast, mental and emotional disorders can lead to behaviors that endanger fitness. For example, an estimated 2 million people in the United States suffer from eating disorders. An eating disorder is a condition in which chronic abuses in an individual's eating patterns can endanger life itself.

DIET COMPARISON

	FOOD GROUPS (DAILY SERVINGS)					
	Milk	**Meat**	**Fruit**	**Vegetable**	**Grain**	**Fats, oils, and sweets**
Maintenance diet	3*	2–3	2–4	3–5	6–11	**
Weight-loss diet	3*	2	2	3–5	6	**
Carbohydrate-loading diet	3*	3 or more	7 or more	5 or more	11 or more	**

*Teenagers and young adults; 2 for older adults
**You can select foods from the fats, oils, and sweets category only if you can afford the kcals after eating the recommended servings from the essential food groups.
Note: The diets listed in this table are approximations based on information from the U.S. Department of Agriculture's Daily Food Guide. *These do not constitute dietary recommendations.* Individuals should check with their physician before going on any diet.

Figure E7.17   Diet comparison.

Toxins. The consumption of **toxins** also influences performance. Toxins are substances that ultimately cause diminished performance or impairment of health. Even medications such as anti-inflammatory drugs (ibuprofen, for example) may be toxins under certain circumstances. This is especially true if they are taken at higher doses than directed.

Illegal, or so-called "street drugs," diminish performance as do legal toxins such as alcohol and tobacco. While illegal drugs may produce temporary feelings of pleasure, they also cause negative, long-term consequences. Our bodies respond to some drugs by building up a tolerance to them. Increasingly larger amounts are required to produce the same effect. Our bodies may become dependent on addictive drugs. An addicted person cannot function normally without the drug. Withdrawal from the drug can be an extremely painful and difficult experience.

Alcohol is a drug that is legal for individuals over a specific age. However, consuming it can have negative consequences. The consumption of alcohol may initially produce a temporary sense of well-being. Thus, under the influence of alcohol, we may think we are feeling and performing better. Actually, alcohol depresses the central nervous system. This causes a loss of coordination and impaired performance. Alcohol causes cells to use oxygen less efficiently and to produce less energy. Consuming large amounts of alcohol over long periods of time damages brain and liver tissue. As noted previously, even small quantities of alcohol impairs judgment.

Like alcohol, the purchase of tobacco is legal, but restricted. Tobacco contains many substances that can adversely influence performance. Burning tobacco produces carbon monoxide. Carbon monoxide binds to hemoglobin faster than oxygen can. (Hemoglobin is the molecule in red blood cells that is designed to carry oxygen to the cells in the body.) Hemoglobin that is bound to carbon monoxide cannot carry oxygen. A smoker who smokes two cigarette packs per day generates enough carbon monoxide to reduce his or her blood oxygen level to that of a nonsmoker who is experiencing the thin air of high mountain altitudes (3,048 meters or 10,000 feet) for the first time. Both tobacco smoke and unburned tobacco such as chew or dip release high levels of nicotine into the bloodstream. Nicotine affects performance directly. It constricts blood vessels, thus impairing oxygen delivery. In addition, nicotine is one of the most addictive drugs known.

Other important aspects of lifestyle that affect fitness include the amount of sleep a person gets and how one handles stress. By the choices that we make, humans can control many, though not all, of the factors influencing fitness.

Technology. Technology can help us both measure and improve our individual fitness. Athletes use weight machines and computerized aerobic exercise machines to build and measure fitness. Specialized clothing and equipment enhance performance by increasing comfort level and efficiency. Computers can model the stresses that various activities produce and help researchers design athletic shoes for specific sports. Sports equipment companies continually use

technological advances to produce better equipment. For example, lighter-weight tennis rackets and more flexible vaulting poles can give athletes a competitive edge.

Athletes also use devices that simulate competitive conditions to improve their skills. At the Olympic Training Center in Colorado Springs, Colorado, swimmers test their fitness in a device called a *flume*, shown in Figure E7.18. A flume is a simulator containing water that runs at gauged speeds. The swimmer can swim in place against moving water to increase speed and endurance. Ski team members can practice all year long on roller skis that duplicate the feel of cross-country skis. Therefore, snow is not a training requirement!

The use of such technologies may raise ethical questions. For example, do these technologies give an unfair advantage to competitors who can afford them? Do wealthy nations produce superior athletes? Are these uses of technology fair? To address

Figure E7.18 Swimmers training for the Olympic Games can test their speed and endurance by swimming in a flume. This equipment controls the speed and direction of water flow through the swimming tank.

those and other issues, regulatory agencies exist for each major sport and for large events such as the Olympics. Many of these agencies are international in scope.

We have seen that several factors affect human physical performance. These include genetic, behavioral, and technological factors. They all are related to how effectively we use our body's energy supplies. ◆

Matter and Energy Are Related

If someone asked you to describe how skin, plant roots, water vapor, and a plastic cell phone are different, could you do it? Humans are usually good at identifying differences between things that we encounter in our physical world. This is because we can directly observe many characteristic features through our senses. If we can see, touch, smell, or hear differences, then we use those characteristics to help recognize our surroundings. However, identifying similarities can be more challenging. What do skin, plant roots, water vapor, and a plastic cell phone have in common? By now, you should recognize that all are examples of matter. In addition, they are also made of atoms.

Atoms are the basic building blocks of all matter. These microscopic particles are found in matter that makes up everything from the smallest virus to the stars in the largest galaxy (see Figure E8.1). Because we cannot see atoms with the naked eye, the importance of atomic interactions is often overlooked. However, these interactions are critical to understanding the relationship between matter and energy.

Individual atoms are microscopic. But the matter that atoms make up is visible. The way that atoms assemble together determines the characteristics of the matter that we see. For example, skin is made up of a different combination of atoms than is the

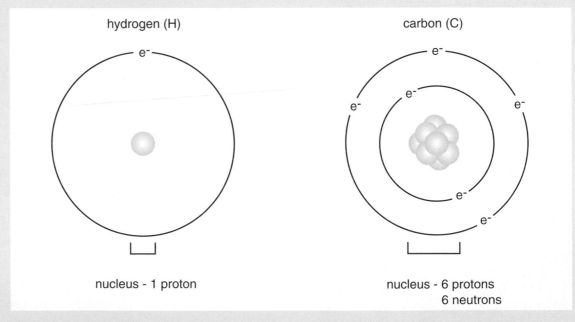

Figure E8.1   Atoms.   All matter is composed of elements, the simplest forms of matter. An atom is the smallest particle of an element that still has the properties of that element. The unique properties of an element are the result of the number and type of subatomic particles present in its atoms. For instance, six electrons, six protons, and six neutrons are characteristics of the element carbon (symbol, C). Electrons are extremely lightweight, negatively charged subatomic particles. They orbit rapidly around the nucleus of an atom. The nucleus is located at the center of an atom. It is composed of two heavy subatomic particles: protons, which are positively charged, and neutrons, which have no charge at all and thus are neutral. Scientists have identified more than 100 different types of atoms, or elements.

plastic in a cell phone. The arrangement of atoms in skin enables it to be flexible and to allow substances to move either in or out of the body; the arrangement of atoms in the plastic of a cell phone make it rigid and waterproof. As Figure E8.2 shows, the source of this important atomic organization is chemical bonds. **Chemical bonds** hold atoms together in predictable ways to form molecules. Energy is stored within the structure of a molecule's bonds and atoms.

It is difficult to describe exactly how energy exists in the structure of chemically bonded atoms. But let's try to imagine it by thinking about the following example. For this example, magnets represent atoms. Consider what happens when you arrange two round, flat magnets so that opposite poles are close to each other. The forces of attraction between the north and south poles pull the individual magnets tightly together. If you arrange several magnets in this way, the forces of attraction will cause them to form a solid, cylindrical stack. The energy stored in this new large magnet (the cylindrical stack of small magnets) is much greater than the energy stored in any of the small magnets individually. The force of attraction between the magnets is somewhat similar to the energy in chemical bonds between atoms.

Magnetic energy is one familiar type of energy. What other forms of energy can you name? Energy comes in a variety of forms. These include heat, light, electrical, solar, nuclear, mechanical, and chemical energy. Heat energy is a commonly recognized form. Most people are familiar with this type of energy through their experiences with friction. A rug burn is the result of the friction between a carpet and someone's moving skin. Bald tires are the result of friction between a road surface and rotating rubber treads. Heat also occurs at the molecular level. When molecules move, they encounter other molecules and generate friction. They, too, produce heat. The greater the motion, the

greater the heat that is released. For example, the coils on an electric stove heat up because an electrical current in the metal coils causes the metal atoms to move rapidly.

When molecules slow down, heat decreases and objects feel cold. In addition, many substances can absorb heat. This happens when matter from one substance absorbs the heat energy caused by the molecular motion of matter in a nearby substance. For example, a hot pan placed in cold water becomes cool as the hot metal transfers its heat energy to the surrounding water molecules. The cold water molecules respond to the transfer of heat energy by moving faster and becoming warmer.

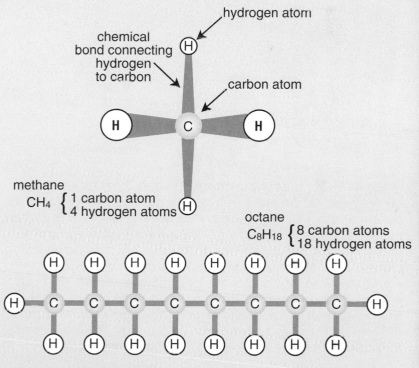

Figure E8.2 **Molecules.** Molecules are formed when atoms are organized by chemical bonding. Combinations of different atoms are organized in unique ways through chemical bonds. This accounts for the unique properties of macroscopic materials. For instance, in one ordered arrangement, carbon and hydrogen form a smelly gas called *methane*. In another arrangement, carbon and hydrogen form octane, a flammable liquid used in gasoline. Note that in both molecules, hydrogen always has one chemical bond and carbon always has four chemical bonds. The number of electrons orbiting around a particular atom determines its number of bonds.

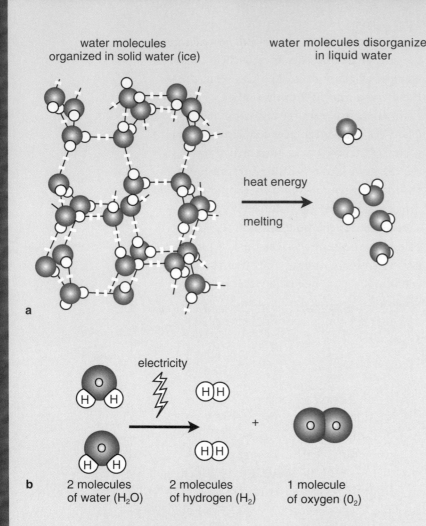

water molecules
organized in solid water (ice)

water molecules disorganized
in liquid water

heat energy

melting

a

electricity

O H H   H H   +   O O

b   2 molecules
of water (H_2O)

2 molecules
of hydrogen (H_2)

1 molecule
of oxygen (O_2)

Figure E8.3 Endothermic processes and chemical reactions take in heat. **(a)** An input of heat energy is necessary to melt ice. Note that there is no change in the chemical bonds of the water molecules that make up the ice. During the endothermic process of melting, the solid water molecules that are held rigidly in place in ice simply change state and become liquid water molecules. These molecules are free to move around. **(b)** In an endothermic chemical reaction, an input of energy causes the chemical bonds to break and reform. Adding electricity to water molecules breaks and reforms chemical bonds. This leads to the formation of two new molecules, hydrogen and oxygen.

Not all heat is the result of friction between a material and its surroundings. Chemical reactions can also release heat. Such reactions are called **exothermic reactions** (*exo* = out, *thermic* = heat). In an exothermic chemical reaction, heat is *released* when the atoms in molecules are reorganized. During a chemical reaction, the chemical bonds between atoms or molecules break and form

new ones. If this atomic reorganization results in the production of heat, then the chemical reaction releases energy. For example, the explosive combustion of grain dust is a chemical reaction. Here molecules are quickly reorganized in the presence of oxygen (an element present in the air) and a spark. Such a reorganization of matter can cause the uncontrolled release of a tremendous amount of energy.

Chemical reactions that absorb, or take in heat, are called **endothermic reactions** (*endo* = in, *thermic* = heat). Such reactions require an *input* of energy to reorganize atoms in the molecules. For instance, the oxygen atom and the hydrogen atoms in a water molecule are quite stable when bonded to each other. It is necessary to add energy, in the form of a spark or ultraviolet light, to reorganize the atoms and form a molecule of oxygen (O_2) and two molecules of hydrogen (H_2). This endothermic process is a chemical reaction because it involves the rearrangement of chemical bonds.

Some endothermic processes that you are familiar with do not involve chemical reactions. For example, when ice melts, it requires an input of heat energy from another source. Think about the glass and surrounding liquid in a container of iced tea. When ice absorbs heat, which occurs any time it is in contact with something warmer than itself, the organized water molecules in it begin to move and become disorganized. In other words, an input of energy alters the molecular organization (but not the chemical bonds). The ice melts as a result. Many complex factors determine whether a particular molecular reorganization will be endothermic or exothermic. As Figure E8.3 illustrates, the melting of ice is an *endothermic process*. But it is not an *endothermic chemical reaction*. This is because no breakage or formation of chemical bonds takes place. What happens is only a change in state. (The *solid* water molecules become *liquid* water molecules.)

The formation of water from oxygen and hydrogen is typical of how matter and energy interact in chemical reactions. Recall the magnet example given earlier. The force of magnetic attraction can be seen as a model. This model helps us understand how energy occurs in the chemical bonds that organize atoms and molecules. Rearranging the magnets transfers the magnetic force from one magnet to the group of magnets. In a similar manner, rearranging chemical bonds through chemical reactions transfers the energy stored in the matter. So, when water forms or decomposes, energy transfers from one form to another as a result of its chemical bonds rearranging.

Understanding this link between energy and matter is important in biology because all living systems require energy and matter for survival. In the case of humans, the thousands of different chemical reactions that constantly occur in our cells depend primarily on chemical energy. Evolutionary adaptations enable these reactions to take place in a controlled manner—without sparks and explosions. ◆

Energy Is Converted and Conserved

When electricity flows through the metal coils on a stove burner, it makes the coils red hot. But this does more than make the teapot ready for tea. It illustrates an essential property of energy. *Energy can be converted from one form into another.* In this case, electrical energy is converted into heat energy. This property of energy has enabled scientists and engineers to develop techniques and tools for making energy accessible to humans. For example, power-generating dams harness the mechanical energy of water by passing water over turbines. The turbines rotate and convert the water's movement into electrical energy.

Without energy conversion, gasoline would not be much more than a smelly, toxic liquid. In fact, gasoline is a useful tool in technologically advanced societies. In liquid form, gasoline stores a large amount of chemical energy in its molecular structure. Gasoline can be a dangerous substance because it is highly flammable. It is exactly that property, however, that makes it valuable as a fuel for industry and transportation. As Figure E8.4 suggests, we have learned how to control the explosive property of gasoline. A

gasoline engine converts the gasoline's stored chemical energy into a form of mechanical energy—a form that can be used to power machinery.

Exploding grain elevators are another example of energy converting from a stored form to heat. Such explosions illustrate that energy exists in two forms: an inactive form

Figure E8.4 Energy conversion. Molecules of the chemical gasoline store energy. Combustion can reverse this energy and convert it into mechanical energy in an automobile. What other energy conversions can you think of?

and an active form. The inactive form is called potential energy. **Potential energy** is stored in the structure of matter and is available for use. When the potential energy in grain dust is released, it becomes active.

Active energy is called **kinetic energy**. A boulder sitting at the top of a hill contains a great deal of potential energy simply because of its position, as Figure E8.5 shows. When the boulder falls off the cliff, however, its potential energy is released in the form of kinetic energy, or the energy of movement. The potential energy poses no threat to you. You can sit on the boulder as it rests at the top of the hill. However, you would not want to come into contact with the boulder as it rolls down the hill, displaying its kinetic energy. Likewise, you are not afraid to pump gas—a tremendous amount of potential energy—into a car's gas tank. But you don't want to light a match at the same time. If you do, you'll see all of that potential energy converted into a dangerous amount of kinetic energy very quickly.

Once potential energy has been converted into kinetic energy, one of two things can happen. The kinetic energy may be captured and made useful, or it may be wasted. For example, what if the boulder at the top of the hill were attached to a rope that, in turn, was attached to a wheel on a well? As the boulder rolled down the hill, it would turn the wheel and raise water from the well spilling most of it as the bucket smashed against the wheel axle. In this example, the kinetic energy of the boulder would be captured and made useful. On the other hand, if the boulder were not attached to the rope, it would simply roll until it stopped, wasting its kinetic energy. The fact that the boulder would eventually stop indicates that yet another energy conversion occurs. Each time the boulder turned, its kinetic energy would cause molecular movements in the grass, soil, and stones. The kinetic energy would be converted to heat. In this case, the release of heat would be wasted energy because it was not captured and used to do work. No energy would be created or destroyed. The energy would simply be *transferred* from the boulder to the surrounding grass, soil, and stones.

a

b

Figure E8.5 Potential energy and kinetic energy.   **(a)** The boulder resting at the top of the cliff has a great deal of potential energy and no kinetic energy. **(b)** The falling boulder has a great deal of kinetic energy but less and less potential energy. How much kinetic or potential energy does the boulder have after it comes to rest at the bottom of the hill?

Energy transfer also takes place in your body when your digestive system removes nutrients and energy from food and supplies them to your body cells. Heat also is produced in this process. Even through all of the intermediate steps necessary for this transfer, no energy is lost or created. This property of energy is called the **conservation of energy**. It means that even though the amount of energy at one location can change, the total amount of energy in the universe remains the same.

In living organisms, the chemical bonds between the atoms of molecules conserve energy. Suppose a large molecule contains eight units of energy. What happens to the energy in this molecule when it is broken down into two smaller molecules? Together, the two smaller molecules plus any small amount of heat from the breakdown will contain eight units of energy as well. The conservation of energy and the ability to transfer energy both play key roles in maintaining the energy balance in organisms. The energy needs of organisms vary from time to time. The ability to convert energy from one form to another means that organisms can use the form that best matches their current energy needs. As Figure E8.6 illustrates, when energy needs are low—for example, during sleep—organisms store potential energy in

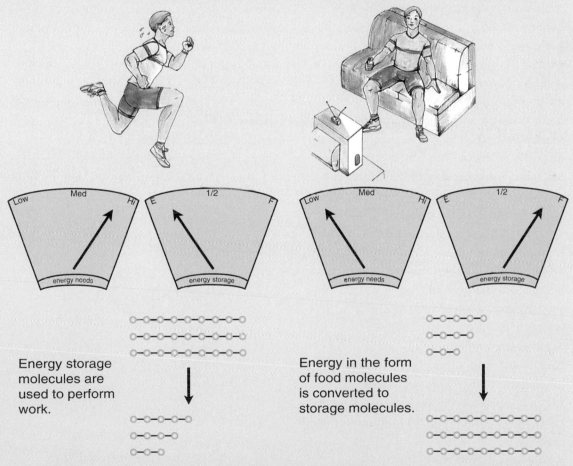

Energy storage molecules are used to perform work.

Energy in the form of food molecules is converted to storage molecules.

Figure E8.6   Living systems regulate energy storage.   When the energy needs of humans are high, our bodies convert storage molecules such as glycogen into a form of chemical energy. This energy can be used to perform work. When energy needs are low, our bodies convert food molecules into storage molecules. These molecules can be used to meet future needs. Are your energy needs high or low right now? Is your body trying to store energy? Or is your body using previously stored energy to perform work?

large storage molecules. These molecules contain many bonds and atoms, and thus, much energy. When energy needs are high—for example, during exercise—organisms convert some of this stored potential energy into mechanical energy, such as the contraction of muscles.

The source of energy in molecules.

What is it about a molecule that enables it to store energy? The arrangement of atoms within a molecule affects its energy properties. The arrangement of atoms within a molecule is determined by the chemical bonds holding it together. There are several types of chemical bonds, or forces of attraction, between atoms. These forces vary in strength. The stronger the bond, the greater the energy needed to break it. Most of the differences between two molecules' energy properties are due to the type of chemical bonds between their atoms.

Some chemical bonds occur between atoms that lose or gain electrons. These atoms are now called *ions*. They become positively or negatively charged. Oppositely charged ions attract each other. These forces of attraction are called **ionic bonds**. Ionic bonds are responsible for holding together the sodium and chloride ions in a crystal of NaCl, or common table salt. Ionic bonds are relatively weak, a fact you can demonstrate for yourself. Dissolve some salt in ordinary tap water. As the salt dissolves, the ions (Na^+, Cl^-) separate from each other and mix with water molecules.

Stronger bonds result when the atoms that make up a molecule *share* their electrons. These bonds are called **covalent bonds**. Figure E8.7 illustrates the electrons that are shared between hydrogen and oxygen in a water molecule. The carbohydrate molecules glycogen (in muscles and liver) and starch (in plants) are complex molecules. They are also rich sources of potential energy. Each is a macromolecule with many covalent bonds. A great deal of energy is needed to make or break covalent bonds. In most cases, enzymes promote these reactions in organisms.

The role of enzymes.

Most chemical reactions require some "start-up" energy before they will occur. This energy is called the energy of activation. Often a fairly large amount of energy of activation is needed. This characteristic of most molecules is actually beneficial because it makes them stable molecules. Certainly it would not be good for the chemical bonds in the molecules of your muscles to break apart suddenly. Nevertheless, it is important that some reactions occur often and quickly in organisms.

One way to provide the energy of activation for a reaction is to add heat to the molecules. Heat increases the kinetic energy of molecules. The molecules will then have the required energy of activation, and the chemical reaction will take place. However, this is not a useful strategy for organisms. This is because increasing the heat in a body will increase *all* chemical reactions, not just the ones that a cell needs. For example, increased heat would increase the breakdown of food molecules (reactions the body needs for digestion). But it would also increase the breakdown of molecules that make up the

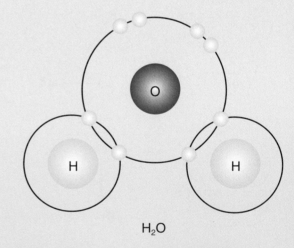

H_2O

Figure E8.7 Covalent bonds in molecules. A water molecule consists of one oxygen atom (which has six electrons in its outer orbit) sharing two of its electrons with two hydrogen atoms (which have only one electron each). These shared electrons represent a force of attraction known as a covalent bond.

muscles and other tissues (reactions that break down the body itself). Organisms solve this problem by using enzymes.

Enzymes are large molecules that help the right chemical reactions take place in cells at the right time. Two characteristics of enzymes allow them to do that. First, they reduce the amount of start-up energy (energy of activation) that a reaction needs. Second, they do that very specifically. Each enzyme reduces the energy of activation for a particular chemical reaction that involves just one particular molecule, or a small set of similar molecules.

The specificity of enzymes and their ability to reduce the energy of activation are both related to their structure. Enzymes are large molecules. They are usually much larger than the molecules they cause to react. The reacting molecules, or substrates, fit into grooves or notches on the enzyme's surface. The grooves or notches are called *active sites*. Only the specific molecules (substrates) involved in the reaction will fit in an enzyme's active site. The enzyme holds the substrate in its active site in such a way that the reaction is more likely to happen. This is how the enzyme reduces the energy of activation.

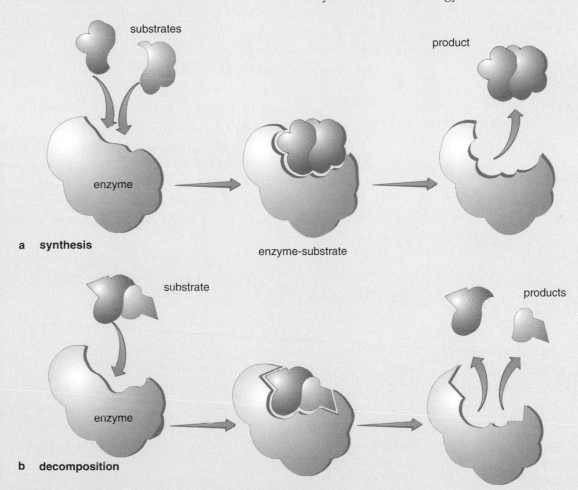

Figure E8.8 Enzymes reduce the amount of energy needed to start a reaction. (**a**) In synthesis, two or more substrate molecules join at the active site on the enzyme. They form one larger molecule. Less energy is needed to start the reaction because of the enzyme. (**b**) In decomposition (breakdown), the substrate combines with the enzyme and is split into two or more smaller molecules. Again, the reaction requires less energy to start because of the enzyme. The amino acid sequence of the enzyme doesn't change during the reaction, but its 3-dimensional shape may change. The shape of the enzyme reverts to its original shape after the reaction is over.

In synthesis reactions, two substrates are held close to each other in the right position for chemical bonds to occur between them (Figure E8.8a). In decomposition reactions, the substrate is held at the active site in a way that distorts one of its chemical bonds. This makes it more likely for the bond to break (Figure E8.8b).

Figure E.8.8 illustrates another important characteristic of enzymes. Enzymes themselves are not changed in the chemical reactions. This means that a single enzyme can help a particular reaction to happen many times. Enzymes are truly amazing molecules. The collection of all the enzymes in an organism allows all of the needed reactions to take place rapidly and precisely at relatively low energies. Cells also can regulate the activity of enzymes. Enzymes allow cells to accelerate and control the particular biological reactions they need.

Energy for cellular activity. Enzymes reduce the energy needed to start chemical reactions. However, nearly all biological reactions require the input of some energy before they can proceed. The source of this energy is long-term storage molecules such as glycogen. But these molecules are too large to be used directly. To make the energy stored in these molecules useful, the energy must be converted into a form that cells can use *directly*. This form is a special type of molecule called **a**denosine **trip**hosphate, or **ATP** (see Figure E8.9). ATP is commonly used in organisms as a direct source of energy.

An analogy may help here. It is good to have a lot of $100 bills. But breaking them down into $10 bills provides buying power in more easily used amounts. Just so, ATP is "small change" in the energy world. You also can think of ATP as a *carrier*. A carrier is a molecule that carries or transfers useful amounts of energy to other molecules in the cell so that needed chemical reactions can occur.

The direct source of energy for most cellular work is ATP. This valuable energy source is many steps removed from the original energy sources. If you trace the path of energy flow backward, you will see that the energy in ATP comes from the breakdown of long-term storage molecules. The energy in long-term storage molecules comes from the food consumed or made by living organisms. An enzyme regulates each of the many steps in these processes. The transfer of energy from matter in the form of food to matter in the form of ATP is one of the most important processes in all of biology. ◆

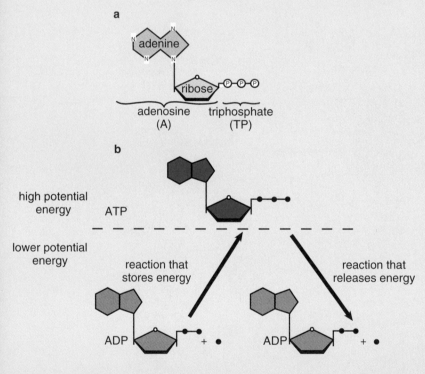

Figure E8.9 Structure of ATP. (a) This diagram shows the structure of ATP (adenosine triphosphate). ATP is one of several energy carriers found in all living organisms. Each ATP molecule is made up of a main section (the A of ATP). Attached to this main section are three identical groups of atoms called *phosphates* (the TP of ATP). **(b)** Energy is stored in ATP until it is released by reactions that remove the third phosphate group. This forms a molecule of ADP (adenosine diphosphate). ATP acts as an energy carrier by alternately storing and releasing energy.

Historical Connections between Matter and Energy

Two thousand years ago the Greeks had a thriving society that focused on the pursuit of knowledge and fitness. These people understood that there is a connection between the fitness of the mind and the fitness of the body. They started the Olympic Games to let men show their athletic skill in different events. (Women were not permitted to participate in the ancient Olympics, although the Greeks had a contest for women called the Heraea. The Heraea was held every 4 years and had fewer events than the men's games.) One of the principal events of the games was the marathon. This was a foot race that commemorated the feat of a Greek messenger who ran from the city of Marathon to the city of Athens, a distance of 26 miles 385 yards.

While some Greeks were showing what their bodies could do, some were extending the limits of their minds by developing explanations for the natural world. A key assumption of their explanations was that the world was composed of four primary elements: fire, water, earth, and air. They described the composition of everything in the world by some combination of these four elements. These ideas were held to be true until the beginning of the 18th century.

By the mid-1700s, scientists were using new explanations to describe the natural world. One of the ideas they focused on was the composition of fire. What was it made of? Unlike the Greeks, who assumed that fire was a primary element, 18th-century scientists experimented with fire and relied on observations to guide their explanations. They noted that when something like coal was burned, it gave off an oily substance. They named this substance *phlogiston*, meaning "fatty earth." The better something burned, the more phlogiston they assumed it contained. Coal apparently contained much phlogiston.

Joseph Priestley used the idea of phlogiston to explain the results of one of his experiments. He stated that a mouse in a glass container with a burning candle dies quickly because phlogiston is poisonous. The more the candle burns, the more phlogiston is produced.

A few years later, in 1772, a Frenchman named Antoine Lavosier generated an

Figure E8.10   Discus thrower (*Diskobolos*). This marble statue is a Roman copy of a bronze made by the Greek sculptor Myron. The original statue was life-sized and sculpted about 450 BC.

alternative explanation for the death of the mouse in Priestley's experiment. Lavosier reasoned that the mouse died not because phlogiston was *added* to the air, but because the fire *removed* something from the air. On the basis of additional experiments, he concluded that to burn, the candle flame required an element in the air. Lavosier called this element *oxygen*. When all of the oxygen was consumed, the mouse would die.

Thus, not only does a flame require oxygen to burn, but mice require oxygen to live.

Lavosier's ideas form the foundation for today's understanding of fire and the release of energy when matter is burned. Later scientists examined these processes on a cellular level. They realized that energy is released systematically and, for most organisms, oxygen is required for the systematic release of energy from food. ◆

Controlling the Release of Energy from Matter: An Overview of Cellular Respiration

Figure E8.11
The three stages of cellular respiration. Glycolysis, which occurs in the cytoplasm of the cell, breaks glucose into smaller molecules. These molecules are transported into the mitochondria. They are further broken down to carbon dioxide in the Krebs cycle. In the electron transport system, the hydrogen atoms released from glycolysis and the Krebs cycle are used to form many molecules of ATP.

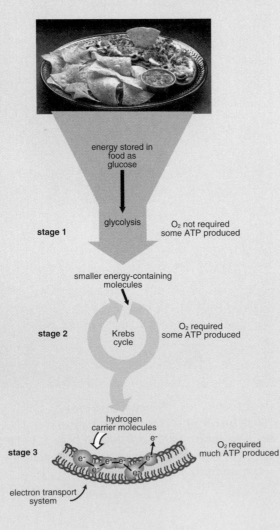

In the example of the grain storage explosion, energy was released from matter suddenly and dramatically. When you eat bread or cookies, however, you do not explode. Clearly, your body must release the energy stored in grain in a more controlled way. When you eat flour made from grain, the cells in your body release the energy one small step at a time. Enzymes catalyze certain chemical reactions to make this slow release of energy from the starch molecules possible. **Cellular respiration** is the process by which enzymes convert the energy stored in macromolecules (such as starch and glycogen) or small molecules (such as glucose) into the usable form of ATP. Just like the explosion, cellular respiration requires oxygen. You need oxygen because of cellular respiration.

Three main stages divide the steps of cellular respiration, as illustrated in Figure E8.11. The stages are known as **glycolysis**, the **Krebs cycle**, and the **electron transport system**. Glycolysis occurs in the cytoplasm of the cell. The Krebs cycle and the electron transport system occur in the mitochondria of the cell. The first stage, glycolysis (*glyco* = sugar, *lysis* = to split), occurs in nearly every living cell. Glycolysis splits glucose into two smaller molecules. This produces a small amount of ATP. These two molecules still contain much stored energy, however. In the Krebs cycle, enzymes break down the two small molecules into carbon dioxide. This produces several more ATP molecules. When you breathe out, most of the carbon dioxide comes from the chemical reactions that occur in the Krebs cycle.

After the first two stages of cellular respiration, some of the glucose molecule's energy has been captured in the form of ATP. Most of the remaining energy is in the form of hydrogen atoms. These atoms have been transferred to hydrogen carrier molecules. These carrier molecules transport the hydrogen atoms to the last stage of cellular respiration, the electron transport system. In this stage, the energy from the hydrogen atoms is transferred to ATP. In fact, most of the ATP made from glucose comes from the last stage of cellular respiration.

In the electron transport system, the hydrogen atoms first are separated into electrons (e^-) and protons (H^+). (Hydrogen atoms are made up of one electron and one proton.) The electrons are transferred to a chain of electron carrier molecules that are embedded in the inner membranes of the mitochondria. The electron carriers relay the electrons from one carrier to another. This process releases a small amount of energy at each step. This energy is used to pump the protons to one side of the inner membrane. A complex diffusion process involving the protons finally converts the energy into many ATP molecules. At the end of the electron transport system, the electrons and protons combine with oxygen (O_2) to form water (H_2O). The end result of cellular respiration is many ATP molecules (from all three stages), carbon dioxide (from the Krebs cycle), and water (from the electron transport system). Cells can use ATP directly for cellular work, like muscle contractions. ◆

Cellular Respiration: A Closer Look at Converting Food Energy into Cell Energy

Let's take a broader and deeper look at the process of cellular respiration. One of the unifying principles of biology is that all living systems require a source of energy for survival. What is the energy needed for specifically? The specific energy needs of organisms include mechanical work such as the contraction of muscles and active transport. Organisms need energy for synthesis, that is, the building of new molecules, cells, and higher structures. Tissue repair and growth require all of these processes. Where does the energy come from? The potential energy in food molecules supplies the energy needs of organisms. However, the structure of these molecules does not store energy in a form

that can be used *directly* for cellular work. Food energy must be converted into a more usable form.

Through the selective pressures of evolution, such metabolic processes exist. Not surprisingly, the simplest of these metabolic processes is remarkably similar in all living organisms. Organisms that are as different as bacterial cells and humans have nearly identical metabolic processes for producing ATP. This fact suggests that these biochemical pathways evolved a very long time ago, before simple organisms became more complex. How do organisms convert food energy into energy that cells use easily? Let's follow the path of a glucose molecule to see how and where a cell harvests its potential energy. Remember, specific enzymes control every chemical reaction in cellular respiration.

The process begins in the cytoplasm. Glucose first enters glycolysis. This process does not require oxygen (see Figure E8.12).

A glucose molecule has six carbon atoms. It is quite stable. That is, the bonds holding its atoms together are not easily broken. Because of this stability, the cell must use a small amount of energy to begin the glucose-splitting reactions (step a). This is similar to lighting a match to start a fire.

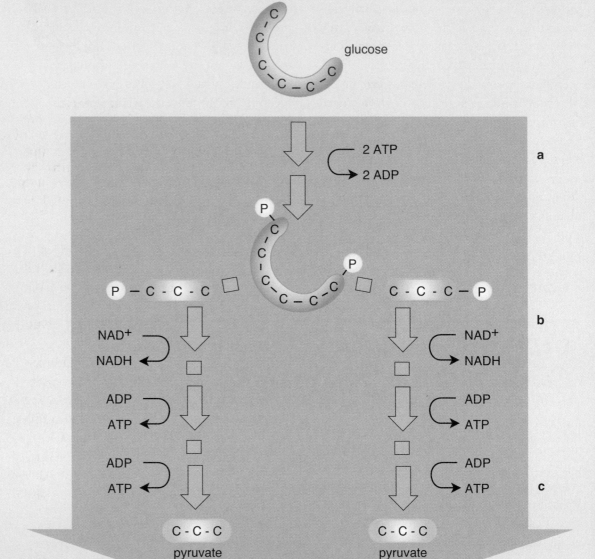

P = phosphate group

Figure E8.12   A molecular view of glycolysis.   In glycolysis, glucose is broken down into two molecules of pyruvate. This takes place in many enzyme-catalyzed steps. In this process, the energy from some ATP is needed to begin the glycolysis reactions. (See [a] where ATP gives up some of its energy and becomes ADP.) ATP also is produced in later steps, as is NADH, a hydrogen carrier molecule.

Glycolysis breaks glucose down into two molecules that each have three carbon atoms (step b). Enzymes rearrange the atoms in these molecules to form two molecules of pyruvate (step c). Glycolysis produces a small amount of ATP. Most of the original glucose molecule's energy, however, remains in the two pyruvate molecules. Some prokaryotes and muscle cells with depleted oxygen supplies use only glycolysis for their energy needs. Many prokaryotes, as well as eukaryotes, proceed to the next two stages of cellular respiration.

In addition to the ATP, glycolysis produces two molecules of NADH (**n**icotinamide **a**denine **d**inucleotide with a **h**ydrogen atom). Some of the energy from the glucose molecule transfers to these two molecules. Cells sometimes use energy directly from NADH to do work. However, most of this energy is converted to ATP in the third stage of cellular respiration, the electron transport system.

The pyruvate molecules now enter the second stage of cellular respiration, the Krebs cycle. These reactions release most of the remaining energy in

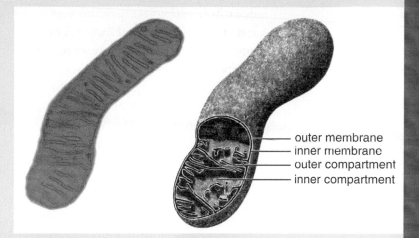

Figure E8.13 A mitochondrion. The reactions of aerobic respiration take place in this cellular organelle. Mitochondria have two membranes, an inner and an outer. The highly folded inner membrane forms the inner compartment. The space between the two membranes forms the outer compartment. The enzymes involved in the oxygen-requiring steps of cellular respiration are located inside the mitochondrion.

- outer membrane
- inner membrane
- outer compartment
- inner compartment

pyruvate. The reactions occur in the cell compartments called *mitochondria* (see Figure E8.13). Because the Krebs cycle requires oxygen, it is called *aerobic respiration*. During aerobic respiration, enzymes convert pyruvate into a 2-carbon molecule by removing a molecule of carbon dioxide.

Next, the 2-carbon molecule enters the Krebs cycle (Figure E8.14a). The Krebs cycle is a stage of aerobic respiration that involves many enzymes and molecular rearrangements. This cycle completes the release of energy from pyruvate by breaking it down to carbon dioxide (step b). This produces a little more ATP (step c). It also produces several more hydrogen carrier molecules, including NADH (step d). In humans, the

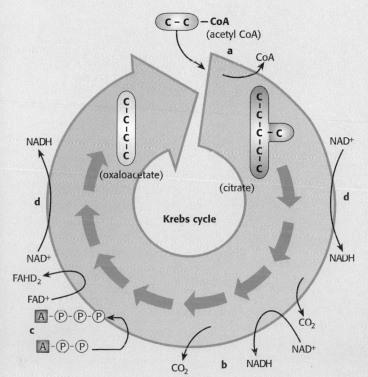

Figure E8.14 The Krebs cycle. The starting molecule for aerobic respiration is a 2-carbon molecule. This molecule is derived from the pyruvate that glycolysis generates. The 2-carbon molecule combines with a 4-carbon molecule to produce a 6-carbon compound. Then many enzyme-catalyzed reactions occur. These reactions release two molecules of carbon dioxide (**b**) and produce some ATP (**c**). In addition, several NADH molecules are produced (**d**).

circulatory system transports to the lungs the carbon dioxide produced here and in the conversion of pyruvate to the 2-carbon molecules. You exhale the gas as a waste product.

Following the first two stages of cellular respiration, the energy from glucose has been converted into energy in ATP molecules and hydrogen carriers like NADH. NADH is an energy carrier *and* a hydrogen carrier. The energy in each NADH molecule is converted into approximately three ATP molecules. This takes place in the third stage of cellular respiration, the electron transport system. Figure E8.15 outlines the electron transport system. This stage also is aerobic. Here, the energy stored in NADH is used to produce large amounts of ATP.

The electron transport system consists of a series of electron carrier molecules that are embedded in the inner membrane of a mitochondrion. The hydrogen atoms carried by NADH are separated into their component electrons and protons. The electrons are passed to the chain of electron carrier molecules. As the electrons move from

one carrier to the next, they release energy. Some of this energy pumps the protons (H^+) across the inner membrane of the mitochondrion. The protons accumulate in the outer compartment of the mitochondrion.

The difference in concentration of protons inside and outside the inner compartment of the mitochondrion produces a concentration gradient. A concentration gradient is a source of potential energy. The protons (H^+) tend to diffuse from the outer compartment, where they are in high concentration, back across the membrane into the inner compartment, where their concentration is lower. To diffuse into the inner compartment, the protons must pass through an enzyme complex located in the membrane. The enzyme complex works much like a waterwheel that captures the potential energy of a flowing stream to grind wheat. In this case, the flow of protons through the enzyme complex makes ATP from ADP and phosphate. In this way, the energy from NADH is transferred to ATP. The transferred electrons then combine with protons (H^+) and molecular oxygen (O_2) to form water (H_2O).

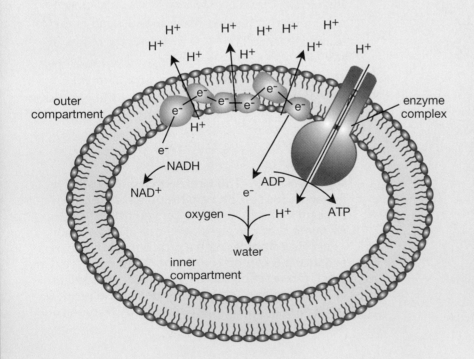

Figure E8.15 Electron transport. The final step in aerobic respiration is the transfer of electrons. Electrons transfer from NADH to a chain of electron carriers embedded in the inner membrane of the mitochondrion. The electrons pass from one electron carrier to the next. As this happens, energy is released and protons are pumped into the outer compartment. The resulting proton concentration gradient drives the production of ATP. Protons flow back into the inner compartment of the mitochondrion, through an ATP-producing enzyme complex. At the end of the electron transport chain, the electrons join with oxygen and protons to form water.

The requirement of oxygen at this point in the electron transport system explains why humans—as well as other animals, plants, fungi, protists, and many prokaryotes—require oxygen for their survival. ATP is the ultimate product of cellular respiration. Carbon dioxide and water are by-products that we release when we exhale. ATP can serve as the energetic *push* that starts many chemical reactions in the cell. ◆

Figure E8.16 How is perspiration related to electron transport?

Regulation and Energy Production

Cellular respiration, like nearly all important processes in living systems, is carefully regulated to maintain an organism's homeostatic balance. In this case, the condition that the organism must sense and respond to is the available energy supply (see Figure E8.17). In general, living organisms need a supply of ATP at all times, even when inactive. For instance, individual cells must maintain an osmotic balance with their surroundings. They do this by continually transporting sodium (Na^+) and potassium (K^+) ions across their cell membranes. This process requires the energy that ATP provides. Recall that ATP provides energy to another molecule by releasing one of its phosphate groups to it. ATP (adenosine triphosphate) then becomes ADP (adenosine diphosphate). What happens when an organism needs more energy than usual? Cells use up ATP rapidly, and ADP levels rise. The mitochondria detect increased ADP levels and respond by increasing the rate of respiration.

The level of ADP is not the only signal that influences energy production in cells. The level of oxygen is another critical signal.

Remember, the Krebs cycle and the electron transport system cannot proceed without oxygen. Glycolysis, on the other hand, is an anaerobic process—it does not require oxygen. The presence or absence of oxygen in the cell dictates the fate of the pyruvate formed in glycolysis. Figure E8.18 shows these possible fates.

Under aerobic conditions, enzymes convert pyruvate into a 2-carbon molecule. This molecule can then enter the Krebs cycle and the electron transport system. During vigorous exercise, however, muscles do not receive enough oxygen for cellular respiration. Under anaerobic conditions such as that, cells must rely on anaerobic energy production. Anaerobic energy production converts pyruvate into lactic acid or alcohol. The process produces less ATP because it does not involve the Krebs cycle and the electron transport system. However, the cell can continue to produce a small amount of ATP until oxygen becomes available again.

Another name for anaerobic energy production is fermentation. Yeast cells carry

Figure E8.17
Regulation of energy.

Cells can detect and adjust the supply of available energy. When energy needs are low, there are low levels of ADP. ATP is made at a slow rate. When energy needs are high, there are high levels of ADP. The electron transport phase of cellular respiration speeds up. How does this system help maintain homeostasis? Is this an example of positive or negative feedback?

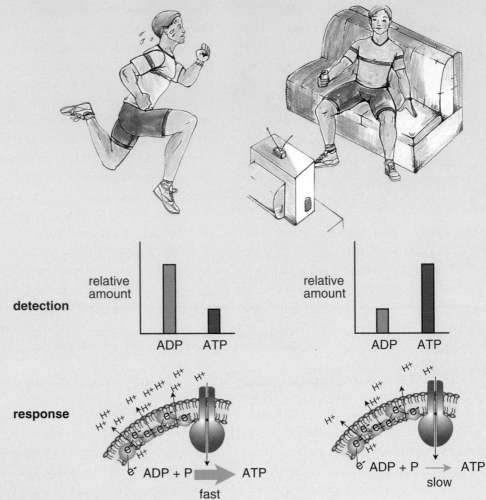

detection

relative amount

ADP   ATP

relative amount

ADP   ATP

response

H^+ ... e^- ... ADP + P → ATP

fast

H^+ ... e^- ... ADP + P → ATP

slow

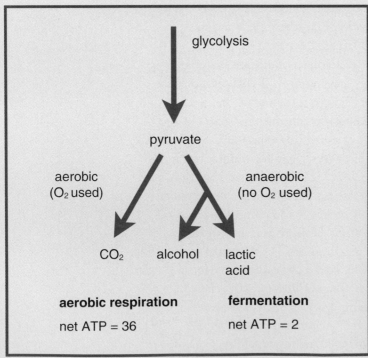

glycolysis

pyruvate

aerobic (O$_2$ used)

anaerobic (no O$_2$ used)

CO$_2$ alcohol   lactic acid

aerobic respiration

net ATP = 36

fermentation

net ATP = 2

Figure E8.18   Aerobic and anaerobic energy release. When oxygen is present, pyruvate enters the Krebs cycle. It is converted into carbon dioxide. Hydrogen carriers transport electrons to the electron transport system. This system produces much ATP. In the absence of oxygen, pyruvate can be converted into alcohol or lactic acid. What are the advantages of each process?

out a type of fermentation that produces alcohol. Certain bacteria, such as those responsible for souring milk or making yogurt, produce lactic acid. In fact, the first organisms on earth were bacteria that acquired their energy through fermentation. Aerobic respiration did not evolve until about 2.5 billion years ago. The level of oxygen in the atmosphere was too low to sustain it until then. What changed? Photosynthetic organisms evolved. Photosynthesis releases oxygen as a by-product. That changed the earth's atmosphere forever.

The process of aerobic respiration made the evolution of complex organisms possible. The amount of ATP produced during aerobic respiration is about 18 times greater than that made in anaerobic glycolysis. This difference in the efficiency of energy release from glucose is significant. Remember that entropy means all things move toward disorder *in the absence of energy*. With an input of energy, however, order and organization in living systems can be increased. Complex, multicellular organisms developed, in part, as a result of aerobic respiration.

The greater efficiency of aerobic respiration also explains why aerobic conditioning gives humans an advantage in performance. During aerobic conditioning, muscle tissues produce more mitochondria. This provides the potential for greater energy release. In addition, circulation to the muscles improves. This provides a greater supply of oxygen. As a result of these two changes, aerobic respiration can convert a greater proportion of the energy in glucose into usable cellular energy. That makes an exercising muscle work more efficiently. ◆

Whose Discovery Is This?

Two students working at the same library table looked up long enough to catch the librarian's stiff glare. They were talking too loud, again. Changing to a whisper, Inez asked, "What's your report on?"

Fernando whispered back, "The guy who discovered photosynthesis. Well, actually the guy who first figured out that plants use light and carbon dioxide from the air to make their own food. What's yours about?"

"Same thing," Inez replied.

"So you're looking up stuff on the Dutch physician Jan Ingen-Housz?" Fernando asked.

"Ink and who?" Inez said. "No, a Swiss botanist and naturalist by the name of Jean Senebier. He was the first person to figure out photosynthesis."

By this time the librarian, Mrs. Drexler, had heard enough of their talking and got up from her chair. "What's going on here?" she asked.

"We're trying to figure out who discovered photosynthesis," Fernando explained.

Mrs. Drexler relaxed, smiled, and said, "I was on the Internet yesterday and found that scientists have now described 80 separate, but interdependent reactions that make up photosynthesis. I suggest that you focus your research on the history of photosynthesis

rather than on trying to find one person responsible for discovering it."

Three days later, Inez and Fernando presented their science teacher, Mr. O'Brien, with the results of their research. "We ran across dozens of men and women who contributed to understanding photosynthesis," Inez said. "Some things are still being discovered about it."

"Yeah," Fernando said. "The list got so long we decided to pick out just a few people who played major roles in developing the whole idea of photosynthesis. Here's our list."

- During the 17th century, a physician named Jean Baptiste van Helmont did an experiment to support his belief that water could be changed into the substance of a willow tree.

- In 1772, Joseph Priestley, an English chemist and clergyman, did some experiments showing that plants release a type of air that allows combustion. Although Priestley did not know about oxygen, his work showed that plants release oxygen into the atmosphere.

- Jan Ingen-Housz (Fernando's candidate for discovering the process) discovered that sunlight is necessary for photosynthesis and only green parts of plants can release oxygen. He performed more than 500 experiments during a 4-month period in 1779 to isolate the variables that he thought affected oxygen production by plants.

- In 1796, Jean Senebier (Inez's candidate for discovering the process) discovered that carbon dioxide is required for photosynthetic growth.

- Nicolas de Saussure, a Swiss chemist and plant physiologist, showed that exposing a plant to sunlight increases its weight by more than the weight of the carbon dioxide it absorbs. In the early 1800s, Saussure published a book in which he concluded that plant growth results from the intake of both carbon dioxide and water.

- In 1845, Julius Robert von Mayer, a German physician and physicist, proposed that plants absorb light energy and convert it into chemical energy. This chemical energy is then stored in compounds.

- From 1936 until his death in 1991, Robert Hill made significant contributions to understanding photosynthetic processes. One of his areas of research demonstrated that oxygen came from water, not carbon dioxide, as was the hypothesis at the time.

- In the 1940s and 50s, Melvin Calvin, with several colleagues, used radioactive carbon dioxide to identify a series of biochemical reactions that resulted in the formation of sugar. He has been honored by having the reactions called the "Calvin cycle."

Fernando and Inez anxiously watched Mr. O'Brien read their report. They hoped he would be pleased that they had focused on so many scientists instead of just one individual. When he finished reading, Mr. O'Brien asked, "What have you learned from your research?"

Fernando and Inez replied together, "No one person discovered photosynthesis. Understanding photosynthesis developed over a long period of time, like most scientific ideas. It involved the ideas and work of many people. We listed only a few of the many scientists who contributed to our understanding of photosynthesis."

Mr. O'Brien smiled; Fernando and Inez were thinking like scientists. ◆

Getting Energy and Matter into Biological Systems

There is a saying that you must have money to make money. A similar loop exists in biological processes: you need energy to get energy. For instance, cellular respiration releases usable energy from storage molecules. But a certain amount of energy is needed to start the process. Likewise, food supplies the energy and matter requirements of many organisms. But the food itself is usually derived from other organisms. How, then, do energy and matter get into organisms in the first place? The main way is through photosynthesis. **Photosynthesis** is the series of reactions by which plants, algae, and some bacteria use light energy from the sun to synthesize large, energy-rich molecules from smaller ones.

You might think of a plant as a solar-powered factory that converts the radiant energy of sunlight (solar energy) into potential energy. The potential energy is stored in chemical form (molecules). Solar energy varies in its strength, from the warming rays of infrared to the damaging rays of ultraviolet. Visible light is only a small fraction of the total energy coming from the sun. Visible light consists of a spectrum of colors. Each color has a different wavelength and energy content, as shown in Figure E8.19. Photosynthesis uses only certain wavelengths, or colors, of visible light. The green color of plants emphasizes that fact. Most plants appear green because their pigments reflect green light rather than absorb it.

Photosynthesis depends on particular wavelengths of light. It also works more or less efficiently depending on the intensity of the light. The ideal intensity of light varies for different plants. Of course, many factors, such as the availability of water and nutrients in the soil, also affect photosynthesis.

Three major events occur in plant cells during photosynthesis: (1) absorption of light energy, (2) conversion of light energy into chemical energy (ATP and NADPH), and (3) storage of potential energy in carbohydrates. These three events take place in two distinct but interdependent sets of reactions (phases). Figure E8.20 summarizes the two phases. In the first phase of photosynthesis, chlorophyll absorbs light energy. Enzymes use this energy to produce small, energy-carrying molecules. These molecules, ATP and the hydrogen carrier NADPH, then power the second phase

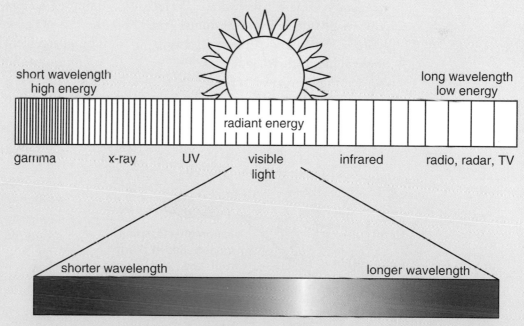

Figure E8.19 **Spectrum of light energy.** The sun is the source of different types of radiant energy. These include damaging ultraviolet (UV) light, light that can be detected by the human eye (visible light), and warming infrared light. Photosynthesis uses only a small portion of this spectrum of light energy.

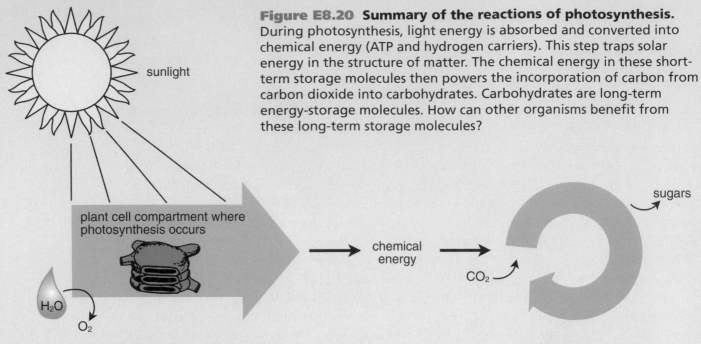

Figure E8.20 Summary of the reactions of photosynthesis. During photosynthesis, light energy is absorbed and converted into chemical energy (ATP and hydrogen carriers). This step traps solar energy in the structure of matter. The chemical energy in these short-term storage molecules then powers the incorporation of carbon from carbon dioxide into carbohydrates. Carbohydrates are long-term energy-storage molecules. How can other organisms benefit from these long-term storage molecules?

sunlight

sugars

plant cell compartment where photosynthesis occurs

H_2O

O_2

chemical energy

CO_2

1. absorption of light energy
2. conversion of light energy into chemical energy

3. incorporation of carbon into carbohydrates

of photosynthesis. In the second phase, carbon and oxygen from atmospheric carbon dioxide combine with hydrogen that came from water to form carbohydrates. Photosynthetic organisms use these carbohydrates for long-term energy storage (much as humans use glycogen). Nonphotosynthetic organisms use them indirectly when they eat the photosynthetic organisms.

Bringing Solar Energy into Living Systems. The reactions of photosynthesis take place in **chloroplasts**, small compartments inside certain plant cells. Figures E8.21 and E8.22 show the location of the chloroplast-containing cells in a plant leaf. The enlargement in Figure E8.22 illustrates the organization of a chloroplast. Within the chloroplast is a system of membranes called

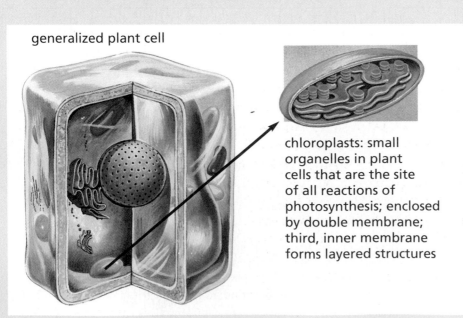

generalized plant cell

chloroplasts: small organelles in plant cells that are the site of all reactions of photosynthesis; enclosed by double membrane; third, inner membrane forms layered structures

Figure E8.21 Plant cells (and photosynthetic protists) contain *chloroplasts*. Photosynthesis takes place in chloroplasts.

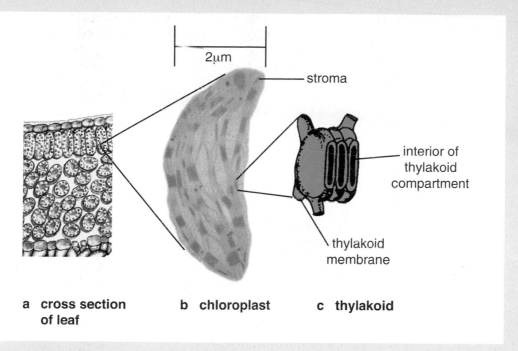

| a cross section of leaf | b chloroplast | c thylakoid |

Figure E8.22 The conversion of light energy into chemical energy occurs in subcellular compartments known as chloroplasts. **(a)** The green disks in the cells in this diagram of a leaf cross section are chloroplasts. **(b)** This electron micrograph of a chloroplast shows the layers and stacks of thylakoid membranes. **(c)** The thylakoid membranes contain chlorophyll and other pigments. These form subcompartments within the chloroplast in which the light-trapping reactions occur. What other subcellular compartments are in a plant cell?

the **thylakoids**. The thylakoids are folded so that they form smaller compartments—somewhat like the infoldings in a mitochondrion. Surrounding the thylakoids is a colorless fluid known as the **stroma**. The internal structure of the chloroplast is important to the process of converting light into chemical energy.

Embedded in the thylakoid membranes are organized arrangements of pigment molecules. These molecules include the green pigments called **chlorophylls**. Chlorophylls and additional pigments give plants their color. These pigments absorb light energy in the visible wavelengths. The absorbed energy sets up a flow of electrons (e⁻) in the chlorophyll molecules, as shown in Figure E8.23. The electrons from chlorophyll are passed to an electron transport system. This system is also embedded in the thylakoid membranes. As this happens, some of the energy that is released is used to pump

protons (H^+) across the thylakoid membranes. The protons accumulate inside the thylakoids and form a concentration gradient. Just as in cellular respiration, the protons then diffuse down the concentration gradient through an enzyme complex in the membranes. The enzymes synthesize ATP as the protons pass through the complex.

In addition to producing ATP, the flow of electrons produces NADPH. This molecule is an energy and hydrogen carrier similar to the NADH formed during cellular respiration. Remember that the solar energy absorbed by chlorophyll in the first phase of photosynthesis provides the energy for the production of energy-rich ATP and NADPH.

Photosynthesis cannot take place without water. Plants absorb water through their roots. Enzymes that are associated with the pigment molecules in the thylakoid membranes remove electrons from the water. These electrons replace those that were

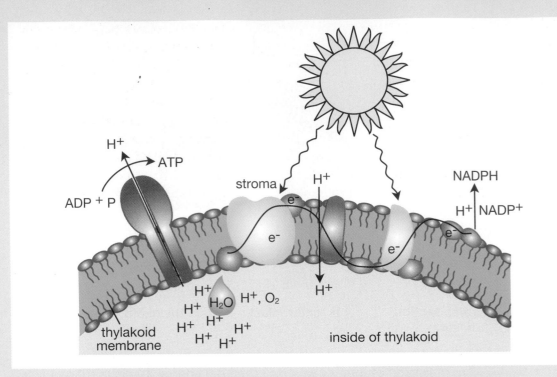

Figure E8.23 ATP production in the chloroplast during photosynthesis.
Absorption of light energy sets up a flow of electrons from water through pigments and other molecules in the thylakoid membranes. Protons accumulate on the inside of the thylakoids. The resulting proton gradient functions much like that in a mitochondrion. The gradient supplies potential energy. This energy enables a membrane-spanning enzyme to synthesize ATP from ADP and phosphate.

Figure E8.24 This *Anacharis* plant is actively engaged in photosynthesis. What gas is likely present in the bubbles?

originally lost by chlorophyll. When the electrons are removed, water splits into oxygen (O) and protons (H^+). The plant releases the oxygen from the water as oxygen gas (see Figure E8.24). Thus, oxygen is a by-product of photosynthesis. However, this by-product provides the oxygen on which animals, plants, and all aerobic organisms depend for respiration.

The first phase of photosynthesis forms three products. These are oxygen gas, ATP, and NADPH. The products ATP and NADPH are now available to provide energy for the second phase in photosynthesis. In the second phase, the reactions form carbohydrates. This important process converts the energy trapped in ATP and NADPH into long-term energy storage (sugars and starch).

Bringing Carbon into Living Systems. The final reactions of photosynthesis use ATP and NADPH from the first phase of photosynthesis and atmospheric carbon dioxide to form carbohydrates. Imagine, atmospheric carbon dioxide, an invisible gas in the air around you, provides the matter that becomes plant leaves, stems, and roots. The process of converting atmospheric carbon dioxide into carbohydrate molecules is called **carbon fixation**. The reactions incorporate, or *fix*, carbon into carbohydrates. Figure E8.25 is a simplified diagram of those carbohydrate-producing reactions. These reactions take place in the stroma of the chloroplast. ATP and NADPH provide the energy (and hydrogen atoms) for those reactions.

First, carbon dioxide from the air enters the plant through the stomates (look back at Figure E5.2 on page 230). The carbon dioxide is added to an existing 5-carbon sugar. This creates a 6-carbon sugar. The 6-carbon sugar quickly splits into two 3-carbon sugars. These 3-carbon sugars have several possible fates.

In a cycle of reactions, these 3-carbon sugars are rearranged into a variety of other sugars. Some become the 5-carbon sugar that first combines with carbon dioxide. Others are exported from the chloroplast and used to form sucrose and starch. The carbon also can be used to form lipids, proteins, chlorophyll, and other molecules the plant cell needs. Sucrose can be transported to nonphotosynthetic tissues of the plant such as the roots. Plant cells use sucrose as a source of matter (carbon) for producing new tissues

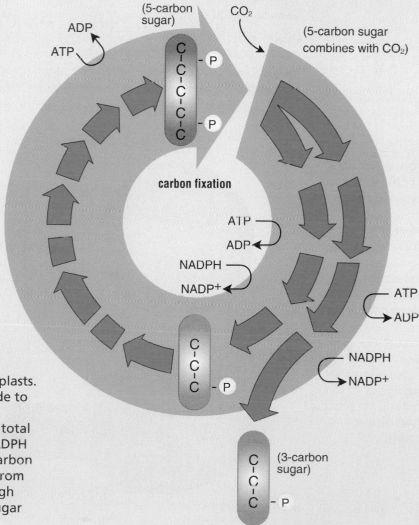

Figure E8.25 Carbon fixation. Carbon fixation takes place in the stroma of chloroplasts. This process uses carbon from carbon dioxide to build carbohydrates. The carbon fixation reactions organize matter and increase the total amount of carbon in the plant. ATP and NADPH provide energy for these reactions. The 3-carbon sugars that are produced can be exported from the chloroplast. Or, they can proceed through many steps that regenerate the 5-carbon sugar that combines with carbon dioxide.

and for energy. In that way, plant cells that cannot perform photosynthesis can obtain energy to live. Some plant cells cannot carry out photosynthesis. Some of these cells have no chloroplasts. Some are cells that are prevented from doing photosynthesis (during winter, for example). Those cells use the process of cellular respiration to break down sucrose and produce ATP. For that reason, plants are said to be producers. They produce their own "food" as well as food for other organisms. ◆

Metabolism Includes Synthesis and Breakdown

Have you ever thought about growth in terms of efficiency? Think about the latest highway expansion project. Lanes are closed; the old surface is torn up and hauled away. Only after much time and inconvenience is new asphalt laid to create a wider, more efficient roadway. Similarly, to build a large office building in a densely packed city requires a lot of preparation. Older, smaller buildings first must be torn down and the debris cleared away. In both cases, the raw materials from the outdated structures are broken down and often recycled. Only then can new materials be used to make newer, larger, or more useful structures.

Living systems function in much the same way. Except living systems continuously break down and build up molecules (see Figure E8.26). Energy links the reactions responsible for both processes. For example, when you eat potatoes, your body breaks down potato starch. It breaks down the starch into the small glucose molecules that make up the starch. The glucose then can be broken down further to obtain energy from the chemical bonds that hold the molecule together. For

Figure E8.26
Synthesis and breakdown.
Both plants and the organisms that consume plants use the sugars made during photosynthesis for biological synthesis and breakdown. These processes are necessary for life. Is photosynthesis a synthesis or breakdown process? What about digestion?

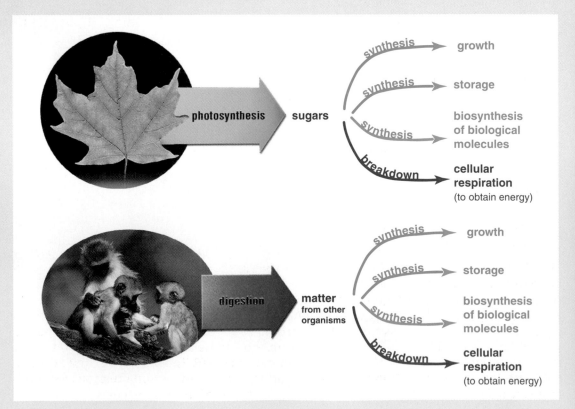

immediate energy, the glucose is broken down during cellular respiration. This makes energy available in the form of ATP. For storing energy, the glucose can be transported to your liver or muscles and combined with other glucose molecules to form glycogen. **Glycogen** is a large, energy-storage molecule. Your body uses some of the energy that is released during cellular respiration to build, or synthesize, the glycogen.

All the chemical activities and changes that take place in a cell or an organism are collectively known as its **metabolism**. Generally, *breakdown reactions* (such as cellular respiration) release energy. *Synthesis reactions* (such as photosynthesis) require energy. The ATP produced by the breakdown reactions becomes the source of energy for many cellular activities, including processes like muscle contraction. Thus, ATP, as well as other energy carriers, provides a critical link between reactions that produce energy and those that require it. Without such links, the energy released from breakdown reactions would be wasted. Without ATP, no energy would be available for biosynthetic reactions. Those reactions are necessary for growth, repair, and routine life processes. Organisms die without ATP.

The breakdown processes in cells produce a variety of smaller molecules that can be converted into the intermediate compounds. Those compounds are formed in *glycolysis* and the *Krebs cycle*. That makes metabolism more efficient because those intermediate molecules can be used in cellular respiration just as glucose is used. For example, *fats* can be broken down into *glycerol*, a 3-carbon molecule, and *fatty acids*, long chains of carbon and hydrogen. Glycerol can be converted into one of the 3-carbon intermediates of glycolysis. The 3-carbon intermediate can enter cellular respiration, the highly efficient, energy-releasing, breakdown process. Fatty acids can be converted into the same 2-carbon molecule that enters the Krebs cycle.

Similarly, *proteins* can be broken down to *amino acids*. After the nitrogen-containing group has been removed from the amino acid, the remaining carbon skeleton can be broken down to intermediates. Those also can enter glycolysis and the Krebs cycle, as shown in Figure E8.27.

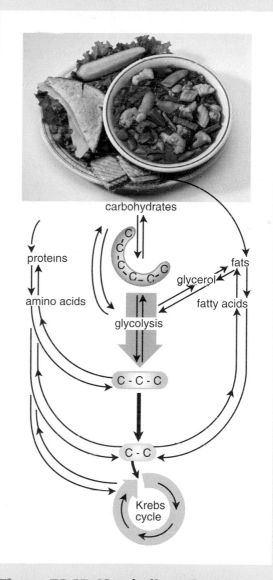

Figure E8.27 Metabolic pathways.
Macromolecules in food are broken down to smaller molecules. These smaller molecules can be converted into the intermediates that are formed in glycolysis and the Krebs cycle. These intermediates then can be used in cellular respiration to produce ATP. The same intermediates also are a source of carbon skeletons for the synthesis of macromolecules.

Intermediate compounds can be used in synthesis reactions as well (see Figure E8.27). Organisms require many different types of macromolecules for their structures and activities. For example, each of the many chemical reactions that take place in an organism requires a specific enzyme (protein). The organism must synthesize these enzymes from amino acids. Cell membranes require specific lipids. These must be synthesized as well. Whether a protein, carbohydrate, or fat, each molecule must be synthesized from the matter that the organism takes in.

Only a few elements compose the tissues of most species. And the same types of macromolecules are found in vastly different organisms. The particular molecular arrangements in a given organism, however, are different from all others. That is why the protein that you consume in your diet, which a plant or animal of a different species made, cannot be used directly as a prefabricated protein in your body. Instead, the protein that you consume is broken down into its component amino acids. Then your cells assemble the amino acids into the specific protein patterns that your body requires.

Synthesizing new proteins is the body's most efficient use of amino acids. During starvation or in the extreme stages of anorexia nervosa, however, the body's cells must compensate for the lack of carbohydrates and fats in the diet by breaking down proteins for energy. The human body does that in an effort to maintain homeostasis. Unfortunately, when this happens, the muscles of the body are consumed as fuel. Although the breakdown of protein is a last resort, it indicates how flexible cells can be in their metabolism. ◆

Garbage among Us—From Then until Now!

Matter—lots of it. Wood. Paper. Glass. Metals. Plastics. Rubber. Cloth. Food. Yard waste. All of these types of matter end up in our landfills. In fact, did you know the following?

- In the United States, each person throws away an average of 1,600 pounds of garbage each year. This is more than any other nation in the world.

- A convoy of garbage trucks long enough to encircle the earth six times would be required to carry all the municipal waste generated in the United States in 1 year.

- In 1960, 63 percent of waste generated went to a landfill, 30.6 percent was burned, and only 6.4 percent was recycled or composted. In 2000, 53.3 percent of waste went to a landfill, 16.7 percent was burned, and 30 percent was recycled or composted. However,

we must improve recycling efforts and reduce our total waste generation to cope with the increasing burden on landfills (223 million tons produced in the year 2000, alone). More than half of the states in the United States are having problems finding places to dump trash. Sometimes trash travels great distances before it is dumped (Figure E9.1).

Figure E9.1 Overloaded with waste and no place to go.

- Lettuce buried in a landfill may take more than 7 years to decompose completely.

- A hot dog can last more than 10 years in a landfill.

- A steak buried in a landfill can retain its fat 15 years after burial.

- In spite of recycling efforts, waste paper is still a major component of landfills nationwide. It makes up 30–35 percent of the waste in landfills.

You throw away things every day. But did you ever wonder what people could tell about you if they sorted through your trash? Garbage and waste can tell us quite a bit about how organisms acquire and use the matter and energy in their community. Let's consider a few different communities and reflect on the cycling of matter through them. How is this process similar and different in these communities? How does matter move from one organism to another? How much and what type of waste does each community produce? What happens to the waste in each community?

Bats in Mammoth Cave National Park, Kentucky. Two bats flit about in the sky at twilight, barely visible in the last light of evening. They dart about catching insects. One bat descends briefly, flying just above the surface of a pond to take a drink. Another nips a moth in midair. Soon, the bats dart into the entrance of a cave that is partially hidden by evergreens (see Figure E9.2).

Several fleas, ticks, and mites have latched onto the bats' coats during the evening. As the bats sit on a cave ledge, resting and cleaning themselves, some of the insects fall to the cave floor. There they become food for the organisms that dwell there. During the night, many bats excrete their wastes—a substance called *guano*. Guano is not solid like human feces, but rather thick and mudlike. It covers the floor of the cave like carpeting. Bacteria, fungi, and other one-celled organisms grow on the guano and use it as their food—their

source of energy. In turn, many of these small organisms are destined to become the food for insects, and some of these insects may become food for the bats.

The Earliest Ancestral Puebloans. The year is AD 950. As a hint of daylight appears in the east, a young Ancestral Puebloan woman awakens and checks on her two young children still asleep beside her in their cliff dwelling (Figure E9.3). They live along a basin in the high-plateau region of the American Southwest. As the woman rises and starts a fire, her mate begins to stir. She retrieves some kernels of corn from a

Figure E9.2 Brown bats live in caves throughout Mammoth Cave National Park, Kentucky.

Figure E9.3 **Cliff dwellings.** The Ancestral Puebloans lived in cliff dwellings. These structures can be found throughout the Four Corners region of the American Southwest.

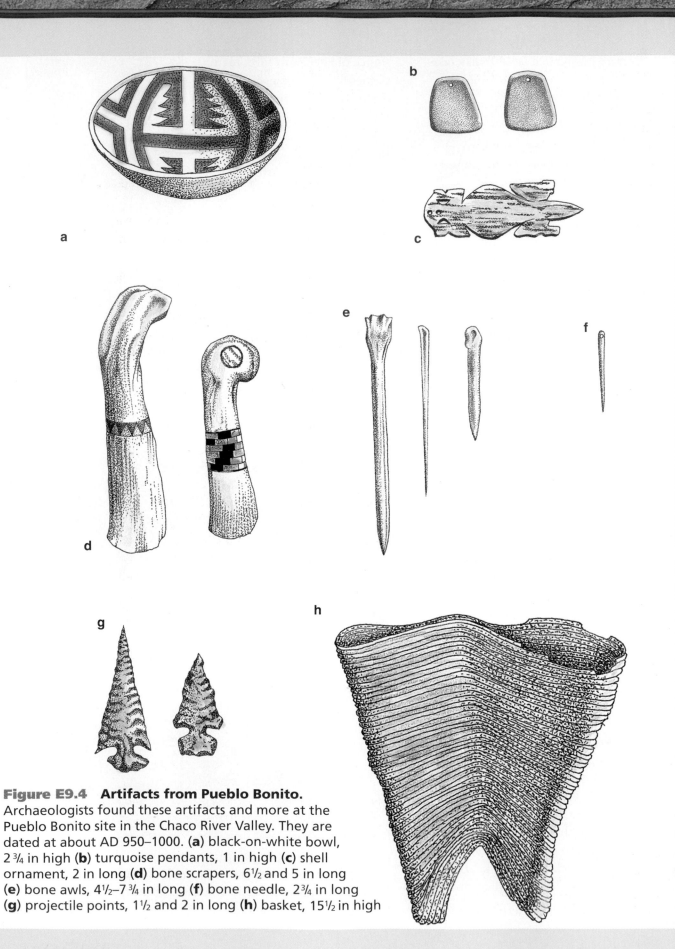

Figure E9.4 Artifacts from Pueblo Bonito.
Archaeologists found these artifacts and more at the
Pueblo Bonito site in the Chaco River Valley. They are
dated at about AD 950–1000. (**a**) black-on-white bowl,
2 ¾ in high (**b**) turquoise pendants, 1 in high (**c**) shell
ornament, 2 in long (**d**) bone scrapers, 6½ and 5 in long
(**e**) bone awls, 4½–7 ¾ in long (**f**) bone needle, 2¾ in long
(**g**) projectile points, 1½ and 2 in long (**h**) basket, 15½ in high

slab-lined hole and begins to grind them into a coarse meal. It is late spring, and the couple hopes to finish planting the corn today. They want to work in the morning before the day becomes hot. To plant, they use a stick to make holes in the ground, drop kernels of corn into each hole, and then cover them with soil.

Later, the woman and her children join other women and children to gather yucca from the plateau. The Ancestral Puebloan families will not only eat the fruit and seeds of the yucca, but they will use the roots for soap and shampoo, and the strong, sturdy fibers from the leaves for making intricate baskets, sandals, aprons, mats, and cradle boards. Small pieces of the yucca and other plant material are discarded in a pile along with cornhusks and cobs, worn-out mats, and broken tools made out of bone.

Some mornings the woman's mate joins other men in the community to hunt for rabbit and deer. In addition to preparing and eating the meat, the Ancestral Puebloans make clothing for the winter months from the rabbit pelts, and tools and utensils such as needles from the bones. Unused bones are discarded in the small but growing pile of waste. At the bottom of this pile, the organic material has decayed enough so that it is almost indistinguishable from the soil beneath it.

Family in Malneville, Ohio. A single mother looks in on her 8-year-old daughter Sonya, who has the flu. She has a big box of tissues beside her bed and a pile of used ones in the wastebasket nearby. Sonya also has finished one carton of juice and has begun another. One of the family's three cats is resting at the foot of the bed. (Someone needs to clean the litter box today.)

This family lives in a three-bedroom, two-bathroom house at the end of a quiet street in a small community north of a major city. Sonya has a 15-year-old brother, Matt, who is keeping his distance because he doesn't want to get sick. He has a huge history report due Monday. He works away at the computer most of the afternoon and prints the entire report four times before he is satisfied. He places the rejected copies in the recycle bin in the kitchen.

The mother is an architect and has been working at home all day on a balsa-wood model of a hospital addition. (Scrap wood seems to be everywhere.) In the evening on the way home from the grocery store (with 10 bags of groceries), the mother stops at a fast-food restaurant and picks up some chicken dinners, which everyone enjoys—even Sonya who is beginning to feel better. As Matt tosses the last dinner carton into the garbage, he notices that it's full again. Whose week is it to take out the garbage, anyway? ◆

Matter in Nature Is Going Around in Cycles . . . What Next?

Imagine a riverbed similar to the one where the Ancestral Puebloans lived 1,000 years ago. It might look something like the illustration in Figure E9.5. In such a riverbed ecosystem, matter is on the move from one place to another or from one organism to another. Water runs through it. Nutrients move from the soil into plants rooted along the river. Beavers gnaw through branches and twigs and use them to build their dams. A great blue heron nabs an unsuspecting fish from the river. When the types and amounts of matter in such an ecosystem remain essentially the same across time, the ecosystem remains in balance. When the types or amounts of matter in an ecosystem change, the ecosystem changes as well.

Figure E9.5   A beaver busy at work. What effect might this beaver have on the movement of matter in its ecosystem?

Let's look more closely at the riverbed ecosystem. There are two types of material components—biotic and abiotic. Biotic matter is living matter. Abiotic matter is matter that is not living. Both types of matter cycle within an ecosystem.

Beavers are part of the biotic matter along this riverbed. In the spring, two to four young beavers are born into each family along the river. During the months while young beavers grow and become more self-sufficient, the local beaver community can withstand the temporary increase in its population. Eventually, however, many of last year's young will move out of the community to establish their homes elsewhere along the river. A few of last year's young may remain, replacing the beavers that die. But the total population of beavers in this area will remain relatively stable. If the number of beavers in this area increased significantly, it might place a stress on the available resources. These resources include the food supply and the sites and materials for building dams, for example. If a situation such as that continued for several seasons without a similar increase in the

resources that beavers need, the resources might be depleted to the point that the environment would be unable to support any beavers. They then would die off or move elsewhere. Such a scenario would cause the community to change.

Not only does matter move through an ecosystem, but some of it makes a complete cycle within it. For example, when beavers die along the river, their bodies gradually decay. The nutrients derived from their bodies eventually mix with the soil. Plants then acquire some of these nutrients from the soil. In turn, various animals (including beavers) feed on these plants. In this way, nutrients that once were part of an animal can cycle through various types of matter and be taken up by another animal.

Water is an example of abiotic matter that moves through and cycles within an ecosystem. Water is constantly moving through this river. The water flowing through the river at a certain spot today is different from the water that flowed through this same spot yesterday. Water also is part of a cycle. Some is added to the river by rain or snow and from tributaries and groundwater reserves in the plateau. Some water leaves the river through evaporation. (See the drawing of the water cycle in Figure E9.6.)

Through time, when the net inflow is the same as the net outflow, the river remains essentially the same. A significant increase or decrease of the inflow changes the river. A significant increase in the water flow would cause the banks to flood, destroying many plants along the riverbed. A sustained increase in the amount of water, however, may support a different number and variety of plants and animals in the community and consequently change its makeup. Similarly, a decrease in the water flow may cause certain plants and animals to disappear as competition for water increased. Again, if such a change were sustained, the makeup of the community would change as well.

These same principles of movement and cycling of matter apply to the many other, less obvious components that make up the riverbed ecosystem. Consider, for example, a single atom of carbon. If you could follow a single atom of carbon in the riverbed community through time, you would see it cycle through many different molecules. At one point, it may form part of a protein molecule in a floating leaf of duckweed. At another time, it may become one of the atoms within a DNA molecule in the genetic material of a fish or a frog that ate the duckweed. At still another point, the carbon atom may remain for a long period within dead plant or animal material in the mud of the river until it is finally used by bacteria or fungi and rejoins the biotic community. Figure E9.7 illustrates some of these interactions and relationships in the carbon

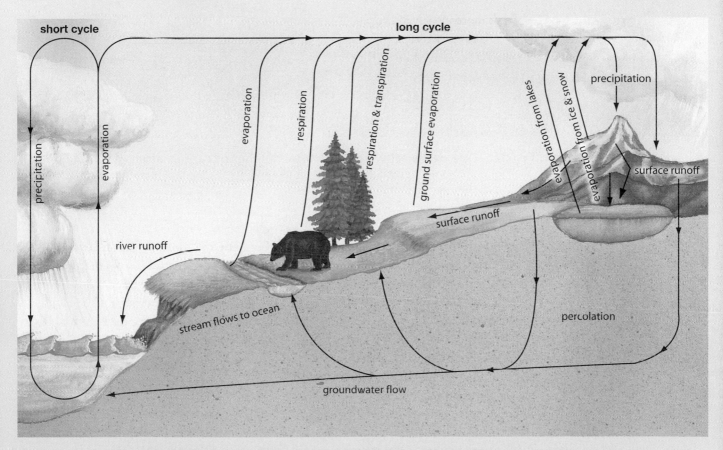

Figure E9.6 The water cycle. The water cycle collects and redistributes the earth's water supply.

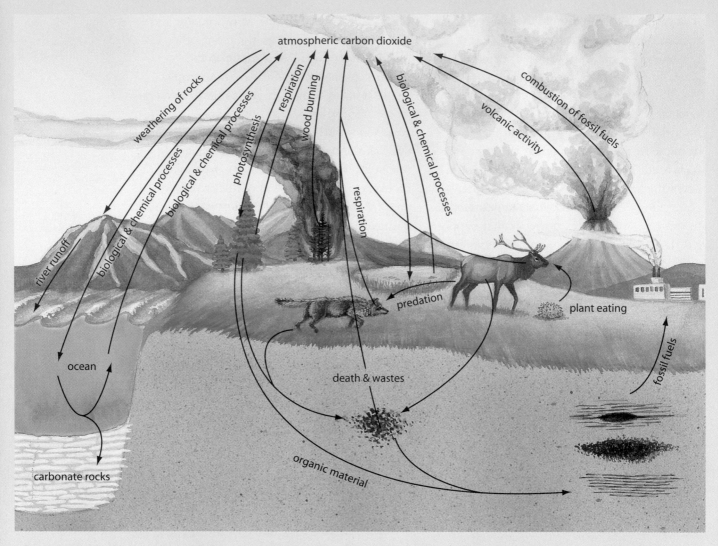

atmospheric carbon dioxide

weathering of rocks

biological & chemical processes

biological & chemical processes

photosynthesis

respiration

wood burning

respiration

biological & chemical processes

volcanic activity

combustion of fossil fuels

river runoff

ocean

predation

plant eating

carbonate rocks

death & wastes

organic material

fossil fuels

Figure E9.7 The carbon cycle. In a stable ecosystem, the total number of carbon atoms will remain approximately the same.

cycle. Again, when the total number of carbon atoms in an ecosystem remains approximately the same along with the proportion of carbon atoms to other atoms, the ecosystem remains essentially stable. When the number or proportion of carbon atoms changes significantly, the community changes.

Other less obvious cycles of matter in ecosystems depend on the existing environmental conditions. Essential elements, such as calcium, potassium, and phosphorous, are available to the biological community only after they dissolve in the groundwater and are

taken up by the roots of plants. Through experience, people have discovered that many desert lands will produce large crops, at least for a time, if they are irrigated. Often, essential elements are abundant in these soils, but they are not readily available to plants due to the shortage of water.

A contemporary issue that is important in the tropics involves a change that humans have introduced. Humans have been removing native communities of plants and animals and growing crops in their place. In addition to the loss of the native plants and animals, a change such as this disrupts the cycling of elements. It may also result in an additional loss of soil fertility.

Consider another issue that is related to the cycling of matter. Various organisms in a community often cannot efficiently metabolize foreign compounds such as pesticides. As a result, foreign compounds may accumulate at toxic levels in the tissues of some organisms. They also may build up in the environment and persist there for long periods of time before they are returned to the cycle.

Taken as a whole, when a community is stable within an ecosystem such as the riverbed, it exhibits a type of large-scale dynamic balance that resembles the homeostasis of individual organisms. The same is true in other communities such as those found in a desert, a temperate pond, a pine forest, or the arctic tundra. On a larger scale, the same also is true for the entire biosphere. The biosphere includes all the organisms as well as the soil, water, and air that surround and support them. As the environment changes, communities may change as well. Homeostasis continues around a balance point, but that point of balance can change through time. ◆

Worms, Insects, Bacteria, and Fungi—Who Needs Them?

Did you know that 100 million bacteria can live in a single gram of fertile soil? Did you also know that 250,000 earthworms can live in a 1¼-acre field of rich topsoil?

This is one reason why earthworms are considered a farmer's best friend. Earthworms are organisms that decompose decaying organic matter. They can work through 10 tons of topsoil a year, aerating it and increasing its fertility.

The quality of the topsoil is important because topsoil serves as a link between the living and nonliving world. Abiotic nutrients enter the living world when they are absorbed by plants. They are returned to the nonliving world when they are excreted by animals as waste. The waste ends up in the topsoil. Here it is broken down into simple nutrients by the soil's inhabitants. At this point, the cycle can begin again as plants reuse these nutrients.

Earthworms play a vital role in keeping the nutrient levels in the soil high because they consume partially decomposed organic matter such as dead leaves and roots. They then excrete nutrient-rich waste. This mixes with the soil and creates humus. Other organisms that perform a similar function in the soil are insects, bacteria, and fungi. Together these organisms help return vital elements, such as phosphorous, calcium, and nitrogen, to the environment where other organisms can use them.

The importance of recyclable elements to the health of most communities emphasizes the role of organisms that decompose organic matter. This is particularly apparent in the tropics. Here the layer of topsoil is thin, the temperature is high throughout the year, and rains are frequent. Under such conditions, nutrients break down rapidly. Those nutrients that are not returned quickly to the living part of the ecosystem flow away in groundwater and are lost to the community. Figure E9.8 illustrates this situation for a tropical rain forest. The community appears extremely lush because most of the nutrients are held in living material almost continuously. The matter recycles rapidly from one organism to another. The critical location for this rapid

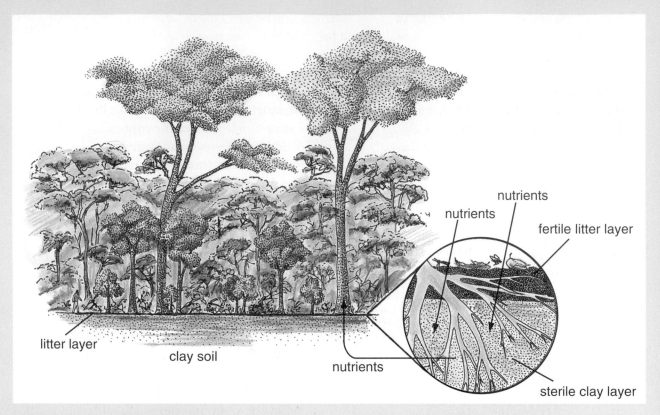

litter layer

clay soil

nutrients

nutrients

nutrients

fertile litter layer

sterile clay layer

Figure E9.8 **Tropical rain forest.** In a tropical rain forest, most of the nutrients are held in living organisms because of the rapid recycling of matter, particularly in the thin layer of topsoil. What might happen to the nutrient levels if the number of living organisms were greatly reduced?

recycling is the relatively thin layer of dead plant material that forms the topsoil on the forest floor. In the constant heat and moisture of the tropics, a group of small organisms in this layer quickly breaks down much of the fallen leaves and other dead organic matter. The nutrients they release into the groundwater then move downward toward the sterile clay beneath where the rich network of tree roots quickly reabsorbs them. The nutrients move up through the tree's roots, trunk, and branches to its leaves.

It is here that the nutrients are recycled into living matter through photosynthesis.

In environments with less extreme conditions, decomposition is much slower and virtually stops in the winter. In these environments, dead organic material can remain in the topsoil much longer without losing its nutrients. If the community is to persist, however, the processes of recycling eventually must return the nutrients in fallen leaves and other dead organic matter to the plants. ◆

Let's Ask Drs. Ricardo and Rita

Drs. Ricardo and Rita, long-time colleagues at the same university, answer questions and concerns about relationships in communities.

Dear Dr. Ricardo,

I am a biology student who has just completed drawing a food web for class. As I was making it, I learned that a food web is the sum of all feeding interactions. I've included a sample (Figure E9.9).

I understand the concept that a food web involves feeding interactions among producers, consumers, and decomposers. Producers are organisms that can make their own food by using matter and energy from the nonliving world. Consumers are organisms that feed on other organisms. Decomposers are organisms that feed on decaying organic matter.

However, I still need your help. In our food webs, we listed our producers on the bottom. Then we listed the herbivores. Above these we included the omnivores and carnivores. We also included decomposers in our webs. Because we have included virtually everylevel of interaction and type of relationship, I was wondering if this is basically what a community is?

—Juanita Perez, Eco High School

Dear Juanita,

How observant you are! You've done a terrific job of describing a community. A community is a collection of organisms that live and interact with each other in a given area. You also described what biologists call biomass. **Biomass** refers to the mass of all living organisms in a given environment. As you probably know, some herbivores may not eat an entire plant. For example, a rabbit may eat only part of a violet. A carnivore, such as a mountain lion, may not eat the bones of the rabbit. What these creatures eat is considered the **consumable biomass**.

What happens to the remaining parts of the violet and the bones of the rabbit? These types of biomass, the leftovers, often represent a substantial portion of the total amount of energy and biological material in a community. This resource does not go to waste, however. Remember the **decomposers** in your food web? These organisms (for example, fungi and bacteria) specialize in using the matter that other organisms do not consume. Though generally not as visible as the other groups, these decomposers serve a vital function in communities. They reduce dead biomass, such as the partially consumed violet and rabbit, into molecules that the producers can reuse. So, you see, you could have drawn arrows from all the creatures to the decomposers.

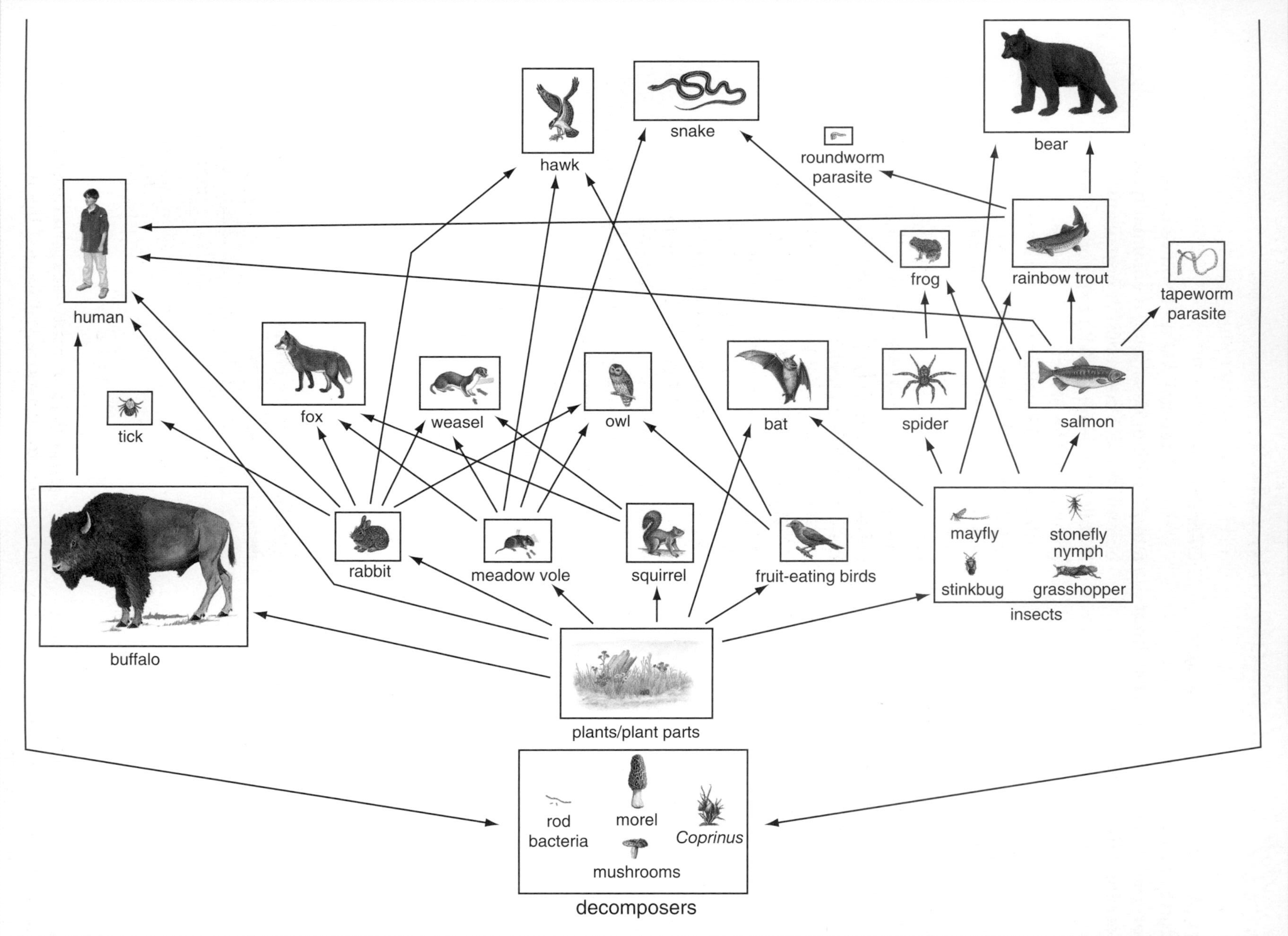

Figure E9.9 A food web. Food webs in a community can be very complex. Can you find any more relationships?

Dear Dr. Rita,

I drew a food web in my class. But I still don't understand what it means in terms of the real world. Can you make this more realistic for me?

—Alfonso Washington

Dear Alfonso,

Thanks for your comment. I would love to help. Think of a riverbed that the Ancestral Puebloans might have lived near. Study the detailed drawing of such a riverbed (Figure E9.10).

In the open water of the river, algae and microscopic water plants are the main producers. These producers are consumed by insects and small aquatic animals such as the tiger salamander and various fish. Higher-level consumers, such as the great blue heron, live by eating either first-level consumers (organisms that have eaten the producers) or smaller predators. Note that at every step in the process, some biological matter passes to the decomposers. This can be in the form of inedible plant or animal parts, organic waste products, or whole dead organisms. The decomposers then break down this matter to simple molecules that the producers can use.

The food web of the river ecosystem is based on solar energy that the producers convert into food. Not all ecosystems, however, support themselves in this manner. The seashore is a good example of a rich, natural ecosystem that is not self-supporting. Virtually all of the organisms that inhabit the zone between high and low tides are consumers. They ultimately depend on plant material and other living or dead organic matter that is brought in by each high tide. Many of the seashore creatures feed on this matter directly. For example, mussels and clams filter seawater for

cottonwoods
sycamores

willows
service-
berries
dogwoods

monkshood
elephantellas
violets
sedges

great blue herons
dippers
racoons

tiger salamander
beavers
algae
watercress

Figure E9.10   **Cross section through the edge of a riverbed in southwestern United States.**
The interactions among organisms in an ecosystem involve the cycling of matter and the flow of energy. What is the ultimate source of energy?

microscopic bits of food. Many other species are predators, such as the sea star, which preys on clams and mussels. The organisms in this community also depend on solar energy. But most of that energy is converted into food by producers that live in deeper ocean communities.

Dear Dr. Ricardo,

I keep hearing about trophic levels when people talk about food webs. What are trophic levels? Are they some sort of tool used to measure food webs? Are they important? Thanks for helping me.

—Lydia Bellissimo

Dear Lydia,

I used to be confused about trophic levels, too. Let me explain. A food web almost looks like a layered wedding cake. Each higher level has fewer organisms. The feeding level that an organism occupies is its trophic level. (This is depicted by the pyramid in Figure E9.11.)

Herbivores occupy the first trophic level in a food web. Small predators occupy the second trophic level. And larger predators occupy the third.

Producers do not belong to any trophic level because they do not eat. They can use solar energy directly to fuel their own metabolism and to produce new biomass. All other organisms are

Figure E9.11 **A pyramid of trophic levels.** Trophic levels provide one way to represent the interactions of the organisms in a community.

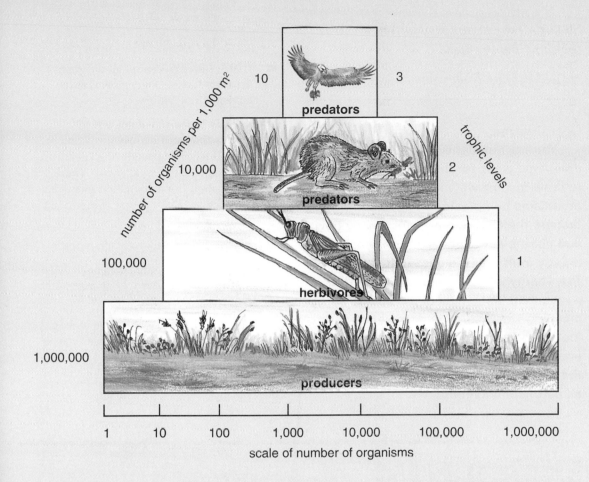

number of organisms per 1,000 m²

10   3   predators

10,000   2   predators

trophic levels

100,000   1   herbivores

1,000,000   producers

| 1 | 10 | 100 | 1,000 | 10,000 | 100,000 | 1,000,000 |

scale of number of organisms

Figure E9.12   **A pyramid of trophic levels showing numbers of organisms.**   This idealized pyramid shows the number of organisms per 1,000 square meters (1,196 square yards) of grassland habitat.

consumers. These consumers cannot make all of the biological molecules they need to build tissue and support their metabolism. After all, when was the last time you raised your arms to the sun, captured solar energy, and converted it into glycogen? We consumers can obtain chemical energy only by consuming biomass, that is, by eating other organisms. Let's use a second pyramid to demonstrate the number of consumers that occupy each trophic level (Figure E9.12).

What about omnivores? What about decomposers? What trophic levels do they occupy? They can occupy more than one. A decomposer can exist in the first trophic level when it breaks down the remaining biomass of a plant that was

partially eaten by a herbivore. The same decomposer also might exist in the third trophic level when it breaks down the bones of a carnivore. Omnivores also occupy different trophic levels. When you eat a salad and a steak for a meal, you are occupying two trophic levels. You see, organisms of a community interact with each other in many ways. One way is through acquiring food, as I've described here.

Dear Dr. Rita,
I am convinced that the food web I drew is all wrong. When I drew arrows between organisms, I pointed the arrow toward the organism that does the eating.

Shouldn't the arrow be pointing toward the thing being eaten?

—Dwayne Robertson

Dear Dwayne,

You are not alone. Often students who draw food webs for the first time want to draw the arrows pointing toward the organisms being eaten. Remember, though, the arrows represent energy flow and not the act of eating. For example, energy from grass is passed to a rabbit. The energy from the rabbit is passed to a mountain lion. Think of the arrows as meaning "the energy is passed to." A food web helps us understand the flow of energy through a community. Ultimately, the sun is the source of energy for nearly all earth communities. ◆

Did you know that . . .

☞ Thirty-three percent of all the grain harvested on earth each day is fed to livestock and poultry.

☞ It takes 16 pounds of grain and soybeans to produce just one pound of beef. It takes six pounds of grain and soybeans to produce a pound of pork, four pounds for a pound of turkey, and three pounds for a pound of eggs or a pound of chicken.

☞ There are currently 1.28 billion cattle populating the earth.

☞ Cattle graze on nearly 24 percent of the landmass of the planet.

☞ Cattle consume enough grain to feed hundreds of millions of people.

☞ Cattle grazing contributes to the increasing numbers of deserts on the earth.

Losing Heat

Each time that an organism uses energy, it loses part of the energy in the form of released heat. This means that only a portion of the solar energy that producers take up is stored in biomass that herbivores can eat. In turn, only a portion of the plant material that herbivores eat is converted into body parts that could become food for predators. Each transfer of energy from organisms at one trophic level to those at the next level results in a decrease in the amount of energy that is available.

Ecologists can estimate the amount of energy that is stored in the biomass at each trophic level. They do this by taking a sample from a community and harvesting the total biomass represented by the producers, herbivores, and higher-level consumers. They then determine the caloric value of this organic matter.

Say we begin with 1 million kcals of solar energy entering the ecosystem. Producers convert only a small fraction (0.8 percent) of it into plant biomass (see Figure E9.13). This biomass represents 8,000 kcals of stored chemical energy. The herbivores, such as the grasshoppers, incorporate only 800 kcals into their biomass. This is only 10 percent of the 8,000 kcals of plant energy available to them. Similarly, the predators, such as the mice that

What happens	Percent
Converted to heat	46.0
Reflected	30.0
Evaporation/precipitation	23.0
Photosynthesis	0.8
Wind, waves, currents	0.2
Total	100.0

Figure E9.13 What happens to the solar energy that reaches earth? Only 0.8 percent of the solar energy reaching the earth is used directly in the production of food.

feed on the herbivores, incorporate only 80 kcals into their biomass. This is 10 percent of the 800 kcals available to them. Finally, the secondary predators, such as the hawk, that feed on the first level of predators, incorporate only 8 kcals into their biomass. Again, this is 10 percent of the 80 kcals available to them. Think about this pattern of reduced energy amounts at successive trophic levels. The secondary predators acquire *only* 8 kcals of the 8,000 kcals of energy that became part of the food web at the producer level. We can use the pyramid in Figure E9.14 to illustrate the reduction in the amount of energy available.

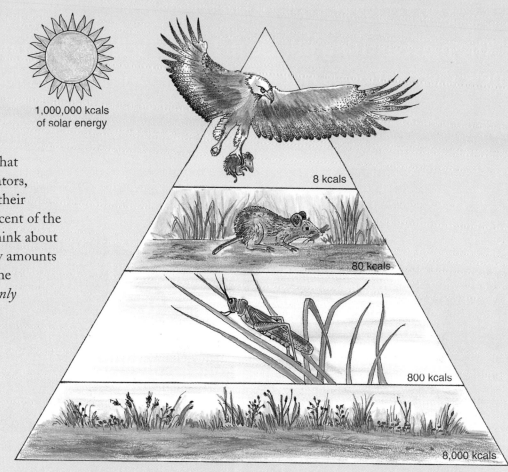

1,000,000 kcals of solar energy

8 kcals

80 kcals

800 kcals

8,000 kcals

Figure E9.14   Energy pyramid.   This idealized energy pyramid illustrates that only a portion of the energy available at one trophic level is available at the next higher trophic level.

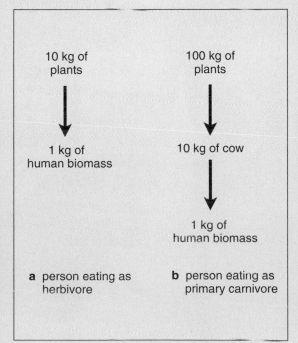

10 kg of plants

1 kg of human biomass

100 kg of plants

10 kg of cow

1 kg of human biomass

a person eating as herbivore

b person eating as primary carnivore

The flow and accompanying loss of energy from one trophic level to the next is the basis for the suggestion that people should eat lower on the food web. For example, a person eating as an herbivore can create 1 kilogram of human biomass by eating 10 kilograms of plants. It takes about 100 kilograms of plants, however, to create 1 kilogram of human biomass if the person eats as a primary carnivore. You are eating as a primary carnivore if you eat the cow that ate the plants, instead of eating the plants directly (see Figure E9.15). ◆

Figure E9.15   Human as herbivore and human as primary carnivore.   The energy relationships between trophic levels are the basis for the suggestion that people should eat low on the food chain.

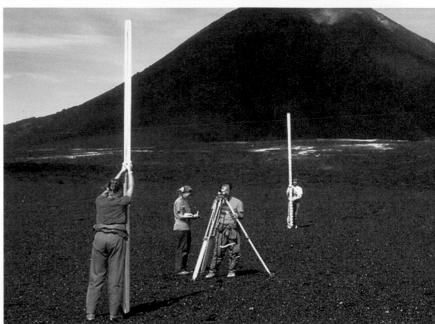

Conducting Your Own Inquiry

Science can be a career, as it is for the people pictured here. Science is a way of studying and knowing the world around you, whether you make it a career or use it to make informed decisions. In this section, you will exercise your inquiry skills. The activities throughout this course involve scientific inquiry. By now, you should have enough experience with those skills to realize that thinking scientifically is a valuable way of answering many questions. In this Explain Section, you will be asked to think like a scientist and apply your critical-thinking skills to evaluate new information.

In the activities in this section, you will look first at examples of science in the popular press and critique the coverage for adequacy. You will consider questions such as, Is the science accurate? Was the coverage complete? Do the scientists or investigating agencies have an unbiased perspective? Next, you will investigate a scientific question of your own. You will need to decide what you want to study, where you will find background information, and how you will conduct your experiment. The choices for your inquiry are yours to make.

The goals of this section are to

- give you the opportunity to evaluate new scientific information using your inquiry skills, and
- allow you to conceive, design, and conduct a scientific investigation of your own choosing.

ACTIVITIES

Engage	Science All Around You
Explore	
Explain	
Elaborate	Being an Experimental Scientist
Evaluate	

Science All Around You

One reason to study biology is to learn to use the methods of science to study the organisms, interactions, and processes around you. Another reason is to understand the events that influence your life. The article *Researchers Find Evidence That Prenatal Exposure to Ecstasy Can Cause Long-Term Memory Loss and Other Impairments in Offspring* is an example of how science and technology are often reported in a newspaper. The write-up describes experiments related to research that led to a new understanding about the drug ecstasy. What can you tell from the article about how the scientists got their results? Can you tell what questions the scientists asked?

Materials   (per person)

newspaper or news magazine
scissors
tape, stapler, or glue

PROCESS AND PROCEDURES

1. Scan the newspaper or news magazine for articles about science.

2. Cut out the article that most interests you, and attach it to a page in your journal.

3. To analyze this news article, answer the following questions in your journal:

   Base your answers on the information in the article itself and what you infer.

   ◆ What question did the scientists ask?
   ◆ What background information informed the scientists?
   ◆ What type of investigation did the scientists conduct?
   ◆ What tools did the scientists use?
   ◆ What results did the scientists get?
   ◆ What conclusions did the scientists draw?
   ◆ What new questions did the scientists ask?

Analysis

1. Discuss your article and analysis with a partner.

2. Record in your journal at least two scientific questions that you would like to research.

   These may be related to the article you analyzed or to another area of science.

SCENARIO

Researchers Find Evidence That Prenatal Exposure to Ecstasy Can Cause Long-Term Memory Loss and Other Impairments in Offspring

Researchers today reported the first evidence that a mother's use of MDMA (ecstasy) during pregnancy may result in specific types of long-term learning and memory impairments in her offspring.

The research, published in the May 1, 2001, issue of the Journal of Neuroscience, was conducted by scientists from Children's Hospital Research Foundation and the University of Cincinnati College of Medicine. The researchers administered MDMA to two groups of newborn rats. One group received ecstasy twice a day for 10 days after birth (analogous to early third-trimester brain development in humans); the other group received ecstasy twice a day during days 11 through 20 (analogous to late human third-trimester brain development). To determine the effects of ecstasy on cognitive abilities, a series of maze and swimming tests were conducted on the rats when they reached an average age of 60 days. While no cognitive changes were noted in the rats given ecstasy at an earlier age, memory and learning deficiencies were noted in the group exposed to ecstasy during days 11–20. The ecstasy-induced disruption in both sequential and spatial reference memory-based learning was long-term and was still apparent after this group reached adulthood.

"This study adds to the evidence that ecstasy is a dangerous drug. Unfortunately, its popularity remains high, in part because some individuals still perceive that taking ecstasy is safe. As its use continues, increases in the number of users who are pregnant will inevitably occur. This study indicates that users may be damaging not only their own cognitive abilities but those of their children as well," says Dr. Alan I. Leshner, former director of the National Institute on Drug Abuse.

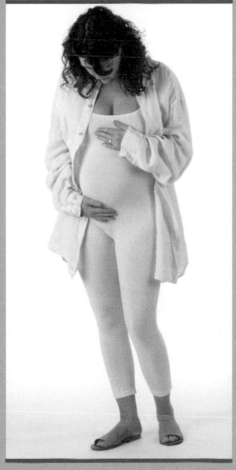

The timing of ecstasy exposure during brain development may be critical as evidenced by cognitive changes in the 11–20-day-old group. "The differences between the responses in newborn rats after MDMA administration most likely occurs because of the stage of maturation of the central nervous system at the time of exposure to MDMA," explains Dr. Vorhees, lead investigator.

He further explains that in adult animals, ecstasy exerts its effects by significantly decreasing serotonin levels and the number of re-uptake sites in the brain. However, in this study, only small changes in serotonin levels were noted in the brains of the newborn rats receiving ecstasy suggesting that developmental exposure to ecstasy may induce cognitive deficits in the fetus through different mechanisms than those of adults.

"These findings raise new concerns about ecstasy when exposure occurs during brain development in the human fetus," Dr. Vorhees concludes.

Source: NIH (National Institute on Drug Abuse), May, 2001

Being an Experimental Scientist

In the Engage Section at the beginning of this course, you investigated the way that scientists think when they do their work. You conducted experiments to test a hypothesis. Although the termite activity was not an actual situation, it was based on a realistic scenario. For this activity, you will *be* a scientist as you carry out a full inquiry of your own design. Remember that each of the *thinking* steps, such as asking a good question, deciding how to test it, and analyzing the meaning of the data you collect, is just as important as the hands-on step of *doing* an experiment. Your performance in this activity will demonstrate both your understanding of the particular area of biology that you investigate and your ability to explain and use scientific processes.

Materials   (per person)

Materials needed will depend on the experiment you design. You will need your teacher's approval before you assemble materials.

PROCESS AND PROCEDURES

Part A   Preparation

1. Use Figure Ex.1 to answer the following questions in your journal:

   a. Which of these steps were evident in the article that you analyzed in the previous activity? Give specific examples, and explain how they were evident.

   b. Identify 3–4 specific times or activities in this course when you have used these steps.

      Looking through your journal may help you answer this question.

2. Obtain from your teacher a scoring rubric for being an experimental scientist. Examine the criteria for the "excellent" categories on the rubric. Tell your partner what you think an "excellent" project would look like when it is finished, and what it would be like to complete an excellent project.

Part B   Conducting a Full Inquiry

Now you will carry out your own full inquiry by following these steps:

I. Asking the Question

1. Choose an area of biology that interests you. Identify a testable question.

   If you are having difficulty thinking of a question, look back at your response to the Analysis questions from the previous activity. Or do some library research about a topic that interests you. The new information will provide useful background and may give you an idea for a testable question.

Figure Ex.1
The processes of science: asking questions, gathering information, and proposing explanations.

a. In your journal, record the question in 1 or 2 sentences.

b. Explain why your question is significant.

To do this, you will need to write several sentences describing what already is known about the topic that you wish to investigate.

c. Restate your question as a hypothesis that can be tested.

d. Record which of the 6 unifying principles of biology (see need to know box below) is most related to your hypothesis.

NEED TO KNOW

Unifying Principles of Biology

Which of these principles is related to your inquiry?

Evolution: Patterns and Products of Change in Living Systems

Homeostasis: Maintaining Dynamic Equilibrium in Living Systems

Energy, Matter, and Organization: Relationships in Living Systems

Continuity: Reproduction and Inheritance in Living Systems

Development: Growth and Differentiation in Living Systems

Ecology: Interaction and Interdependence in Living Systems

2. Show your question to your teacher for approval before you proceed.

II. Gathering Information

1. Use the library, local scientists, the Internet, or other available resources to gather information related to your question.

Scientists use data that others collect as well as data that they gather directly through experimental investigations. You should use a similar process at this time.

2. Design an experiment to test or answer your question by doing the following:

a. Describe your experimental design in your journal and include these sections:

◆ Rationale, that is, how this experiment will test your question (include a description of your controls and the role that they will play)

◆ Hypothesis (explain what you think the answer to your question may be and why you think so)

◆ Procedure (include the materials you will need)

◆ Data analysis (explain how you will analyze the data)

Your teacher may have specific suggestions about the length of time that you will have or the equipment that is available.

b. Write in your journal a safety plan for your experiment. In your procedures, record the precautions that you will follow when you

- ◆ use chemicals,

- ◆ handle equipment, and

- ◆ handle biological hazards such as bacteria or yeast.

Ask your teacher to explain any hazards that you do not understand. Your teacher should also help you identify the precautions necessary to prevent harm from an accident.

Review Appendix A, *Laboratory Safety*, on pages 683–689. Be sure that you understand all the safety considerations involved in your experimental design. Make sure that you have read and understood the hazards and precautions described on the labels and Material Safety Data Sheets for all the chemicals you plan to use in your experiment. Report all accidents, no matter how small, to your teacher.

3. Discuss your library research, experimental design, and safety plan with your teacher before you continue. If your plans are reasonable and safe, your teacher will approve further work.

4. When you have your teacher's approval, carry out the experiment you have designed to test your hypothesis.

Remember, record data carefully in your journal. Use the proper controls to make it a valid test.

Figure Ex.2 Scientists protect themselves by following safety procedures while working in the laboratory. What safety precautions has this scientist taken?

III. Analyzing Your Data

1. Organize your data in a way that makes it easier to see patterns or understand what the data show you (see Figure Ex.3).

This step will help you when you present your work in Part V.

2. Decide what your data tell you, and record your preliminary conclusions. Include a description of any limitations of your experimental design and any unexpected results that you may have found.

IV. Drawing Conclusions

1. In your journal, explain what your conclusions indicate about the question you asked.

Support your conclusions by making specific references to your data.

2. Describe how your work connects to the unifying principle most related to your inquiry.

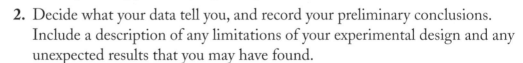

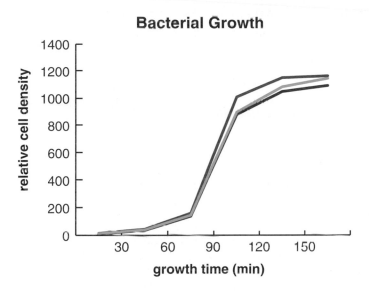

Bacterial Growth

Figure Ex.3   Bacterial growth graph.   Graphs can be a useful way to display data. This graph shows the growth profile of three different bacterial strains. Can any of your data be presented conveniently using a graph?

V. Communicating Your Results

1. Assemble a presentation of your full inquiry that makes it possible for someone else to understand what you did, why you did it, and what you found out.

    A poster, a written or verbal report, or a videotape are some examples of how you can communicate your results.

2. Be sure to identify the connections between your inquiry and the following aspects of biology:

    ◆ The unifying principles of biology

    ◆ Technology

    ◆ Culture

    ◆ History

    ◆ Ethics

    All inquiries will have connections to at least 1 of the unifying principles of biology. However, your inquiry may not have connections to all of the other aspects of biology. If you cannot identify a technological, historical, cultural, or ethical connection relevant to your inquiry, explain this in your presentation.

3. As you listen to other students present their results, look for evidence or examples that illustrate why the approach they took to answering their question was scientific.

UNIT
4

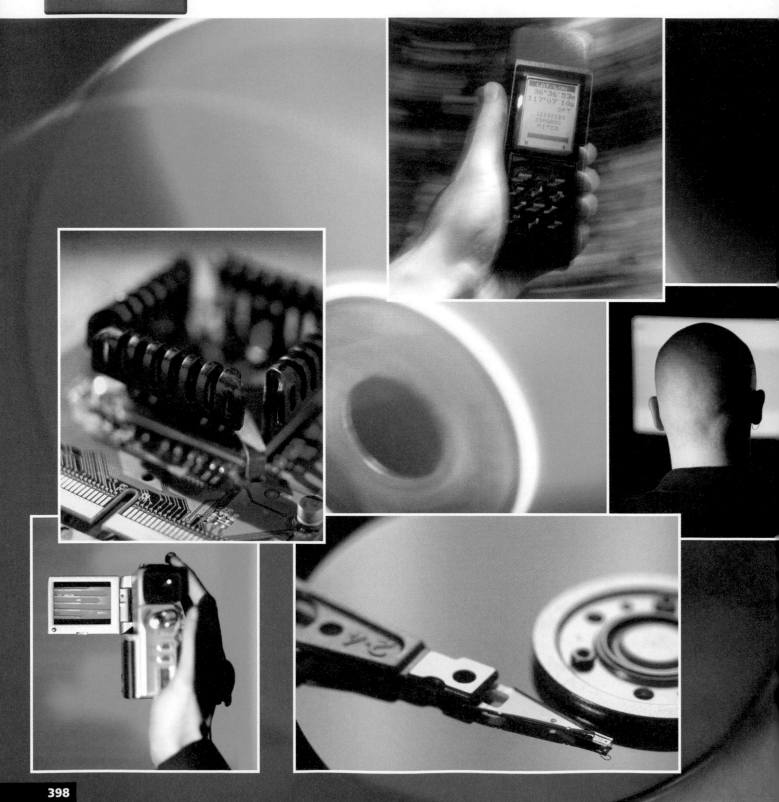

Continuity:
Reproduction
and Inheritance
in Living Systems

What do the items and organisms shown in this collage have in common? Consider how each can store or transfer information, or do both. Though each thing stores or transfers information, how it does that varies a great deal. In this unit, you will explore the idea of continuity. You will examine the complex mechanisms that make the storage and transfer of genetic information possible in living organisms.

By the end of this unit, you will be able to

- explain that the continuity of a species depends on the transfer of genetic information,

- compare different strategies for how information is transferred and preserved through reproduction,

- describe the structure of genetic material,

- explain how genetic information is expressed,

- illustrate how sexual reproduction and mutation increase genetic variation and why this is important for the evolution of a species,

- realize that human reproduction takes place within a cultural setting and involves ethical issues, and

- appreciate the current and potential impact that genetic engineering technology has on our lives.

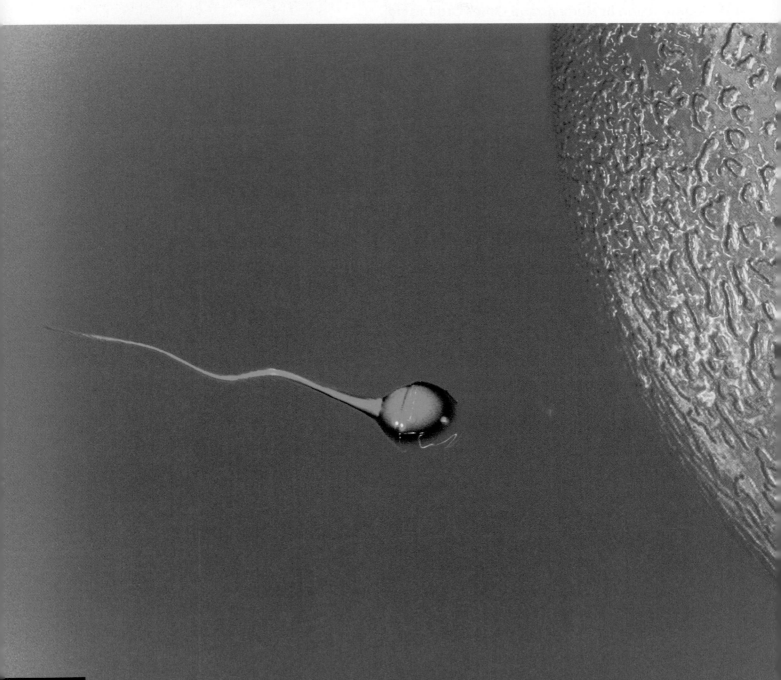

"If a single cell, under appropriate conditions, becomes a man in the space of a few years, there can surely be no difficulty in understanding how, under appropriate conditions, a cell may, in the course of untold millions of years, give origin to the human race."

Herbert Spencer, 1820–1903, English philosopher

Reproduction in Humans and Other Organisms

Chapter 10

This photograph captures the moment of fertilization as a human sperm makes its way into an ovum. While technology has made new fertilization methods possible, all human development begins with the union of genetic information from two individuals. Not all organisms begin this way, however. Among the diversity of organisms, there are several ways to make more offspring. Certain organisms are even capable of reproducing by themselves, without another organism contributing. In this chapter, you will explore concepts about reproduction in general and about human reproduction, specifically. As you do so, you will consider how reproduction contributes to both the continuation of life on earth and the continuity of species.

ACTIVITIES

Engage	A Zillion Ways to Make More
Explore	Making Sense of Reproductive Strategies
Explain	Making Sense of Human Reproduction
Elaborate	Observing Reproductive Behavior in Nonhuman Animals
Elaborate	Cultural Influences on Human Mating Behavior
Evaluate	A Reproductive Strategy for Your Critter

A Zillion Ways to Make More

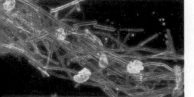

You probably know how humans reproduce. But have you considered how squid or seaweed reproduce? Humans are just one of millions of organisms on earth that reproduce. Let's see what you really know about reproduction. This activity will introduce you to several of the reproductive strategies that exist.

Materials

DVD and player

PROCESS AND PROCEDURES

1. How does a small cluster of trees become a forest? To begin thinking about that question, read *The Aspen Story*.

2. What other ways are there to make more? To give you some idea of the range of reproductive strategies and behaviors that exist, watch the DVD segment "What's Going on Here?" Think about what is happening in each of the images.

Analysis

Now that you have begun to think about how organisms reproduce, create a concept map in your journal that shows what the term *biological continuity* means to you at this point in your study of biology. Begin your map as shown in Figure 10.1. Add other factors that represent your current understanding of biological continuity. Leave room to add more concepts and to make changes to your map later in the chapter. Be sure to include descriptors on the links between concepts that explain how the ideas are related.

This concept map is a way for you to record your *early* ideas on the subject. You will refer back to it and reflect on how your view changes as you work through this chapter and unit.

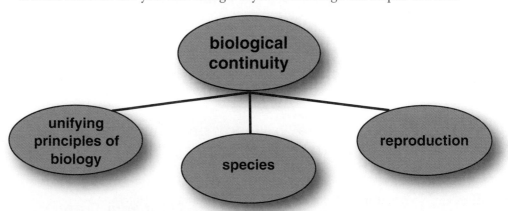

Figure 10.1 Biological continuity. In your journal, begin your concept map with the elements pictured here. Add other factors that represent your understanding of what biological continuity means at this point. You will build on this map throughout the unit. Be sure to include descriptors on the links between concepts that explain how the ideas are related.

The Aspen Story

The pleasant fragrance of evergreen trees surrounded the small group of students and their teacher. They had stopped by a stream for a rest before continuing their field trip.

"How tall is that tree?" Kim asked, pointing at a ponderosa pine.

"Oh, I'd say around 100 feet tall," estimated the teacher. "Is that the largest tree you see here?"

"Yeah, but it's not all that big," observed another student, Paul. "Last summer I went to Yosemite Park in California, and they've got huge trees there, called sequoias. They're much taller than this."

"How do you know?" the teacher asked Paul.

"Well, there were pine trees like this nearby, and the sequoia just towered over them. And the trunk was much thicker, like five or 10 of these other pines put together. And the big sequoias are old. I read that some are close to 2,000 years old," Paul replied.

"Wow! Think of how many cones and new trees it must have made during that length of time," said Maria. "It's amazing the whole forest wasn't just sequoias!"

"Look at this cluster of trees with the heart-shaped leaves," the teacher said. "Does anyone know what they are?" asked the teacher.

"Aspens," several students said simultaneously.

"Well, here's a puzzle: If I tell you this aspen is even bigger than the sequoia, how could that be true?"

"I know! I read about that in a magazine," Meagan said. "All these aspen trees are really like branches coming off one giant tree trunk underground. Some parts die, but others grow up from the underground part that connects them all. So this whole group of aspens is really just one big tree."

"Then how do you explain that lone one over there?" Kim asked, pointing to a tree on a slope far beyond the stream.

"Aspens can also grow new individuals from seeds in the same way that oaks and pines reproduce," explained the teacher. "That one probably is a separate tree, not part of the cluster here."

"So if that lone tree grows some more tree-looking sprouts from its roots, has it reproduced?" Paul asked.

"What do you think?" his teacher asked in return.

Making Sense of Reproductive Strategies

Explore

Reproduction, the making of offspring, is an essential process for the continuation of a species. But is it essential for an individual? In humans, reproduction requires the genetic information from a male and a female. Is that true of all species? To begin to answer these questions and to develop your understanding of reproduction, you will look at similarities and differences in the reproductive strategies of a number of species.

Materials   (per team of 2)

2 reproduction cards
felt-tipped marking pen
large sheet of paper or poster board

Figure 10.2 Make your presentation interesting and informative. Before you present, practice pronouncing the names of your organisms and the terms used to describe their reproductive strategies. If either of your organisms is unusual, be prepared to describe it for your classmates.

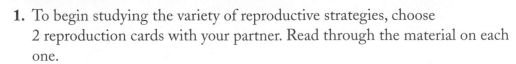

PROCESS AND PROCEDURES

1. To begin studying the variety of reproductive strategies, choose 2 reproduction cards with your partner. Read through the material on each one.

   Your teacher will provide these cards. The glossary on page 705 will help with unfamiliar terms.

2. With your partner, look for similarities and differences in the reproductive strategies described on your cards. Record this information in your journal.

3. Prepare a short (3- to 5-minute) presentation that compares and contrasts the reproductive strategies of the 2 organisms that you and your partner studied. In your presentation, answer the following questions:

   a. What are some characteristics of each organism's reproductive strategies?

      You might include these characteristics:

      ◆ Number of offspring produced during each reproductive cycle

      ◆ Frequency of the reproductive cycle

      ◆ Structures that are involved in reproduction

      ◆ Age of sexual maturity

      ◆ Length of gestation

      ◆ Length of the period of offspring dependency

      ◆ Life span of individuals

      ◆ Mating behaviors

   b. How are the reproductive strategies similar? How are they different?

   c. What are the advantages and disadvantages of the reproductive strategies of your 2 organisms?

      For example, consider the amount of time and energy each strategy requires and the survival rate for the offspring.

   d. How does each strategy ensure survival of the species?

      The essay *Continuity through Reproduction* on page 474 has important background information to help you with this task. Your teacher may have other resources available for you as well.

PAGE 474

4. Create a visual diagram to use with your presentation.

   Make your presentation interesting and informative. Practice pronouncing the names of your organisms and the terms used to describe their reproductive strategies before you present. If either of your organisms is unusual, be prepared to describe it so that your classmates have an idea of what it is like.

5. Make your presentation to the rest of your classmates.

   As you listen to the other presentations, take notes in your journal. Record the similarities, differences, and patterns in reproductive strategies.

6. When the presentations are finished, participate in a class discussion of the patterns that are emerging.

7. Read the essay *Cloning* on page 476 for background information about laboratory cloning techniques. In your journal, explain the difference between *somatic cell nuclear transfer* and *fertilization*.

PAGE 476

8. In your journal, make a list of 3 concepts related to reproduction and continuity that you think are important to the study of biology.

   Consider general ideas about reproduction rather than reproductive structures. For example, you might list the idea that reproduction can be a sexual or an asexual process.

9. Add your 3 concepts from step 8 to the concept map on biological continuity that you started in the previous activity. Include appropriate descriptions for how the concepts are related.

10. Compare your concept map with your partner's. Discuss any differences or similarities that you see. Make any additions to your concept map that reflect your current understanding of biological continuity.

Analysis

Complete the first item as a class. Then complete the two remaining items individually.

1. Participate in a class discussion and construction of a biological continuity concept map.

   Contribute ideas and explanations from your own concept map.

2. Think about the following questions. Record your responses in your journal.

   a. Is reproduction necessary for the survival of an individual? Explain.

   b. Is reproduction necessary for the survival of a species? Explain.

   c. Explain the relationship between changes in a species' environment and the effectiveness of that species' reproductive strategies.

      Consider whether a species' reproductive strategies might change over time. How might fast or slow changes in the environment affect those changes?

3. Explain the connection between natural selection and reproduction in a way that describes their importance to biological continuity.

NEED TO KNOW

Background Information: A Glossary of Reproduction Terms

Figure 10.3
Two examples of asexual reproduction in a plant and an animal.
(a) The sprout on the potato grew from a bud that can produce an entirely new potato plant. (b) If cells from the central body remain on a severed arm, the sea star can regenerate a new body from the one arm.

Asexual reproduction involves the growth of a new organism without the fusion of nuclei (which occurs in sexual reproduction). Asexual reproduction usually involves one parent and leads to offspring that are genetically identical to each other. Growing a new plant from a cutting is an example of asexual reproduction.

Binary fission is the division of a cell into two cells of equivalent size. It involves a replication of genetic material (DNA) in the parent cell before the cell divides. Binary fission is asexual. It is the chief means of asexual reproduction in prokaryotic cells.

Budding is a type of asexual reproduction. Here new individuals begin as outgrowths on the body of a single parent. The offspring eventually separates from the parent and becomes independent.

Cloning is another type of asexual reproduction. Here new individuals receive genetic information from a single parent cell. The resulting offspring is genetically identical to the parent.

Fertilization is the fusion of nuclei from two gametes during sexual reproduction. The result is one nucleus in a zygote.

Fragmentation is a type of asexual reproduction. Here a piece broken from a parent organism grows into a new individual.

Gametes are special reproductive cells. They are produced in eukaryotes through a type of cell division called *meiosis.* Each gamete contains only one set of unpaired chromosomes. This is half as much genetic information as a body cell. During sexual reproduction, the nuclei of gametes fuse and become the first cell of the offspring (called a *zygote*).

Gestation is the internal incubation of embryos or the carrying of young, usually in a uterus, from conception until delivery.

Meiosis is a special process of cell division in eukaryotes. It produces reproductive cells known as gametes. Each gamete contains only one set of unpaired chromosomes. This is half as much genetic information as a body cell.

Mitosis is the production of two identical nuclei in one cell. This is usually followed by the cell dividing into two cells. Each new cell that results from a mitotic division has the same genetic makeup as the original cell. Asexual reproduction in most unicellular protists occurs by mitosis. Cell growth in multicellular organisms also takes place by mitosis.

Ova (singular: **ovum**) are the gametes that females produce. Also known as eggs, ova are larger than sperm. They contain substances that influence the zygote's early development. Eggs also contain organelles that pass on to the offspring and nutrients needed to sustain the earliest stages of a developing organism.

Sexual reproduction involves the fusion of the nuclei of two gametes. Most often, the gametes are produced from two parents. Because each parent contributes information, the offspring of sexual reproduction are not genetically identical to either parent.

Sperm are the gametes that males produce. They consist of a compact nucleus surrounded by a membrane, a flagellum for propulsion, mitochondria that provide energy, and a small sac at the tip containing enzymes that help them penetrate the ovum.

Spores are asexual reproductive cells that can develop directly into a complete organism. By contrast, most gametes must join with another gamete before development can take place.

Sporulation is the process of reproducing asexually by producing spores that grow directly into new individuals.

Vegetative reproduction involves parts of an organism that are not specialized for sexual reproduction. Examples include fragmentation, budding, and sprouting from roots as aspen trees do or sprouting from runners as strawberries do.

Zygotes are the cells that result from the fusion of gamete nuclei. A zygote is produced when an ovum and a sperm unite to form a fertilized egg. Zygotes contain a full set of genetic information. They receive half from each parent's gamete.

Making Sense of Human Reproduction

Explain

SCENARIO

Family Planning: A Historical Perspective

Since ancient times, people have attempted to regulate the size of their families. Their reasons were as varied as the families themselves. These reasons included cultural, social, physical, emotional, and economic considerations. A 4,000-year-old papyrus (a written scroll) found near the Nile River delta documents the first known use of artificial birth control. It prescribed a recipe for a substance that would block the cervix, to be applied in the vagina before intercourse. Egyptian illustrations of a condom, drawn 3,000 years ago, provide the earliest evidence for condom use.

In the 1800s, the *rhythm method* was a common practice. (Using this method, one calculates when a woman is ready to conceive and abstains from intercourse at that time.) It was not effective, however, because little was known about the menstrual cycle. Based on observing other mammals, it was thought that women were most likely to conceive during menstruation. It was not until the late 1920s that Carl Hartman, a reproductive biologist, established that ovulation in humans occurs midway between menstrual cycles.

Today, scientists have developed a variety of effective birth control methods that can be used by men and women to prevent pregnancies. As we continue to learn more about the human body, birth control devices and methods continue to become safer and more reliable.

In most mammals, females and males are drawn to mate by powerful instincts that happen only when the female's body is ready to conceive. In humans and some other primates, however, the female may be receptive to sexual activity at any time. Her body, however, can conceive only for a short time during each menstrual cycle. Humans differ from other mammals in that we understand that intercourse can lead to conception.

As scientists better understood the biology of the human reproductive system, that knowledge led to improved birth control methods through new technologies. Your task in this activity is to explain the *biological basis* for birth control methods. In other words, you will explain how birth control technologies work and *why* they differ in their degree of effectiveness. You also will explain how the chances for conception might be improved for couples hoping to conceive. To complete this task, you will have a variety of resources.

Materials   (per person)

art supplies (colored paper, markers, etc.)
DVD and player (watch as a class)

PROCESS AND PROCEDURES

As you work, use the following resources, as well as others that you have available, to help you complete this activity:

PAGE 477

PAGE 481

PAGE 484

◆ The NOVA video *Miracle of Life* (The first half shows events related to fertilization.)

◆ The essays *Making More People* on page 477, *Hormones and Sexual Reproduction* on page 481, and *Sexual Activity and Health Hazards* on page 484

◆ The DVD segments "Human Menstrual Cycle" and "Conception"

◆ Additional materials (Your teacher may supply these, or you may find them on your own.)

SC**LINKS**®
NSTA
Topic: birth control
Go to: www.scilinks.org
Code: human3E408

1. Classify the birth control methods from the examples in the need to know box. Place them into the following categories: physical barriers, chemical methods, and behavioral methods.

   In your journal, record the birth control methods and the way that you classified them. Remember that you have a variety of resources to help you decide how to categorize these methods.

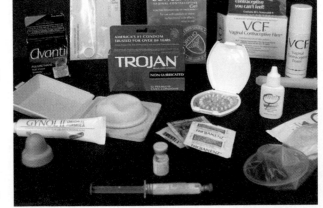

Figure 10.4 Categorize the birth control methods listed in the need to know box into three categories: physical barriers, chemical methods, and behavioral methods.

2. Using the available resources, prepare a brochure about 1 contraceptive method from each category in step 1. Your brochure should give the *biological* explanation for how the contraceptive methods work.

NEED TO KNOW

EXAMPLES OF BIRTH CONTROL METHODS

Device/method	Description	Failure rate* (pregnancies per 100 women per year)
Abstinence	Abstaining from sexual contact. (Completely prevents sexual transmission of AIDS.)	0
Cervical cap	Small dome-shaped rubber cap that is inserted through the vagina to closely cover the opening entrance to uterus (cervix).	22.0
Condom	Thin sheath made of latex or animal skin that is placed over the penis. Often coated with spermicide. *Only latex* will help protect against AIDS. **	7.3 (if spermicide is not used) ***
Diaphragm	Flexible wire circle covered with latex that is placed over entrance to uterus (cervix). Generally used with spermicide.	10.0 (if spermicide is not used) ***
Douche	Vagina is rinsed after sexual activity.	40.0
Injectable progesterone-like substance	An injection for females that lasts up to 3 months. May cause menstrual irregularities.	1.0
Implant devices	Capsules containing synthetic progesterone that are inserted surgically under a female's skin. They slowly release hormones for 3–5 years.	1.0
Intrauterine device (IUD)	Small plastic or copper device placed (by a physician) inside the uterus. Effective for 10 years. Probably causes mild inflammation of uterine wall.	1.0
Natural family planning (rhythm method)	Systematic monitoring and recording of data to determine time of ovulation. Then abstaining from sexual intercourse for several days around the time of ovulation.	26.0
Oral contraceptives (birth control pills)	Synthetic estrogen and synthetic progesterone (or progesterone only) that a female takes in tablet form throughout menstrual cycle.	0.3
Spermicide	Foam, cream, jelly, or suppository preparations that contain chemicals that kill sperm. Spermicides are placed in the vagina prior to sexual activity.	15.0 (if used alone)
Tubal ligation (sterilization)	Oviducts in female are surgically severed and tied off.	0.5
Vasectomy (sterilization)	Vas deferens in male is surgically severed and tied off.	0.6

*Failure rate can be *much* higher if the method is not used properly. For example, if the condom is used *after* sexual intercourse has begun, some sperm already may have been released.

**Natural membrane condoms, as compared with latex condoms, have larger micropores. These condoms may permit passage of pathogens such as HIV.

***Combined use of spermicide with condom or diaphragm is more effective than either of these methods used alone.

You will know you have developed a good brochure if you do each of the following:

◆ Describe how each birth control method interferes with reproduction.

◆ Explain how each method affects the reproductive systems of males or females. (For example, does the method alter the hormonal levels of the male? the female?)

◆ Explain why each method needs to be used at a particular time.

◆ Explain the differences in the effectiveness of the methods that you chose in each category.

You can develop 1 brochure that describes all of the methods, or 1 brochure for each method. Remember, your goal is to show that you understand the *biology* behind these methods. For example, you will discuss how birth control pills influence the hormone cycles during the menstrual cycle.

Analysis

Join the class in a discussion of the following:

1. The word *progesterone* means "to promote gestation." *Estrogen* means "to generate estrus." Explain why these are appropriate names. What do you think the prefix *contra-*, as in *contraception*, means?

2. Explain the role that gametes play in sexual reproduction. How do they ensure the *continuity of information* that must take place for a species to survive?

3. Consider the rhythm method of birth control. Explain how a couple that desires children could modify and use it to increase the chances of conception.

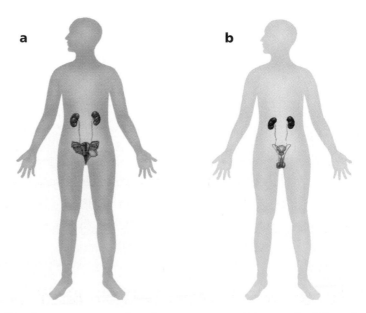

Figure 10.5   The human reproductive system.   (a) Female (b) Male

4. Imagine that a couple wants to have children. But tests show that the man has a low sperm count and the female has blocked oviducts. Read the short essay *Infertility* on page 486 for background information. In your journal, explain whether the use of pharmaceutical drugs alone will improve their chances for beginning a pregnancy.

PAGE 486

Further Challenges

1. Research and report on current progress in developing oral contraceptives for men.

2. Research and report on current technological methods that are being used to assist couples who are having difficulties conceiving a child.

Observing Reproductive Behavior in Nonhuman Animals

Elaborate

Throughout the animal kingdom, the males and females of many species put on a show of behavior aimed at attracting a mate. When a peacock wants to attract a peahen, he displays his extravagant plumage, he struts, and he shakes his colorful tail. Similarly, a male elk (bull elk) calls out loudly (bugles) during mating season. The bugling of a bull elk has at least two effects. It attracts potential mates, and it announces his presence to other bulls with the goal of steering them away. Such animal displays often are showy and complicated. **Ethologists** are biologists who develop and test hypotheses about animal behavior. They are interested in learning more about the connections between various behaviors and mating. In this activity, you will observe some animals' mating behaviors and explore the costs and benefits these behaviors have for individuals and populations.

Materials

DVD and player

PROCESS AND PROCEDURES

1. Study the mating behavior of the animals in the DVD segment "Animal Mating Behaviors." In your journal, record your observations.

2. Read the essay *Mating Behaviors of Nonhuman Animals* on page 486. Take brief notes about the advantages and disadvantages of showy mating behavior.

PAGE 486

Analysis

Work individually to answer the following questions. Record your responses in your journal.

Topic: mating behaviors
Go to: www.scilinks.org
Code: human3E412

1. List three showy mating behaviors in nonhuman animals that were not used as examples in the essay *Mating Behaviors of Nonhuman Animals*.

2. For each of the mating behavior examples listed above, explain one benefit and one cost each behavior brings to the individual organisms or populations who exhibit the behavior.

   Refer specifically to the behaviors that you have chosen. Explain whether the costs and benefits affect the individual, the population, or both.

Elaborate

Cultural Influences on Human Mating Behavior

In the activity *Making Sense of Human Reproduction*, you explained the physical aspects of human reproduction and how it is regulated. In this activity, you will extend that understanding to include cultural behaviors that are associated with human reproduction.

Materials (per team of 4)

scissors
poster board or large sheets of paper
materials collected earlier
tape or glue

Figure 10.6   A Hmong couple.   The traditional marital union of Hmong families includes rituals that resolve any existing conflicts between clans and sets rules for the future. (Clans are families that share the same paternal ancestry.) Traditional Hmong marriages are arranged according to customary patterns of authority and respect.

PROCESS AND PROCEDURES

1. Use the materials that you have collected to create a display that demonstrates various cultural behaviors associated with human reproduction. You may focus on either American (USA) culture or another culture that you know something about. Include characteristics of human behavior that you think are similar to those of other animals and those that you think are distinctive.

   Include at least 5 different types of cultural influences on your poster. Consider both modern influences, like the subtle messages included in television commercials, and long-standing influences that have been in our culture for many generations.

   Read and use the 2 essays *Human Mating Behaviors* (page 489) and *Cultures and Mating Patterns* (page 489), and any other valid resource to support your claims. Reading about cultures other than your own helps you realize the variety of patterns that exist. This often helps you observe your own culture more objectively.

PAGE 489   PAGE 489

2. Set up your display in your classroom.

3. Study the displays of other teams. Look for patterns in the cultural influences that lead to human mating behaviors.

   Remember that you are looking for patterns about behaviors that might lead to mating, not about the mechanisms of mating.

Analysis

Work in your team to respond to the following. Record your responses in your journal, and be prepared to discuss your responses with the class.

1. List the various aspects of American culture that you think most influence human mating behaviors today. For example, you may think American music has an important influence.

2. Compare and contrast human mate selection in the United States 200 years ago with mate selection today. Explain three specific examples of changes in American culture that contributed to differences in mate selection now and then.

Figure 10.7
What might these images convey about mate selection in American culture?

Further Challenges

1. An ongoing debate in the scientific community is whether or not most human sexual behavior is biologically based. Research the scientific literature to learn about this debate. Report the conclusions that your evidence supports.

2. In the United States, families historically use the surname of the father. Perhaps for this reason, Americans may think automatically of the male as the head of the household. That view, however, is changing as most women now work outside the home. Males do not play the same role in all cultures. For instance, among some Native American tribes in the Pacific Northwest, each tribe is composed of clans that are linked through the mothers' lines.

    Consider the following observations. Then discuss how societies draw their conclusions about the importance of men and women.

    ◆ A human embryo automatically develops with female characteristics unless it receives male hormones such as testosterone very soon after conception.

    ◆ The ancient Greek philosopher Aristotle suggested that the female is a defective male because she does not have a penis.

Evaluate

A Reproductive Strategy for Your Critter

When one egg sac of a spider hatches, swarms of tiny spiders emerge. Although there are huge numbers of spiders born, each one lives a relatively short time. In contrast, an elephant gives birth to one baby. But this young elephant has the potential to live for almost a century. In both cases, mechanisms exist that provide for a continuation of the species, even though the individual organisms eventually will die. In this activity, you will demonstrate and evaluate what you have learned about reproduction.

Figure 10.8 Many spiders are born at one time, but each spider has a short life span.

Materials   (per person)

your critter
blank paper

PROCESS AND PROCEDURES

1. Revisit the critter that you discovered earlier this year. Think about how it might reproduce. To give you sufficient opportunities to show everything that you have learned from this chapter, your critter must reproduce, either sexually or asexually.

   Consider the habitat where it lives and the factors that likely would lead to a successful reproductive strategy. Use your journal notes, the essays, and DVD segments to help you develop complete ideas.

2. Obtain a critter rubric from your teacher, and study the criteria. Participate in a class discussion about the criteria for this project.

3. Write a detailed description of your critter's reproduction method. You may be creative and invent new reproductive strategies for your critter. However, you must be able to logically explain the biological basis for the strategy and demonstrate your knowledge. Be sure to address the following:

   ◆ The reproductive structures involved

   ◆ A description of the role that hormones and other factors play in regulating reproduction

   ◆ An explanation of the mating behaviors it uses to ensure the production of offspring

   ◆ An analysis of the advantages and disadvantages for the number of offspring produced, their approximate life span, and the nurturing they receive

   ◆ How the organism's overall method of reproduction compares and contrasts with human reproduction

   You may want to include a drawing or diagram with your description.

Analysis

   Return to the concept map for biological continuity that you started at the beginning of this chapter. Study the ideas and relationships that it represents. Think about how your understanding has increased, and add three or four more ideas or relationships to your map. Make any necessary changes so that your concept map accurately shows your current understanding of biological continuity. Either add these ideas and changes to your existing diagram or create a new one that your teacher can read and evaluate easily.

> "It is certainly desirable to be well descended, but the glory belongs to our ancestors."
>
> *Plutarch (AD 46–AD 120)*, Morals, *AD 100*

Continuity of Information through Inheritance

Chapter 11

Are there certain distinct traits that many members of your family share? For example, some families might refer to a distinct chin type that shows up from generation to generation as the *family chin*. Look at this photograph. Can you identify any similarities between members of the different generations? In this chapter, you will begin to explore the processes involved in the transfer of genetic information. You will investigate what the results mean for various populations of organisms, including humans.

For instance, you will learn how a disease was inherited by several generations of royal families in Europe. You will see how this disease was especially tragic for the family of Nicholas and Alexandra Romanov, the last czar and czarina of Russia. You also will learn how the laws of probability make it possible to predict trait inheritance, how cellular processes account for patterns of inheritance, and how genetic concepts explain much of human variation.

ACTIVITIES

Engage	Gifts from Your Parents
Explore	Game of Chance
Explore / **Explain**	Patterns of Inheritance
Explain	Understanding Inherited Patterns
Explain / **Elaborate**	Can You Sort It Out?
Elaborate	The Genetic Basis of Human Variation
Evaluate	Continuity and Change

Gifts from Your Parents

"You have your mother's nose." "You smile just like your grandfather." "You'll be as handsome as your uncle." Comments such as those often are heard when families get together. They remind us of the biological link from one generation to the next. The processes of reproduction ensure that species can survive through many generations. Exactly what is it that survives? It is not the organism itself. Because, regardless of species, all organisms eventually die. Yet, the survival of a species or a family line shows that something is handed down from parents to offspring.

Throughout this chapter, you will investigate the mechanisms of inheritance that underlie reproduction. As you work, consider what biological mechanisms exist that allow families to continue and species to survive even though individuals die.

SCENARIO

A Royal Tragedy

In 1904, a great wave of celebration and public enthusiasm swept through the vast Russian Empire. At long last, after four successive daughters, the czar and czarina produced a son—an heir to the throne. This little boy, who was given the name Alexis, seemed destined for a great future. In addition to having been born heir to the throne of the world's largest country, he was kin to many of the royal and aristocratic families then existing in Europe. His great grandmother, Victoria, who died only 3 years before, reigned as Queen of England for more than half a century. That was the period when the British Empire reached its greatest heights of power and influence. The kings of England and of Spain, the prince of Prussia, and the kaiser of Germany all were cousins of Alexis on different family branches. His own mother, Czarina Alexandra, was the daughter of one grand duke of Hesse and the sister of another. Even though the huge empire of his father,

Nicholas II, was troubled by unrest, everyone expected that this new little heir would provide a sense of stability as he and the new century grew together. In time he would preside over a more modern and progressive Russia.

Unfortunately, the little boy was not well. He had been born with hemophilia A. In this disease, the blood clots so slowly that the person can bleed to death from a minor injury. Today, treatments are available that allow people with hemophilia to lead fairly normal lives. But this was not the case in little Alexis's time. For him, even the most minor childhood accidents meant bouts of painful and potentially fatal illness.

Czar Nicholas was so obsessed with the poor health of his only son that he failed to devote adequate attention to the many problems of Russia. The boy's mother, Czarina Alexandra, became even more preoccupied than the czar. She may have been tormented by the possibility that her son's illness came to him from her side of the

In this activity, you will study how genetic information transfers from one generation to the next. Specifically, you will examine the biological inheritance of one trait in the family of the last czar of Russia.

PROCESS AND PROCEDURES

1. Read *A Royal Tragedy*. This story describes a disease that was inherited through several famous families.

2. Discuss the following questions as a class:

   a. How did the young czarevitch come to have hemophilia?

   b. How is it possible that the mother and father showed no signs of the disease?

   c. Suggest some traits that people acquire during their lifetime. What is the difference between acquired traits and inherited traits?

   d. How might cultural practices have influenced the frequency of hemophilia occurring among the czar's family?

family. A number of male relatives in different branches of her family were afflicted or had been afflicted, including one of her brothers (see the pedigree shown in Figure 11.1). Desperate, the czarina became an easy victim for a succession of quacks and mystics whose undue influence at court was viewed with suspicion and alarm by regular government officials and the nation at large. Indeed, the preoccupation of the czar's family with Alexis's hemophilia may have contributed to the downward spiral of social disorder that triggered the Russian Revolution of 1917. Ultimately, this revolution led to the murder of the entire imperial family by agents of the Bolsheviks in July of 1918.

The story of young Alexis and his family is filled with drama and tragedy. It also illustrates a number of features about the inheritance of biological traits in both humans and other complex organisms. In this chapter, we take a closer look at the basic systems that govern both the continuity and change of genetic information.

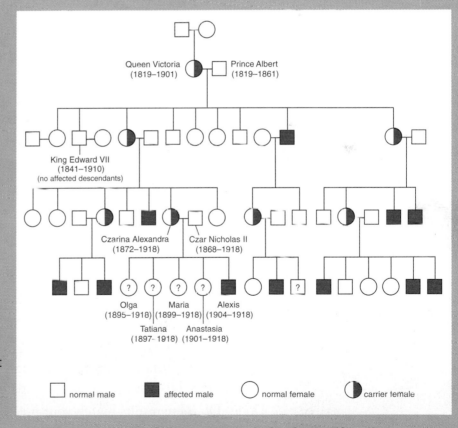

Figure 11.1   Hemophilia in Czarevitch Alexis's family.
A pedigree is a family tree that enables us to trace the transfer of a specific genetic trait through several generations.

(continued on page 449)

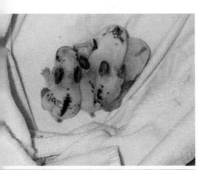

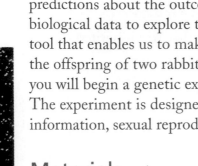

Game of Chance

If someone flips a coin, you know that there are two possible outcomes: heads or tails. You can predict how likely either is to happen. Can you make similar predictions about the outcomes of genetic events? In this activity, you will use biological data to explore the concept of probability. Probability is a mathematical tool that enables us to make predictions. We will provide you with information about the offspring of two rabbits, and you will look for patterns in the results. In addition, you will begin a genetic experiment that you will conduct throughout this chapter. The experiment is designed to help you see the relationship between genetic information, sexual reproduction, and inherited traits.

Materials (per team of 2)

coin
calculator

PROCESS AND PROCEDURES

Part A   Predicting Inheritance Patterns

1. Work with your teammate to solve the following problems. Record your answers in your journal.

   a. A pair of rabbits mated and produced 10 offspring. How many males and how many females would you predict are in those offspring?

   Explain how you made your prediction. Did you need additional information?

   b. Even if you are reasonably confident that your prediction is correct, can you guarantee how many males and females will be born in the litter? Explain your answer.

2. Test your prediction by using a coin to simulate the sex of the 10 offspring.

   a. In your journal, prepare a table to record your team's predicted and actual results.

   b. Flip the coin 10 times. Record your results.

   c. Explain the role of chance in determining your results.

3. Look at the data under the heading Small Sample Size in the need to know box titled Results of Rabbit Matings. These data show the results of 3 rabbit matings. Discuss the following with your teammate:

   a. Do these results match your predictions from step 1 or your test results from step 2? Explain your answer.

   b. The result of each of these 3 crosses obviously is not the same. Explain why the actual outcomes vary from 50 percent males and 50 percent females.

NEED TO KNOW

RESULTS OF RABBIT MATINGS

Small sample size

Trial	# of offspring	Males	Females
1	10	4	6
2	10	6	4
3	10	6	4

Large sample size

Trial	Total # of offspring	Males	Females
1	600	279	321
2	600	296	304
3	600	316	284

4. Next, investigate the relationship between probable outcomes, actual results, and sample size. Examine the data under the heading Large Sample Size in Results of Rabbit Matings. Note that the total number of offspring is 600. Calculate the percentage of male rabbits for each group of 600 offspring. Record these results in your journal.

   Percentage males = [(# males) ÷ (total # offspring)] × 100.

5. Answer the following questions with your teammate. Record the answers in your journal.

   a. Are these results generally closer to 50 percent than those in the small sample size (step 3)? Explain your answer.

   b. Based on your observation, what effect does sample size have on the match between probable outcomes and actual results?

6. You can test the accuracy of large sample sizes by generating your own data with coins and combining the data of the entire class.

   a. This time, instead of flipping the coin 10 times, flip it 20 times. Record the results in your table from step 2.

   b. What is the percentage of heads for this sample size of 20 flips?

   c. Contribute your data to a class data table that your teacher develops on the chalkboard.

   d. What is the percentage of heads for this large sample size?

   e. What do these results suggest about the effect of sample size on the match between probable outcomes and actual results?

Analysis

1. Use what you have learned about the importance of sample size to evaluate the following medical study reported in a local newspaper.

> "A study reported in the medical journal *Acta Artifacta* appears to link ownership of fast cars with premature balding. The study, consisting of 17 men who own sports cars, found that nearly 60 percent suffered from premature balding. The authors of the study conclude that because this percentage of balding is much higher than in the general population, there is an increased chance of suffering from premature baldness if one owns a fast car."

Topic: probability
Go to: www.scilinks.org
Code: human3E422

2. If you flip a coin five times and get heads every time, what is the probability that you will get tails on the next flip?

Part B   Yeast Genetics

When your teacher indicates, you will begin a genetic cross experiment that will continue throughout the chapter. The procedure for this experiment, which uses baker's yeast, *Saccharomyces cerevisiae,* is described in the Yeast Genetics Protocol.

NEED TO KNOW

The Life Cycle of a Yeast

Baker's yeast (*Saccharomyces cerevisiae*) is a unicellular organism that reproduces both sexually and asexually. Because the cells have a characteristic shape at each stage, it is possible to distinguish all the major stages of the yeast life cycle under a microscope. A brief description will help you understand the stages that you observe.

Certain types of yeast cells are referred to as **haploid cells**. This is because they contain only one chromosome from each chromosome pair. These yeast cells can occur in two mating types (or "sexes"): mating type **a** and mating type α (alpha). When cells of opposite mating types (**a** and α) come in contact, they secrete hormonelike substances called **pheromones**. These pheromones cause haploid cells of the opposite mating type to develop into gametes, which are pear-shaped. The gametes then can fuse and produce zygotes. These appear as peanut-shaped cells. When cultured on a solid growth medium, the fused peanut-shaped cells can reproduce asexually by budding (they appear as cloverleaves). These cells may grow into a visible colony that contains up to 100 million cells. In times of stress, however, these cells cease to bud. They undergo a process that produces reproductive cells called **spores**. Spores can survive stressful environmental conditions. When growth conditions become favorable, the spores can germinate and reenter life stages that lead once again to reproduction by budding.

Figure 11.2
Petri dishes.   A petri dish is a flat dish made of plastic or glass with a cover.

In this experiment, you will use 2 yeast strains of opposite mating types. In this way, you can complete an entire yeast life cycle. You will mate the yeast and let them grow through a complete life cycle until you regenerate the original mating types.

As you progress through this sequence, you will come across some important principles. You will learn how genetic material interacts when it is combined, how it is sorted during preparations for reproduction, and how it is transferred through inheritance.

PROTOCOL

Yeast Genetics Protocol

Materials   (per team of 2)

microscope slide
coverslip
dropping pipet
glass-marking pencil
compound microscope
container of sterile flat toothpicks
bottle of water
6 zip plastic sandwich bags labeled *waste* (1 for each day)
MIN medium agar plate
3 YED medium agar plates
"unknown" medium agar plate
YED medium agar plate with pregrown yeast strains of **a** and α mating types
   (labeled *Plate I*)
DVD and player (watch as a class)

Topic: yeast life cycle
Go to: www.scilinks.org
Code: human3E423

Procedure

Remember to record all of your results in your journal.

Day 0

1. Observe the techniques in the DVD segment "Yeast Monohybrid Cross."

   These techniques will help you perform the steps in this experiment.

2. Obtain Plate I from your teacher. Use a microscope to examine some yeast cells of either mating type. Use the following procedure:

   a. Put a small drop of water on a microscope slide.

   b. Gently touch the flat end of a sterile toothpick to the streak of either the **a** mating type or the α mating type on Plate I. (The strain for the **a** mating type has a red or pink phenotype. The strain for the α mating type has a cream phenotype.)

   c. Mix the material on the toothpick with the small drop of water on the slide.

   d. Place a coverslip over the drop.

   e. Discard the toothpick in the plastic waste bag.

   f. Examine the cells with the high-power lens of the microscope.

   g. In your journal, sketch the cells. Note the phenotype of each mating type.

   Use a new sterile toothpick for each step that requires a toothpick. Be careful not to touch the ends of the toothpicks to anything except yeast or the sterile agar. Discard the used toothpicks in the plastic waste bag. **Keep the lid on the plate except when transferring yeast.**

   (*continued*)

Yeast Genetics Protocol (continued)

3. Prepare fresh cultures of both mating types on Plate II as follows:

   a. Touch the flat end of a sterile toothpick to the **a** mating type.

   b. Gently drag the toothpick across the surface of a YED medium plate. You will make a vertical streak about 1 cm long and 1 cm from the edge at a 12 o'clock position (see Figure 11.3).

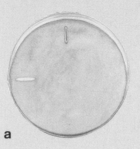 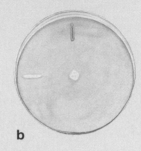

a   b

Figure 11.3
Yeast culture plates.
(**a**) Appearance of Plate I on day 0. (**b**) Appearance of Plate II on day 1 after the mating mixture has grown.

   c. Discard the toothpick in the waste bag.

   d. Use a glass-marking pencil to label the plate with an **a** near the streak.

   e. Use a new sterile toothpick to put a horizontal streak of α mating type at 9 o'clock on the same plate.

   f. Label this streak α.

   g. Label this culture *Plate II*, and add your names.

4. Prepare a mating mixture on Plate II as follows:

   a. Use a new sterile toothpick to transfer a small amount of the **a** mating type from the streak in Plate I to the middle of the agar in Plate II.

   b. Use another sterile toothpick to transfer an equal amount of the α mating type to a point just next to the first spot.

   c. Use a 3rd sterile toothpick to mix the 2 dots of yeast thoroughly to make a mating mixture.

   Be careful not to tear the agar surface. Discard used toothpicks in the waste bag.

5. Invert Plate II. Incubate at room temperature for 3 hours so that the cells can begin mating. Then refrigerate the plate until the next lab period.

   If your class meets in the afternoon, you can refrigerate the plate immediately. Then incubate it at room temperature for 4–5 hours before step 7.

6. Wash your hands thoroughly before leaving the laboratory.

Day 1

7. Examine Plate II. Discuss the following with your partner:

   ◆ What is the phenotype of the mating mixture?

   ◆ After you have completed *Patterns of Inheritance*, Part A, compare the yeast phenotype results with the results of your bean cross. Which color bean is equivalent to the yeast **a** mating type?

8. Use the procedure in step 2 to examine the mating mixture through the microscope.

   a. Sketch what you see. Compare it with your earlier drawings.

   b. Describe any differences in the types of cells you see. Explain why those changes may have taken place.

9. Make a subculture of mating type **a**, some of mating type α, and some of the mating mixture. Use sterile toothpicks to transfer the yeast to a MIN medium agar growth plate.

   Use the same pattern that you used on Plate II. Make the 2 different mating type streaks and the circular mating mixture colony in the middle. Discard used toothpicks in the waste bag.

10. Label this subculture *Plate III*, and add your names.

11. Invert the plate and incubate overnight.

12. Wash your hands thoroughly before leaving the laboratory.

Day 2

13. Examine Plate III. Discuss the following with your partner:

    ◆ What do you observe about the colonies on Plate III after incubation?

    ◆ Explain how the information present in the fused cells differs from the information in either of the original mating types.

14. Use the procedure in step 2 to examine the freshly grown mating mixture in Plate III through the microscope.

15. Discuss the following with your partner:

    ◆ What types of cells are present? Sketch each type.

    ◆ Have any of the types seen in step 8 disappeared? Explain what happened to them.

16. Make a subculture by transferring some of the mating mixture with a sterile toothpick to a fresh YED medium agar plate.

    a. Streak the cells in 1 horizontal line across the middle of the plate.

    Discard used toothpicks in the waste bag.

    b. Label this subculture *Plate IV*, and add your names.

    c. Invert the plate and incubate overnight.

17. Wash your hands thoroughly before leaving the laboratory.

Day 3

18. On a plate of "unknown" medium, make several thick streaks of the freshly grown subculture from Plate IV.

    Discard used toothpicks in the waste bag.

19. Label this culture *Plate V*, and add your names.

20. Invert the plate. Incubate at room temperature for 3 or more days.

21. Wash your hands thoroughly before leaving the laboratory.

(*continued*)

Yeast Genetics Protocol (continued)

Day 7

22. Use the procedure from step 2 to examine yeast from Plate V through the microscope.

    You may need to use the fine adjustment on the microscope to distinguish cells at different levels.

23. Discuss the following with your partner:
    - ◆ What cell types are present now that were not present before? Sketch these cell types.
    - ◆ Compare these cell types with those you saw at other stages.
    - ◆ How do you think the unknown medium differs from the growth medium?

    Refer to the introduction of Part B, Yeast Genetics.

    - ◆ If the cells in the sacs are most frequently found in groups of 4, what process do you think produced them? Explain.
    - ◆ Are the cells in the sacs haploid or diploid? Explain.

24. Transfer some yeast from Plate V to a fresh YED medium agar plate.
    - ◆ Use sterile toothpicks to streak the cells as shown in Figure 11.4.

      Discard used toothpicks in the waste bag.

Figure 11.4 Pattern used to streak the spores. First streak one line of cells across the top of the plate. Then use a second sterile toothpick to streak some of these cells in a zigzag pattern across the rest of the plate. When this is done properly, individual yeast cells at the end of the second streak will grow into isolated colonies.

25. Label this culture *Plate VI*, and add your names.

26. Invert the plate. Incubate at room temperature for about 5 hours. Then refrigerate until the next lab period.

    If your class meets in the afternoon, refrigerate immediately. Then incubate at room temperature for 5 hours before step 28.

27. Wash your hands thoroughly before leaving the laboratory.

Day 8

28. With your partner, discuss and explain what you observe about the colonies on Plate VI.

29. Use the procedure in step 2 to examine the growth from Plate VI through the microscope.

30. Sketch the cells. Compare them with the stages you observed before.

31. Discard used culture plates as your teacher directs.

32. Wash your hands thoroughly before leaving the laboratory

Patterns of Inheritance

Why is it that children look like their parents? Think of your own family or the families of your friends. In many cases, you can see physical resemblances among family members even when they are different ages. Even more striking is the similarity of physical characteristics in domestic animals that are purebred, such as breeds of dogs. This similarity of characteristics happens only if matings take place between members of the same breed such as the border collies illustrated in Figure 11.5a. In asexual reproduction, the similarity of inherited traits among individuals is even greater. For example, tulips that reproduce through bulbs.

Natural populations generally are not as uniform as purebred lines of domesticated organisms. For example, dogs running free in a city can choose their mates naturally. They do not always mate with dogs that look similar to themselves. Such matings produce offspring with a mixture of traits. Consider the mixture of traits that results when a Great Dane mates with a collie, as shown in Figure 11.5b. A mixture of traits is common among human offspring as well.

In this activity, you will begin to model how genetic information is passed from one generation to the next.

b

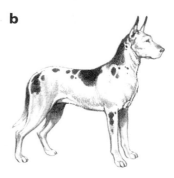

parent

a

Figure 11.5   Continuity of form in animals.   (a) Purebred dogs, such as this family of border collies, pass their characteristic traits to offspring almost unchanged. (b) Mixed mating, however, produces a mixture of traits.

parent

Materials   (per class of 30, teams of 2)

opaque container (hat, bucket, or similar)
50 red beans
50 white beans
sheet of poster board (optional)
overhead projector and transparency (optional)

offspring

PROCESS AND PROCEDURES

Part A   Inheritance of One Trait

In this model, you will use 2 colors of beans to represent the genetic information that contributes to the trait for straight or floppy ears in rabbits.

1. Select 2 beans randomly from the container that your teacher provides.

2. In your journal, record the color of your beans. Also, note whether your pair is homozygous or heterozygous.

   Each bean represents the genetic information in 1 of the parents. If the beans are the same color, the pair is **homozygous** (*homo* = same). If the beans are different colors, the pair is **heterozygous** (*hetero* = different).

3. Shake both in your hands, and then select 1 without looking.

   Each parent contributes only half of his or her own genetic information to each offspring. Parents do not know which half they contribute.

4. Add this bean to the bean your partner selected.

5. Record the color of the 2 beans in the new combination. Indicate whether the pair is homozygous or heterozygous.

   The new bean combination represents the genetic information that will determine the condition of the ears in the rabbit offspring.

6. Use the color key that your teacher displays. List in your journal the ear trait that your beans corresponded to initially and finally.

   a. To which condition did your 1st bean combination correspond?

   b. To which condition did your partner's 1st bean combination correspond?

   c. To which condition did the new combination correspond?

7. As part of a class discussion, use the key once again and the shared results of the class to consider the following:

   a. Did 1 bean color (which corresponds to 1 piece of inherited genetic information) have a greater influence in determining the ear trait than the other bean color?

PAGE 492

   b. Read the essay *Phenotype and Genotype* (page 492). This essay introduces the genetic terminology you will need throughout the rest of this unit. In your journal, correctly label the combinations and conditions that you recorded in steps 2, 5, and 6 as phenotype or genotype.

   c. Using genetic terminology, write 1 paragraph that describes the events in steps 1–6.

Part B   Inheritance of Two Traits

What will you observe if you follow the inheritance of 2 traits at once? Continue working with your partner as you study the inheritance of ear type and sex in rabbits.

1. Examine the tables in the need to know box titled Following the Inheritance of Two Traits. These tables show the results of a cross that follows 2 traits in rabbits: ear type (floppy ears or straight ears) and sex (female or male).

   Male rabbits that had floppy ears were mated with female rabbits that had floppy ears. The results for 100 offspring are shown.

NEED TO KNOW

Following the Inheritance of Two Traits

# of offspring	Male rabbits, floppy ears		Female rabbits, floppy ears	
	Males		Females	
	Floppy	Straight	Floppy	Straight
100	52	0	48	0

# of offspring	Male rabbits, straight ears		Female rabbits, floppy ears	
	Males		Females	
	Floppy	Straight	Floppy	Straight
100	0	47	0	53

2. Based solely on the results of this cross, what conclusions can you draw about these 2 traits?

3. Next, male rabbits that had straight ears were mated with female rabbits that had floppy ears. The results for 100 offspring are shown. Calculate the data for sex (female/male) and ear type (floppy ears/straight ears) as percentages.

   Percentage with trait = [(# with trait) ÷ (total # offspring)] × 100.

4. Discuss the following questions with your teammate:

   a. What overall conclusions can you draw about the inheritance of straight ears versus floppy ears?

   b. Do you think the type of ear a rabbit is born with is affected by whether a rabbit is female or male? Explain your answer.

Analysis

PAGE 496

Work individually to develop responses to the following questions in your journal.

Base your responses on your experiences so far in this chapter and on the information in the essays *Phenotype and Genotype* (page 492) and *Case Studies of Two Genetic Disorders* (page 496).

Topic: Mendelian genetics
Go to: www.scilinks.org
Code: human3E430

As you work on and discuss questions that involve genetic disorders, be sensitive to the possibility that some of your classmates may have, or be close to someone who has, one of the genetic disorders we are studying. *Anyone* can be born with a genetic disorder.

1. Although Huntington's disease is a dominant trait, the symptoms do not appear until late adult years. Imagine that you are a doctor treating a young man who has a parent with Huntington's disease. What concerns might you have for your patient and why?

2. Restate the following accurately: One out of every two offspring that result from a cross between parents with the genotypes *Hh* and *hh* definitely will have Huntington's disease.

3. Two healthy individuals marry and produce three children. The first two are healthy. But the third is born with cystic fibrosis, indicating that she is homozygous *cc* for the cystic fibrosis alleles. What can you conclude about the genotypes of the other people in the family?

4. What is the probability for the couple in question 3 that their future children will have cystic fibrosis? What does this mean for their healthy children?

5. In cocker spaniels, black (*B*) is dominant over red (*b*). Solid color (*S*) is dominant over white spotting (*s*). A red male was mated to a black-and-white female. They had five puppies, as follows: one black, one red, one black-and-white, and two red-and-white.

   a. What genetic principle explains the phenotypes of these offspring?

   b. Write one or two paragraphs to describe how that principle worked in this cocker spaniel family. Show the genotypes of the parents and their offspring in your explanation. Include the following terms:

gene	phenotype
dominant trait	chromosome
recessive trait	allele
genotype	

6. Consider how tall you are. How tall will you likely be when you are fully grown? How tall might you have been if you were raised in a very different situation? How do your genes and the environment interact to determine how tall you will be?

Modify the diagram (Figure 11.6) below to illustrate your answer.

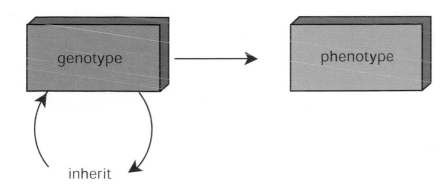

Figure 11.6 Relationship between genotype and phenotype.

Understanding Inherited Patterns

Explain

In the activity *Patterns of Inheritance*, you used phenotypic patterns of inheritance to derive information about an organism's genotype. Recall from your work in Chapter 10 that in sexual reproduction, genetic information is passed from generation to generation by cells called *gametes*. Gametes such as egg and sperm have only *half* the genetic information of other body cells. If they had more, each zygote would start life with more genetic information than its parents. The amount of genetic information would continue to build up generation after generation if this were true. For that reason, the number of chromosomes in gametes must be reduced.

How and when does this reduction occur? Most of the solution to this question was worked out just before the beginning of the 20th century. The key is a process called *meiosis*. In this activity, you will use information presented on the DVD and in an essay to model the mechanism through which meiosis produces gametes.

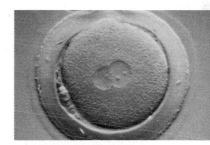

Figure 11.7 The sperm and egg each contribute one-half of the genetic information contained in the nucleus of the zygote.

Materials (per team of 2)

red and blue modeling clay
large sheet of paper
small sheet of scratch paper

scissors
DVD and player (watch as a class)

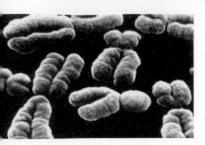

PROCESS AND PROCEDURES

Part A   Meiosis

Meiosis is the mechanism that reduces the amount of genetic information in a cell by one-half before gametes are produced. Meiosis also explains why patterns of inheritance often are predictable.

Work with your team to complete the following tasks:

1. Write a description in your journal of how the major events in meiosis lead to a reduced amount of genetic information in gametes.

2. Through meiosis, how many gametes does a single parent cell produce? Explain why the process results in this number of gametes.

3. Create a flowchart to record the steps for how an individual chromosome behaves during the process of meiosis.

PAGE 498

You may use the essay *Meiosis: The Mechanism behind Patterns of Inheritance* (page 498) and the DVD segment "Meiosis" as resources.

Part B   Tracking Genes through Meiosis

Consider a cell from a male diploid animal that has 2 pairs of chromosomes. Use Figure 11.9, your journal notes, and modeling clay to track how meiosis affects the distribution of the 4 chromosomes. You will do this by identifying a specific gene associated with each chromosome.

Figure 11.8 Human chromosomes. These chromosomes have replicated and are joined to their sister chromatids.

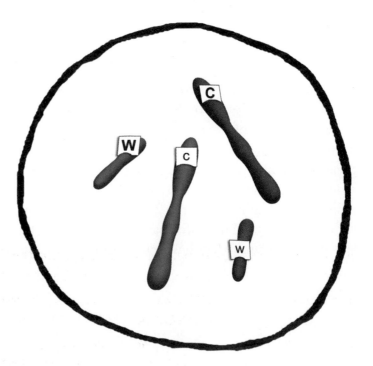

Figure 11.9   Clay models of chromosomes in a diploid animal cell.

1. On a large sheet of paper, draw circles to represent a cell undergoing meiosis.

   Draw a large circle at the top of the page. Draw 2 smaller circles below that and 4 circles below the 2. Finish up with 4 circles with tails (to represent sperm) at the bottom of the page.

2. Use the modeling clay to form 2 pairs of chromosomes about as thick as a pencil. Make 1 pair about 6 cm long. Make the second pair about 3 cm long.

   Use red modeling clay to represent the chromosome of each pair that came from the female parent. Blue modeling clay will represent the chromosomes from the male parent.

3. From the sheet of scratch paper, cut enough 0.5-cm squares to make gene labels for each chromosome. Mark the labels as follows: C = cream eye, c = tan eye, W = white wing, and w = spotted wing. Press the labels into the clay models.

   Put the labels for eye color on the long chromosomes and the labels for wing color on the short chromosomes (refer to Figure 11.9).

4. Place your chromosome models in the large circle at the top of your sheet of paper.

5. Prior to meiosis, the chromosomes *replicate*. Make more clay models with labels to represent this step.

6. Using your cell-diagram circles, move your chromosome models through the process of meiosis and into the sperm.

   In your journal, sketch how you line up the chromosome models during each meiotic division.

7. Answer the following questions:

   a. In your model, what is the genotype of each sperm for eye color and wing color?

   b. What other genotypes are possible?

      Check the results of other teams.

   c. At what point(s) would you change how you positioned your chromosome models to obtain the other possible genotypes?

Topic: meiosis
Go to: www.scilinks.org
Code: human3E433

Analysis

1. Explain how your cell diagrams and answers to the questions in Part B illustrate the connection between the segregation of alleles and meiosis.

2. If an organism has the genotype *AA*, what can you say about the alleles present in the gametes that gave rise to that organism?

3. Use the principle of segregation to write one or two paragraphs that explain how the alleles of different genes are mixed during mating.

   Use genetic terminology to describe your ideas accurately.

Can You Sort It Out?

In the activity *Understanding Inherited Patterns*, you saw that the key to inherited patterns is a process called *meiosis*. Meiosis results in the production of gametes. Each gamete carries genetic information from one of the parents. In this activity, you will examine the results from the mating of different strains of garden peas, much as Gregor Mendel did in his monastery garden more than 150 years ago. You will learn how to use a Punnett square as a tool to help you predict simple crosses. Then you will apply your understanding of genetics to determine the relationships between the phenotypes and genotypes of the parents and offspring. Finally, you will investigate the patterns of inheritance in linked traits and in X-linked traits.

Materials   (per team of 2)

calculator
DVD and player (watch as a class)

PROCESS AND PROCEDURES

Part A   A Mendelian Trait: Pea Pod Color

View the DVD segment "Mendel's Peas." Work through the steps of this **monohybrid** (1 trait) **cross** with your partner. Answer the questions from the DVD.

Part B   Two Mendelian Traits: Pea Pod Color and Shape

When you follow the inheritance of 2 traits (a **dihybrid cross**), more complex patterns result. In garden peas, the genes for the traits of pod color and pod shape are on different chromosomes. As a result, their inheritance conforms to Mendel's law of independent assortment.

Green pods (G) are dominant over yellow pods (g). Expanded pods (E) are dominant over constricted pods (e) (see Figure 11.11). Peas that are homozygous for both green and expanded pods are crossed with peas that have yellow, constricted pods.

Figure 11.10
Gregor Mendel dedicated his life to practical experiments in inheritance.

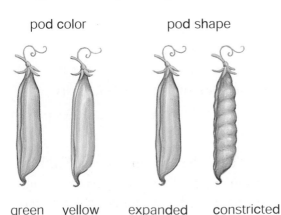

pod color   pod shape

green   yellow   expanded   constricted

Figure 11.11   Pod color and shape in garden peas.

1. With regard to pod color and pod shape, record in your journal the genotypes of gametes that can be formed by these parental types. List the genotypes and phenotypes of the F_1 (first generation) offspring.

2. The F_1 individuals are crossed with each other. Use a Punnett square, as described on the DVD, to show the possible genotypes of the offspring. Record your work in your journal. Include your Punnett square.

3. Based on the data in your Punnett square, what fraction of the offspring would you predict to have each of the following phenotypes?

   a. The dominant phenotype for pod color and pod shape

   b. The dominant phenotype for pod color and the recessive phenotype for pod shape

   c. The recessive phenotype for pod color and the dominant phenotype for pod shape

   d. The recessive phenotype for pod color and pod shape

4. If there were 288 offspring, how many would you predict to have green, expanded pods? green, constricted pods? yellow, expanded pods? yellow, constricted pods?

   In your journal, record how you calculate your predictions.

5. Compare your predictions with the actual results that your teacher provides. Answer the following questions:

   a. Do the results match your predictions?

   b. How can you explain any discrepancies between the result and your predictions?

Part C   Linked Traits

Because there are many more genes than chromosomes, it is not surprising that many different genes are located on the same chromosome. When gametes are formed, alleles of genes that are located on the same chromosome tend to end up together in the same gamete. The term **linkage** is used to describe this tendency. Linkage can be disrupted during meiosis, however. This happens when chromosome segments are broken and exchanged between matching chromosomes during **crossing-over** (see Figure E11.11 on page 504).

1. Repeat steps 1–3 in Part B. But this time, suppose that the genes for pod color and pod shape are on the same chromosome. (That is, G and E are linked, and g and e are linked.)

2. Describe the effect that crossing-over might have on the results.

   The DVD segment *Crossing Over* may help you with your description.

Part D   X-Linked Traits

1. In the fruit fly *Drosophila melanogaster*, red eye color is dominant over white eye color (see Figure 11.12). Predict the genotypes and phenotypes you would expect in the F_1 generation when a homozygous red-eyed female fly is mated with a white-eyed male fly.

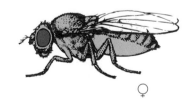

Figure 11.12   Eye color in fruit flies.

First, you might want to list the gametes you would expect the parents to produce. Then combine the gametes to show the F₁ offspring. A Punnett square may be useful.

2. Your teacher will list the actual results of such a cross on the chalkboard. Compare them with your predictions.

3. Say you mated red-eyed *male* flies with white-eyed *female* flies (instead of red-eyed females with white-eyed males). Would you expect similar F₁ results to those obtained in step 2? (When males and females are switched with respect to the traits used in a cross, it is called a *reciprocal* cross.)

4. In the early 1900s, biologist Thomas Hunt Morgan performed a similar cross. But instead of getting all red-eyed flies, he got half red-eyed flies and half white-eyed flies. However, all the red-eyed flies were females, and all the white-eyed flies were males. How might you explain these seemingly unexpected results?

The following information may help you explain this phenomenon.

NEED TO KNOW

Autosomes and Sex Chromosomes

In humans and many other organisms, one special chromosome *pair* does not always occur as a *matching* pair. That special pair is the sex chromosomes. As their name indicates, these specialized chromosomes carry genes that control the sex phenotype of the individual. The other, nonsex chromosomes are called **autosomes**. Autosomes are designated by numbers. In humans and many other animals, the sex chromosomes are designated by the letters X and Y. In humans, other mammals, and fruit flies, the females have two X chromosomes. Males have a single X chromosome, and it is paired

SCiLINKS
NSTA

Topic: chromosome, chromatid
Go to: www.scilinks.org
Code: human3E436

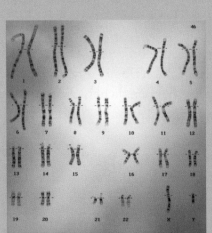

with a Y chromosome. Thus, in many animals, females have two equivalent sex chromosomes. Males have two different sex chromosomes. Figure 11.13 shows a diploid set of human chromosomes arranged in matching pairs. Are these chromosomes from a male or a female?

Very few genes have been detected on the Y chromosome, although it has at least one gene that causes maleness. The X chromosome, on the other hand, carries hundreds or thousands of different genes. These genes are said to be X-linked. Most of the genes that the X chromosome carries control phenotypes that have nothing at all to do with sex. A good example is Alexis's hemophilia in the story *A Royal Tragedy*.

Figure 11.13   A diploid set of human chromosomes.   Except for gametes, nearly every human cell contains a matching pair of each chromosome. One member of each pair is from the mother. The other member is from the father. At the beginning of meiosis, the chromosomes condense and thicken. Images of these condensed chromosomes are cut from a photograph and arranged in pairs, as shown, to create a karyotype. Karyotypes are used in genetic testing.

5. Use what you know to date to solve the following problems:

   a. A superscript letter designates the allele. Often it is used with the chromosome symbol to diagram a cross of a trait that is carried on the X chromosome. For example, the allele for white eyes might be represented by X^r, and the allele for red eyes by X^R. The symbol Y can represent the Y chromosome and does not carry a gene for eye color. Using these symbols, diagram the cross described in step 3. Show the expected genotype and phenotype fractions.

      Show your work in your journal.

   b. Diagram the cross that would result if the F_1 offspring were mated. Show the genotype and phenotype fractions you would expect in the F_2 generation.

Analysis

Be prepared to respond to the following as part of a class discussion:

1. Predict the possible phenotypes and genotypes of the offspring from a mating of two beagles. A heterozygous female with the dominant phenotype for droopy ears (D) mates with a male with the recessive phenotype for upright ears (d).

2. Describe the role of a Punnett square in predicting the potential ratio of genotypes that may result from a particular cross.

3. Recall that crossing-over causes some genes on the same chromosome to assort independently. What relationship might you expect between the spacing of genes on the chromosome and their frequency of independent assortment?

4. Revisit step 1 of Part D. Remember that the gene for eye color in fruit flies is linked to the X chromosome. Predict the F_2 results of that mating.

5. Explain why males are more likely than females to display the phenotypes associated with X-linked recessive traits.

6. Use your knowledge of X-linked traits to explain the inheritance of hemophilia in the story *A Royal Tragedy*.

The Genetic Basis of Human Variation

Elaborate

   Look around at your classmates. Consider how different they are from one another. Think about the tremendous variety of physical characteristics, such as hair type, skin color, body type, and facial features. All distinguish one human from another. The degree of variation is limited, however. Despite the physical distinctions of humans, you easily can recognize a stranger from a distant country as a member of *Homo sapiens*. What might be the genetic basis for such variation? How might natural selection affect the variety of characteristics exhibited by humans? In this activity, you will begin to answer these questions. You will experience some of the nature and range of variation in human populations and acquire additional information about how genotype affects phenotype.

Figure 11.14
In this activity, you will analyze two human traits.

Materials (per person)

white 3 × 5-in card
colored 3 × 5-in card
pencil

masking tape
small squares of paper

PROCESS AND PROCEDURES

Part A   Measuring Variation

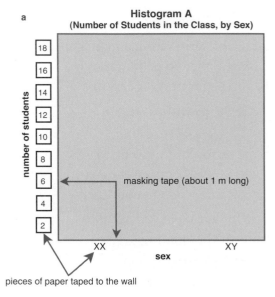

a
Histogram A
(Number of Students in the Class, by Sex)

number of students

18
16
14
12
10
8
6
4
2

masking tape (about 1 m long)

XX   XY
sex

pieces of paper taped to the wall

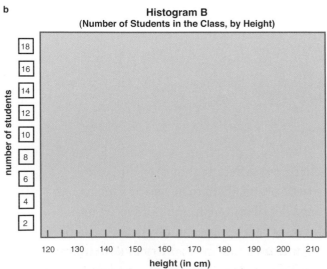

b
Histogram B
(Number of Students in the Class, by Height)

number of students

18
16
14
12
10
8
6
4
2

120 130 140 150 160 170 180 190 200 210
height (in cm)

Figure 11.15   **(a) Histogram A (b) Histogram B**

1. Work with your classmates and teacher to construct the axes for the 2 histograms shown in Figure 11.15. Use the masking tape and small pieces of paper. Make and label the axes on a large wall in your classroom, in the hall, or in another large open area.

2. Next, write XX on a white 3 × 5-inch card if you are a female. Write XY if you are a male. This is your chromosomal sex. On a colored card, write your height in centimeters—round off to the nearest 5 cm.

3. Use masking tape to affix your cards to the proper places on the histograms.

4. When the histograms are complete, work with your partner to answer these questions. Record your answers in your journal.

   Use the data in the histograms and your understanding of genetics to help you.

   a. How many different types of individuals are represented on Histogram A?

b. How many different types of individuals are represented on Histogram B?

c. In your journal, draw and label the 2 histograms. Describe how their shapes differ.

d. What is responsible for the shape of Histogram A?

e. What is responsible for the shape of Histogram B?

f. What would happen to the shapes of the histograms if you added data from the rest of the students in your school?

g. List 3 other human traits that would result in the same type of pattern as Histogram A. Do the same for Histogram B.

Part B Variation and Evolution

SCENARIO

Catastrophe Survivors

Imagine that a terrible disaster has befallen humankind. The survivors of the catastrophe are forced underground to live in cramped tunnels and caves. Because it is impossible to survive aboveground, these tunnel-dwellers never venture outside. The hard earth and the scarcity of digging tools force the

inhabitants to dig passageways that are as small as possible. The resourceful inhabitants live primitive lives. They eat roots, insects, and rodents; sleep huddled together; and reproduce within these constricted surroundings. For many generations, through thousands of years, no human ever experiences wide open spaces.

Complete the following with your teammate. Read the essays *The Role of Variation in Evolution* (page 503) and *Genetic Complexity* (page 507) for important background information.

PAGE 503   **PAGE 507**

1. Describe the change in Histogram B that you might expect to see if the inhabitants of this underground world were to participate in the Part A activity 5,000 years after moving underground.

   Be creative. Feel free to illustrate your description. Or expand the story to explain your response.

2. How do we define "normal" for traits such as height? What, for example, is "normal" height? Where does "short" end and "tall" begin? How do we define other complex traits such as behavior? Where does "intelligent" end and "really intelligent" begin?

3. What evolutionary interpretation can you give to human traits that exhibit a continuous pattern of variation? Consider the effects of natural selection as you develop your answer.

Analysis

Respond to the following tasks individually. Contribute your answers to a class discussion.

1. One of the most important lessons from Charles Darwin's work is that natural selection acts on naturally occurring variations in populations. How might traits that vary continuously, such as height, arise from the mechanisms of evolution?

2. Look again at the shape of Histogram B. What part of the histogram represents inhabitants of the underground world who are likely to fare well in this new environment? Why are so many people represented by the measurements in the middle and so few at the extremes—the "outliers"?

3. Is the variation observed in Histogram B of the same type as that which causes genetic disorders such as cystic fibrosis? Explain.

4. Explain the underlying genetic difference between complex traits and simple traits. (Complex traits are those traits that exhibit continuous patterns of distribution. Simple traits are those traits that exhibit discrete patterns of distribution.)

5. What does human variation, including variation in genetic disorders, have to do with natural selection and evolution?

Further Challenges

Biologists have discovered that there are genes that make certain people susceptible to heart disease. Other people who have these genes, however, do not develop heart disease. What does that information tell you about the role of natural selection in common disorders such as heart disease? What does it indicate about our ability to identify people at risk and about the likely effectiveness of various treatments?

Evaluate

Continuity and Change

In this activity, you will apply your understanding of the basic concepts of genetics by using genetic terminology to summarize your yeast experiment results. You also will compare the patterns of inheritance in yeast and humans, and analyze data from human genetic disorders. Remember that your work in this activity is evidence for what you have learned about biological continuity to this point. It will be evaluated by your teacher.

Materials   (per team of 2)

results from yeast experiment

PROCESS AND PROCEDURES

Part A   Genetic Mechanisms in Yeast

1. Obtain a rubric from your teacher for analyzing your yeast experiment. Study your yeast experiment results in enough detail to respond in your journal to the following.

    Use the introduction to the Yeast Genetics Protocol (page 423) as a resource.

    a. Compare the final colonies to the original mating type colonies. Describe how they are alike or different.

    Remember to use drawings to illustrate your descriptions whenever appropriate.

    b. What life-cycle stages are present in these final colonies? How do you know they are present?

    c. What evidence is there that a new life cycle has started?

    d. Use the results of your yeast experiment to explain the statement, *The genetic plan of yeast cells can be transmitted through reproduction*.

Figure 11.16 Recall the pattern that you used to streak the yeast spores.

2. Apply your understanding of genetics to the yeast reproduction diagrams on the Copymaster *Yeast Reproduction*. Complete the following tasks:

    a. At each position where new cells are represented in the sequence, describe whether the cells are haploid or diploid. Justify your responses.

    b. In the appropriate diagram, label the position where meiosis occurs.

3. Working individually, write 1 or 2 paragraphs in which you compare the mechanisms that yeast and humans use to maintain genetic continuity. In your comparison, include a description or illustration with labels of the following:

    ◆ The haploid and diploid cells in each species

    ◆ The meiotic process each organism uses that leads to gamete formation

    ◆ An obvious phenotype that can be inherited from one generation to the next

    ◆ The life cycle and method of reproduction of each species

Part B   Genetic Variation and Human Genetic Disorders

Analyze the following questions. Use what you know, the essay *Incomplete Dominance* (page 510), and the material in the need to know box on page 442 titled Human Genetic Disorders.

PAGE 510

1. Which disorders show X-linkage? Explain whether you would expect to see them in males or females, or possibly both.

2. Write 1 or 2 paragraphs that describe how young Czarevitch Alexis (from the activity *Gifts from Your Parents* on page 418) could have been affected by hemophilia even though neither parent was affected. Use genetic terminology to accurately describe the biology underlying the situation.

3. Although Huntington's disease is very rare in the total population, it appears at a rate of 50 percent in affected families. Explain this statement in genetic terms.

4. Alleles that cause cystic fibrosis occur at a rate of about 1 in 25 individuals of European descent. Alleles that cause red-green color blindness occur at a rate of about 1 in 20 males in the United States. Picture a school with 500 students (50 percent male and 50 percent female). Would these statistics *guarantee* that 20 students are heterozygous carriers of the cystic fibrosis gene or that at least 12 males are color-blind? Explain your response.

5. Look at the disorders listed in the table. How does the genetic abnormality of trisomy 21 differ from the others?

6. Use the concept of natural selection to help explain why the frequency of hemophilia A is so different from the frequency of color blindness.

7. Charles Darwin did not have an understanding of genetics when he proposed his theory of evolution. Now that you have some understanding of genetic mechanisms, how would you use that knowledge to help explain evolution and the diversity seen in populations of living organisms?

8. How might the mechanisms of evolution explain how harmful alleles, such as those that lead to sickle-cell disease, are retained in a population?

SCI*LINKS*
NSTA
Topic: genetic diseases/
genetic screening/
genetic counseling
Go to: www.scilinks.org
Code: human3E442

NEED TO KNOW

Human Genetic Disorders

Disorder	Genotype	Phenotype	Genetic incidence
Cystic fibrosis (CF)	Autosomal recessive	Life-threatening respiratory illness and blockage Digestive problems Salty sweat	European American heterozygous 1:25 General population homozygous 1:2,000 African American homozygous 1:17,000 Hawaiian Asian homozygous 1:99,000
Tay-Sachs	Autosomal recessive	Accumulation of lipids in the brain and other organs and tissues Progressive retardation in development Paralysis Dementia Blindness Death by age 3 or 4	Jewish American of Eastern European descent heterozygous 1:30 Non-Jewish heterozygous 1:400,000
Sickle-cell disease	Autosomal recessive	Sickle-shaped red blood cells Reduced oxygen-carrying capacity Under certain conditions, some sickling in heterozygotes	African American heterozygous 1:10 African American homozygous 1:400
Familial hypercholesterolemia (FH)	Autosomal dominant	Heterozygotes Heart disease Blockage of blood vessels Homozygotes Large buildup of fat deposits in arteries Fat deposits in tendons and under skin Heart attacks in childhood	General population heterozygous 1:500 General population homozygous 1:1,000,000

Disorder	Genotype	Phenotype	Genetic incidence
Huntington's disease	Autosomal dominant	Neurological disease, fatal in middle age, characterized by uncontrollable twitching	In general, very rare General population heterozygous 1:20,000 In affected families 50%
Hemophilia A	X-linked recessive	Lack of blood clotting, can result in fatal hemorrhage	General population males 1:7,000 General population females almost nonexistent
Red-green color blindness	X-linked recessive	Inability to distinguish the colors red and green Reduced night vision	General population males 1:20 Homozygous females 1:400
Trisomy 21 (Down's syndrome)	3 copies of chromosome 21	Mental retardation Poor skeletal development Weak muscle tone Altered facial features Heart and organ abnormalities Males are sterile; females may be fertile Life span of 30–50 years	Incidence increases with mother's age

Ákohgo ts' ídá haiit' éego
ááhyi ní nahalingo, éí baa
nitsídzíkees doolee?

Gene Action

Chapter 12

Do you have any idea what the words in the picture inset mean? How might you begin to understand the information that is stored in an unfamiliar language? During World War II, 29 Navajo Indians, members of the United States Marine Corps, used their language to code and transfer secret information. Called *code talkers,* those men played an important role in securing an Allied victory.

On July 26, 2001, President George W. Bush presented the Congressional Gold Medal to four of the five living code talkers and relatives of the other 24 men. The presentation, pictured left, was held at the Library of Congress in Washington, D.C.

The military chose the Navajo to be code talkers because their language is complex and little-known. Consequently, if a message were intercepted by people outside of the United States, it was unlikely to be decoded. Imagine how difficult it would be to decode the words written on the picture inset. Translated into English, that Navajo sequence means, "What does this sentence really mean when you think about it?"

The symbols that make up words function like a code to store and transfer information. The molecules of genetic material also store and transfer coded information, in this case, from one generation to the next. In addition, the information stored in the molecular code of genetic material can be expressed in a form that is useful to living systems. The importance of the genetic code has motivated scientists for decades to study it in more and more detail to uncover its rules and mechanisms.

In this chapter, you will learn about and model the genetic code, as well as understand other aspects of molecular genetics. You also will learn about the field of genetic engineering and consider the consequences and implications of advances in this field.

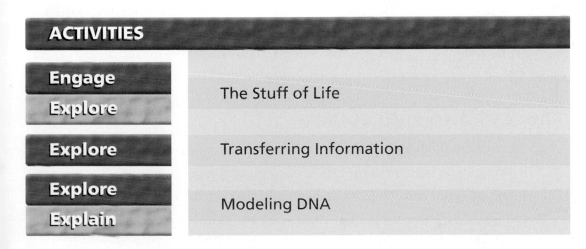

ACTIVITIES

Engage **Explore**	The Stuff of Life
Explore	Transferring Information
Explore **Explain**	Modeling DNA

Explain	Gene Expression
Elaborate	A Closer Look at Protein Synthesis
Elaborate	Genetic Technology
Evaluate	Words to Live By

Engage

Explore

The Stuff of Life

In Chapter 11, you studied the importance of inheritance for the continuity of species. At this point, you should be able to explain the relationship between genotype and phenotype. The key to all of these processes is deoxyribonucleic acid, DNA. In this activity, you will begin to look more closely at DNA. You will need to understand the complex role that DNA plays in all living systems. This will help you appreciate the impact that new genetic technologies are having on biological research, medicine, public policy, and the judicial system. Because those technologies have the potential to affect the lives of all citizens, an understanding of DNA and its molecular function is now everyone's concern, not just the scientists. But first, what is this stuff we call DNA?

Figure 12.1
Barbara McClintock, an accomplished geneticist, won the Nobel Prize in Physiology or Medicine in 1983.

Materials (per team of 2)

2 safety goggles	test tube rack
2 lab aprons	hot plate
2 pairs gloves	glass-marking pencil
2 15-mL culture tubes	ice bucket with ice
500-mL beaker	1 mL Woolite cold water wash or Dawn
calibrated pipet or graduated cylinder	dishwashing detergent
glass stirring rod	6 mL 95% ethanol
thermometer	5 mL bacterial suspension from lima beans

PROCESS AND PROCEDURES

1. Answer the following questions as part of a class discussion:

   a. When you hear the term DNA, what images come to mind?

   b. If you could see DNA, what do you think it would look like?

2. On a half page in your journal, draw what you think or predict that DNA looks like.

3. Investigate some of your ideas about DNA by using the DNA Isolation Protocol to isolate real DNA from bacteria. This process is called *extraction*.

DNA Isolation Protocol

CAUTION: During this investigation, wear safety goggles and gloves at all times. Keep the lids on all of the solutions when not in use. Do not inhale fumes. Be sure to wash your hands after this investigation.

Caution **Safety Goggles**

Lab Apron **Lab Gloves**

1. With your partner, collect the materials that your team will need to complete this extraction.

   Your teacher will tell you which materials you will need for your team and which materials you will share with several other teams at stations.

2. Use the glass-marking pencil to label 1 culture tube as your bacterial suspension. You and your partner will want to be able to identify it later.

3. Carefully add 5 mL of bacterial suspension to this culture tube.

4. To release the DNA from the cells, you must break open the cells with a detergent. To accomplish this, do the following:

   a. Add 1 mL of Woolite or Dawn to the bacterial suspension that is in your culture tube.

   b. Cap the tube tightly. Invert it very slowly 2 times.

      It is important to do this step carefully and extremely slowly (as if in slow motion). We don't want the DNA to break into small pieces. If the DNA breaks, the rest of the procedure will not work.

   c. Let the tube stand undisturbed for 5 min.

5. According to your teacher's instructions, place your tube in a hot-water bath that has been preheated to 65°C–70°C (149°F–158°F). Let your tube stand in the bath (incubate) for 15–20 min. Closely monitor the temperature of the bath to keep it within this range.

WARNING: Hot water will scald, causing second-degree burns. Do not touch the hot-water-bath beaker or allow the hot water to contact your skin. If a burn occurs, *immediately* place the burned area under *cold* running water; then call the teacher.

Warning

   Exposure to this high temperature and the detergent will help separate the DNA from the other macromolecules that make up the cell. A temperature greater than 80°C will break apart the DNA.

   While the suspension is incubating, continue with steps 6 and 7.

6. Pour 6 mL of ethanol that has been stored in a freezer into the 2nd culture tube. Cap it, and place it in a bucket of ice.

WARNING: Ethanol is *flammable* and is a *poison*. Do not expose the liquid or its vapors to heat, sparks, open flame, or other ignition sources. Do not ingest; avoid skin/eye contact. If contact occurs, flush affected area with water for 15 min; rinse mouth with water. If a spill occurs, flood spill area with water; *then* call the teacher.

Warning **Poison!**

   For this extraction to work, the ethanol must be ice cold.

7. Allow the bacterial suspension to warm up and the ethanol to cool down.

   While you are waiting, go on to step 4 in the Process and Procedures.

(continued)

DNA Isolation Protocol *(continued)*

8. After your bacterial suspension has been in the hot-water bath for 15–20 min, remove it. Allow it to cool to room temperature in a test tube rack.

   This will take about 5 min. Handle the tube carefully; it should remain still. Do not put it on ice or wave it around to cool it.

9. Add the cold ethanol to the suspension. Do this by tipping the tube containing the bacterial suspension at an angle. Then pour the ethanol slowly down the side of the tube.

   This method will prevent the 2 layers from mixing. The ethanol causes the DNA previously dissolved in the detergent solution to become insoluble (no longer able to be dissolved). The insoluble, white precipitate in the ethanol layer (upper layer) is DNA.

10. With your partner, take turns spooling the DNA as follows:

    a. Hold the tube at a 45° angle.

    b. Place the glass stirring rod into the tube. Rotate the rod slowly.

       Fibers consisting of many molecules of DNA should come out of the solution and attach to the glass rod as you rotate it. This process is called *spooling.* It is possible because the DNA is insoluble in alcohol. Spooling causes the DNA to separate from the solution, allowing you to gather it with the rod. Remember to rotate the rod slowly. Look carefully for fine white threads accumulating around the rod.

    c. Continue this process until no more DNA comes out of the solution.

    d. Describe in your journal whatever you can observe about the DNA you have extracted.

11. Return the materials as your teacher directs. Wash your hands thoroughly before leaving the laboratory.

4. During the waiting period in step 7 of the DNA Isolation Protocol, contribute to a team list of questions that come to mind as you read the story *A Royal Tragedy (continued).*

5. Participate in a class discussion that your teacher guides.

Analysis

Complete the following tasks in your journal:

1. Make a list of your observations on the process of isolating DNA and on what the DNA looked like. Compare these observations with your previous impressions from step 1 of Process and Procedures.

2. Is it likely that the cells of living organisms other than bacteria could serve as a source of DNA? Explain your answer.

3. The story *A Royal Tragedy (continued)* illustrates one example of how the legal system uses DNA technology. What other applications of DNA technology

Topic: Romanovs
Go to: www.scilinks.org
Code: human3E448

SCENARIO

A Royal Tragedy (continued)

In the minds of the Russian Bolsheviks, the success of their revolution demanded that the imperial family be arrested and imprisoned. Czar Nicholas II, his wife Alexandra, their four daughters, Olga, Tatiana, Maria, Anastasia, and their son, Alexis, were arrested in late April 1918. The anti-Bolshevik White and Czech armies were closing in on the Siberian town of Ekaterinburg where the family was imprisoned. Around midnight on July 17, 1918, the family—along with three servants and a doctor—was taken to a small room in the basement of the house that had been their prison for 78 days. The guards told them that they were going to be photographed. Instead, Yakov Yurovsky, the leader of the executioners, took a small paper into his hand and began to read: "In view of the fact that your relatives are continuing their attack on Soviet Russia, the Ural Executive Committee has decided to execute you." With the reading, he condemned the 11 people to death.

The order for execution also commanded that the bodies of the imperial family be totally destroyed so that no evidence of their execution remained. The executioners loaded the bodies into a truck and drove deep into the forest. They dug one large grave. After putting the bodies in the grave, they doused them with sulfuric acid so they could never be recognized. Next, they placed boards on top of the bodies and filled the hole with dirt. Finally, the assassins drove trucks back and forth over the burial site to conceal the digging. They intended that the grave should never be found.

Yakov Yurovsky returned to Moscow and wrote a detailed report of all the events of July 17 and 18, 1918.

He concluded his report with the precise location of the secret grave. In 1978, the eldest son of Yurovsky gave to Gely Ryabov, a famous filmmaker, a copy of his father's report to the Soviet government on the execution of the imperial family and the disposition of their bodies. His reason for giving his own, handwritten copy of the document to Ryabov was to repent for "the most horrible page" in his father's life. In late May 1979, Ryabov and Alexander Avdonin, a geologist, led a small group to the site identified in Yurovsky's report. They began to dig and within minutes saw three skulls. Afraid of the consequences of this discovery, they returned the three skulls to the grave. They could not tell anyone. It was not a time in Soviet history to make public sensational news about the imperial family.

By the autumn of 1989, the disintegration of the Soviet empire was under way. On June 12, 1991, the first nationwide election of a political leader in the thousand-year history of Russia took place. Russians elected Boris Yeltsin as president. Now was the time. Avdonin had a regional governor ask Yeltsin's permission to exhume the bones of the imperial family. Yeltsin nodded yes. On July 11, 1991, a convoy of trucks, loaded with police officers, detectives, forensic experts, excavating equipment, and Alexander Avdonin left Ekaterinburg. They drove to the burial site vacated by Avdonin and Ryabov 12 years before. Everyone took a spade and began to dig.

The searchers quickly found the three skulls that Avdonin and Ryabov had reburied. Digging wider, they encountered more skulls, ribs, leg bones, arm bones, and vertebrae. The skeletons lay in disarray, one on top of

(*continued*)

another. After weeks of careful digging, more than 950 bones and bone fragments were uncovered. Sergei Abramov, a leading forensic anthropologist, spent more than 3 months assembling the bones and fragments into nine skeletons. The remains of two of the 11 executed were never found. President Yeltsin and many of the Russian people wanted to know for certain if these were the remains of the imperial family.

Investigators proposed that a definitive answer could be found using genetic testing. Dr. William Maples of the University of Florida, and Dr. Peter Gill, director of the Forensic Science Service in London, began the task of linking the newly discovered bones with the imperial family. The process sounded simple. Match DNA found in the bones to DNA found in living blood relatives of the imperial family. Researchers proposed using small pieces of the nine femurs for the analysis. Although the pieces of femur were small, they could use DNA technology to make enough DNA copies for testing. A partial family pedigree in Figure 12.2 illustrates how one famous relative could help solve the mystery.

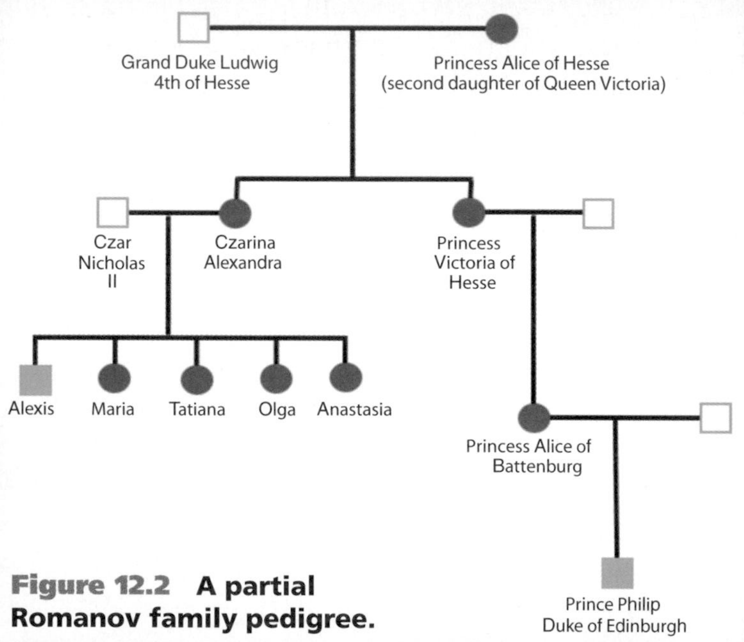

to travel. Sperm rely on energy released by their mitochondria to power their movements. The mitochondria, however, are found only in the upper tail section of the sperm. During fertilization, only the sperm nucleus penetrates the ovum. The tail and mitochondria are left behind. Thus, only the ovum contributes mtDNA to the zygote and resulting embryo. Unlike chromosomal DNA that undergoes recombination and assortment, mtDNA stays intact from one generation to the next. In summary, only the mother transmits mtDNA to her children. Furthermore, mtDNA remains the same for generation after generation. The maternal mtDNA continues to be passed from mother to child, through the generations. Males never pass mtDNA to any of their children.

Now, back to our story. Look at the pedigree in Figure 12.2. We see that Czarina Alexandra's mother, Princess Alice of Hesse, passed her mtDNA to her great grandson Prince Philip, Duke of Edinburgh. Prince Philip, the husband of the reigning Queen Elizabeth II of England, was perfectly suited for an mtDNA comparison

Figure 12.2   A partial Romanov family pedigree.

Before we continue with the events in our story, let's look at human DNA. We know that our 23 pairs of chromosomes are packages of DNA. We refer to them as chromosomal DNA. We also have DNA in our mitochondria (mtDNA). The way that we inherit our mtDNA is different than how we inherit chromosomal DNA. This is because mtDNA is not located in the cell's nucleus. Egg and sperm do not contribute mtDNA equally to the zygote they form through fertilization. That is because of the size difference between sperm and eggs and the different travel distances involved for sperm and egg to unite.

During intercourse, sperm swim through the female's vagina and uterus into the fallopian tubes. That path represents an enormous distance for the tiny sperm

with bone material of the murdered Russian czarina and her daughters. Five times, researchers matched the mtDNA from Prince Philip with Alexandra's bone material and that of her daughters. All of the matches produced perfect results. Czar Nicholas's mother passed mtDNA through four generations to the now living Countess Xenia. When scientists compared mtDNA from the bones thought to be those of Nicholas to the mtDNA from Countess Xenia, it was a perfect match. Five times, researchers matched the mtDNA from Nicholas's bone material to that of his great grandniece. Using genetic evidence, Drs. Maple and Gill declared that there is no doubt that the bones were the remains of the imperial family.

have you heard about? Describe one example from a news story or personal experience.

4. Read the essays *Genetic Information Is Stored in Molecular Form* (page 512) and *Landmark Discovery: DNA May Be the Stuff of Genes* (page 513). Then answer the following questions: Do you think you could extract the same material from your skin cells? a leaf? your teeth? a rock? Why or why not?

PAGE 512

PAGE 513

Transferring Information

Explore

How often does someone in your school use a photocopier to duplicate an important document? As recently as the 1970s, photocopiers were uncommon. People used manual typewriters and carbon paper or mimeograph machines to make copies. Compared with modern technology, those methods seem inefficient. Consider how much more difficult duplication was before the widespread use of movable-type printing presses in the late-1400s. Before then, expert scribes made handwritten copies of entire books. Imagine how many errors a person might make while copying this whole biology book by hand. Examples of how often errors *did* happen during that process are easily found by reading historical documents.

Aside from occasional errors, written language is a powerful technology for storing and passing on information. How does it compare with the methods that cells use to pass on genetic information to every new cell or new organism? Cellular mechanisms must copy (or replicate) enormous amounts of DNA, the genetic material. In this activity, you will model and explore the general process of information transfer. As you participate, consider the importance of accuracy when information is transferred from one place to another.

Figure 12.3 Copy machines are commonplace today. Duplication of written materials was difficult and frequently contained errors before Pi Sheng invented printing with movable woodblocks in China (1040), or the use of movable type (invented in Korea around 1392), or the introduction of a European printing press in the mid-1400s.

Materials (per team of 8)

1 or 2 large sheets of paper
pen or pencil

PROCESS AND PROCEDURES

1. To begin thinking about information transfer in living systems, join your teammates to discuss the following questions. Record your answers in your journal.

   At this point in the chapter, your answers may be brief and simple.

   a. All molecules store energy. But not all molecules store the information that affects inheritance. Which molecules contain the information that results in an organism's genotype and phenotype? What ideas do you have about how information is stored in molecules?

b. What is the role of genetic information in the life of an individual organism?

c. Why is replication (copying) of DNA important to the continuity of a species?

d. Why is it important that genetic information be passed on, or transmitted, accurately?

2. Join with another team. Briefly discuss your answers to the questions in step 1. Revise your answers if you wish.

3. According to your teacher's instructions, create a team of 8. Follow your teacher's directions for carrying out 2 tests of information transfer.

Analysis

1. Examine the results of each test you conducted in step 3. In your journal, explain how each set of observations might apply to the genetic mechanisms that are responsible for storing and transferring information.

2. In your own words, or in a concept map, briefly describe the relationships among DNA, genes, chromosomes, accurate information transmission, cells, an organism, and offspring.

Explore

Explain

Modeling DNA

In the activity *Transferring Information*, you experienced some challenges to accurate information transfer. You were asked to begin thinking about how cells manage this task. Now, you will build a model of DNA. This will help to explain how this molecule can store genetic information and transfer it accurately to new cells.

As you build your model, keep in mind that modeling is a tool for understanding structures and processes that may be difficult to observe directly. James Watson and Francis Crick are the scientists credited with proposing the first detailed description of DNA's structure. They used model building extensively in their work. When they began developing their DNA model, they could not explain all of the physical data collected from DNA. Their first attempts did not match the actual structure of DNA very well. They then modeled arrangements of atoms suggested by the X-ray photographs of Rosalind Franklin and Maurice Wilkins. They also applied a great deal of chemical insight. Eventually, their model began to mimic the natural situation more closely.*

Remember also that even the best model only partially imitates the phenomenon it is constructed to illustrate. Models are useful for showing *some* aspects of an actual structure or process. But they do not portray every characteristic perfectly. The power

---

Source: Watson, J. D. (1968). *The Double Helix.* Atheneum Publishers.

of models comes from their ability to help us picture structures and processes that we cannot actually see. Keep in mind that people have a tendency to assume that every feature of a particular model is accurate. This activity will help you learn not only to develop but also to critique a biological model.

Materials   (per team of 4)

pop beads or colored paper clips
twist ties
rubber bands
double-sided tape
wire
DVD and player (watch as a class)

PROCESS AND PROCEDURES

Part A   Modeling DNA Structure

Imagine that you are on a team of research scientists involved in an effort to describe the likely structure of the DNA molecule. You have decided to tackle this task by modeling. You will build physical representations of a variety of possible structures and change these models to reflect new information as it becomes available.

> Although you will work as a team to share information, each of you should build your own model. This will allow you to compare different ways of representing the same physical characteristics of the DNA molecule.

Model 1

1. Build your 1st model. Use both the pop beads and the following observations about the structure of DNA:

   - DNA is a polymer. A polymer is a very long, chainlike molecule composed of small subunit molecules. Subunit molecules are like the links in a chain. They are attached to each other by covalent bonds.
   - Four different types of subunit molecules exist.

2. Compare your model with those built by the other members of your team. Discuss any differences that you notice.

3. Analyze your model by responding to the following in your journal:

   a. What features of your model represent the properties of DNA described above?

   b. Look closely at your model. How do you think that the structure of DNA might allow it to store information? How might DNA store different information along different parts of its length?

Model 2

4. Modify your DNA model. It should reflect the following additional information:

   ◆ DNA consists of 2 long chains of subunits twisted around each other to form a double helix. (A helix is the shape a pipe cleaner takes when you wrap it around a pencil.)

   ◆ The 2 helical chains are weakly bonded together. Subunits on 1 chain or strand bond to subunits on the other strand.

   ◆ The diameter of the DNA molecule is uniform along its length.

5. Compare your new model with those built by the other members of your team. Discuss any differences that you notice.

6. Analyze your 2nd model by responding to the following in your journal:

   a. How well does your pop bead model represent each of the 5 structural characteristics of DNA listed so far? Briefly list these 5 characteristics. Then explain how your model represents each.

   b. Examine the figures that your teacher presents. Compare the superficial resemblances with a spiral staircase and with a zipper. List the strengths and weaknesses of using a spiral staircase or a zipper to illustrate DNA structure. How do these models compare with your pop bead model?

Model 3

7. Now add another layer of detail to your model of DNA. Consider the following observation. Modify your design accordingly:

   ◆ The order of subunits in 1 strand of DNA determines the order of subunits in the other strand.

   As you try to solve this portion of the model, consider that the aspect of DNA's structure that you now are modeling is the key to how DNA is replicated (copied).

8. Compare your new model with those built by the other members of your team. Discuss any differences that you notice.

9. Analyze your 3rd model by responding to the following in your journal:

   a. Use your modeling results to describe the relationship between subunits bonded to each other on opposite strands of the DNA double helix.

   b. Think about this last characteristic of DNA. Consider how the relationship between the subunits on each strand might suggest a means of replicating the molecule. Describe your ideas.

Part B   Analyzing a DVD Model

1. With your class, view the DVD segment "DNA Structure." This segment will give you more information about DNA structure (the 4 subunits and the

interactions between subunits on each strand). It will also help you understand the importance of this structure to the replication of DNA molecules.

As you watch the DVD segment, look for information that will help you answer the following questions. Take notes in your journal. The new information that you gather will help you better understand the structure of DNA.

a. What characteristic of the subunits allows for a uniform diameter of the double helix? What type of interaction takes place between the subunits of each strand that encourages a double helix to form?

b. How does the sequence of subunits on 1 strand provide a template (a pattern or guide) for the sequence of subunits on the other strand? Is that important to replication? Explain your answer.

2. Use the new information that you gathered from the DVD segment and the tasks below to reevaluate your 3rd model.

◆ Write a short paragraph in your journal that describes how you would have to modify your 3rd model to reflect this new information.

◆ List 3 ways in which pop beads limit your ability to create a more detailed or more accurate model of a DNA molecule.

◆ State what materials (other than pop beads) you would use. How would you assemble them to model DNA more accurately? (Alternatively, you may use these materials to construct another model on your own.)

Part C   Modeling DNA Replication

As you saw in Part A of this activity, one of the reasons that scientists build models is to help them picture and better understand *structures* that are difficult to observe directly. Models also can help scientists picture and better understand a variety of complex and hard-to-observe *processes*.

Imagine that you now have determined the structure of DNA. Your research team has turned its attention to the task of explaining how DNA replicates. In particular, your team has decided to try to answer the 2 research questions that follow.

Read the essays *DNA Structure and Replication* (page 513) and *Replication Errors and Mutation* (page 519). The essays and the DVD segment "DNA Replication" contain important background information to be used in your responses to the following questions and tasks.

Topic: DNA replication
Go to: www.scilinks.org
Code: human3E455

PAGE 513   PAGE 519

Research Question 1

What are the critical characteristics of DNA that allow both the lasting storage of information and the transfer of information through copying (replication)?

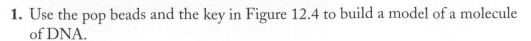

1. Use the pop beads and the key in Figure 12.4 to build a model of a molecule of DNA.

   Although you will work as a team to share information, each of you should build and manipulate your own model. You will need to demonstrate to your teacher your *own* understanding of replication.

2. Manipulate your pop bead model to illustrate the process of replication.

PAGE 521

3. Read the essay *Landmark Discovery: Why the Fuss about Watson and Crick?* (page 521). Consider the work that Watson and Crick did now that you have gone through the process of constructing a DNA model. Discuss the following statements and questions with your team and with your teacher when he or she visits your group. Record your conclusions in your journal. It is important that you understand these points before you attempt to complete step 4.

   a. Scientists use the phrase *complementary base pairing* to refer to the pairing of G with C and A with T in the DNA molecule. How does complementary base pairing make accurate replication possible?

   b. The bonds that attach adjacent nucleotide subunits in a strand of DNA are covalent bonds. Hydrogen bonds are strong. How would strong bonds improve the DNA molecule's ability to store information accurately for a long time?

   c. The bonds that attach the 2 DNA strands to each other in a double helix are hydrogen bonds. Hydrogen bonds are much weaker than covalent bonds. How would weaker bonds favor the capacity of the DNA molecule to replicate?

   d. How does your model reflect the difference between the bond strength between nucleotide subunits and the bond strength between the 2 strands of a DNA molecule? Illustrate your answer with specific references to your pop bead model.

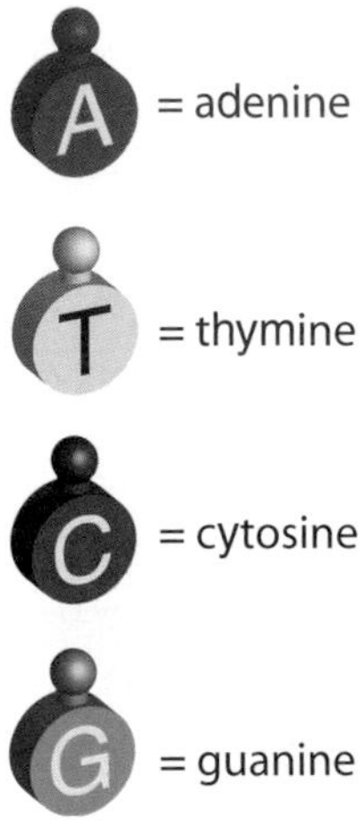

4. Analyze your work in steps 1–3 above. Then develop an answer to research question 1. Record your answer in your journal.

 = adenine

 = thymine

= cytosine

= guanine

Figure 12.4 What components of DNA do these pop beads represent?

Research Question 2

What are the advantages and disadvantages of an information transfer system that uses a physical pattern, or template?

5. Use your pop bead model to demonstrate a mutation in your DNA molecule.

6. Use your pop bead model to demonstrate what would happen to this mutation as your DNA molecule replicates.

7. Discuss the following questions with your team and with your teacher when he or she visits your group. It is important that you understand the answers to these questions before you attempt to complete step 8.

a. Think back to the tests of information transfer that you conducted in the previous activity, *Transferring Information*. How did the accuracy of the orally transferred information compare with the accuracy of the written transfer?

b. Under what conditions might the extremely high accuracy of replication be advantageous to a species?

c. Under what conditions might such accuracy be disadvantageous?

8. Review your work in steps 5–7. Then develop an answer to research question 2. Record your answer in your journal.

Figure 12.5
Dr. Leticia Márquez-Magaña (left), a molecular biologist at San Francisco State University, and one of her students.
Dr. Márquez-Magaña studies the soil bacterium *Bacillus subtilis*.

Analysis

During this activity, you used scientific modeling to explore two important characteristics of DNA: (1) its ability to *store* information, and (2) its ability to *transmit* that information to future generations. Fit these characteristics into the big picture of genetic continuity and reproduction by completing the following tasks:

1. Copy Figure E12.1 (page 512) into your journal. Label the portion of the figure that specifically illustrates the *storage* of genetic information. Label the portion of the figure that specifically illustrates the *transmission* of information to subsequent generations. Label the portion of the figure that specifically illustrates the *use* of genetic information to maintain life.

2. In your journal, explain the relationship between DNA structure and

a. information storage, and

b. accurate information transfer during the reproduction of organisms (meiosis).

Include a diagram to illustrate your explanation.

3. Imagine that a mutation takes place in an organism's genotype.

a. Explain *in molecular terms* how this change might have happened. How can it be passed along to offspring and to the next generation of offspring after that?

b. What effect might this mutation have on an organism carrying it? Why? Refer to Figure E12.7 (page 520) in your answer.

Further Challenges

Briefly review the tests of information transfer that you completed in the activity *Transferring Information*. Those tests used written and spoken language instead of the language of DNA. However, each test was a rough model of the process by which information transmits from one cell to another (or one organism to another) following DNA replication. As a model, each test had strengths and weaknesses. Each test portrayed the processes of information transfer with varying degrees of accuracy.

Ask yourself how accurately each test represented the replication of DNA, as you understand the process now. Then answer the two questions below.

1. How does the copying of coded, written words compare with DNA replication? How is it similar? How is it different?

   Remember, DNA replication is the biological process by which one molecule of DNA produces a second, identical molecule.

2. How does the transfer of coded, written words compare with reproduction? How is it similar? How is it different?

   Reproduction is the biological mechanism by which genetic information maintains the continuity of a species.

Explain

Gene Expression

You have studied how a DNA molecule can act as a template for its own replication. You should now be able to explain how genetic information maintains the continuity of a species from one generation to the next. In this unit, you also have studied the concept that genetic information is used to build and maintain the phenotype of individual organisms. But how is the information in DNA used by each organism that possesses it? How do your cells use the information in the sequence of nucleotides in your DNA to build and maintain the physical being that is you?

In this activity, you will develop your own explanation of the relationship between genotype and phenotype. You will do this by tracing the series of events that lead to gene expression. The gene you will study is that for sickle-cell disease. Sickle-cell disease is the potentially fatal condition that you read about in Chapter 11. As you and your partner work through this activity, you will create a poster that illustrates the molecular basis of sickle-cell disease. When you have completed your poster, you will use your understanding of gene expression to suggest explanations for how other genes may exert their effects.

Materials   (per team of 2)

poster board   scissors
assorted construction paper   tape or glue
felt-tipped markers or crayons   DVD and player (watch as a team)

PROCESS AND PROCEDURES

Part A   Looking at Sickle-Cell Disease

1. Begin your study of the molecular basis of sickle-cell disease by reading the information in the need to know box. You will learn about this inherited disorder and its associated gene.

2. Review the essay *Incomplete Dominance* on page 510. Consider what the phenotype might be for a person with the genotype $Hb^A Hb^S$.

Hemoglobin and Red Blood Cell Abnormalities in Sickle-Cell Disease

Each year, about one in 625 African American children is born with sickle-cell disease. This disease is caused by an abnormality in **hemoglobin**. Hemoglobin is the protein in red blood cells that carries oxygen to body cells. When the oxygen supply in the blood is low, these abnormal hemoglobin molecules clump together. Normal hemoglobin molecules remain separate. Figure 12.6a shows the difference between the behavior of sickle-cell hemoglobin and normal hemoglobin under conditions of low oxygen.

In a person with sickle-cell disease, the clumping of the hemoglobin molecules at low oxygen levels causes the red blood cells to become long and rigid like a *sickle* instead of remaining round and flexible (Figure 12.6b). That change in cell shape causes a variety of problems in the body. For example, as cells become sickled, they tend to block small blood vessels. This causes pain and damage to the areas that do not receive an adequate blood supply. The long-term effect of repeated blockages may permanently damage a person's internal organs. This includes the heart, lungs, kidneys, brain, and liver. For some people, the damage is so severe that they die in childhood. With good medical care, however, many people with sickle-cell disease can live reasonably normal lives.

As you may recall from Chapter 11, sickle-cell disease is associated with the genotype $Hb^s Hb^s$. People who have this condition have two abnormal genes, one inherited from each parent.

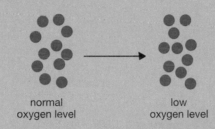

normal   low
oxygen level   oxygen level

normal hemoglobin

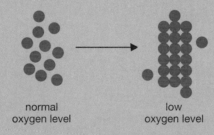

normal   low
oxygen level   oxygen level

sickle hemoglobin

Figure 12.6a Comparison of the behavior of normal and sickle-cell hemoglobin under conditions of low oxygen.

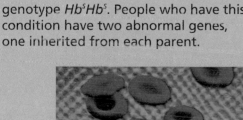

normal red cells   sickle-shaped red cells

Figure 12.6b Comparison of the shapes of normal and sickle-cell red blood cells under conditions of low oxygen.

3. Discuss the following questions with your partner. Contribute to a class discussion as your teacher directs.

   a. What medical symptoms might a person with sickle-cell disease experience?

   b. What problem in the red blood cells causes these symptoms to happen?

   c. What problem in the behavior of the hemoglobin molecules is associated with these changes in an individual's red blood cells?

   d. Think back to your knowledge of DNA structure. What might be the *molecular basis* for the phenotype of sickle-cell disease?

4. Work in teams of 2 to create a poster that illustrates the molecular basis of sickle-cell disease. Use the materials that your teacher provides and the information in Figure 12.7. Your poster should have a place for a title (you will add this later). It should have each of the numbered sections that you see in Figure 12.7.

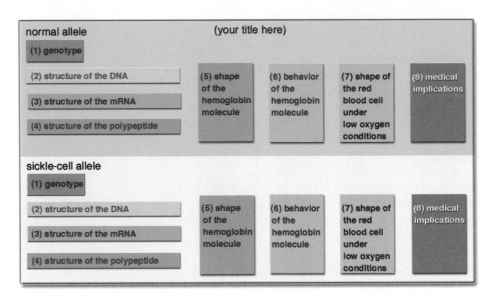

Figure 12.7 Sample poster design. Use this outline as a model for the poster that you will create to explain the molecular basis of sickle-cell disease.

5. Use the information that you gathered in steps 1 and 2 to complete areas 1, 6, 7, and 8 of your poster. Refer to Figure 12.7 to determine the information required in each of these sections.

   On your poster, include pictures and words that you think would be appropriate and helpful. Add a descriptive label to each area so that a viewer will understand what each section is displaying.

Part B   Looking at the Structure of the Gene Involved in Sickle-Cell Disease

1. To understand in more detail how the information present in the hemoglobin gene is related to sickle-cell disease, refer to the DNA sequences on the copymaster that your teacher provides. Use these sequences as paper models of the same portion of 2 different alleles of the hemoglobin gene.

2. Compare the 2 nucleotide sequences.

   a. Draw an arrow or a circle on your poster to indicate the nucleotides in the sickle-cell sequence that differ from those in the normal sequence.

   b. What type of mutations exist in the sickle-cell allele?

3. Cut out and attach your DNA sequences to the appropriate places on your team's poster.

Part C   Looking at the Expression of the Gene Involved in Sickle-Cell Disease

1. Determine how the difference in sequence between the normal and sickle-cell alleles of the hemoglobin gene results in the symptoms associated with the disease. Determine the messenger RNA (mRNA) sequence that corresponds to the DNA sequence that you examined in Part B. This will help you understand how protein synthesis, using the 2 DNA sequences, results in the production of different proteins.

One member of your team should generate an mRNA based on the DNA sequence that represents the allele for normal hemoglobin. The other member of your team should generate an mRNA based on the DNA sequence that represents the sickle-cell allele.

To complete this step, you will need more information about messenger RNA and the process by which mRNA is synthesized. Read the essay *The Expression of Genetic Information* (page 521), and watch the DVD segment "Transcription."

PAGE 521

2. Attach your mRNA models to the appropriate places on your team's poster.

3. Compare (a) the mRNA that results from the transcription of the normal allele of the hemoglobin gene to (b) the mRNA that results from transcription of the sickle-cell allele. On your poster, use an arrow or a circle to indicate the nucleotides in the sickle-cell mRNA that differ from those in the normal sequence.

4. Refer to the genetic code table (Figure E12.13, page 526). Use the table to determine the sequence of amino acids that would result from translating the mRNA that you built from your original DNA sequence.

Each member of the team should translate 1 of the mRNA molecules.

To complete this step, you will need more information about the genetic code and how mRNA is translated into protein. Read the essays *Translating the Message in mRNA* (page 524) and *Landmark Discovery: White-Coated Sleuths Decipher Genetic Code* (page 527).

PAGE 524

PAGE 527

5. Post your amino acid sequences in the appropriate places on your team's poster.

6. Compare (a) the amino acid sequence that results from transcription and translation of the normal allele for the hemoglobin gene with (b) the amino acid sequence that results from transcription and translation of the sickle-cell allele. On your poster, use an arrow or a circle to indicate the amino acids in the sickle-cell protein sequence that differ from those in the normal sequence.

7. Read the information in the need to know box. You will learn about the relationship between the sequence of amino acids in a hemoglobin molecule and the molecule's shape.

The Sequence of Amino Acids Determines the Hemoglobin Molecule's Shape

Inside the environment of a red blood cell, a molecule of normal hemoglobin consists of four protein chains folded into a globular shape. The molecule remains folded in this manner because attractive forces occur between amino acids in different parts of the molecule's protein chains.

A change in the amino acid sequence can take place because of the single nucleotide mutation in the hemoglobin gene. This, however, has no effect on the molecule's overall shape when oxygen levels are normal. For that reason, sickle-cell hemoglobin behaves just like normal hemoglobin under such conditions.

When oxygen levels are low, however, the change in a single amino acid alters the attractive forces inside the molecule. That causes molecules of sickle-cell hemoglobin to assume a different shape from those of normal hemoglobin. As Figure 12.8 shows, it is the change in molecular shape under low oxygen levels that causes sickle-cell hemoglobin to form the rigid rods characteristic of the condition.

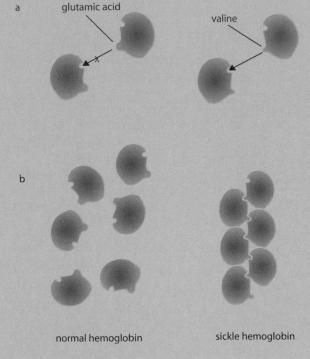

normal hemoglobin   sickle hemoglobin

Figure 12.8   Normal and sickle hemoglobin. The difference in behavior of sickle-cell hemoglobin is related to a change in shape that takes place at low oxygen levels. This shape change results from the amino acid valine replacing a glutamic acid. **(a)** Molecules of normal hemoglobin will not associate with each other. This is because the bulge created by the glutamic acid is too large to fit into a pocket in another hemoglobin molecule. Molecules of sickle hemoglobin, however, will associate with each other. This is because the bulge created when valine replaces the glutamic acid is small enough to fit into the pocket. (The size of the pocket does not change.) **(b)** Molecules of normal hemoglobin remain in solution, even under conditions of low oxygen. In contrast, molecules of sickle hemoglobin associate together to form rigid cells under low oxygen conditions.

8. Add what you learned in step 7 to the appropriate places on your team's poster.

9. Complete your team's poster by adding a descriptive title. Include any other details that you think would help someone else understand the information that it presents.

> Take this opportunity to check your poster. The information on your poster should reflect what you understand about how human cells use the information stored in the nucleotide sequence of their DNA to build and maintain the human being that those cells compose.

Analysis

Use the information on your poster and in the essays to respond to the following. Record your responses in your journal. Your teacher will use your journal to evaluate your understanding of gene expression.

1. Draw Figure 12.9 in your journal. Leave room on your drawing to add components (when necessary) and labels for the following:

amino acid	nucleotide
cytoplasm	protein
mRNA	tRNA
nucleus	

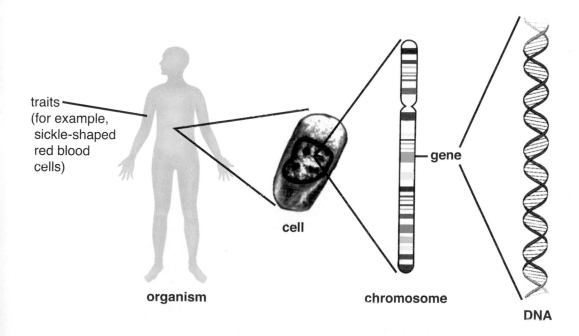

Figure 12.9 This diagram shows the relationships between an organism, a cell, a chromosome, and DNA. An organism is made up of cells. Cells contain chromosomes. Chromosomes consist of DNA. Sections along the DNA that provide information are called *genes*. (Note: This diagram is not drawn to scale.)

2. In Chapter 11, you read about cystic fibrosis, a common recessive condition. The gene involved in cystic fibrosis normally codes for a transport protein that affects the flow of ions across membranes. When mutated, the now faulty version of that protein limits the body's normal ability to secrete fluids into the respiratory and digestive systems. Think about what you now know about gene expression. Create a flowchart that illustrates how the genotype *cc* might lead to the medical problems associated with the phenotype of cystic fibrosis.

   The poster that you made on sickle-cell disease may suggest a general scheme for your outline.

3. Refer back to the copy of Figure E12.1 in your journal. Redraw that figure. Add the processes of transcription and translation. Explain the locations that you chose.

Elaborate

A Closer Look at Protein Synthesis

In the activity *Modeling DNA*, you discovered the structure and replicating mechanism of DNA. Each team made its own model. Each sequence was unique. This variety of DNA sequences mirrors real life. Not all DNA sequences are exactly alike. Even the genes that give instructions for the same thing, for example, eye color, are not exactly alike. The variation in the nucleotide sequence of DNA helps to explain the diversity of life. All organisms use the same mechanism to give instructions and transfer information. But the sequence of nucleotides contributes to the variation within a species and among all living organisms.

DNA sequences code for the production of proteins within an organism. But isn't a protein something you find in meat, nuts, and dairy products? In an organism, proteins are much more than that. Proteins play a role in almost all of life's natural processes. For example, enzymes are proteins that help reactions take place. Some enzymes in your stomach help break down the food you eat. Replication enzymes help DNA to replicate. Insulin is another protein. It is a type of hormone that aids in controlling the level of sugar in your body. Other proteins produce pigments that determine the color of your eyes and hair. Collagen is a protein that helps make your skin and bones strong. Proteins like hemoglobin help move oxygen around your body. Antibody proteins help your body fight off illness. Proteins help give cells their structure and shape. Those are just a few examples of the variety of proteins and what they do. DNA contains the original instructions to make all of the different types of proteins.

Of course, one set of instructions cannot be used to make many different types of proteins. Like different recipes give instructions for different food dishes, different DNA sequences give instructions for different proteins.

When scientists describe protein synthesis conceptually, they generally focus on the translation process as the final step in the transfer of information from DNA to RNA to protein.

However, scientific inquiry into protein synthesis does not end with this general appreciation of the important role of translation. The details of this process are the focus of much current research. Scientists investigate the cellular mechanisms that control how the language of nucleic acids is translated into the language of proteins. This helps them to understand exactly how the final transfer of information from nucleic acid to protein takes place. In this activity, you will elaborate on your understanding of gene expression. You will examine the intricate and elegant details of translation.

Materials

DVD and player

PROCESS AND PROCEDURES

Part A   Understanding Translation

1. Copy the symbols from Figure 12.10 into your journal. Label them.

   You will need to know these symbols to explain the events in the DVD segment.

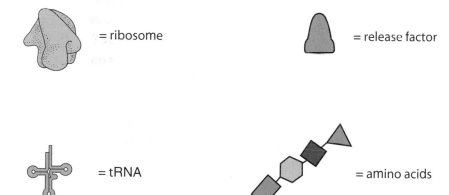

= ribosome

= release factor

= tRNA

= amino acids

Figure 12.10   Symbols used in the DVD segment on protein synthesis.

2. Watch the animated DVD segment "A Closer Look at Protein Synthesis: Translation" according to your teacher's instructions.

   Record notes in your journal that describe the steps involved. Watch the segment as many times as necessary.

3. Read the essay *Cellular Components in Protein Synthesis* (page 527). Take brief notes to use as you complete the rest of this activity.

PAGE 527

4. With your partner, write an explanation of the translation process. Your teacher will collect your explanation. A thorough explanation will include answers to the following questions:

   a. What structures are necessary for protein synthesis?

   b. How is the ribosome involved in protein synthesis?

c. How does the nucleotide sequence of each mRNA codon help position each tRNA? How many nucleotides are involved in this positioning?

d. Think about the mechanism of positioning tRNA on mRNA. How is this similar to the mechanism that holds DNA together as a double strand?

e. What happens to adjacent amino acids once they are positioned on the ribosome?

f. How is the sequence of mRNA nucleotides related to the sequence of amino acids in the protein?

g. What events cause protein synthesis to stop? Is there a special mRNA nucleotide sequence or another factor that contributes to stopping translation?

h. What happens to the protein after translation?

5. Watch the 2nd part of the DVD segment "A Closer Look at Protein Synthesis: Translation." Discuss with your partner how that translation sequence differs from the 1st.

6. Participate in a class discussion of the explanations that you developed in step 4. What is the significance of what you observed in step 5?

The essay *Cellular Components in Protein Synthesis* should help to clarify the process of protein translation.

Part B   Predicting the Effects of Mutations

Topic: genetic mutation
Go to: www.scilinks.org
Code: human3E466

What happens when a mutation occurs? The consequences of a mutation might or might not have an effect on the message the DNA is sending. Imagine a blueprint for a building. The length of a wall might be written on the blueprint as 100 feet. What if the architect accidentally spills her lunch on the blueprint? The carpenter begins to measure the boards according to the lengths on the blueprint, but reads 10 feet instead of 100 feet. The carpenter may notice this mistake and repair it. (Some DNA repairing enzymes do this in the cell.) If the carpenter does not fix it, it may affect the structural properties of the building.

Changes in DNA take place spontaneously. Some changes happen naturally. Human influence causes other changes. Sometimes changes are due to environmental or chemical effects. Chemicals in tobacco smoke, charcoal-grilled foods, and toxic wastes contain substances that can cause mutations. Certain types of radiation also are known to cause mutations, such as ultraviolet (UV) radiation. UV radiation from the sun can damage DNA. Sometimes there are mistakes that take place spontaneously during the normal process of DNA replication. The cell has repair enzymes that patrol the DNA for defects. If a mutation is detected, damaged nucleotides are cut out and replaced with correct nucleotides. However, the mistakes are not always caught. Just as the carpenter might not detect the mistake in the blueprint, the repair mechanisms in a cell might not always catch or be able to repair mutations.

Because DNA is so important to life, significant numbers of copying errors would result in serious consequences. Complete the following steps to develop a deeper understanding of the possible effects of mutation on an individual's phenotype.

1. Write the mRNA sequence that would be produced by transcription from the following DNA strand:

   TACTTCGATCAGTAAGCTATGGACGACCAGAGCACGATCGACT

   The single strand of DNA nucleotides shown above is the strand that is transcribed into mRNA. This ultimately gives rise to a protein.

2. Refer to the genetic code table (Figure E12.13, page 526). Determine the sequence of amino acids that would result from translation of the mRNA from step 1.

3. Use the same process you used in steps 1 and 2 to determine the effect of the following mutation:

   TACTTC_TATCAGTAAGCTATGGACGACCAGAGCACGATCGACT

4. Identify the mutation in the following strand of DNA. Specify its effect.

   TACTTCGATCGTAAGCTATGGACGACCAGAGCACGATCGACT

   Use the DNA strand from step 1 as your reference.

5. Identify the effect of the following DNA mutation:

   TACTTCGATCAGTAAGCTATGGACGAGCAGAGCACGATCGACT

6. Which of the 3 mutations in Part B most likely would give rise to a functional protein?

Analysis

Review the essay *Replication Errors and Mutation* (page 519). Discuss the following with your partner. Record your responses in your journal.

1. Describe how mutations take place.

2. When would you expect mutations to be passed from parent to offspring? When would you not expect this to happen?

3. What kinds of effects might mutations have? Explain two different examples.

4. Provide a specific example. How might mutations influence evolution?

5. Describe why protein synthesis is important to living systems.

Genetic Technology

Elaborate

In this activity, you will apply your understanding of the basic principles of gene action. You will learn how scientists study and manipulate genetic material. You also will discuss the potential positive and negative effects of gathering genetic information and manipulating the genes of organisms. Then you will simulate these genetic manipulations by conducting a DNA-based genetic screening test. When you have completed this activity, you will understand how it is that in recent years, geneticists have started to identify and document the molecular similarities that make us all human. You will also appreciate the molecular variability that uniquely identifies each of us.

Materials   (per team of 2)

pop beads or colored paper clips

PROCESS AND PROCEDURES

Part A   Gene Manipulation: Science and Society

In this part of the activity, you and your partner will study two rapidly growing areas of genetic research and technology. You then will analyze the ethical consequences that may result from those technologies.

1. Decide with your teammate who will study genetic engineering and who will study the Human Genome Project.

2. Working individually, read the appropriate essays for your topic. Read carefully so that you will be well prepared to analyze the subject and teach your partner about it.

   If you are studying genetic engineering, read the essays *Landmark Discovery: Extraordinary New Technique Changes Biology Forever* (page 529) and *Manipulating Genetic Material* (page 530).

   If you are studying the Human Genome Project, read the essays *Landmark Discovery: New Technique Discovered While Driving* (page 536), *Informatics: Mapping and Sequencing the Human Genome* (page 537), and *Genetic Screening: A Dilemma for All of Us* (page 539).

3. Use the information from your assigned essays and any other reliable resources to complete the following tasks. Record your responses in your journal. Be prepared to explain your topic and answers to your teammate.

   a. Identify and summarize at least 2 major ethical issues related to the technology associated with your topic.

   b. Explain at least 1 benefit and 1 concern related to each of the major ideas that you summarized in step 3a. Be sure to include discussion of the issue from different views.

   c. Describe how the issues that you explained have already affected or might affect you and others in the future.

   d. Explain your own opinions with regard to the balance between benefits and concerns that you identified in step 3b.

   e. Recommend what you think should be done about the issues that you have summarized.

4. With your teammate, take turns teaching each other about your topics.

   Discuss the responses that you wrote in step 3a–e. Be sure that you respect your teammate's right to have a different opinion than you.

5. In your journal, write 2 or 3 paragraphs that summarize your teammate's topic. Include the benefits and concerns that are tied to the related technologies.

Topic: Human Genome Project
Go to: www.scilinks.org
Code: human3E468a

 PAGE 529   PAGE 530

 PAGE 536   PAGE 537

 PAGE 539

Topic: genetic engineering/ recombinant DNA
Go to: www.scilinks.org
Code: human3E468b

6. Write 1 paragraph that explains how recombinant DNA technology influenced genetic engineering. Write a 2nd paragraph that explains how polymerase chain reaction techniques influenced the Human Genome Project.

Part B   Getting a Handle on Molecular Variability

1. To deepen your understanding of variability at the molecular level, read the following information:

You had a basic understanding of human variability long before you started this course. Even as an infant, you used differences in smell and sound to distinguish some humans from others. (You likely did not know what you were doing, however.) As you got older, you noticed other differences among people as well. These included differences in appearance, in attitude and behavior, and in health. Gradually, you began to understand that variability intellectually. You began to understand that humans are similar. We can easily identify each other as human. Yet, we are also significantly different.

In Chapters 10 and 11, you focused on the molecular level of human characteristics. You studied the similarities and differences that we see. You learned how these characteristics reflect underlying similarities and differences in our genetic materials—the structures of our DNAs. Although we are more similar than we are different, the study of genetics tends to focus on differences. Until about 1980, it was only through tracing such phenotypic differences (many of them health-related) that scientists were able to recognize and describe either the ways in which we are similar or the ways in which we are different.

Hypothetical DNA Sequences

Sequences A and B in Figure 12.11 below represent two slightly different versions (two different alleles) of a nucleotide sequence within the same portion of a human autosomal chromosome. Some people carry Sequence A; other people carry Sequence B. Because each of us carries two chromosomes of each type, some people may carry both sequences.

Sequence A:

CCTGCAGAATTCGTTGAATTC

Figure 12.11
Hypothetical DNA sequences.

Sequence B:

CCTGCAGAATTCGTTGATTTT

Do all genotype differences result in visible phenotype differences? A hint for the answer to that question was provided in the opening story about the investigation into the Romanov murders. Scientists used DNA "fingerprinting" evidence to identify human bones. Why do you think that such a procedure is possible? What is it about the structure of DNA that makes one person's genetic material distinct? Are all such molecular differences associated with some physical effect? What tools do we have available today that can help us study these differences?

2. Use pop beads and the key in Figure 12.12 to make a model of each sequence in Figure 12.11.

   One team member will make a model of Sequence A. The other team member will model Sequence B.

3. Examine the sequences. Identify any differences.

4. What is the term for an individual carrying both sequences in their DNA?

5. Discuss the following questions with your partner. Record your answers in your journal.

   a. What is the molecular difference between Sequence A and Sequence B? Answer specifically.

   b. Would you expect that the polypeptide produced by transcription and translation of Sequence A would differ from that produced from B? Why or why not? Support your answer with specific evidence.

      Review the essay *Translating the Message in mRNA* (page 524) before you answer this question. Be sure to support your answer with specific evidence.

   c. Think about your answer to question 5b. Do you think that you could detect a difference in phenotype between a person with Sequence A and a person with Sequence B? Why or why not?

6. A **restriction enzyme** is a particular kind of protein that cuts DNA at a specific location between nucleotide base sequences. The restriction enzyme *Eco* R1 recognizes the DNA sequence GAATTC. It cuts the DNA between the G and the A each time it encounters that sequence. Locate the places on your model of Sequence A that *Eco* R1 would recognize. Break the strand at the appropriate points. Do the same for Sequence B.

7. Discuss the following questions with your partner. Record your answers in your journal.

   a. When *Eco* R1 cuts Sequence A, how many bases long is each fragment?

      You can determine this by counting the beads in each fragment.

   b. When *Eco* R1 cuts Sequence B, how long is each fragment?

   c. Special laboratory tests exist that can distinguish DNA pieces of one length from DNA pieces of another length. How could you use *Eco* R1 and these lab tests to distinguish a person carrying Sequence A from another person carrying Sequence B?

   d. How does this procedure give you a way to identify molecular variability?

 = adenine

 = thymine

 = cytosine

 = guanine

Figure 12.12 Use this key to make a model of each DNA sequence.

Analysis

You have just used RFLPs (pronounced "riflips") to test for the presence of a particular genotype difference that occurs among members of the human population. RFLP stands for **R**estriction **F**ragment **L**ength **P**olymorphism. In the laboratory, scientists use **electrophoresis** to determine the lengths of DNA fragments. These fragments are produced when a piece of DNA is treated with a restriction enzyme. During electrophoresis, an electric field is used to draw DNA fragments through a gel medium. Fragments of different lengths will travel different distances through the gel medium. Small fragments will move through the gel more rapidly than do large fragments.

As you have seen, differences in the fragment lengths reveal differences in the nucleotide sequence of the DNA sample. Those sequence differences are examples of variability *at the molecular level*. Some of those differences appear to be associated with detectable phenotypic differences among humans. Others do not appear to be associated with any differences.

1. Read the information in the need to know box. It describes how a similar test can help scientists distinguish chromosomes that carry the sickle-cell allele from those that carry the normal allele for human hemoglobin. Discuss with your partner the questions that follow. Record your answers in your journal.

Topic: RFLP
Go to: www.scilinks.org
Code: human3E471

NEED TO KNOW

A Genetic Test for Sickle-Cell Anemia

As you saw in the activity *Gene Expression*, a mutation in the DNA that codes for hemoglobin is the cause of sickle-cell disease. The mutation changes the amino acid glutamate in normal hemoglobin to the amino acid valine in sickle hemoglobin. The mutation also eliminates a restriction enzyme recognition site. The presence or absence of this restriction site is the basis for an accurate prenatal DNA test. This test determines whether a developing fetus has sickle-cell disease, sickle-cell trait, or normal hemoglobin.

a. Look at Sequences A and B on the copymaster that your teacher provides. These sequences represent the same nucleotide sequence sections of the normal and the sickle-cell alleles of the human hemoglobin gene. What is the difference between Sequence A and Sequence B?

b. Think about this difference and your knowledge of the genetics that underlie sickle-cell disease. What can you predict about an individual who has only Sequence A in his or her genetic makeup? What if the individual has only Sequence B?

c. The restriction enzyme MstII recognizes the DNA sequence GGTCTCC. It cuts the DNA between the first T and the first C each time it encounters that sequence. How could you use MstII to distinguish the gene for sickle hemoglobin from the gene for normal hemoglobin? Answer specifically in terms of the fragment lengths you would expect to see in each case.

d. Assume that a woman undergoes prenatal diagnosis to determine whether her fetus has sickle-cell disease. Below are two possible test results for the developing fetus. What is the diagnosis for each result?

test result 1: fragment sizes = 4, 14, 10, 5

test result 2: fragment sizes = 4, 24, 5

PAGE 540

2. Read the essay *Shaping the Future* (page 540). In your journal, choose one issue that you discussed in this activity. Explain how it relates to Loren Eiseley's idea that the power humans have carries with it a responsibility.

Evaluate

Words to Live By

You have been learning about DNA, its structure, and how it functions. DNA is an incredible code that provides instructions for life. It is a constant in all living organisms. Through its sequence, it provides the variety of life that you see. This has been a chapter with many detailed concepts. One good way to keep track of those details and demonstrate your understanding is through diagrams such as concept maps. In this activity, you will use what you have learned to describe how the concepts you have studied are distinctive and how they overlap. You will work in teams of two for this activity.

PROCESS AND PROCEDURES

A Venn diagram is a figure that compares the characteristics of 2 or more concepts. To create a Venn diagram, you need to ask yourself what you know about the concepts that you will include. You create a list of all you know. You then categorize the characteristics that you listed as either being unique or shared. When you transfer the concepts and characteristics to your diagram, the overlapping areas on the diagram will represent shared characteristics. The Venn diagram in Figure 12.13 shows how 2 concepts might overlap.

1. Copy the Venn diagram in Figure 12.13 into your journal. Your teacher also will have the Venn diagram drawn on the board.

2. Think about characteristics of DNA replication and protein synthesis. Contribute your ideas to a class list on the board. Copy these ideas into your journal.

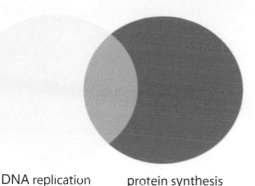

Figure 12.13 The outline of a Venn diagram relating DNA replication and protein synthesis.

DNA replication   protein synthesis

3. Participate in a class discussion about the characteristics listed. In the Venn diagram, list those characteristics that are distinctive to 1 concept or the other (replication or protein synthesis). Then list those characteristics that are common to both concepts. Put characteristics that are common to both concepts in the area where the 2 circles overlap. Put characteristics specific to each concept in the portions of the circles that do not overlap.

Analysis

You have generated a list of characteristics that describe DNA replication and protein synthesis. How do they relate? In Chapter 10, you used another type of diagram, a concept map, to describe visually how some genetic concepts are related. In this part of the chapter evaluate, you will create a new concept map. This map will reflect your understanding of continuity and gene action.

1. Obtain a rubric from your teacher. Study the guidelines that will be used to evaluate your concept map.

2. Create a concept map about continuity and gene action that follows these guidelines:

   a. Identify the key concepts. In this activity, use the concepts and characteristics your class generated in the Venn diagram.

   b. Start with a main idea. Subdivide it into categories that go from general concepts to more specific ones.

   c. Look for cross-links between concepts on different parts of the map.

   Concept maps can be done in different ways. But it is important that you know how the terms are related to each other. Your concept map is evidence of the understanding that you have developed in Unit 4. Think carefully. Use your journal as a resource for genetic terminology and concepts to include in your map. Remember, your teacher will use your concept map to evaluate your understanding.

Continuity through Reproduction

Four thousand new bacteria in 6 hours. Six kittens in 2 months. One elephant in a little under 2 years (see Figure E10.1). More, more, more! What biological function is served by making more organisms? Whether it is a bacterium, a cat, a tree, or an elephant, every individual organism results from some type of reproductive process. **Reproduction** is the making of offspring by one or more parents. All species depend on reproduction for continued survival.

You may think of birth and death as abrupt events. Life, however, is a continuous process for a species. Your individual existence came about through the fusion of your parents' egg and sperm cells. The genetic blueprints within those egg and sperm cells were passed through millions of generations. The evidence for evolution indicates that you are part of a living journey that began on this planet more than 3 billion years ago. Reproduction made this journey possible. We can trace human ancestry back through the millennia using fossil records and biochemical methods. Using these methods, scientists have discovered evidence that links humans to other species. This evidence also shows how new species slowly emerge.

Do you ever think about your ancestors? Do you wonder about future children and grandchildren? In our own lives, we place great importance on individual life—on how long an individual human lives. When we think of other species, however, we focus on the species as a whole, not on individuals. For example, we think of a blue jay as a member of a living species. We rarely mark the life and death of a single blue jay. We view continuity as the ongoing presence of blue jays. Because all individuals eventually die, the existence of any species depends on reproduction.

You, like all mammals, had two biological parents. Each parent contributed to your genetic plan. Your genetic plan is a combination of information from two sources. It is possible through **sexual reproduction**. Sexual reproduction requires the union of

Figure E10.1 Elephants have the longest pregnancy of any mammal in the world—close to 22 months. The young nurse for 3 or 4 years.

specialized reproductive cells called **gametes**. Gametes differ from all other cells. They have only half of the genetic information that other cells have. The female parent produces the gametes known as eggs or **ova** (singular: ovum). The male parent produces the gametes known as **sperm**. Figure E10.2 shows ova and sperm of several species. When ova and sperm come together during sexual reproduction, their nuclei fuse. The product of their fusion is a **zygote**. This zygote has the potential to develop into a new organism. It carries a unique combination of genetic information contributed by the ova and the sperm. Humans, plants that grow from seeds, cockroaches, and elephants are all products of sexual reproduction. They all come from the union of gametes produced by two parents.

Not all organisms result from two parents. A hydra, for example, is a tiny animal that lives in water. Hydras can reproduce sexually by forming ova and sperm. They also can reproduce asexually by forming buds on the side of their bodies, as illustrated in Figure E10.3b. The bud enlarges until it grows into a new hydra that breaks off from the parent. Unless a mutation alters a particular trait, the offspring will have the same genetic pattern as its parent. Offspring produced from a single parent are called **clones**. This type of reproduction is called **asexual reproduction**, the making of offspring from a single parent. The offspring have a genetic pattern identical to that parent.

Other species reproduce both sexually and asexually. Grass grows from seeds

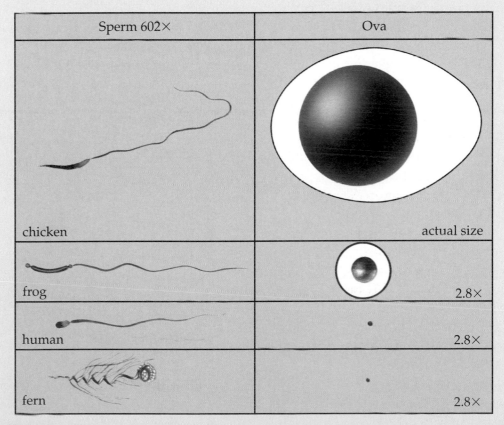

Sperm 602×	Ova
chicken	actual size
frog	2.8×
human	2.8×
fern	2.8×

Figure E10.2 Gametes (ova and sperm) from several species. In each species, sperm are much smaller than the ovum. This difference is apparent when you notice the number above the first column. This number shows that the illustrations of sperm have been enlarged more than those of the ova. Chicken eggs are an example of ova that are incubated outside the body of the mother. These ova have a hard protective shell.

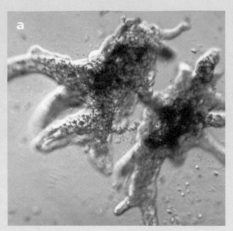
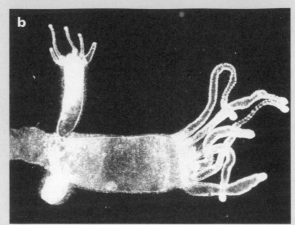
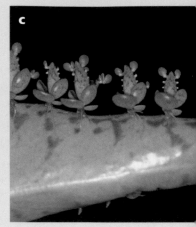

Figure E10.3   Three examples of asexual reproduction.   (**a**) Amoeba (100×) reproduce by simple cell division (binary fission). (**b**) Hydra (100×) can reproduce by forming a bud that grows into a new individual. (**c**) The *Bryophyllum* leaf (1×) sprouts small plantlets that may grow into a new *Bryophyllum*.

(sexual reproduction). It also grows by sending out underground runners (asexual reproduction). Yeast cells produce sexual gametes or asexual buds. Being able to reproduce both sexually and asexually is just one of many reproductive strategies that exists in the five kingdoms of organisms. Other reproductive variations include the following:

- Number of offspring produced
- Length of time and energy the reproductive strategy requires
- Ability of the gametes and offspring to survive

In all of these cases, however, the species survives by continually producing new organisms that replace those that die. ◆

Cloning

Cloning is defined in different ways by various groups and organizations. A commonly used definition is that cloning is the production of genetically identical organisms. Identical twins fit that definition. Yet, accepting identical twins as clones would yield a variety of negative and positive responses. A more widely accepted definition comes from the American Medical Association (AMA): "Cloning is the production of genetically identical organisms via somatic cell nuclear transfer."

Somatic cell nuclear transfer refers to the process of removing the nucleus of an ovum and replacing it with the nucleus of a somatic cell. In that way, the ovum gains a full set of genetic information from the existing organism, without fertilization. The genetic information transferred into the ovum may

have no relation to the ovum. The last four words of the AMA's definition gives a much more complete picture of what cloning means to most people today.

One of the world's most famous clones was a sheep named Dolly. We will use Dolly to illustrate the last four words of the AMA's definition. A cell was removed from the udder of a 6-year-old white-faced ewe (a *somatic cell*). An egg cell was removed from a black-faced sheep, and its nucleus was removed. The somatic cell was fused with the egg cell, from which the nucleus had been removed (*nuclear transfer*). Thus, the ovum gains a whole set of genetic information from the existing organism, without fertilization. At this point, the egg cell contained its original cytoplasm, including mitochondria and DNA. But it had the nucleus of another sheep. An electric shock was used to stimulate the egg cell to divide and develop. The egg cell developed normally to an early embryonic stage. It was then transplanted into a surrogate, black-faced ewe. On July 5, 1996, 148 days later, Dolly was born. Dolly appeared to have all the traits of the white-faced ewe whose somatic cell had been used in the cloning procedure.

Since Dolly, there have been clones of mice, cattle, and pigs. Does this mean that in the near future there will be human clones? Few doubt that the biological processes of human cloning could be successful with further research. However, the ethical implications—the "rights" and "wrongs"—of human cloning must be explored. We must develop an acceptable, comprehensive, and intelligent plan before human cloning has a chance to become a reality.

Dr. Arthur Caplan is the director of the Center for Bioethics and professor of bioethics at the University of Pennsylvania. He was asked to describe the ethical pros and cons of cloning. He stated, "The pros are that you might be able to help infertile individuals and couples have children, and by making cloned cells, you might find a way to make tissues and organs to treat diseases. That's called therapeutic cloning. The cons are that human cloning is not safe. Animal cloning has produced many dead, deformed, and diseased animals. However, I do favor making cloned cells for research" (2001). Some data that support Dr. Caplan's objection come from experiences in cloning Dolly. It took scientists 277 tries before Dolly was created. In 277 nuclear fusions, only 29 embryos developed. Only 13 embryos appeared normal

Figure E10.4   Dolly and her lamb. Dolly, a clone, was able to breed normally to produce her first lamb in April 1998.

enough to implant in 13 ewes. Only Dolly's surrogate mother gave birth. Experts say that the technique that produced Dolly fails 97 percent of the time. In addition, Dolly developed arthritis at age $5\frac{1}{2}$, raising other concerns.

In 2003, scientists decided to euthanize Dolly because she had a serious lung infection. Dolly was relatively young when she got arthritis and the lung disease. Scientists, however, do not know whether the early onset of disease was a result of the cloning process.

As of this writing, a high percentage of scientists and bioethicists seem to oppose human cloning. However, cloning tissues and organs falls under a different category than cloning humans. The majority think that type of cloning would be beneficial to science. ◆

Making More People

On the New Guinea island of Trobriand, a woman completes a long labor and delivers a healthy baby boy. Although the woman has a husband, she and the others present at the birth do not congratulate the father. People in Trobriand emphasize the mother's

contribution to a child's development. Not much importance is placed on the biological link between the baby and his father. The islanders believe that ancestral spirits plant the seeds that enable a fetus to grow. This belief establishes a link between the past and the future. The father does have a role to play, however. They expect him to have intercourse with the mother throughout the pregnancy. Trobriands believe that continued intercourse helps the fetus to grow.

One aspect of the Trobriand view fits with the scientific view. Like the Trobriands, we believe offspring are related to their ancestors. However, science has demonstrated that offspring acquire their genetic heritage from both parents. We also know that pregnancy is not caused by spirits planting seeds in the mother. Instead, pregnancy is caused by an ovum and a sperm coming into contact with each other. To understand more fully how humans reproduce, you need to understand how reproductive structures function and are regulated.

Female anatomy. Did you know that a woman is born with all the ova she will ever have? The ovaries of a female baby contain approximately 2 million **ova**, or gametes. **Ovaries** are the human female **gonads**—the gamete-producing organs. A 7-month-old female **fetus** (prebirth baby older than 8 weeks) has about 7 million ova. But about 5 million die before birth. Approximately 400 of the remaining 2 million mature into healthy ova. These are capable of being fertilized. Ova begin maturing in the ovaries when a female reaches sexual maturity, or **puberty**. Puberty typically happens between the ages of 9 and 14.

Each month, one of the two ovaries (see Figure E10.5) releases a mature ovum. The mature ovum bursts out of the ovary into the body cavity. The ovum then enters a long

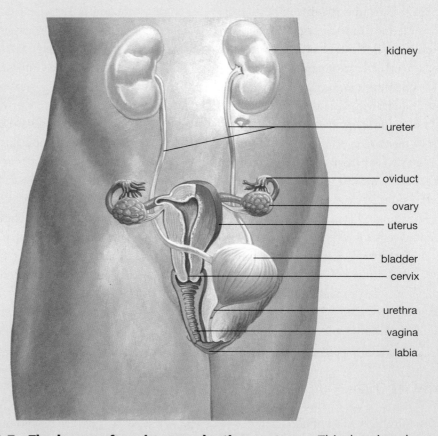

kidney

ureter

oviduct

ovary

uterus

bladder

cervix

urethra

vagina

labia

Figure E10.5   The human female reproductive system.   This drawing shows the internal organs (ovaries) that produce gametes. It also shows the pathway (called the oviduct) that leads from each ovary to the uterus. The uterus expands to accommodate a developing embryo if fertilization occurs. An opening (cervix) at the base of the uterus leads to the vagina, the birth canal. The vagina opens to the external environment. Notice the long path a sperm must travel to join an ovum in one of the oviducts.

tube called an **oviduct**. As you can see in Figure E10.5, there are two oviducts, one near each ovary. If fertilization does not occur, the ovum disintegrates within 24 hours. The oviducts lead to the uterus. The **uterus** is a thick-walled, pear-shaped organ located between the bladder and the rectum.

The vagina connects the uterus and the external reproductive organs. The **vagina** is a muscular and tubular cavity that is penetrated during vaginal intercourse and is the exit canal for menstrual flow. The external female reproductive organs, together, are called the **vulva**. The external reproductive organs include the mons pubis, clitoris, and labia. The **mons pubis** is a pad of tissue covering the pubic bone. During puberty, it becomes covered with hair. The **labia** are folds of skin that protect the genitals. They cover the clitoris and the vaginal and urinary openings. The **clitoris** is a small, elongated organ situated at the front of the vulva. The urethra and urinary opening in the female body are not directly connected to the reproductive organs.

Male anatomy. Unlike a female child, a male child is born without any gametes in his body. **Sperm**, or male gametes, form in the testes at puberty (see Figure E10.6). **Testes** are the male gonads. Sperm take about 74 days to develop. Millions of sperm mature each day in a healthy, young adult male. The difference in the numbers of male and female gametes may surprise you. However, very few sperm survive long enough to reach an ovum.

Figure E10.2 illustrates the size difference between male and female gametes. Sperm are much smaller than ova. In fact, the sperm cell is one of the smallest, most specialized cells of the human body. The head of a sperm cell contains the genetic material that fuses with the genetic material in an ovum to produce a zygote. The midsection of a sperm cell contains many mitochondria. Mitochondria power the sperm cell's swim through the female reproductive tract. The sperm's long tail whips back and forth to direct its movement.

After sperm are produced in the testes, they are stored in the long, coiled tubes of the storage compartment called the **epididymis**. Sperm remain in the epididymis until they are mature. From the epididymis, they pass through paired tubes called the **vas deferens** to the two small sacs called seminal vesicles. The **seminal vesicles** contribute to the production of semen. **Semen** is a white sticky fluid that carries and nourishes the sperm. Semen and sperm cells flow into ejaculatory ducts. These ducts connect the seminal vesicles with the opening of the urethra in the prostate gland. The **prostate gland** produces and adds more fluid to the semen. Another gland, called the **cowpers gland**, produces an alkaline mucus. Thus mucus is secreted before ejaculation to protect sperm from the acidic vagina. That secretion also contains sperm. Thus, fertilization can readily take place if a couple relies on withdrawing the penis before ejaculation for birth control.

The **urethra** is the passageway for both sperm and urine. A muscle near the prostate gland contracts so that no urine can flow through the urethra during ejaculation. **Ejaculation** expels semen from the urethra of the penis during orgasm. During ejaculation, up to 5 mL of semen is released. It contains approximately 300 million sperm cells.

The external male reproductive organs include the penis and scrotum. The **penis** is made up of the shaft and the glans. The **glans** is a rounded gland structure at the tip of the penis. It is covered by the foreskin. The foreskin is sometimes removed (usually in infancy) by a surgical procedure known as *circumcision*. The small opening in the center of the glans is the urinary opening where urine and semen are released.

The **scrotum** is a loose sac of skin and muscle that houses the two testicles. The scrotum regulates the temperature of the testicles. This temperature must be approximately 33°C–34°C (91.4°F–93.2°F, cooler than body temperature) for optimum

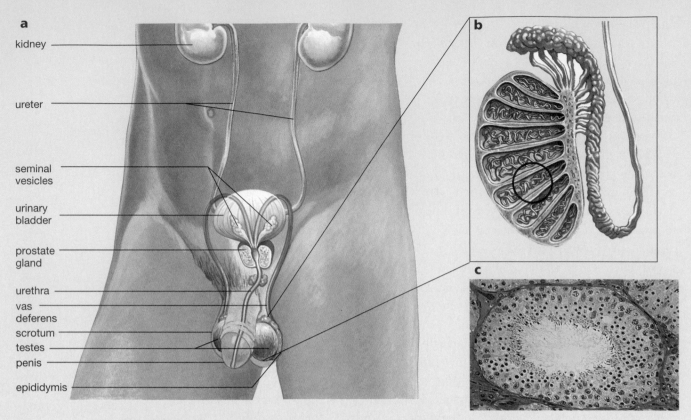

a
kidney
ureter
seminal vesicles
urinary bladder
prostate gland
urethra
vas deferens
scrotum
testes
penis
epididymis

b

c

Figure E10.6   The human male reproductive system.   **(a)** This drawing shows the male sex organs and glands that lie within the body cavity and those that are external. **(b)** Each testis is composed of packed coils of tubules in which sperm develop. **(c)** This photograph is a cross section through a tubule (100×). Around the edge of the central canal are the dark heads of the sperm. Their tails extend into the canal.

sperm production. The male body automatically regulates testicle temperature. It does this by changing the position of the scrotum to be closer or farther from the body.

Sexual intercourse. As a male becomes sexually aroused, the blood flow to the penis increases. Increased blood volume causes the penis to become rigid. This makes it easier to enter the vagina. As the female becomes sexually aroused, blood flow to the vaginal area increases. Glands near the vagina secrete fluids that lubricate the vagina. This eases the movement of the male's penis in the vagina. It also contributes to the mobility of the sperm.

Male ejaculation results from involuntary muscle contractions that follow the stimulation of sensitive nerve endings in the penis. These involuntary muscle contractions take place during male orgasm. **Orgasm** is the peak of sexual stimulation. Ejaculation occurs during

orgasm, releasing sperm-containing semen through the penis. Female orgasm also causes involuntary muscle contractions. These result from stimulation of sensitive nerve endings in the vaginal area, especially the clitoris. These contractions may help transport the sperm upward through the cervix and into the uterus toward the ova. However, fertilization can take place without female orgasm.

The muscle contractions that happen during both male and female orgasm create pleasurable sensations. From an individual human couple's perspective, these sensations enhance the emotional bond between them. From a human species' perspective, the pleasure derived from sexual intercourse helps to ensure continuation of the species.

Fertilization. Fertilization occurs as a result of sexual intercourse. The journey of sperm to the oviducts may take less than an hour. Only a few thousand sperm may survive the trip, however. If an ovum is present in one of the oviducts, sperm swarm around it and release enzymes. The enzymes promote changes in the outer layers of the ovum. This allows the sperm to penetrate these layers. Only one sperm actually penetrates the ovum during fertilization. As soon as penetration takes place, the cell membrane of the ovum changes to prevent entry of any other sperm.

Fertilization usually happens in the oviduct. The single cell that results from the joining of the ovum and sperm is called a **zygote**. The zygote begins a series of cell divisions to produce an **embryo**. The embryo develops as it moves through the oviduct and into the uterus. About 7 days after fertilization, the embryo consists of a ball of cells containing an inner, flattened cavity. At this stage, it begins to implant into the wall of the uterus. The uterus protects the developing embryo. It stretches and grows as the embryo grows.

After implantation, the developing embryo will obtain the nutrients and oxygen it needs from the mother's blood supply. It does this through an organ called the **placenta**. The placenta attaches to the uterine wall. It is connected to the embryo by a ropelike **umbilical cord**. The placenta exchanges nourishment from the mother and waste products from the embryo through the mother's blood. After 8 weeks of growth, the embryo is called a **fetus**.

Birth. Following a 9-month gestation period, uterine contractions push the baby through the cervix into the vagina. The time when a woman's body is undergoing contractions to deliver a baby is called *labor*. Hormones and regulatory feedback loops determine when a woman will begin labor. During labor, contractions become more frequent as the baby nears the vagina and the cervix expands. The vagina functions as the birth canal. The fetus usually travels head first down the birth canal.

The moment when the fetus, followed by the placenta, exits the mother's body is called *delivery*. After delivery, the umbilical cord is cut and clamped near the naval. Finally, mucus is cleared from the baby's mouth, nose, and throat. From that moment forward, the baby's body takes over the processes of maintaining homeostasis. These processes had been taken care of by the mother's body only hours before. ◆

Hormones and Sexual Reproduction

For human females and males, the joining of ova and sperm is highly regulated. Hormones are molecules that regulate the reproductive system during development and after sexual maturity. This regulation mainly involves communication between endocrine glands in the brain and the reproductive organs.

Changes in certain hormonal levels control the onset of puberty. There are many external indicators of sexual maturity. Body proportions change. Underarm and pubic hair grows. An interest in sex begins. Vocal cords lengthen and the voice deepens, especially in males. Facial hair grows.

In addition to those external indicators, there are internal indicators of sexual maturity. In both males and females, the hypothalamus directs the anterior pituitary to release **follicle stimulating hormone (FSH)** and **luteinizing hormone (LH)**. In males, FSH stimulates the testes to produce sperm. LH stimulates the release of the major male sex hormone, **testosterone**, from the testes (see Figure E10.7). In females, FSH and LH are involved in regulating ovulation.

After maturity, hormones continue to signal the events that lead to the production of gametes and that promote sexual behavior.

In a mature male, testosterone stimulates continuous sperm production. Erection of the penis and ejaculation depend on sufficient levels of testosterone in the bloodstream. As shown in Figure E10.7, negative feedback loops between the testes, the hypothalamus, and the anterior pituitary reduce the level of LH and FSH. When the level of testosterone in the blood rises too high, the hypothalamus signals the anterior pituitary to release less LH. Less LH translates into less testosterone released from the testes.

In females, hormonal interactions are similar, but more complex. The ovaries produce the major female sex hormones. These are **estrogen** and **progesterone.** After puberty, these hormones regulate reproductive function. In contrast to sperm, which are produced continually, ova mature and are released from the ovaries as part of a monthly cycle. The **menstrual cycle** is depicted in Figure E10.8. FSH signals an ovum to mature inside a sac, or follicle, on the surface of one ovary. The maturing follicle releases estrogen.

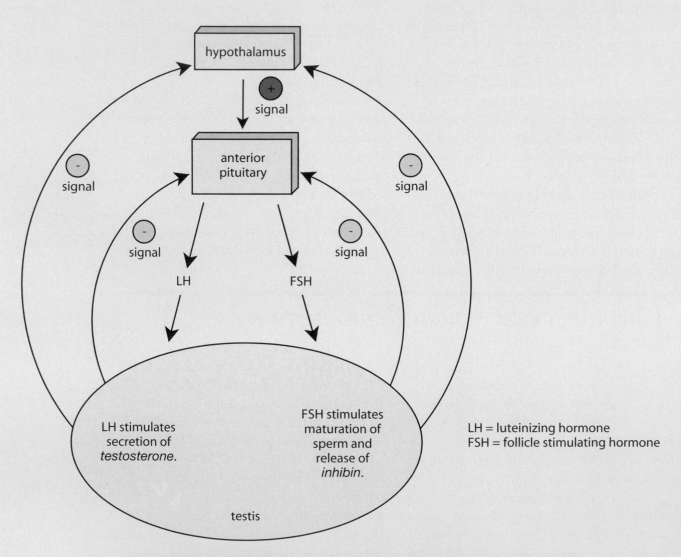

Figure E10.7 **Interaction of hormonal signals between the brain (hypothalamus and anterior pituitary) and the testes in the human male.** Testosterone is the major male sex hormone. But production of viable sperm depends on the action of LH and FSH as well. The involvement of the hypothalamus suggests a mechanism for sexual arousal in response to sexual thoughts.

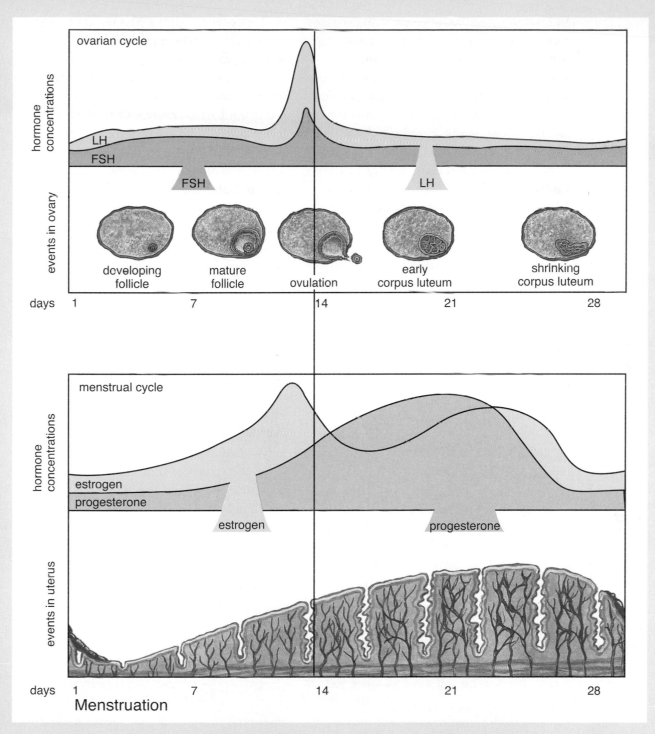

Figure E10.8 The human menstrual cycle. Interactions between the nervous system and several organs, glands, and hormones regulate the cycle. Note how the hormone levels change at ovulation. This makes two very different phases to the cycle.

Estrogen stimulates the secretion of LH. The dramatic rise of LH stimulates ovulation. During **ovulation**, the mature ovum bursts out of the follicle. Ovulation occurs around the middle of the cycle. The entire cycle lasts about 28 days, although it may range from 24 days to more than 35 days.

Estrogen and progesterone also prepare the uterus for a possible pregnancy. During the first half of the cycle, the level of estrogen increases. Estrogen stimulates the inner lining of the uterus to thicken with increased blood vessels. If sperm enter the vagina anytime between a few days before ovulation to a day or so afterward, a sperm and ovum may join. Pregnancy will occur if the resulting embryo implants in the uterus.

An ovum can be fertilized only during a 10- to 15-hour interval after ovulation. Sperm, however, can survive up to 72 hours. This means that sexual intercourse several days before ovulation still may result in pregnancy. Because individual menstrual cycles vary so much, it is extremely difficult to predict exactly when a female will ovulate. Because the timing of ovulation is not predictable, pregnancy can occur if sexually active individuals do not use birth control. No birth control measure (except abstinence) is 100 percent effective. Pregnancy can occur even when these preventive measures are used.

During the second half of the menstrual cycle, the level of progesterone increases (see Figure E10.8). After the ovum leaves the follicle, the follicle reorganizes into a structure called the corpus luteum. The **corpus luteum** secretes progesterone. Progesterone is the hormone responsible for maintaining the thickened, blood-rich inner lining of the uterus. The corpus luteum disintegrates after about 12 days, unless pregnancy occurs. If an embryo implants in the lining of the uterus, a placenta develops from embryonic and maternal tissue. The placenta nourishes the growing embryo. It also secretes progesterone. Progesterone helps maintain the lining of the uterus.

If fertilization does not occur, hormone levels drop. The lowered hormone levels decrease the blood supply to the inner lining of the uterus. Part of the lining then disintegrates and passes from the uterus through the vagina and out of the body. The shedding of the lining is called **menstruation**. During menstruation, a small amount of blood is expelled (between 50 mL and 150 mL—about ¼ cup to a little more than ½ cup). Menstruation begins on day 1 of the cycle.

In humans, fertility declines with age. For females, just as menstruation marks the beginning of sexual maturity, **menopause** marks the end. At menopause, females no longer have a menstrual cycle and no longer ovulate. The effects and timing of menopause vary widely. Menopause usually takes place between the ages of 45 and 50.

For males, sperm production continues. The number and health of their sperm cells, however, may decline as they age. If enough healthy sperm are produced, a male of advanced age is still capable of impregnating a female. ◆

Sexual Activity and Health Hazards

Sexual behavior involves risks. Pregnancy and childbirth pose life and health risks to the mother. Using birth control methods greatly reduces the possibility of pregnancy. However, some birth control methods themselves cause health risks. For example, some people have allergic reactions to spermicidal preparations. Intrauterine devices (IUDs) can cause cramps, increased bleeding during menstruation, and even pelvic inflammatory infections. Oral contraceptives (birth control pills) may increase the chance of stroke, especially among women who smoke.

Sexually transmitted diseases (STDs). Sexual behavior can also increase the risk of contracting a sexually transmitted disease (STD). Sexual behavior usually involves the exchange of body fluids. This exchange provides an excellent route of infection for pathogens. Sexually transmitted pathogens include the viruses that cause AIDS and genital herpes. Other pathogens include the bacteria that cause syphilis, chlamydia, and gonorrhea.

AIDS (acquired immune deficiency syndrome) leads to many devastating illnesses and often death. Casual contact, such as shaking hands with an infected person, does not transfer HIV. HIV is the virus that causes AIDS. Infection requires a transfer of body fluids such as blood, semen, or vaginal secretions. HIV infection most often occurs during intercourse (heterosexual and homosexual) and through the sharing of needles by drug users. A regimen of multiple antiviral drugs slows the progress of the disease. When individuals are first infected by HIV, they usually have no symptoms. But they can still transmit the virus to others. AIDS takes several years to develop. Its symptoms include extreme fatigue, weight loss, reduced resistance to other infections, and cancer.

An estimated one in five of the total adolescent and adult population of the United States is infected with genital herpes. The virus that causes this disease is related to the viruses that cause chicken pox and cold sores. Symptoms of genital herpes are painful sores on the male's penis or the female's vulva, vagina, or cervix. There is no cure for genital herpes. The sores heal and recur throughout an infected person's life. Genital herpes is transmitted through direct contact with the infected area. Infection can occur whether or not sores are present. Although there is no cure, antiviral drugs help relieve the painful symptoms. Outbreaks of sores also become less frequent and milder over time. Genital herpes may be transmitted to babies of infected mothers as they pass through the birth canal. Herpes can cause serious neurological damage to infants. To avoid this, doctors recommend that women with active herpes sores deliver their children by C-section.

The symptoms of syphilis vary depending on the stage of the disease. Each stage is separated by a long period without symptoms. In the early stage, a hard sore called a chancre develops on the male's penis or the female's vagina, or on the hands and lips. Although no symptoms are present after the chancre heals, a blood test would reveal that syphilis bacteria are present. During the second stage, a skin rash develops. This can happen even on the palms and the feet. Individuals are highly infectious during this stage. During the final stage, tissue damage occurs throughout the body, particularly to the nervous system. Untreated, late-stage syphilis causes severe damage to the circulatory and nervous systems, and even death. An estimated 35,000 new cases of syphilis occur annually in the United States. Antibiotics can cure syphilis.

The most common sexually transmitted disease is chlamydia. Chlamydia is caused by a very small bacterium. An estimated 3 million new cases occur in the United States each year. Most people who are infected with chlamydia do not have symptoms and, therefore, do not seek treatment. When symptoms are present, females have inflammation of the opening to the vagina or cervix. Males have inflammation of the epididymis and a watery discharge from the penis. Untreated, chlamydia can cause serious reproductive and other health problems. For example, chlamydia may cause pelvic inflammatory disease in females, resulting in infertility. Babies born to women who have chlamydia may be infected and develop eye inflammations or pneumonia. Antibiotics can cure chlamydia.

Gonorrhea, like syphilis, is a bacterial disease that has afflicted humans since ancient times. Symptoms may or may not be present. If they are, males experience painful urination and pus from the penis. In females, the cervix is infected, causing a discharge from the vagina. If left untreated, gonorrhea may lead to infertility in females. A pregnant woman with untreated gonorrhea may transmit the bacteria that cause the disease to her baby as it passes through the birth canal. The resulting eye infection can lead to blindness, so physicians routinely treat newborns with eyedrops that prevent the disease. An estimated 800,000 new cases of gonorrhea occur each year in the United States. Antibiotics can cure gonorrhea most of the time. However, there has been a dramatic increase in antibiotic-resistant strains of gonorrhea.

The most effective way to avoid contracting a sexually transmitted diseaseis to avoid sex with an infected person. However, infection is not always obvious or known. The use of condoms helps prevent the transmission of many sexually transmitted diseases, although they do not guarantee protection. ◆

Infertility

Couples trying to conceive children are not always successful. Approximately 15 percent of couples in the United States experience infertility. A variety of factors may cause infertility. If the male's sperm count is low or the female does not ovulate or ovulates irregularly, the chances of fertilization decrease dramatically. Oviducts also can become blocked. This prevents the ovum and sperm from meeting and uniting.

Some of these problems can be overcome so that natural fertilization takes place. Vitamins and minerals, hormones, and fertility drugs have been used successfully. Fertility drugs often stimulate the release of more than one ovum. This increases the likelihood of multiple births.

In more difficult cases, however, technology may be used to carry out **in vitro** (literally, "in glass") fertilization. Doctors administer drugs to stimulate ovulation. They then remove several ova from a female's body. They mix the ova with sperm in a glass dish. If fertilization takes place, the zygotes are allowed to develop for a few days inthe glass dish. The resulting embryosare monitored for health and normal development. The doctor then implants several healthy embryos into the woman's uterus. Doctors implant more than one embryo to increase the likelihood that at least one will develop and result in a healthy baby. In some cases, couples elect to freeze some of the embryos for future use.

Medical technology solves many fertility problems, but it also creates ethical dilemmas. For example, what happens to those frozen embryos if a couple decides not to use them? Should they be destroyed? Can they be sold? Can they be used for medical research? If a couple divorces, who gets "custody" of the embryos? ◆

Mating Behaviors of Nonhuman Animals

Pacific salmon leave the ocean and swim hard against the current of a freshwater river. The salmon are driven upstream by their instinct to return to a specific location to reproduce. Sexual drive is a physiological mechanism that leads to a wide variety of mating behaviors. Because reproduction is essential for continuity of a species, behaviors that promote mating and reproduction are advantageous. Some behavioral and physical traits give individuals a competitive edge in mating and producing offspring. These traits contribute to sexual selection. **Sexual selection** is a process of natural selection. It involves specific characteristics that one sex prefers in the other. The animal world provides many striking examples.

Bighorn sheep provide an example of dramatic mating behavior. They live in the mountainous regions of western North America. The males often engage in competitive sparring, bashing their heads together as shown in Figure E10.9. These spars take place only during the winter mating (rutting) season. During this time, the males fight to control the areas where females in estrus gather. Massive horns and unique sparring movements may provide an advantage to a particular male. The winners mate more frequently than the losers. This makes it more likely that their traits are passed on to offspring. Fighting is expensive in terms of expended energy, lost time, and injury. Losers do not challenge the winners again. Sometimes young males challenge the dominance of older males in later years.

In many species, actual fighting may not be part of the competitive strategy to attract or gain access to a mate. Simple behavioral displays may be adequate. Males of certain species of grouse, for instance, dance. They gather on a lek, or dancing ground, and begin a synchronized, elaborate display for the females. The males spread their tail feathers, inflate their neck pouches, and produce a booming call to accompany the dance. Females select a mate from the group of displaying males. A male's plumage and the subtle features of his dance may improve the chance that a female will select him. Males of some species, such as the bird of paradise, have extremely elaborate plumage that enhances their courtship display.

Male songbirds frequently express sexual readiness in the form of songs and calls. These vocalizations may announce the male's defense of his territory or his invitation to mate. In wetland areas in the springtime, an evening chorus of male frogs croak to attract

Figure E10.9 **Male bighorn sheep (*Ovis canandensis*) in a competitive sparring match.**

a Male (right) threatens other males.

b Male's red underside attracts female.

c Male starts zigzag dance toward nest; female follows male.

d Male guides female into nest.

e Male taps female near tail; female lays eggs.

f Male bites female; female leaves nest. Male enters nest and fertilizes eggs.

Figure E10.10 **The courtship and reproductive behavior of sticklebacks.**

females. In some species of fish, courtship and mating movements mimic aggressive behaviors. Figure E10.10 illustrates courtship and mating in one such fish, the American stickleback.

In many species, females provide primary care for the young. For these females, being conspicuous can be a disadvantage. Bright colors and elaborate plumage may increase the danger of predation to the mother and her young. Frequently, striking external features are reserved for males. The elaborate plumage of male birds may become a disadvantage, however, because it makes them more visible to potential predators.

Most nonhuman mating behaviors only take place periodically. Those periods happen around the times when species are able to reproduce. For example, most nonhuman mammals have cycles known as *estrus*, or "heat." Estrus takes place only once or a few times a year. Hormones and environmental factors regulate the frequency of the estrus cycle. Unlike the human menstrual cycle, ovulation takes place *during* estrus. Those nonhuman female mammals who have estrus are receptive to males only during that cycle. Animals such as deer, elk, and moose enter into estrus once a year. Most dogs go into estrus twice a year. Mating behavior occurs in those animals around the times when females enter estrus. That behavior is absent or greatly reduced at other times. ◆

Human Mating Behaviors

How do human males and females attract each other's attention? Think about the behaviors, attire, and fragrances of people at dances and other social gatherings. Do you see any parallels between human behavior and the patterns of other animals?

Some human cultures study the patterns and movements of particular animals and incorporate them into their dances and rituals. These cultural behaviors are not transmitted biologically. But many such practices may be adaptive and enhance reproduction.

In humans, the sexual drive has a genetic and physiological basis. Certain physical attributes, such as facial features and body shape proportions, may initially attract a mate. Other less obvious attributes also may attract a mate. Attributes such as good character, good health, and intelligence also may be advantageous to survival and reproduction. ◆

Cultures and Mating Patterns

Think about ceremonies in your community such as baby showers, weddings, and funerals. In every culture, patterns influence the way humans approach birth, marriage, and death. Cultural patterns also influence how we approach daily events, such as gathering and preparing food and raising children.

Human parents play a unique role in the animal kingdom. Unlike most other organisms, human children are a long-term commitment. Human societies around the world often mark sexual maturity with great ceremony. They approach marriage as a significant event.

In a particular tribe in the Amazon forest, adolescent boys undergo an initiation rite that marks them as young men. Two older men make incisions in the boys' skin and fill the wounds with hot, liquid tar. The tar prevents infection and leaves a pattern of scars on the boys' bodies. Although the ritual is painful, the boys are proud to be entering puberty. Similar scarring techniques are used by the Aborigines of Australia's Northern Territory and by the Abelam of Papua, New Guinea.

Among the Abelam, a girl's first menstruation is a time of great celebration. At this time, women cut designs in the skin of the girl's breasts, stomach, and upper arms, and shave her head. This ritual, too, is painful, but is conducted with great celebration.

Figure E10.11 During a Turkana wedding ceremony in northwestern Kenya, the bride's family brings sheep and goats as part of the bridewealth. Men and women dance in the background.

In some cultures, marriage takes place long before the young pair is ready to reproduce, as the following story indicates.

Cultural ceremonies such as marriage promote pair bonds between males and females. In many cultures, this pair bond formed is monogamous. **Monogamy** is a bond between one male and one female. In some cultures, polygamy is practiced. **Polygamy** is a pair bond between a man or woman and multiple spouses. The biological basis for pair bonding makes sense. Raising human offspring takes a long time. The support a parent receives from his or her spouse may be invaluable. Similar patterns exist in other primates, such as gibbons and marmosets. In these primates, adults mate for life and together raise their offspring to maturity.

Sexual behavior, ethics, and public policy. When two people have a child, their genetic information is combined in that child. This basic biology underlies the marriage patterns of many cultures. In certain historical periods of ancient Egyptian culture, brothers and sisters in ruling families sometimes married. The purpose was to increase the purity of the family line and to avoid the genetic influence of outsiders.

More often, however, cultures developed strong taboos against marriage or sexual activity between close relatives. In the Middle Ages in parts of Europe, for example, ruling families were forbidden to marry anyone to whom they were related in the seven previous generations. With such a strict rule, they ran out of eligible marriage partners. In Navajo

SCENARIO

Ashok's family was very pleased with the dowry that they would receive from his bride's family after the wedding ceremony. As is often the custom among Hindu families in the rural Haryana state of India, the groom's family had visited the family of the bride-to-be prior to the wedding to inspect the gifts. Now the evening of the wedding feast had arrived. All preparations for the occasion were complete.

Kamala watched with anticipation as Ashok, her husband-to-be, arrived on horseback from a neighboring village. The approaching darkness enhanced the fireworks display that heralded Ashok's arrival. A small band played. Villagers in elaborate costumes danced in front of the horse and rider.

At the wedding feast, Ashok's family was served first while Kamala and her family waited patiently. The food included a variety of tasty vegetable curries with roti (flat, unleavened bread).

The festivities continued throughout the evening and into the early morning hours. The wedding ceremony could not conclude until 1:27 a.m., the precise time determined by the family astrologer.

Kamala had celebrated her 11th birthday just 2 weeks earlier. Ashok would be 14 next month. The bride and groom would not live together for several more years. It is common in this part of rural India for a father to arrange the marriage of his daughters well before they are old enough to bear children. By tradition, it also is very important that the bride and groom are virgins when they marry.

Kamala's father had spared no expense for this wedding. He had accomplished his duty now that the last of his three daughters was successfully married. Kamala would remain with her parents until one day, perhaps 4 or 5 years later, Ashok would return, with ceremony, to claim his bride.

traditions, a young person is not to marry within his or her clan or the clan of the father. Clans are subgroups within a culture that trace their descent either through their mother's line or through their father's line. Taboos against **incest** (sexual relations between members of the immediate family) provide protection against inbred diseases.

Laws or public policies define how closely related two individuals may be and still marry. Laws may be based on scientific information, such as knowing that parents contribute genes to their offspring. But they also are cultural. There is more than one cultural approach to the same information. Laws reflect a culture's ethical and cultural values. In some societies, religious practices are not separate from the government, and public policy reflects religious beliefs.

Sexual practices among humans are influenced by cultural values and public policy, as well as by individual choices. Sexual activity can have serious physical, emotional, and financial consequences. Indeed, sexual partners not only expose themselves to potential health risks, but they also expose themselves to the potential responsibility for the human being they produce through their union.

Can humans adopt sexual behaviors that consciously avoid these dangers? There is no completely safe sex, only safe abstinence. Individuals who choose to become sexual partners, however, can choose behaviors that decrease the risk of infection. Both partners may undergo medical examinations to ensure that they are free of sexually transmitted diseases. They also may use a physical barrier such as a condom to reduce the chance of fluid (and pathogen) exchange. Pathogen exchange is further reduced by using spermicide with a condom. Some spermicides may kill HIV. These practices *lessen* the odds of infection or pregnancy. But they are *not a guarantee* against infection or pregnancy.

How are these personal choices related to public policy? For one thing, federal regulations determine which methods of birth control are made available. For another thing, society as a whole bears the burden of high-risk behaviors that result in sexually transmitted diseases. High-risk behaviors increase the pressure on medical services, medical costs, the cost of insurance, and so on. ◆

Phenotype and Genotype

Phenotype. Blood type, ear shape, and petal color. These are physical traits that we observe when the information in an organism's genetic plan is expressed biologically. Observable traits are called an organism's **phenotype**. The term phenotype can refer to either a specific trait or to the collection of traits that characterize an entire organism. For instance, we can say that a collie has a long hair rather than a short hair phenotype. We also can say that a collie has a very different phenotype from a Great Dane. A collie is smaller, has longer hair, and shorter legs than a Great Dane. The genetic plan passed from parents to offspring provides the blueprint for the offspring's phenotype. Thus, offspring usually have a phenotype similar to their parents' phenotypes.

Phenotype is not determined solely by the genetic blueprint, however. Environmental factors play a critical role as well. For example, the average height of Japan's population increased by several inches during theearly and middle 20th century (see Figure E11.1). Did the genetic blueprints for the entire population change? No, the environment for the population changed. Japanese children had more nutritious diets in the early and middle 1900s than did children of earlier generations. An environmental limitation (poor diets) had prevented children of earlier generations from reaching the maximum size permitted by their genetic plan. Interactions between the inherited genetic plan and the environment are typical for complex phenotypes such as height and behavior. Complex phenotypes involve many genetic and environmental factors.

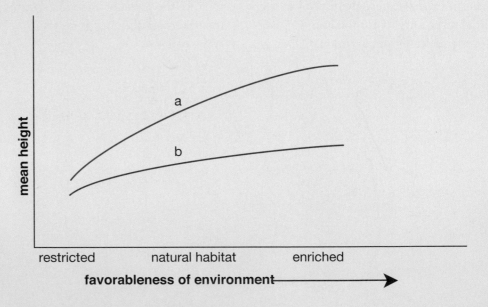

Figure E11.1   Height in Japanese boys and girls in relation to environmental conditions.   Improved environmental conditions in Japan led to a phenotype of increased height during the early and middle 20th century. Curve a represents 15-year-old boys. Curve b represents 13-year-old girls. The units for both mean height and environmental conditions are not to scale. (Based on data from Gottesman, I.I., and L.L. Heston. (1972). *Genetics, Environment, and Behavior.* Academic Press.)

Scientists conducted experiments in the 1930s to test the following hypothesis: *Environmental factors influence how genetic information produces a phenotype.* In a simple yet clever experiment, scientists took cuttings from genetically identical plants. They planted them at varying altitudes. The cuttings grew extremely well at sea level. The cuttings barely grew at higher mountainous altitudes. The results of the experiment demonstrated that the environment affects the phenotype produced from a given genetic plan.

Genotype. If phenotype is the result of a genetic plan that is influenced by the environment, what is the genetic plan itself? The genetic plan, or **genotype**, consists of all of the genetic information in an organism. This genetic information is stored in **DNA** (deoxyribonucleic acid) molecules. The cells of humans and other eukaryotes contain structures called chromosomes. **Chromosomes** are DNA molecules organized around structural proteins. Each human chromosome contains the DNA for just a small part of the total genetic information. However, the DNA in each chromosome contains enough information for many phenotypic traits. The very tip of one human chromosome contains the genetic information that causes the blood to clot. We refer to a particular piece of genetic information as a **gene**. In this example, the gene produces a blood-clotting protein in healthy individuals. (Alexis's hemophilia A resulted from a defective gene. [See *A Royal Tragedy.*] His body could not produce the clotting protein called Factor VIII.)

Each of the 46 human chromosomes contains many genes. The largest chromosome contains about 2,500 genes. The smallest one is the Y chromosome. It contains only about 250 genes. Figure E11.2 illustrates some of the many genes present on two human chromosomes. Each gene occupies a specific location on the chromosome.

Populations include more than one version of most genes. For example, some individuals have a blood type gene that

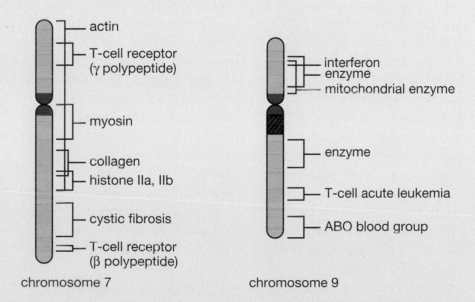

chromosome 7

chromosome 9

Figure E11.2 Each chromosome carries many genes. This illustration shows a few of the genes that have been mapped to two human chromosomes, chromosome 7 and chromosome 9. Humans have two copies of each of 23 different human chromosomes. Each chromosome carries between 250 and 2,500 genes.

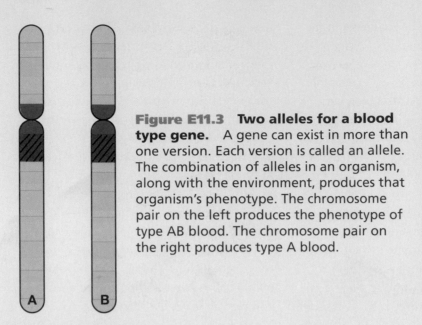

Figure E11.3 Two alleles for a blood type gene.   A gene can exist in more than one version. Each version is called an allele. The combination of alleles in an organism, along with the environment, produces that organism's phenotype. The chromosome pair on the left produces the phenotype of type AB blood. The chromosome pair on the right produces type A blood.

specifies type A blood. Others have a version of the same gene that specifies type B blood. The term **allele** refers to different versions (for example, type A and type B) of the same gene (for example, blood type). The particular combination of alleles determines the organism's phenotype.

Organisms that reproduce sexually generally receive two alleles for every gene. One set of alleles (on one set of chromosomes) comes from the mother's ovum. Another set of alleles (on a second set of chromosomes) comes from the father's sperm. A large variety of allele combinations is possible when gametes combine to form a new organism. This helps explain why there is usually much variation in sexually reproducing populations.

Additional genetics concepts can be illustrated by the blood type example. A person who has type AB blood has one allele for type A and one allele for type B. How can that happen? Either (1) the allele for type A was inherited from the father and the allele for type B was inherited from the mother. Or (2) allele A came from the mother and allele B came from the father. Either way, this combination results in a genotype that is

heterozygous (*hetero* = different) for the blood type alleles. Alternatively, a person who inherits two identical alleles (AA or BB) has a genotype that is **homozygous** (*homo* = the same) for blood type. Figure E11.3 shows some of these combinations.

Some human traits have simple inheritance patterns. Cleft chin is one example. The cleft chin phenotype ranges from a small dimple to a full crease in the middle of the chin. Geneticists have discovered that an individual who inherits just one allele for this trait (from either parent) will show the phenotype. The individual expresses a dominant trait. In this example, this is a cleft chin. A **dominant trait** presents itself whether the individual is homozygous or heterozygous. Is the individual who inherits only one allele for cleft chin homozygous or heterozygous for this trait?

A **recessive trait** presents itself only in homozygous individuals. Individuals who do not have a cleft chin did not inherit the allele for cleft chin from either parent. Is such an individual homozygous or heterozygous for this trait?

Sometimes traits seem to be inherited in a random fashion. For example, baby rabbits inherit genes for the traits of ear type and fur color. Ears can be straight or floppy. Fur color can be white or brown. What combinations are possible from a mother with straight ears and white fur and a father with floppy ears and brown fur? A baby rabbit may be born with straight ears, like the mother, and brown fur, like the father. It may have floppy ears, like the father, and white fur, like the mother. It also is possible for the baby rabbit to look just like the mother or just like the father (see Figure E11.4). All of these possible combinations demonstrate that the inheritance of the alleles for fur color and ear type are independent of each other. Genes governing those two traits undergo **independent**

assortment. In this example, independent assortment takes place because the genes for ear type and fur color are located on different chromosomes. The movement of one chromosome does not depend on the movement of another chromosome.

The principle of independent assortment was discovered more than 150 years ago in a small European monastery garden. A scholarly monk named Gregor Mendel used pea plants to study patterns of inheritance. Mendel experimented with many generations of pea plants. His insights later became the cornerstone for explaining basic patterns of inheritance. ◆

Figure E11.4   Independent assortment of two traits in rabbits.   The same ear type and fur color do not always stay together. Thus, these results demonstrate that the traits for ear type and fur color are assorted independently of each other.

Case Studies of Two Genetic Disorders

Huntington's disease. Rita is a 30-year-old woman. She and her husband would like to have a baby. Rita's father died a few years ago of Huntington's disease (HD). HD is a dominant genetic disorder that causes degeneration of the central nervous system. Symptoms of the disease usually do not appear until age 35 or older. Currently, there is no effective treatment or cure for HD. The disease worsens for 5 to 15 years. Then the patient dies. Because Rita's father had HD, she knows that her chance of developing the disease is 50 percent.

A genetic procedure that requires a small blood sample can determine whether or not

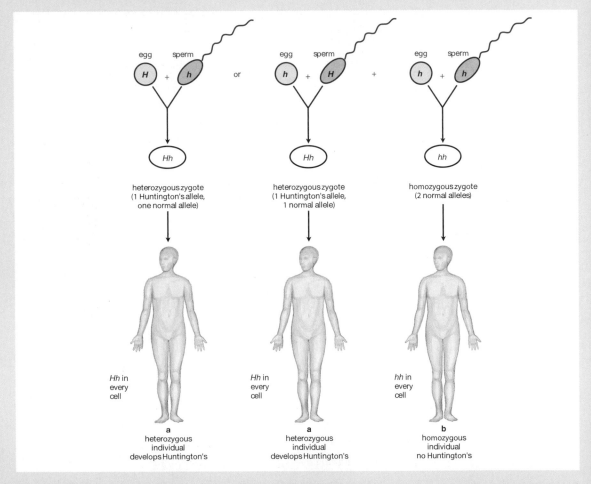

Figure E11.5 Genotypes in Huntington's disease.   Geneticists use a shorthand way of writing genotypes. They assign a capital letter to the allele for the dominant form of a trait. And they assign a lowercase of the same letter to the allele for the recessive form. The allele for Huntington's disease is symbolized by a capital *H.* A lowercase *h* indicates the normal allele. **(a)** The zygotes that gave rise to the first two individuals received the *H* allele in the gamete that came from one parent and the *h* allele in the gamete from the other parent. This resulted in the heterozygous genotype *Hh.* These persons eventually will develop the disease. **(b)** The zygote that gave rise to the third individual received *h* alleles in the gametes from both parents (homozygous *hh*). This person will remain free of the disease. An individual who received *H* alleles from both parents (a relatively rare situation) would have the homozygous genotype *HH.* This person would develop the disease.

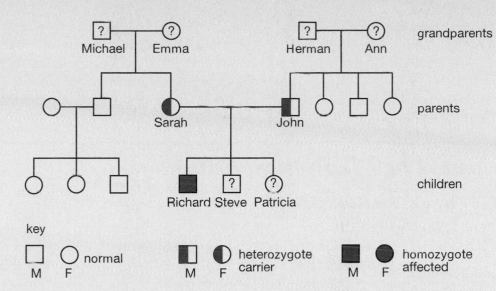

Figure E11.6
Pedigree for a family with cystic fibrosis. What is the likelihood that Richard's two older siblings, Steve and Patricia, are carriers?

key

☐ ○ normal	◧ ◖ heterozygote	■ ● homozygote
M F	M F carrier	M F affected

Rita carries the allele for HD. If you were Rita, would you have the test? What are the advantages of knowing that you have the allele for HD? What are the disadvantages of knowing? Are there advantages in *not* taking the test?

HD often puts tremendous psychological stress on the family and the individual. Many affected parents feel guilty because they may have passed the allele on to their children. Should affected people avoid passing on the allele by deciding not to have biological children?

Cystic fibrosis. Almost from the time his parents brought him home from the hospital, Richard seemed weaker than other infants. He frequently fell ill with coughs and colds. The doctors finally diagnosed cystic fibrosis (CF) when Richard was nearly a year old. CF causes chronic digestive and respiratory problems. CF is the most common single-gene disorder that typically results in death before reproductive age. Richard's grief-stricken parents were confused and angry when they heard the diagnosis.

"How could our son have such a terrible disease when no one in either of our large families has ever had CF?" asked the distraught father.

"The allele for CF is quite common," explained Dr. Cooper, their pediatrician. "In fact, about one in 25 European or Jewish Americans, one in 45 Hispanic Americans, and one in 65 African Americans carry an allele for cystic fibrosis. Unlike Huntington's disease, however, a person must inherit an allele for cystic fibrosis from both parents to be affected."

"So you mean that both of us could get sick as well?" asked Richard's mother.

"No. Neither of you can get CF because it is a recessive trait. You only have the disease if you are homozygous. The fact that Richard is sick indicates that he is homozygous. Each of you must be heterozygous. This means that each of you carries one allele for CF. Let me indicate the allele for cystic fibrosis with a lowercase *c* and the normal allele with an uppercase *C*. Only persons with the genotype *cc*, like Richard, will develop the cystic fibrosis phenotype. Persons with a *Cc* or *CC* genotype will have a normal phenotype. Those with the genotype *Cc*, like both of you, are carriers of CF.

"The allele for CF is widespread in the population. The chance that two heterozygotes will have children with the disease is quite high. The high frequency of the CF allele in the population explains the tragic fact that cystic fibrosis is so common."

The doctor helped Richard's parents understand why they could not have known they were carriers. They were determined to provide the best possible care for Richard. They gave him antibiotics to help his body fight lung infections. They performed a daily routine of chest-thumping therapies to clear the thick mucous deposits from his lungs. Even though illness and unpleasant treatments were a constant part of his life, Richard celebrated his fourth birthday much like any other child. Lots of friends and family members enjoyed cake, ice cream, and balloons with him. He was a happy child most of the time despite his restricted lifestyle and reduced life expectancy. Fortunately, recent medical advances offer the promise of a healthier life for people with CF. ◆

Meiosis: The Mechanism behind Patterns of Inheritance

Meiosis is the special type of cell division that produces gametes (ovum and sperm) in sexually reproducing organisms. Following the chromosomes during meiosis provides a way to understand certain patterns of inheritance. In all cells other than gametes, chromosomes occur in matching pairs. This is called the **diploid** condition. For each pair, one chromosome came from the mother's ovum and one chromosome came from the father's sperm. The maternal and paternal chromosomes of each pair contain genes that affect the same traits. As you learned earlier, however, the alleles for each gene may be different.

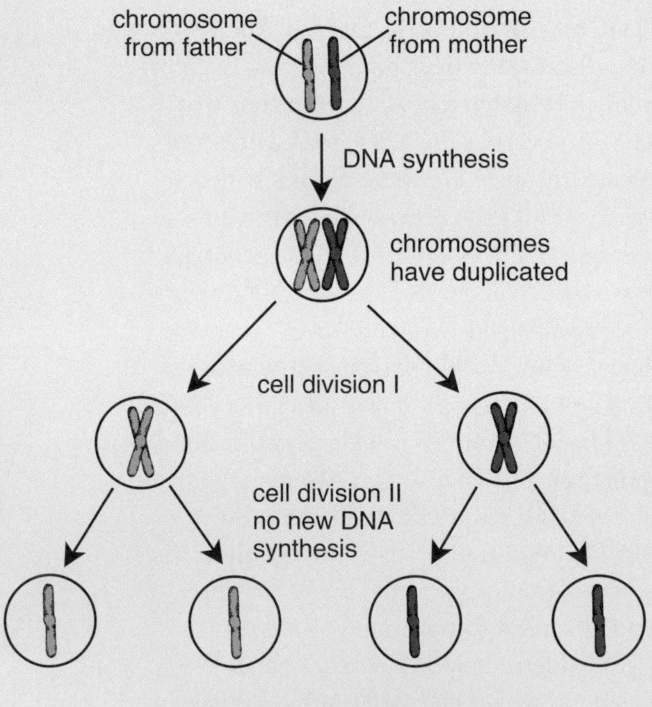

In contrast, gametes (ovum and sperm) contain only *one* chromosome from each matching pair. Gametes are **haploid**. They contain half the number of chromosomes that other body cells such as skin and nerve cells have. When an ovum and a sperm combine to form a zygote, the nuclei of both cells fuse. The zygote will have matching pairs of chromosomes. Each pair is comprised of one chromosome from the ovum and one chromosome from the sperm. Thus, fertilization restores the diploid number of chromosomes in the zygote. What would happen if chromosome numbers were not halved during meiosis? Chromosomes would double in number with each generation! Such a condition in humans and other animals would lead to the death of the zygote.

In meiosis, as in mitosis, the number of chromosomes doubles at the beginning of the process. In mitosis, one cell division follows. This restores the usual diploid number of chromosomes. In meiosis, however, cell division occurs *twice*. The process results in four cells. Each cell has the haploid number of chromosomes. The four cells produced by meiosis each have just one set of chromosomes.

Figure E11.7 illustrates what happens to one pair of chromosomes during meiosis. Let's examine the process in more detail. Just before

chromosome from father
chromosome from mother

DNA synthesis

chromosomes have duplicated

cell division I

cell division II
no new DNA synthesis

cells that mature into gametes

Figure E11.7 Meiosis consists of one duplication of chromosomes followed by two cell divisions.

meiosis begins, DNA synthesis takes place. Each chromosome in the pair doubles. During the first meiotic cell division, the two doubled chromosomes separate into two offspring cells. Each of the offspring cells contains one doubled chromosome.

During the second meiotic cell division, the doubled chromosome in each cell separates into two more offspring cells. This second cell division results in a total of four offspring cells. Each offspring cell contains one chromosome from the original pair.

Figure E11.8 shows the events of meiosis in a cell with two pairs of chromosomes. How many chromosomes do human cells have before meiosis? How many chromosomes do they have after meiosis? How many *pairs* of chromosomes do human diploid cells have? What is the haploid number of chromosomes in humans?

Meiosis and segregation. Gregor Mendel worked out the principles of simple inheritance decades before the cellular mechanisms of meiosis were understood. He achieved this astounding intellectual achievement by designing creative experiments, making keen observations, keeping detailed records, and applying mathematical reasoning to his results.

Meiosis explains Mendel's key discoveries, the **principle of independent assortment**, and the **principle of segregation**. We discussed the principle of independent assortment earlier. Now, let's consider the principle of segregation. Remember that (1) genes are located on chromosomes and (2) alleles are versions of a gene. Alleles on the two chromosomes in a pair segregate (separate) when the two chromosomes separate during meiosis. Each gamete, therefore, receives only one allele for a given gene. Your teacher will lead you in an exercise to help you see how meiosis explains the principle of segregation.

Understanding meiosis also allows us to make predictions about the genotypes and phenotypes of offspring. We can predict the frequency of offspring genotypes when parents of known genotype mate and produce large numbers of offspring. Figure E11.9 presents an example using guinea pigs. Short hair is a dominant trait in guinea pigs. G represents the allele for short hair, g the allele for long hair. Both parents are heterozygous for short hair (Gg). Each parent produces equal numbers of G and g gametes through meiosis. When fertilizations takes place, the gametes join in random combinations. In this case, $\frac{1}{2}$ of the ova and $\frac{1}{2}$ of the sperm contain the G allele. We can, therefore, expect that $\frac{1}{4}$ ($\frac{1}{2} \times \frac{1}{2} = \frac{1}{4}$) of the offspring will have the homozygous genotype GG. Will their hair be long or short?

What about the other half of the ova and sperm—those that carry the g allele? According to the principle of segregation, fertilization of these gametes will probably result in about $\frac{1}{4}$ of the offspring having the homozygous genotype gg. Will their hair be long or short? The rest of the offspring will be heterozygotes. Half of the heterozygotes will come from unions of G ova with g sperm. The other half will come from unions of g ova and G sperm. (Both are written Gg. Biologists record the dominant trait first, regardless of which parent passes it on.) Of the resulting offspring at one mating, $\frac{3}{4}$ will have short hair ($\frac{1}{2}$ Gg plus $\frac{1}{4}$ GG) and $\frac{1}{4}$ will have long hair (gg). Biologists refer to this pattern as a 3:1 phenotypic ratio ($\frac{3}{4}:\frac{1}{4}$, reduced to lowest terms).

The laws of inheritance do not allow us to make exact predictions for a specific mating, however. Each fertilization involves the union of a single ovum and a single sperm out of *many* possible ova and sperm. We cannot predict with absolute certainty that a particular mating will result in a zygote that is Gg, for example.

Flipping a coin illustrates this phenomenon. Is it possible to toss four heads in a row with a coin? What about tossing 100 heads in a row? The predicted result of getting heads in a coin toss is 50:50. This is a prediction that can be verified by observing a large number of tosses. You may not be

diploid parent cell

a This cell has 2 pairs of chromosomes.

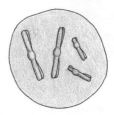

beginning of meiosis prophase 1

b Just before this diploid cell begins meiosis, DNA synthesis takes place. Each chromosome is duplicated.

crossing-over

c The pairs of duplicated chromosomes become closely aligned. They join in several places. At these junctions, equivalent pieces of the chromosome pair may exchange places. This exchange process is called crossing-over. It results in the switching of alleles. The chromosomes involved in the exchange originally came from different parents. Thus, a new combination of information now exists.

metaphase 1

d The joined chromosomes line up along the middle of the cell. Cytoplasmic fibers attach to each duplicated chromosome.

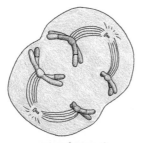

anaphase 1

e The cytoplasmic fibers pull apart each pair of duplicated chromosomes. This happens during the 1st cell division.

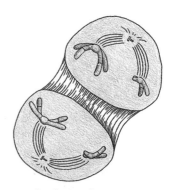

telophase 1

f Each new cell resulting from this division contains 2 doubled chromosomes, 1 from each pair.

Figure E11.8   The stages of meiosis. This figure illustrates the events of meiosis for a cell that has two pairs of chromosomes.

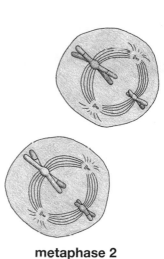

metaphase 2

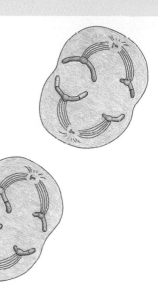

anaphase 2

g A 2nd cell division now takes place with no further DNA synthesis. During this cell division, there are no matching chromosome pairs. Instead, the doubled chromosomes line up in single file.

h Fibers pull apart each doubled chromosome.

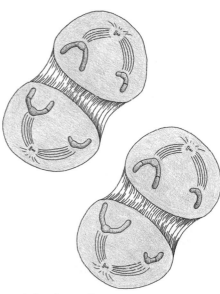

telophase 2

i Each of the resulting 4 offspring cells has a single set of chromosomes and is haploid. Mature human gametes form from the products of meiosis.

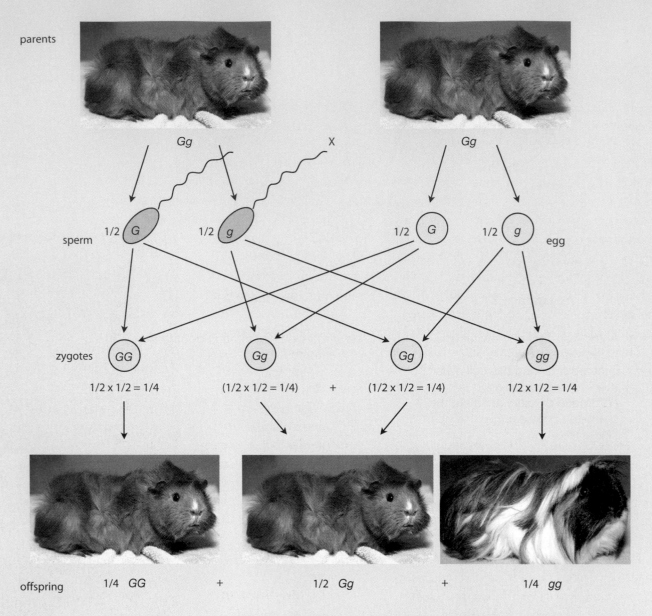

parents

Gg   X   Gg

sperm   1/2 (G)   1/2 (g)   1/2 (G)   1/2 (g)   egg

zygotes   (GG)   (Gg)   (Gg)   (gg)

1/2 x 1/2 = 1/4   (1/2 x 1/2 = 1/4)   +   (1/2 x 1/2 = 1/4)   1/2 x 1/2 = 1/4

offspring   1/4 GG   +   1/2 Gg   +   1/4 gg

Figure E11.9 **The regularity of allele segregation makes prediction of offspring possible.** If the genotypes of the parents are known, then the gametes that result can be known as well. The possible combinations of gametes yield predictable genotypes and phenotypes of offspring.

surprised at tossing four heads in a row. But you would be amazed at tossing 100 heads in a row.

Imagine that the parent guinea pigs in Figure E11.9 have a litter of four. Recall that both parents are heterozygous (*Gg*) for the short hair allele. If we examine *many* such litters, we probably would find that ½ of the offspring had the *Gg* genotype,

¼ the *GG* genotype, and ¼ the *gg* genotype. However, it is quite possible that in any given litter, all may have the *GG* genotype or all have the *gg* genotype. Isn't it possible to toss four heads in a row with a coin? Only when large numbers of matings are considered together do the frequencies of genotypes come close to those predicted by allele segregation. ◆

The Role of Variation in Evolution

Genetic information passes faithfully from one generation to the next, quite impressively. The results from the Human Genome Project show that the DNA in all humans is 99.9 percent identical. (We will talk more about that in Chapter 12.) Such continuity is possible because genes passed from parents to offspring almost always remain unchanged. Nevertheless, variation exists among humans and continues to arise. This is important. Evolution can only take place if variability exists within a population. This variability makes some individuals better adapted to the environment than others.

How do variations happen? They take place in two ways: mutation and recombination. A **mutation** is a physical change to the gene. This results in a change in genotype. It also may change the trait that the gene governs. This results in a change in phenotype. **Recombination** creates new combinations of alleles during meiosis. (For example, refer back to Figure E11.8.) Sexual reproduction promotes variability in a population because of meiotic processes that cause recombination.

Mutation, the direct source of variation. Mutations of alleles are quite rare under natural conditions. For example, say you examined 100,000 corn kernels for a particular phenotype such as altered color or shape. You would find only a few kernels that differed from the rest. Excessive mutations have a negative impact on continuity. Most of them reduce or eliminate the activity of the allele. Indeed, a mutation in the Factor VIII gene causes hemophilia A. This mutation and the disease it causes are passed down through the generations.

Keep in mind, however, that only mutations in the genetic material of a *gamete* can be inherited by offspring. In other words, a mutation in one of your skin or stomach cells cannot be transmitted through inheritance.

The hemophilia A allele that affected Czarevich Alexis apparently arose as a mutation in one of the two gametes that gave rise to his great grandmother, Queen Victoria.

Mutation might appear to be a negative thing. In fact, it is the ultimate source of all new genetic information. Thus, mutations are critical for generating diversity. Natural selection acts on this diversity. This results in the evolution of species. Anything that raises the frequency of mutations increases genetic diversity. Unfortunately, it also increases the proportion of individuals who may be born with developmental errors or other unfavorable phenotypes (see Figure E11.10). Radiation and certain chemicals increase the rate at which mutations occur. This is the reason that biologists are concerned about the environmental effects of pollutants that contain these chemicals.

Recombination, an additional source of variation. Mutations are rare. As a result, they introduce a relatively small amount of variation into most species. Most of the genetic variation in a population is due to processes that take place during meiosis. These processes are segregation of alleles, independent assortment, and crossing-over. Remember that during meiosis, alleles separate from each other. Members of a chromosome pair assort (move into different offspring cells) independently of each other. The exercise you did in

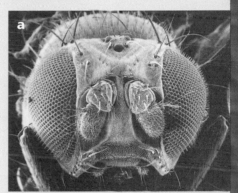

Figure E11.10 Most mutations are not harmful. **(a)** Normal fly **(b)** Mutant fly. In this mutant fly, the antennae structures have developed as legs.

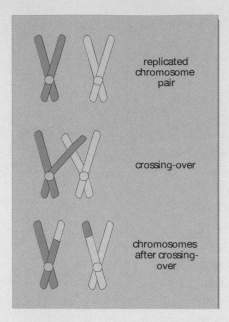

replicated chromosome pair

crossing-over

chromosomes after crossing-over

Figure E11.11 Crossing-over generates new allele combinations within chromosomes during the early stages of meiosis.

class showed how this causes different combinations of alleles.

Crossing-over is another meiotic process that results in new allele combinations. Remember that for each pair of chromosomes, one came from the mother and one from the father. During meiosis, chromosomes line up with their matching chromosomes. The arms of the pairs intertwine or "cross over." At this time, pieces of the chromosome partners exchange places, as shown in Figure E11.11. When the chromosome pairs separate later in meiosis, each has a new and unique combination of alleles. The resulting chromosomes assort independently into gametes. You can compare meiosis to playing a card game. Shuffling the cards gives a new combination of characters in each hand you deal. This is like independent assortment. But crossing-over takes recombination

even further. Take the playing cards analogy. It would be as if you cut some of the cards in half and spliced them onto other cards.

The process of meiosis is not always perfect. Occasionally, mistakes take place. These mistakes can be fatal or detrimental to the offspring. For example, the partners in a chromosome pair may not separate from each other during the first division of meiosis. As Figure E11.12 indicates, both members of this chromosome pair will end up in one offspring cell. The other offspring cell gets neither chromosome. This error in chromosome movement is called **nondisjunction**. At the second division of meiosis, the doubled chromosomes separate in the usual way. This results in two gametes that contain two copies of this particular chromosome and two gametes with no copies of the chromosome. Nondisjunction also can take

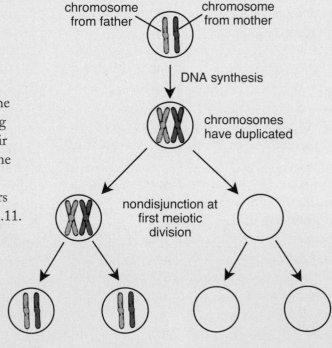

chromosome from father   chromosome from mother

DNA synthesis

chromosomes have duplicated

nondisjunction at first meiotic division

cells that mature into gametes

Figure E11.12   Nondisjunction.   Compare this sequence of events with normal meiosis in Figure E11.8.

place during the second division of meiosis. Among the four gametes produced, two are normal, one has two copies of the chromosome, and one has no copies. Fertilization of an abnormal gamete with a normal gamete from the other parent produces a zygote with either three copies or only one copy of this chromosome.

In humans, the extra set of genes on a third copy of a particular chromosome always produces multiple disruptions. These disruptions show up in the phenotype of the affected individual. Individuals who have three copies of a chromosome can survive. But they only survive when nondisjunction involves the X or Y (sex) chromosomes, or the smallest nonsex chromosome (number 21). Individuals who have three copies of chromosome 21 exhibit a collection of phenotypes known as Down's syndrome. These individuals generally show some degree of mental and physical disability. This disability can range from slight to severe. These individuals are prone to leukemia and heart disease. They have a shorter than normal life expectancy. Individuals who have three copies of any other chromosomes either die as embryos or shortly after birth. Zygotes with only one copy of any chromosome, except the X or Y chromosomes, do not survive.

Observing the consequences of variation. The fossil record shows continuity across generations in all living systems. For example, hard-shelled invertebrates such as trilobites (see Figure E11.13) and snails have been preserved in great numbers by sediment deposits. Their fossils look recognizably the same across hundreds of thousands of years. Through sufficiently long periods of time, however, changes in organisms become clear. Often, these changes can be observed only by following a species across very long periods of time, such as millions of years.

One example is the fossil record of the evolution of modern horses. An extensive series of fossils provides a good record of the change in horses across the last 60 million years. As Figure E3.3 shows, an ancestral form of the horse ran on four-toed feet. This animal was about the size of a small dog. If we saw the ancestral animal today, we might not immediately recognize it as an early horse. As we study more recent horse fossils, we can see adaptations in the feet that more closely resemble modern horses. Over millions of years, changes in the foot took place until only a single large toe, or hoof, remains today. (See Figure E11.14. Relate it to Figure E3.3.) With each change in size and foot shape, we see more and more resemblance to the modern horse. Thus, when we view all of the intermediate forms, the evolutionary connection between the modern horse and its original ancestor becomes obvious.

How do these types of evolutionary changes arise? Natural selection acts on the natural variation in populations. Variations that improve the chances of survival and reproduction tend to remain in the population. We say that such variations are adaptive. That is, they enhance an individual's

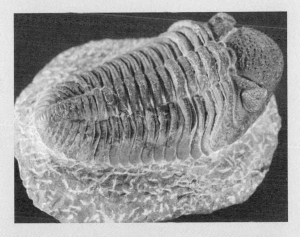

Figure E11.13 Trilobite. Comparison of fossils from sediments of different geological eras shows that there was little change in this species across thousands of years.

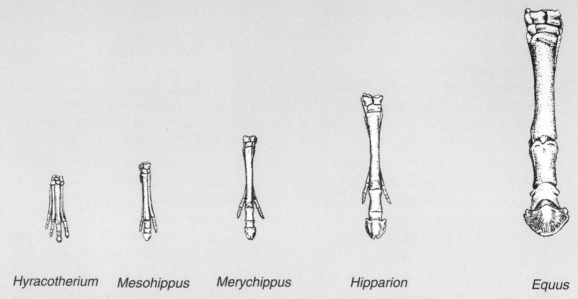

Hyracotherium   Mesohippus   Merychippus   Hipparion   Equus

Figure E11.14 **The evolution of species across time.** During the evolution of the horse, the overall form changed through long time periods. Specialized structures such as the foot also changed. The modern horse's foot contains only a single toe, or hoof. What other features of the legs have changed?

ability to survive and pass those genes on to its offspring.

Natural selection affects all traits, both discrete and continuous. *Discrete* means that the phenotypes for a trait can be placed into distinct categories. For example, people can be placed into two categories with regard to cystic fibrosis: those who have the disease and those who do not. Similarly, people can be placed into four categories for blood type: type A, B, O, or AB. These are discrete traits.

Continuous means that phenotypes for a particular trait include a range with no distinct categories. Height, weight, and skin color are traits that demonstrate continuous variation in human populations. Can you think of other traits that exhibit continuous variation in a population?

Figure E11.15 shows the continuous variation in leg length among horses. A graph of the distribution of leg lengths resembles a bell-shaped curve. Why are most individuals clustered near the middle range? These individuals are the result of selective processes. These processes favored the

survival and reproduction of their ancestors. Smaller numbers of individuals with either very short or very long legs exist in the population. These extreme traits apparently were not adaptive in the past. Horses with very short legs may have been less likely to escape predators than horses with longer legs. On the other hand, horses with very long legs may have been less able to tolerate the stresses of running than horses with shorter legs.

Regardless of the specific trait, all cases of evolutionary change result from the same two steps. First, each new generation expresses variation in traits. Second, natural selection tests each variation in the struggle to survive and reproduce.

How can natural selection result in new species? One way relates to geographical isolation. A species that is confined to one specific and stable habitat tends to express a relatively uniform phenotype. (Refer back to the Chapter 2 essays for a definition of species.) What could happen if a population from this species colonizes a new habitat?

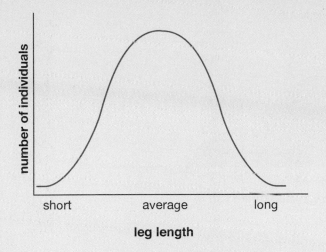

number of individuals

short   average   long

leg length

Figure E11.15 **Continuous variation.** A trait that varies continuously, such as leg length, is examined in a large population. As you can see, most individuals cluster around the average value for that trait. Relatively few individuals exhibit the extreme ranges of the trait. Such traits are called *multifactorial*. This is because they are caused by many genes interacting with many environmental factors. How many other traits that exhibit a continuous pattern of variation can you identify?

In the new habitat, individuals with more extreme traits may be at an advantage. Natural selection would favor these individuals. Across many generations, the population in the new habitat may change considerably from the original population. Eventually, the new population may become notably different from the original population. So different, in fact, that when they are reunited, they can no longer interbreed. A new species has evolved. All evolution is influenced by selective pressures acting on natural variation in populations. ◆

Genetic Complexity

Can all phenotypes be explained simply by following one or two genes through meiosis? Is an understanding of segregation of alleles and independent assortment enough to explain continuously varying traits such as behavior? Geneticists can easily track the inheritance of Huntington's disease. But this disease produces many complex effects on human health and behavior. Scientists cannot yet explain how a mutation in this one gene can cause so many effects.

What about behavioral or physical phenotypes that we consider to be normal? Can genetics explain why you usually are happy while your best friend is usually sullen? It might seem strange to consider genetics when thinking about behavior. Scientists continue to explore the contribution of genetics to behavior.

The influence of genotype on complex behaviors. Direct evidence that genetics can influence behavior was first provided in the 1930s. Scientists studied the maze-running ability of mice. The speed, memory, and decision-making abilities of mice determine how quickly they can complete a maze. The scientists found that in a given population of mice, some made many wrong turns. Others made very few. The scientists mated "maze-dull" mice with other maze-dull mice from this population. Likewise, they mated "maze-bright" mice with other maze-bright mice. Could the ability to run the maze well be inherited? Figure E11.16 shows that after several generations, two distinct populations of mice existed—maze-dull mice and maze-bright mice. Thus, the scientists demonstrated that

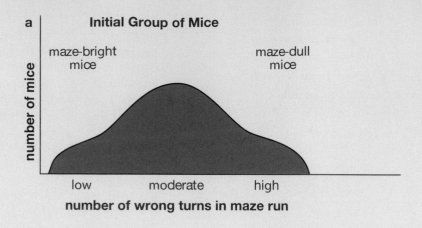

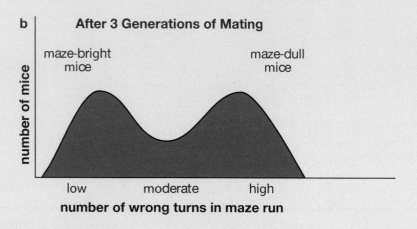

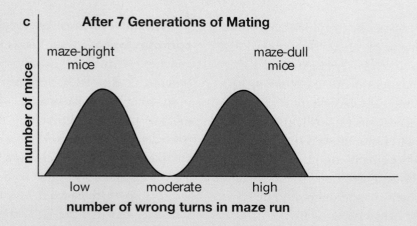

Figure E11.16   A genetic component to behavior. (a) Scientists tested a large group of mice for its ability to run a maze successfully. They found a wide range of behaviors. This graph shows the typical distribution for a trait exhibiting continuous variation. (b) and (c) Scientists chose maze-bright mice from this group and mated them with other maze-bright mice. They eventually ended up with a population of consistently maze-bright mice with only a narrow range of behavior. Likewise, a population of uniformly maze-dull mice can be bred if maze-dull mice are mated with other maze-dull mice from the starting population. This experiment illustrates that complex behaviors have genetic components.

genetic variation for a complex behavior exists. They also demonstrated that it can be passed from one generation to the next. With so much genetic variation, what constitutes *normal* behavior from a population standpoint? Normal behavior is really just an average of the tremendous diversity that exists among the individuals.

Complex traits include behavior, intelligence, and personality. What distinguishes complex traits from simple traits such as a cleft chin or hemophilia? Scientists think that two factors are involved: the environment and the number of genes that influence the trait. You already have seen that the environment can affect the phenotype of genetically identical plants grown at different altitudes. How can the number of genes play a role in inheriting a complex trait? Skin color is an example of a complex trait. Several genes influence the skin-color phenotype. These genes control the production of pigments called *melanins*. How do these genes interact to produce the large variation in skin color exhibited by populations around the world?

Skin color, a complex trait. Consider a model for how multiple genes might influence the complex trait of skin color. Let us imagine that only two genes are involved in skin color. The alleles for the two genes are designated *C* or *c* and *S* or *s*. Only uppercase alleles result in the production of melanin. The more melanin alleles that a person inherits (of the *C* or *S* variety), the darker his or her skin color will be.

As indicated in Figure E11.17, independent assortment and segregation can generate nine possible genotypes. Their corresponding phenotypes illustrate the effect of having more or less melanin-producing alleles. An individual with all melanin-producing alleles (*CCSS*) would have very dark colored skin. An individual with two melanin-producing alleles (*CCss* or *CcSs* or *ccSS*) would have medium colored skin. An individual with no melanin-producing alleles

Genotype	Number of melanin alleles	Skin-color phenotype
Ccss	0	Very light
Ccss or *ccSs*	1	Light
CCss or *CcSs* or *ccSS*	2	Medium
CCSs or *CcSS*	3	Dark
CCSS	4	Very dark

Figure E11.17 A model for the interaction of two genes that cause skin color.

(*ccss*) would have very light colored skin. Notice that this is not simply a case of dominant and recessive alleles. The effects of *two distinct* genes influencing the same trait must be taken into consideration. The genes involved in traits such as skin color are added together to express a given phenotype. In fact, more than two genes contribute to skin color. In addition, the environment also has an impact on this phenotype.

The environment varies from place to place. It exerts selective pressures on the populations in each place. Geneticists propose that environmental factors influenced the evolution of skin-color genes. Skin color can compensate for the varying amounts of sunshine available in different parts of the world. The ultraviolet (UV) rays in sunlight affect human health. The human body needs UV light to synthesize vitamin D. Vitamin D is needed to develop healthy teeth and bones. However, too much UV light can damage DNA and cause skin cancer (melanoma). In ancient populations that lived in southern latitudes, high levels of melanin protected individuals from skin cancer. (Melanin prevents UV light from penetrating the underlying, living layers of skin.) Thus, darker skin was selected in southern latitudes. In northern latitudes, indirect sunlight and cloud cover limit the availability of UV light. In ancient populations that lived in northern latitudes, low levels of melanin allowed UV light to be absorbed into the skin. Increased absorption of UV light reduced the risk of problems that vitamin D deficiency causes. Lighter skin was selected in ancient

populations in northern latitudes. Thus, the frequency of alleles that produce melanin changed across time through natural selection in early human populations. Similar interactions between genes and the environment ultimately account for all of the diversity of life on earth. ◆

Incomplete Dominance

Determining an individual's genotype by observing phenotype is not always easy. For example, a person who does not have cystic fibrosis may have either the genotype Cc or the genotype CC. Both genotypes produce the same phenotype (no disease). For some traits, however, observing the phenotype reveals the genotype. In snapdragons, for example, plants that have the genotype C^RC^R produce bright red flowers. Plants that have the genotype C^WC^W produce white flowers. (Sometimes genotypes are written using superscripts above the gene symbol to designate different alleles.) Plants that have the genotype C^RC^W bear flowers that are neither pure red nor pure white, but pink (see Figure E11.18). **Incomplete dominance** describes this pattern of inheritance. The heterozygous genotype produces a phenotype that falls somewhere between the two homozygous phenotypes. Thus, heterozygous individuals are easily detected.

The human genetic disorder known as sickle-cell disease demonstrates incomplete dominance. Sickle-cell disease occurs most frequently in populations originating from equatorial Africa, the Middle East, or the southern Mediterranean. Defective hemoglobin molecules in red blood cells produce sickle-cell disease symptoms. Hb represents the hemoglobin gene. Individuals with the homozygous genotype Hb^AHb^A produce normal hemoglobin. Individuals with the homozygous genotype Hb^SHb^S suffer from sickle-cell disease.

In these individuals, the hemoglobin molecules clump together when oxygen levels drop. The clumping causes the red blood cells to lose their flexibility and assume an abnormal, sickle shape. A large number of these sickled cells may block small blood vessels. The cells stop the flow of nutrients and oxygen to surrounding tissues. During these episodes, individuals experiences fever and severe pain in their limbs and joints. Eventually, vital organs may be damaged. The individuals may die. Individuals who have the heterozygous genotype Hb^AHb^S produce both sickle and normal hemoglobin. These individuals have sickle-cell trait. Usually, they experience normal health. However, under certain conditions, they may develop sickling of their red blood cells and experience mild symptoms. (An example of such a condition is exposure to reduced oxygen pressure at high altitudes.)

Scientists have discovered an evolutionary association between sickle-cell disease and malaria. A mosquito-borne parasite transmits malaria, a common tropical disease. Worldwide, malaria results in well over a million deaths each year. Individuals with sickle-cell trait (Hb^AHb^S heterozygotes) are less likely to be infected by the malarial parasite than nonsickle cell individuals (Hb^AHb^A homozygotes). The shape of the sickled cells inhibits infection by the malarial parasite. This means that people who live in regions where malaria is common have a better chance of avoiding malaria if they have sickle-cell

$C^R C^R$

red

C^R C^W

$C^W C^W$

white

F$_1$ generation

$C^R C^W$

pink

Figure E11.18 **Incomplete dominance of flower color in snapdragons.** The phenotype of the F$_1$ heterozygote is different from that of either homozygous parent.

trait. Thus, people who carry one sickle-cell allele and live in areas where malaria is common have a selective advantage over those who lack the allele. The trait increases their chances of living long enough to reproduce. In this way, natural selection has preserved the allele for sickle-cell disease in the human population. ◆

Genetic Information Is Stored in Molecular Form

How might advances in DNA technologies affect your life? To answer that question, you need to understand the role that DNA plays. DNA contains information that is critical to the structure and function of your body's cells. In fact, the instructions encoded in DNA play a major role in determining how your body operates. If you have children, their lives will depend on the transmission of genetic information from you and your spouse to them.

DNA instructions preserve species' characteristics. DNA structure and the DNA copying processes are critical to that transmission. DNA is responsible for the accurate transmission of genetic information from parents to offspring. The structure also is responsible for accurately transmitting genetic information from a cell to its offspring cells. In other words, DNA is the *molecular* basis of reproduction.

Figure E12.1 expands on the ideas of Figure 11.6. It looks at the inheritance of genotype and the production of phenotype at a molecular level. Note the arrows that lead from the box labeled *genotype* to the word *replicate* and back to *genotype*. These arrows represent the cyclical events of reproduction.

Those events are responsible for maintaining a species' genetic continuity. The term *replicate* refers to making a copy of a DNA molecule. The replication of DNA allows organisms to keep a set of genetic instructions for themselves while passing on sets to their offspring.

DNA is important both to a *population* and to each *individual* organism. To see why, we must consider the processes by which cells use the information they contain. The use of genetic information is known as **gene expression**. The result of gene expression is an organism's phenotype. Figure E12.1 also illustrates these events. Note the arrows that lead from the box labeled *genotype* to the word *expression* and to the word *phenotype*. These arrows illustrate the flow of information during gene expression. Ultimately, the instructions stored in DNA enable all living organisms to build, maintain, and regulate their cells. In this way, the information stored in DNA is like the information stored in the operating system of a computer. A computer cannot operate without operating system instructions. Living systems cannot function without the instructions for life—encoded in DNA.

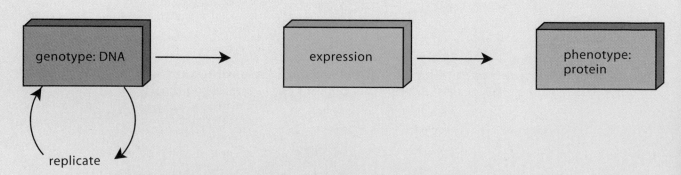

Figure E12.1   Dual role of genetic information.   At the molecular level, your genotype is the instructions encoded in your DNA. Replication allows these instructions to be transmitted to the next generation. Gene expression allows these instructions to produce proteins that can build, maintain, and regulate your body.

As you develop a deeper understanding of how living systems rely on DNA, consider why accurate DNA transmission from one generation to the next is essential. That understanding may help you see how scientists' growing knowledge of DNA influences your life. For instance, DNA analysis now offers hope of early diagnosis and treatment of diseases such as cystic fibrosis. Another example involves using DNA technologies to develop improvements in agriculture such as disease-resistant crops. You also may encounter DNA technologies in the form of genetic fingerprinting. Scientists use this technology to reevaluate historical events and establish guilt or innocence in criminal cases. Who knows, perhaps some day you will be involved in using DNA analysis techniques to solve a great mystery! ◆

Landmark Discovery: DNA May Be the Stuff of Genes

New York (1944): The effort to describe the molecular composition of those mysterious particles that scientists call genes moved a giant step forward this week. A new report indicates that a chemical called *deoxyribonucleic acid (DNA)* may be the so-called "transforming" substance discovered more than 10 years ago by Frederick Griffith.

Griffith observed that mice died when exposed to both live, rough-surfaced, harmless bacteria and dead, smooth-surfaced, harmful bacteria. He then observed that bacteria in the tissues of the dead mice had been *transformed*. The bacteria now contained both the smooth-surfaced and harmful characteristics. That *transformation* is the change in the phenotype of the living bacteria from rough-surfaced to smooth-surfaced and from harmless to harmful. It seems to occur when some information-rich substance moves from the dead bacteria to the live bacteria.

The identity of this transforming substance, however, remained unknown until this week. Oswald Avery, Colin MacLeod, and Maclyn McCarty are investigators at the Rockefeller Institute. They reported a set of experiments that demonstrates that the substance causing the change actually is DNA. This discovery suggests that genes are made of DNA. Genes are the particles thought to carry the information that determines the physical and chemical characteristics of a cell. Scientists do not know much about this powerful substance. But this week's announcement is likely to intensify efforts to describe DNA's structure and function. In addition, scientists will work to explain how DNA can cause such important effects in cells. ◆

DNA Structure and Replication

DNA is required for the building, maintenance, and regulation of all living organisms' cells. That means each new cell must receive a copy of the genetic material from its parent. How are copies made? The process is called **replication**. This complete process of making a copy of the cell's genetic material is complex. The key to understanding this complex process, however, is very straightforward. You simply have to understand a few things about how a cell's genetic material is structured and organized.

In humans (as in all eukaryotes), the genetic material consists of long DNA molecules. These molecules are packaged tightly in chromosomes. In each of our cells (except gametes and red blood cells), we have 23 pairs of chromosomes. Each chromosome, in turn, contains one long DNA molecule and many protein molecules. The DNA and protein molecule organization creates beadlike clusters. As Figure E12.2 shows, DNA wraps tightly around these clusters to form nucleosomes. These nucleosomes pack together to form the condensed and compact structure that we see when we look at a dividing cell under the microscope.

The information storage capacity of genes lies ultimately in the DNA. It does not reside in the protein components of chromosomes. Therefore, the question of how a cell copies its genetic information during reproduction actually is a question of how a cell copies its DNA. Copying DNA accurately is much like communicating a message. It is easier when some form of physical template, or pattern, is used. Games like "pass the message" demonstrate how easily inaccurate copying can happen when there is no physical record, such as a written note, of the transmitted message. Perhaps you can imagine that a physical template also would help carry out the huge task of accurately duplicating genetic information. In fact, that is exactly how biological systems accomplish this task. The DNA molecule itself serves as a template for information transfer. That is, the molecule that contains the genetic information acts as a pattern for its own replication.

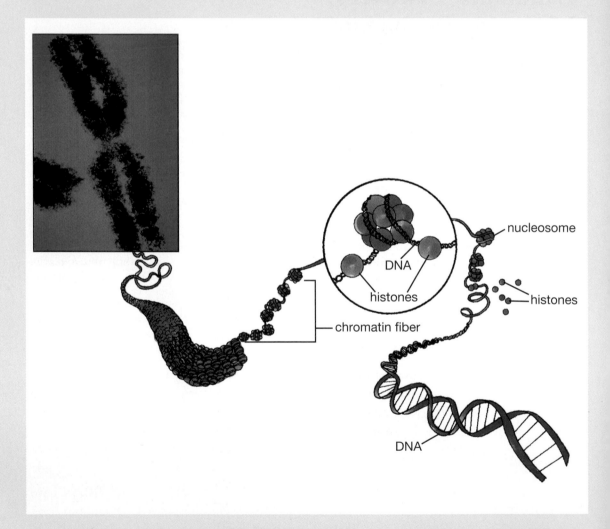

Figure E12.2 Eukaryotic chromosome structure. Each chromosome in a eukaryotic nucleus consists of a long molecule of DNA. This molecule is wrapped around histone proteins to form beadlike structures called nucleosomes. Fully extended, the DNA in one human chromosome would be about 5 centimeters (2 inches) long. Prokaryotes, in contrast to eukaryotes, have only one chromosome. This chromosome lacks the beadlike proteins that aid packing. What advantage might efficient packing of DNA offer a cell?

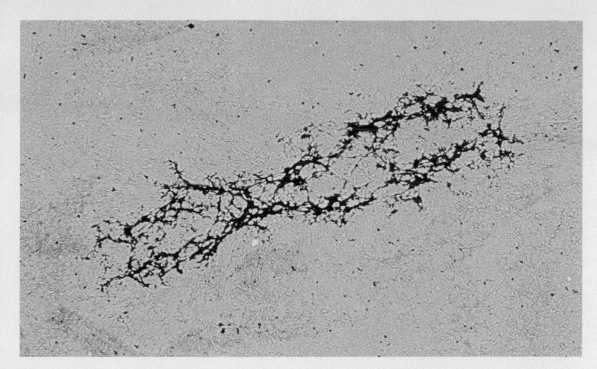

Figure E12.3 Human DNA. This human chromosome is seen through an electron microscope. The chromosone was treated with a substance that disrupted its structure, releasing the DNA.

DNA can serve as its own template because its organization is specific. Look at the drawing of DNA shown in Figure E12.4a. Note that a single DNA molecule is a double-stranded structure. The two strands twist together in a spiral or *helical* form. That aspect of DNA earned it its nickname: the *double helix*.

Examine the two DNA strands more closely. Each of those two strands (Figure E12.4b) is made up of a series of smaller molecules called **nucleotides**. A long strand of nucleotides bonded together is called a **nucleic acid**. Thus, DNA is an example of a nucleic acid.

A closer look at the nucleotides that make up each strand of DNA (Figure E12.4c) reveals even more regularity. Each nucleotide is made up of the same three parts. These are a nitrogen base, a deoxyribose sugar, and a phosphate group. The sugar and phosphate portions are the same in all nucleotides. However, the nitrogen bases vary. As Figure E12.4d shows, a DNA nucleotide may contain one of four different nitrogen bases. The four unique bases are like the letters in a word. Consider how the order of letters in a word determines the information that the word conveys to someone who understands written language. Similarly, the order of nitrogen bases along one strand of DNA conveys information to any part of the cell capable of translating that code.

Do you understand that DNA stores genetic information in the sequence of the nitrogen bases along one strand of DNA? If so, then you already understand a great deal about the structure of genes at the molecular level. In fact, only one question remains to complete your basic knowledge of DNA structure. How can one DNA molecule be replicated to make another identical molecule?

The answer to this question is that there are predictable interactions between the nitrogen bases. On close inspection of the DNA double helix, we find that the pairing between nitrogen bases on opposite strands is always the same. A large base on one strand

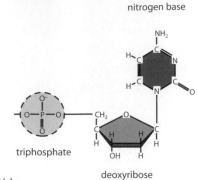
nitrogen base

triphosphate

deoxyribose

c   Parts of a nucleotide.

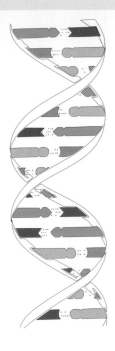

a   The double helix.

Figure E12.4   Structure of DNA.
The sequence of nucleotides along the strand encodes the cell's genetic information. How many different sequences could be made using just 10 nucleotides in a DNA strand?

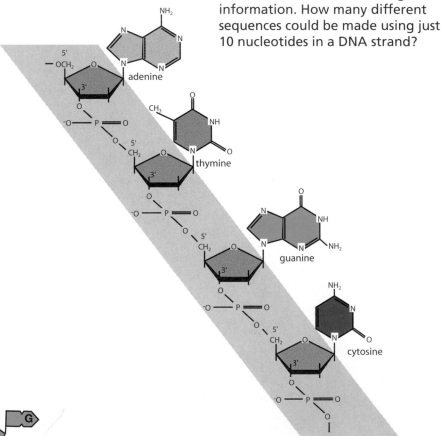

adenine

thymine

guanine

cytosine

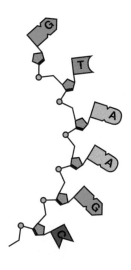

nucleic acid

symbol for nucleotide

b   Nucleotides are covalently bonded to form a strand known as a nucleic acid.

d   Nucleotides may contain 1 of 4 different nitrogen bases. The sequence of nucleotides along the strand encodes the cell's genetic information.

always bonds to the same small base on the opposite strand. Figure E12.5 shows this aspect of DNA structure. Notice that the pairing that takes place between nitrogen bases is *absolutely* specific in DNA strands. Adenine (A), a large base, always bonds with thymine (T), a small base. Guanine (G), a large base, always bonds to cytosine (C), a small base. **Complementary base pairing** describes the bonding pattern that always happens between base pairs.

Complementary base pairing explains how it is possible for DNA to act as a template for its own replication. Like other biosynthesis reactions, specific enzymes are required for replication to take place. Replication begins when those enzymes separate the two DNA strands. Next, enzymes read the sequence of nucleotides on one strand. Finally, enzymes facilitate the synthesis of a new, complementary strand. They do this by adding one nucleotide at a time to the new strand. Remember, A always bonds with T, and G always bonds with C. Thus, the sequence of bases in the old strand *determines* the sequence of bases in the new strand. In other words, each newly added base during replication must *complement* the base in the old strand with which it will pair. In this way, any DNA molecule can serve as a pattern for a new copy of the genetic information that it encodes.

Figure E12.6 illustrates the replication process. As shown in the figure, the double strands of the DNA molecule first separate. That allows the replication enzymes to build a new strand of DNA to match each of the old strands. Separation of the double helix is critical to replication. It is possible because the attractive forces that hold the two strands together are relatively weak hydrogen bonds. Hydrogen bonds are much weaker than the strong covalent bonds that hold neighboring nucleotides together in each strand. That difference in bond strength explains how the two strands of a DNA molecule can

be separated for replication without destroying the strands themselves. Once separated, the base-by-base replication process continues. Eventually, there are two molecules of DNA where previously there had been one. Once complete, each molecule contains one old strand and one new complementary strand. ◆

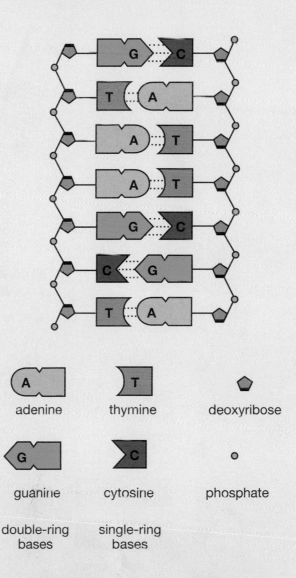

adenine thymine deoxyribose

guanine cytosine phosphate

double-ring bases single-ring bases

Figure E12.5 Complementary base pairing in DNA. Notice the pattern of how the bases pair with each other. The dots between base pairs represent hydrogen bonds. These bonds hold the two strands in a double helix together. Are there any differences in hydrogen bonding between G and C and between A and T?

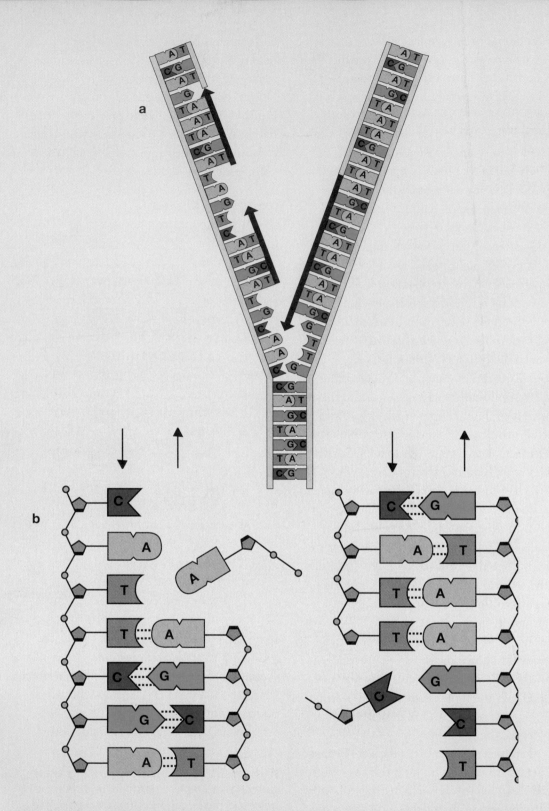

Figure E12.6   DNA replication.   (a) A replication fork at which two new DNA strands are being synthesized. **(b)** Details of nucleotide addition. DNA replication enzymes add nucleotides one at a time to each of the growing strands. In eukaryotic cells, the process of DNA replication takes place in the nucleus. In prokaryotes, replication takes place in the cytoplasm.

Replication Errors and Mutation

Templates provide a very accurate way of transmitting information. They do this whether it is written language or genetic information in DNA. Even with the use of a template for replication, however, errors do occur. In language, these errors appear as misspellings in books and articles. In DNA, these errors are called **mutations**. One type of error takes place when the replication enzymes mistakenly skip a base. In this case, the new strand forms with a missing base. When that strand is replicated, the error is copied onto a new, second strand. This makes a DNA molecule that is missing a nucleotide at that position. Such an error is called a **deletion mutation**.

Another type of error takes place when the replication enzymes mistakenly add the wrong base to a position. Substituting one small base for the other or one large base for the other during replication is called a **substitution mutation**. In that case, the complementary pairing normally seen in DNA is disrupted at the point of substitution. If the DNA is replicated, however, the newly synthesized strand will contain an appropriate base pair for the substitution mutation (Figure E12.7). In that way, the mutation is preserved and carried on in all future offspring cells. Usually, specific repair enzymes detect and repair mutations. Despite the existence of those enzymes, some mutations become a permanent part of a cell's genetic material.

Mutations can take place in the DNA of any cell in the body of an organism. Imagine what could happen if mutations occur in cells that give rise to gametes (sperm and eggs, for example). If those gametes become zygotes and grow, the mutation will be passed along to the offspring. Then the mutation may become a lasting change in that species' genetic information. Take single-celled organisms that make new individuals by simple cell division. Any mutation may be passed along to new individuals. Ironically, the accuracy that results from the template method of copying DNA also means that, once a mutation occurs, *it* copies accurately as well.

Think about those errors that are copied accurately during replication. Does every change in DNA structure give rise to a lasting change in a species' genetic information? No, it does not. Some mutations can cause serious developmental errors. These mutations are so harmful that they may kill the organism long before it reaches reproductive maturity. In those cases, the mutation is not copied again. Less serious, but still harmful mutations, may lead to traits that are troublesome for survival and reproduction. For instance, a mutation may result in a frog with a short tongue. This characteristic may limit the frog's success in catching insects. That may prevent the frog from growing large, becoming strong, and mating successfully. In those cases, the forces of natural selection will tend to reduce how often that genotype happens in the population.

Those mutations that give individuals an advantage *may* result in long-lasting changes in a species' genetic material. Also, there are mutations that are only mildly harmful or have no effect. These mutations may continue to be passed from generation to generation. The genetic variety that results from some neutral or mildly harmful mutations may turn out to be an advantage if the species' environment changes or the individual relocates. In those cases, the *phenotype* that results from the new *genotype* may become an advantage for the individual's survival. For example, individuals who carry one allele for the sickle-cell trait have an advantage if they live in parts of the world where the malaria pathogen is present. That heterozygous

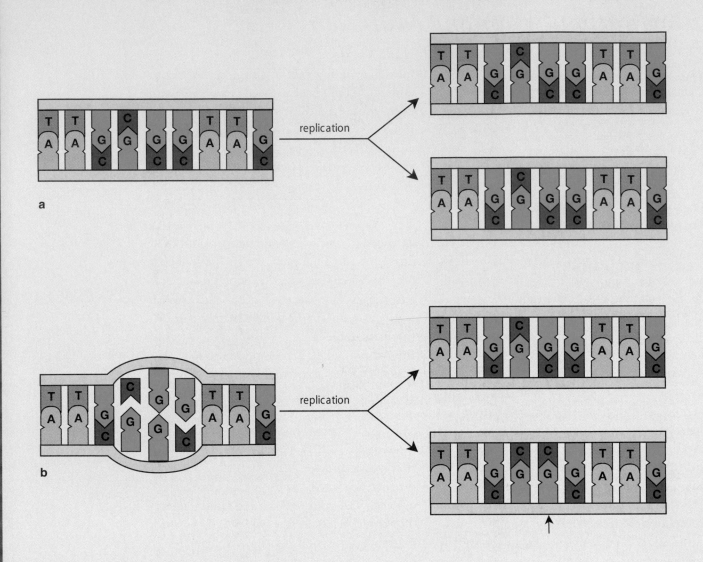

Figure E12.7 Preserving a mutation. **(a)** Normal DNA undergoes replication to produce two identical DNA molecules. **(b)** Mutated DNA (note that a C from the normal DNA has mutated to G) undergoes replication to produce two new DNA molecules. But only one of those molecules is identical to the normal DNA. In that way, replication preserves mutation (arrow).

genotype makes those individuals who have it more likely to survive malaria outbreaks. One effect of this advantage is that the number of individuals in the population who have one sickle-cell allele increases. Under other circumstances, that genotype would be considered rather harmful. In this way, the wide variety of alleles that occur in a population, including some mutations, helps species survive. ◆

Landmark Discovery:
Why the Fuss about Watson and Crick?

London, England (1953): The most recent issue of *Nature* hit scientists' desks this week. This issue contains a landmark paper proposing a physical structure for DNA. DNA is the substance that makes up the genetic material of living organisms. The paper is coauthored by James Watson and Francis Crick, with important contributions from Rosalind Franklin's work. This paper already has the scientific world buzzing with enthusiasm and optimism.

To be honest, though, your humble science club's *What's New?* correspondent didn't see what the fuss was all about. I mean, I thought science was an *experimental* endeavor. How could a paper that only proposes a *model* be exciting? Where is the evidence that these two scientists actually are right? Besides, I think that coming up with a model would be easy. There must be hundreds of different ways to suggest how DNA is put together. So what's the big deal with *their* model?

To get an answer to my questions, I called an old friend of mine, Pete, at the university. Pete is a high-level science type, though you wouldn't know it from his no-pain/no-strain lifestyle. Wow, did he set me straight! First, he pointed out that a good model *explains* all of the known characteristics of

Figure E12.8   Watson, Crick, and Franklin. James Watson and Francis Crick are credited with proposing the first detailed description of the structure of DNA. Their work built on the arrangements of atoms suggested by the X-ray photographs taken by Rosalind Franklin.

the system that you are studying. Take the Watson and Crick model as an example, he said. It explains how DNA can do all the things the genetic material appears to be able to do. Not only can DNA *encode* information, but it also can store that information in a stable manner through time. DNA also

duplicates with very high accuracy. It also has enough structural flexibility to produce the full range of variations that we see on earth.

Then Pete pointed out that a good model also is *consistent* with all the available experimental evidence. In the case of DNA, this includes several pieces of evidence. DNA is shaped like a double helix. The nitrogen bases are stacked inside the molecule in a regular pattern. The big nitrogen bases and the small nitrogen bases are present in the molecule in a 1:1 ratio. And finally, Pete insisted that a good model is testable. He said, "Just look at all the predictions that the new DNA model makes that you could test. For example, you could test that a newly replicated DNA molecule would have one old strand and one new strand. Or you could consider that the two strands at any point on the molecule are complementary, but not identical."

"Okay, okay," I said. So I've learned something about modeling and science. And if Pete and his friends are right about where the study of DNA is going to take us, this is just the beginning of what I'm going to learn. In fact, all of us will be learning a lot in the next few decades. So, hats off to model-building. . . . Got any LEGOS? ◆

The Expression of Genetic Information

When an error in replication takes place, the nucleotide sequence of a DNA molecule is altered. The resulting mutations may be passed on during the next round of DNA replication. Knowing how a change in DNA structure (essentially a change in genotype) can be physically preserved, however, does not tell us what effect the altered DNA structure has on the organism. To see that effect, we must look at the organism's phenotype and

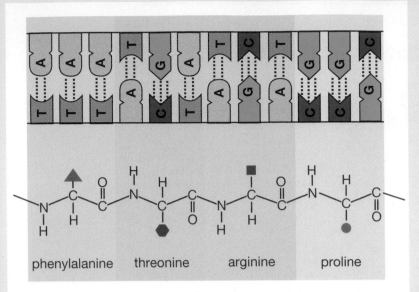

Figure E12.9 **Relationship between DNA sequence and protein sequence.** Each strand of DNA consists of a series of nucleotides. These nucleotides are bonded together in a particular order. The protein that is specified by this DNA consists of a series of amino acids. These amino acids are bonded together in the order encoded by the sequence of nucleotides in the DNA. A set of three nucleotides in the DNA codes for one amino acid in the corresponding protein. The genetic code is examined in more detail in the essay *Translating the Message in mRNA* (page 524).

discover whether it also is altered. In other words, we must look to see whether the mutation caused a change in a gene that is used to control some characteristic of the organism.

The process by which a cell *uses* genetic information is called **gene expression**. Let's look at the first step in understanding how gene expression takes place. Genes contain information that is required to build proteins. Proteins carry out critical biochemical and structural activities inside cells. Those activities include a number of housekeeping functions that almost all cells continually must perform to remain alive. Think about how you must replace burned-out lightbulbs, take out the trash, and grocery shop to maintain a healthy household. Cells must also replace and repair worn out parts, eliminate wastes, and break down glucose for energy to stay healthy. In addition to those basic chores, however, most

cells also conduct very specialized types of activities. For example, plant leaf cells harvest light energy. They use it to build sugars. Muscle cells contract to allow movement of your limbs. Regardless of the activity involved, the information that a cell needs to build proteins is contained in its DNA.

The protein that is expressed is determined by the gene's nucleotide sequence (A, C, T, and G). Through that sequence, DNA directs the formation of proteins. Proteins are sequences of amino acids. The diagram in Figure E12.9 illustrates this process. Notice that there is a relationship between DNA structure and protein structure. Both nucleic acids and proteins are long molecules. Both are made of repeating subunits arranged in a linear manner. Because both nucleic acids and proteins are linear, a code in the sequence of nucleotides can specify the order of amino acids in the protein. That is, the order of nucleotides in a gene determines the order of amino acids in a protein. This is important. The order of amino acids in a protein specifies that protein's shape. Proteins will function properly only when they have folded into a very specific shape.

Genetic information is first expressed as RNA. Let's see how this genetic code determines the sequence of amino acids in a protein. Let's also look at how the cell physically assembles these amino acids into a chain. To do those things, we need to look at some of the specific steps of gene expression. To begin with, it makes no difference what type of information a particular gene contains. In most cases, the first step in making this information available for use in the cell is the construction of another nucleic acid, **ribonucleic acid** (**RNA**). Structurally, RNA is almost identical to DNA. But there are several major differences. RNA contains a ribose sugar instead of a deoxyribose sugar. Thymine (T), one of the bases in DNA, does not occur in RNA. Instead, a related base, uracil (U), is found at positions complementary to adenine (A). In addition, RNA is single-stranded.

Like DNA, RNA is built according to the information that is available in the DNA template. The first step in gene expression is the production of RNA from the DNA template. This is called **transcription** (Figure E12.10). Now you know that RNA is

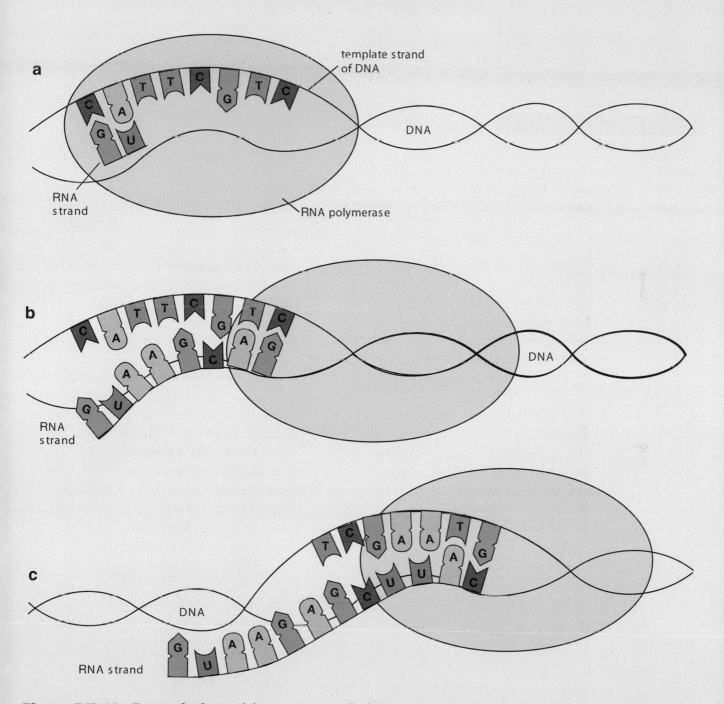

Figure E12.10   Transcription.   (a) An enzyme called RNA polymerase synthesizes RNA from a template strand of DNA. The process of transcribing DNA into RNA is very similar to the process of replication. Except only one RNA strand is made. **(b)** Note that as the enzyme moves along the DNA, the double helix is unwound. Specific base-pair interactions form between the DNA and RNA. **(c)** The DNA strands behind the enzyme then interact again to form the double helix. Eventually, the enzyme that is building the RNA reaches the end of the gene. At that point, the DNA and the RNA are released. Transcription, like replication, takes place in the nucleus of eukaryotic cells.

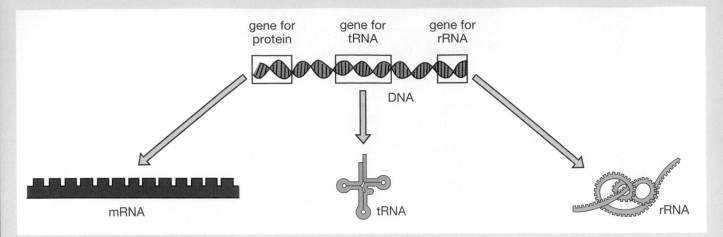

Figure E12.11 Types of RNA. DNA encodes three types of RNA. The information encoded in mRNA will be translated directly into protein. The tRNA and the rRNA participate in the reactions that assemble proteins.

chemically similar to DNA. Can you imagine how DNA serves as a template to make a strand of complementary RNA? The new RNA nucleotides are arranged through base-pairing interactions in an order that matches the DNA template. This is the same way new DNA nucleotides are arranged during DNA replication. In fact, the process of *transcription* is, in many ways, very similar to the process of *replication*.

As Figure E12.11 shows, cells can make three types of RNA. The first type is called **mRNA** (messenger RNA). It has the crucial role of carrying information from the DNA in the cell's nucleus to the cell's cytoplasm. This is where the protein will be made. This form

of RNA logically is called messenger RNA. This is because its only role is to carry a transcript (or message) of the DNA-encoded information. It carries this message to the place in the cell where that information can be translated (or read).

The second and third types of RNA are called **tRNA** (transfer RNA) and **rRNA** (ribosomal RNA). In contrast, they function in the actual process of assembling amino acids to make proteins. These two forms of RNA are transcribed from genes that are not expressed as proteins. Instead, as Figure E12.11 shows, the final product of these genes is RNA. These RNAs play a key role in converting the information in mRNA into protein. ◆

Translating the Message in mRNA

To express a gene for a protein, the cell first makes a molecule of mRNA. This mRNA then acts like a blueprint for building a house or a machine. Cells translate the mRNA blueprints into specific sequences of amino acids that make up proteins. These mRNA blueprints are written in the language of nucleic acids. Those proteins are the cellular equivalent of structures and machines (refer to

Figure E12.12). The name given to the process of converting the genetic code in an mRNA sequence into an amino acid sequence is **translation**. Think about how you would have to translate information in a message that was written in an unfamiliar language. In the same way, your cells must translate the information encoded in mRNA into proteins for it to be useful.

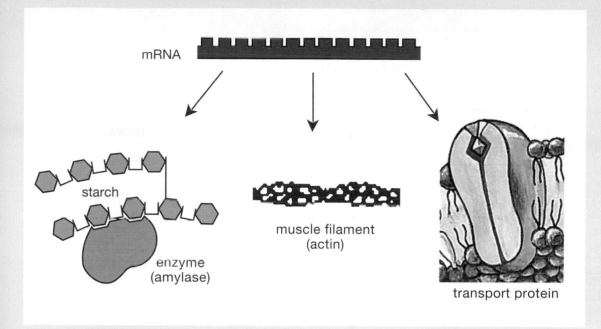

Figure E12.12   Translating mRNA into protein.   The information encoded in mRNA is translated into proteins. Proteins then can function in the cell as enzymes, structural components, or a variety of transport molecules. Translation takes place in the cytoplasm. In eukaryotes, this means that the mRNA first must be transported out of the nucleus.

Next, we will look at the actual steps of protein synthesis (translation). Before we do that, let's examine some of the basic characteristics of the code that links a nucleotide sequence to the amino acid sequence in a protein. This code is called the **genetic code**. Proteins are built from some 20 different amino acids. Each amino acid must be identified specifically by a coding system within the mRNA. The code cannot be a simple one-to-one pairing of nucleotides to amino acids. If it were, the code could only specify (code for) four different amino acids (one for each of the four different nucleotides). Likewise, the code cannot involve a two-to-one correlation (two nucleotides encoding one amino acid). In that instance, the code could specify only 16 amino acids. Instead, the code involves a three-to-one correlation. In other words, the genetic code uses three sequential mRNA bases to identify each amino acid. Each triplet (three-nucleotide combination) is called a **codon**.

Unraveling the details of the genetic code involved determining exactly which amino acid is specified by which codon. This was one of the most exciting series of discoveries ever made in the field of biology. Now, humans actually can read the information encoded in the genetic material of each species.

Study Figure E12.13 carefully. Did you notice that using all four bases, three at a time, results in 64 possible codon combinations ($64 = 4^3$)? Remember, there are only 20 amino acids. The early genetic code researchers discovered that some amino acids have more than one codon. Figure E12.13 lists the triplet codes for each amino acid.

Study the table again. You will notice that some of the possible triplet base combinations do not correspond to any amino acid. Several triplet base combinations begin with U. These signal a *stop* in translation (that is, the end of the protein). Another special codon is AUG. This codon specifies the amino acid methionine. It

First letter	Second letter				Third letter
	U	**C**	**A**	**G**	
U	phenylalanine	serine	tyrosine	cysteine	U
	phenylalanine	serine	tyrosine	cysteine	C
	leucine	serine	stop	stop	A
	leucine	serine	stop	tryptophan	G
C	leucine	proline	histidine	arginine	U
	leucine	proline	histidine	arginine	C
	leucine	proline	glutamine	arginine	A
	leucine	proline	glutamine	arginine	G
A	isoleucine	threonine	asparagine	serine	U
	isoleucine	threonine	asparagine	serine	C
	isoleucine	threonine	lysine	arginine	A
	(start) methionine	threonine	lysine	arginine	G
G	valine	alanine	aspartate	glycine	U
	valine	alanine	aspartate	glycine	C
	valine	alanine	glutamate	glycine	A
	valine	alanine	glutamate	glycine	G

Figure E12.13   **The genetic code.**   The code letters represent bases in mRNA. The words in the boxes are the names of the 20 amino acids most commonly found in proteins. To use the code, follow a codon's three nucleotides to arrive at the corresponding amino acid. You do this by using the rows and columns labeled *First, Second, Third Letter*. For example, GGA codes for glycine. How many of the amino acids have more than one codon?

also is a signal to *start* translation (to begin building the protein).

One of the most remarkable aspects of the genetic code is that it is nearly universal. For example, although prokaryotes and eukaryotes have *many* basic structural differences, they use the same genetic code. That basic similarity is an important piece of evidence that supports the theory of a common origin of all life-forms. ◆

Landmark Discovery: White-Coated Sleuths Decipher Genetic Code

Bethesda, Maryland (1961): It looks as though one of the greatest challenges in scientific decoding soon will be conquered. Hats off to the pioneering work of two modern-day detectives from the National Institutes of Health Marshall Nirenberg and Heinrich Matthaei. Nirenberg and Matthaei were intent on cracking the genetic code. They announced last week the first decoded results from their landmark research. The results showed that three mRNA nucleotides in the sequence UUU correspond to the amino acid phenylalanine, and the mRNA triplet CCC corresponds to the amino acid proline.

The genetic code lies at the heart of all living systems. Thus, this breakthrough truly is a remarkable accomplishment. The existence of a code—the sequence of bases in an organism's DNA—has been known since the mid-1950s. But until now scientists had no idea how to read it. To decipher the genetic code, Nirenberg and Matthaei built an artificial protein-making system in a test tube. They then gave it an artificial message. By knowing the message that they gave the system and analyzing the protein made, they were able to decode the code.

Although the process sounds simple, its execution represents an amazing feat. To read even those first two words (UUU and CCC), Nirenberg and Matthaei had to create a test-tube system that actually built proteins to order. To do that, they extracted enzymes and other necessary protein-assembly components from dead bacteria. For example, their test-tube system contained molecules of rRNA and of tRNA. Both of these molecules are known to be central to the assembly process. In addition, Nirenberg and Matthaei had to build a set of artificial mRNAs. Those mRNAs had to contain known nucleotide sequences. Only after both of those tasks had been accomplished were they able to start deciphering.

What does all of this mean to you? Well, if you have any UUUs or CCCs in your genetic information (and you do), it means that we now know what those codons mean to your cells. We now can *read* them. As we break more and more of the code, who knows? One day we may be able to pull all of the mRNAs out of your cells and read your genes. What would our molecular sleuths say about that? ◆

Cellular Components in Protein Synthesis

Understanding that mRNA codons correspond to amino acids is important to understanding gene expression. The process, however, is complex. It involves identifying the appropriate amino acids, aligning them properly, and joining them together. It also involves a number of *cellular components*, or cellular structures, as Figure E12.13 illustrates. Ribosomes are the primary cellular component. This component is responsible for translating the information encoded in mRNA into a protein.

Ribosomes are large structures. They are made of rRNA and protein. They travel along a strand of mRNA and read the triplet codons (Figure E12.14a). Ribosomes can read any mRNA. As a result, they can produce an unlimited number of different proteins. For each mRNA strand, however, the specific order in which the amino acids are put together is dictated by that mRNA's particular codon sequence.

A second important component of protein synthesis is the cell's population of tRNA molecules (see Figure E12.14b). Those molecules are important. They recognize both specific mRNA codons and the amino acids

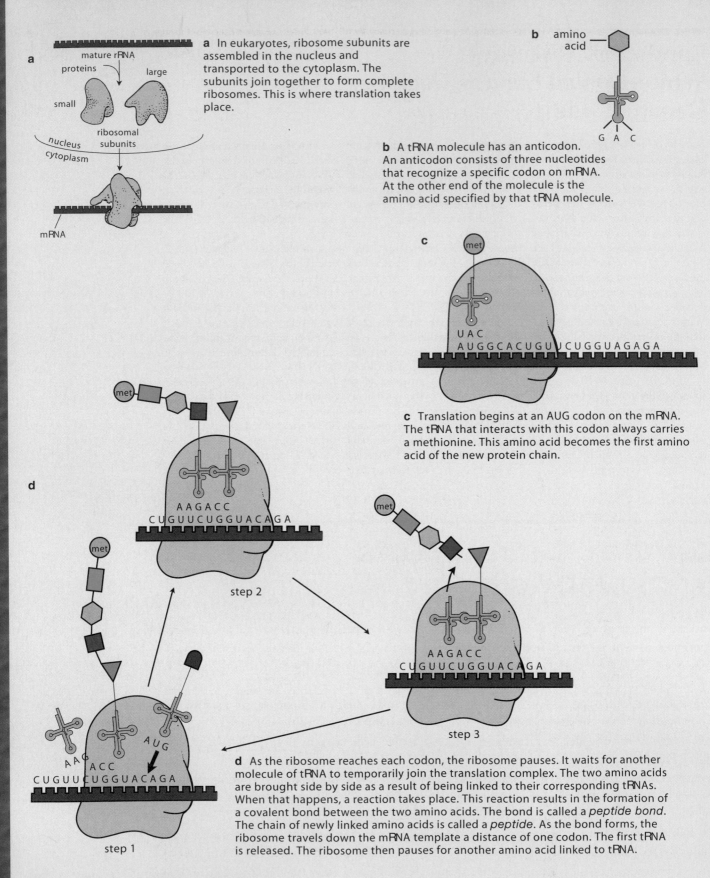

a In eukaryotes, ribosome subunits are assembled in the nucleus and transported to the cytoplasm. The subunits join together to form complete ribosomes. This is where translation takes place.

b A tRNA molecule has an anticodon. An anticodon consists of three nucleotides that recognize a specific codon on mRNA. At the other end of the molecule is the amino acid specified by that tRNA molecule.

c Translation begins at an AUG codon on the mRNA. The tRNA that interacts with this codon always carries a methionine. This amino acid becomes the first amino acid of the new protein chain.

d As the ribosome reaches each codon, the ribosome pauses. It waits for another molecule of tRNA to temporarily join the translation complex. The two amino acids are brought side by side as a result of being linked to their corresponding tRNAs. When that happens, a reaction takes place. This reaction results in the formation of a covalent bond between the two amino acids. The bond is called a *peptide bond*. The chain of newly linked amino acids is called a *peptide*. As the bond forms, the ribosome travels down the mRNA template a distance of one codon. The first tRNA is released. The ribosome then pauses for another amino acid linked to tRNA.

Figure E12.14   Protein synthesis.

Landmark Discovery: Extraordinary New Technique Changes Biology Forever

San Francisco, California (1973): Both the study and practice of biology were radically and irreversibly changed today. Stanley Cohen of Stanford University and Herbert Boyer of the University of California San Francisco reported the first successful attempt to build and to clone a *recombinant* DNA molecule. What makes this accomplishment so remarkable? The recombinant DNA molecule—made by joining together (or *recombining*) pieces of DNA from two completely different sources—never existed before. Today, it exists. It exists in many thousands of copies, and researchers can make thousands more at will.

When congratulated on their accomplishment, Cohen and Boyer quickly acknowledged their debt to many other scientists whose hard work and important discoveries made creating and cloning a recombinant molecule possible. One key advance in just the last few years was the 1970 discovery of the first restriction enzyme. This discovery was made by Werner Arbor of the University in Basel, and Daniel Nathans and Hamilton Smith of Johns Hopkins University. **Restriction enzymes** are proteins that can recognize and cut perfectly a specific sequence of nucleotides in DNA.

Another key advance took place in several research labs at the same time. That discovery involves isolating another important protein. That protein is the enzyme **DNA ligase**. DNA ligase functions during the replication and repair of DNA molecules. It repairs nicks that occur in one DNA strand.

Isolating DNA ligase allows scientists to use it to fasten back together DNA fragments that restriction enzymes have cut. In addition, the DNA that scientists stitch together can come from different organisms. For instance, scientists can combine bacterial DNA with yeast DNA to create *recombinant molecules*.

The idea behind Cohen and Boyer's technique is straightforward. They cut DNA from two different sources with the same restriction enzyme. They then mixed the DNA together with DNA ligase. The DNA ligase caused the cut pieces to stitch together. Then Cohen and Boyer inserted the new, recombinant molecules into living bacteria. As the bacteria reproduced, the tiny recombinant DNA molecules also multiplied. Within hours, their technique produced a colony of reproducing bacteria. They could then extract as many copies of the recombinant molecule as they wanted.

Recombinant DNA techniques are revolutionizing scientific research and technology. Scientists around the world are isolating and inserting a wide range of human genes into bacteria. By doing this, they can both study gene expression and harvest the products that the genes code for. Such techniques may lead to an unlimited supply of human insulin to use in treating diabetes. Or, it could produce unrestricted quantities of human growth hormone to use in treating dwarfism. Imagine the benefits of inserting the genes for a wide range of desirable characteristics into crop plants. (Bigger cucumbers? frost-resistant strawberries? sweeter corn?) Who knows? One day, we may even be able to remove particular genes from peoples' bodies and replace them with other genes.

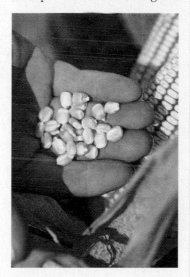

Of course, new technologies come with potential problems as well. Scientists already are pointing out the need to regulate the technology to allow for only beneficial and safe DNA transfers. The deliberate combining of genes from *different* species, however, involves controlling genes and evolution in a different way than has ever been done before. We may not be able to predict exactly the impact that those changes will have. Our world is a different place today from what it was yesterday. It is important that all of us—scientists and nonscientists alike—be knowledgeable. We must all take part in deciding how we will use our new genetic abilities. ◆

that match those codons. One portion of a tRNA molecule interacts with the amino acid that corresponds to a particular codon.

Another portion of the tRNA molecule then interacts with the codons in the mRNA. That interaction is a base-pairing association. It takes place between the nucleotides of the tRNA and the nucleotides of the mRNA. The base pairs form according to the same rules of complementary pairing that take place between nucleotides in DNA. Look at Figure E12.14c–d. The tRNA molecules bring about the *translation* of the language of nucleic acids into the language of proteins.

Translation continues until the ribosome reaches a special codon. This special codon does not specify an amino acid. These codons are called **stop codons**. Stop codons cause the ribosome to pause indefinitely because there are no matching tRNAs. At this point, a release factor—which is itself a protein—binds to the ribosome. The release factor causes the ribosome to separate from the mRNA. The completed protein folds into a shape determined by its amino acid sequence. It is now ready to function.

Each protein that is produced by translation plays some role in the function of a cell, tissue, organ, or organ system. For instance, there are particular alleles that encode the information for producing the protein hemoglobin. The protein produced through the translation of the corresponding mRNA for that allele transports oxygen in red blood cells. The ability of any protein to function properly, however, depends on whether the protein is folded properly.

A protein's final folded form can be altered by mutations. Mutations can alter one or several amino acids. This can cause the protein to fold into a form that is nonfunctional (inactive) or only partially functional. That is how a single amino acid mutation in hemoglobin can result in sickle-cell disease. Think about the change that this mutation causes at the molecular level. Perhaps then you can see why *genotype* is so important in determining *phenotype*.

Protein synthesis is a highly regulated process. The amount and type of protein produced in cells vary. For example, the life stage of an organism, the time of day, and the particular cell types are all factors that determine protein production. That regulation can be accomplished by changing rates of translation and transcription in cells.

Scientists use a variety of techniques to learn more about the role of specific proteins in organisms. They can conduct experiments to investigate what role a protein plays. They can study how the cell regulates the amount of protein that is produced. But first, scientists often need to separate a specific protein from other proteins produced in the cells. One technique that scientists use is **chromatography**. Chromatography is a set of techniques that scientists use to separate mixtures of molecules, such as proteins. Molecules separate based on their mass, charge, or ability to bind to other molecules. Scientists also use procedures such as electrophoresis to learn about the composition, expression, and properties of proteins. By understanding more about specific proteins, scientists can learn how organisms respond to changing conditions and maintain homeostasis. ◆

Manipulating Genetic Material

In the last 40 years, science has greatly increased our understanding of the structure and function of genetic material. Also changed is our ability to work with it in the laboratory. In fact, our increasing ability to study and manipulate molecular processes in a variety of species has led to a revolution in the ways that scientists conduct research. That, in turn, has changed how pharmaceutical firms make medicines and how many industries conduct their day-to-day business.

The technologies are new. But our fundamental interest in studying and manipulating genetic information is not new.

For centuries, humans have selectively bred plants and animals to produce organisms with desirable combinations of characteristics. Traditional methods of agricultural breeding were the earliest forms of genetic engineering. **Genetic engineering** is a process designed to artificially control the genetic makeup of an organism. In *selective breeding*, humans cross plants or animals that have desirable traits to produce new generations. For example, a golden retriever is the product of selectively breeding various Labradors and spaniels. As a result, future generations show more of the desired traits. Less desirable traits sometimes can be eliminated. Selective breeding also can produce new, less desirable traits. For instance, a greater tendency for developing hip dysplasia came out of many selective dog breeding programs. (Hip dysplasia is a common cause of osteoarthritis or degenerative joint disease.)

In recent years, scientists have developed more powerful techniques for examining genetic material at the molecular level. These techniques make it possible to selectively change the genotypes of organisms. Many other new techniques allow scientists to alter the genetic information of a species in much more direct and extensive ways than the older methods of selective breeding. It is now possible to introduce genes into an organism that neither parent possessed. It is even possible for scientists to remove genes from one organism and introduce them into an unrelated organism—one that does not normally possess those genes. The new DNA formed through that process is called **recombinant DNA** (see Figure E12.15).

One example of how scientists are using recombinant DNA technologies to address a specific practical problem involves the cotton plant. Cotton plants often are attacked by a pest called a bollworm. The bollworm damages cotton crops and costs millions of dollars each year to control. Researchers have known for a long time, however, that a bollworm will die if it eats the common

bacterium called *Bacillus thuringiensis*. (*B.t.* for short.) A protein that the bacteria produce is partially digested in the worm's gut and poisons the worm. Because that protein is so effective, for years farmers have sprayed *B.t.* bacteria on their cotton crops to discourage the bollworms from eating them. That protective measure has its drawbacks, though. Sunlight breaks down *B.t.*, and rainfall easily washes it off the plants.

Through genetic engineering, however, researchers have overcome those drawbacks. Figure E12.16 shows how scientists isolated the gene that codes for the poisonous bacterial protein. They then transferred the gene into the cotton plant. The new cotton plants thus contain recombinant DNA. They can produce

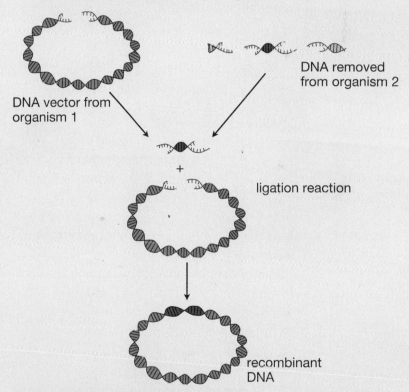

Figure E12.15 Recombinant DNA. Molecular biologists isolate DNA from separate sources and combine them in unique combinations. DNA from Organism 2 can be joined to a small circular molecule of DNA from Organism 1. This takes place in an enzyme reaction called ligation. The circular DNA molecules are called plasmids or vectors. They are found in many bacteria. Because scientists can move vectors in and out of bacterial cells relatively easily, they serve as convenient carriers of DNA. As a result, they allow for the production of recombinant DNA molecules.

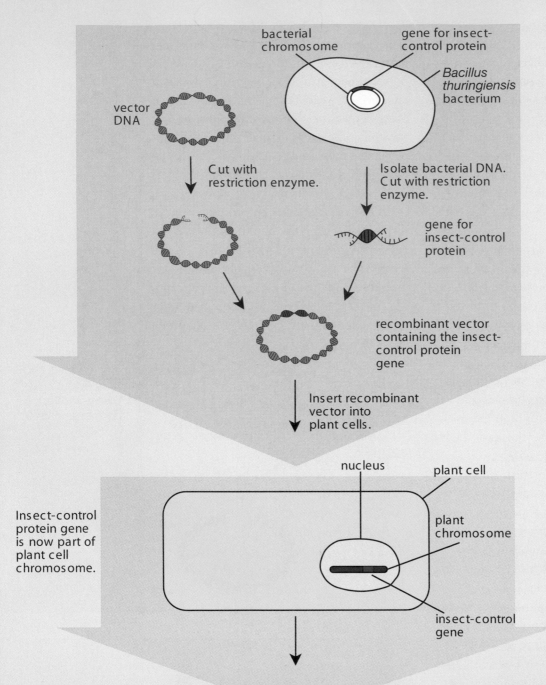

bacterial chromosome

gene for insect-control protein

Bacillus thuringiensis bacterium

vector DNA

Cut with restriction enzyme.

Isolate bacterial DNA. Cut with restriction enzyme.

gene for insect-control protein

recombinant vector containing the insect-control protein gene

Insert recombinant vector into plant cells.

nucleus

plant cell

plant chromosome

Insect-control protein gene is now part of plant cell chromosome.

insect-control gene

A whole cotton plant is grown from 1 altered cell. Every cell in the plant produces the insect-control protein. The plant can now protect itself from bollworm attack.

Figure E12.16 Genetic engineering of cotton. The toxic insect-control protein gene *Bacillus thuringiensis* is isolated. This is done with the same DNA-cutting restriction enzyme that is used to cut the DNA vector. Scientists combine these two pieces of DNA. They then insert the recombinant DNA into a plant cell. An entire plant regenerates from that one cell. The plant can now protect itself from the bollworm.

a bacterial protein, *B.t.* toxin, in their leaves. Those plants are engineered to protect themselves from damage. When a bollworm begins nibbling on the leaves, it eats the *B.t.* protein and dies. Food crop plants also can be engineered to produce the *B.t.* protein because it is not toxic to humans. Farmers can use less insecticide, thereby decreasing the amount of toxic chemicals that enter the water supply and food web. The technology, however, has not been completely effective. Farmers using the engineered cotton in 1996 reported that many bollworms survived in the new crop. Additional pesticides had to be applied, though the total amount was reduced. The surviving bollworms raise concerns, however. What might prolonged exposure to *B.t.* do to the bollworm's resistance to its toxicity? There also are concerns for the other organisms that will encounter *B.t.* through this technique. Current tests show that the *B.t.* toxin is nontoxic for most animals, including beneficial insects. But the toxin has the potential to harm endangered and threatened species of moths and butterflies.

Plants or animals that contain genes from unrelated species, such as cotton plants containing bacterial genes, are called **transgenic**. Transgenic organisms are used widely in research and industry. Other organisms altered by genetic engineering techniques can be just as important, however, even if they are not transgenic. Consider the genetically engineered tomato, which recently was approved for sale in the United States. Tomatoes normally ripen and soften at the same time. That situation encourages farmers to pick the tomatoes while they are still green and ship them to stores before they soften. The less desirable alternative is to ship ripe tomatoes that are easily damaged in transit. Unfortunately, green tomatoes do not ripen well after they are picked. They often have little flavor even after they have turned red.

When scientists discovered that the ripening and softening processes were not the same, a new alternative for farmers emerged. Different genes (and thus different biochemical pathways) regulate the two processes. As a result, scientists could target the softening process and modify it. The result was a genetically engineered separation of the ripening and softening pathways. This allows tomatoes to be ripened on the vine, preserving their flavor. Yet they can be transported to the market without damage and rotting. Farmers and consumers alike benefit from that new technology. Some questions remain, however. What might be the potential effects if a genetically engineered crop interbreeds with a wild type of crop? These concerns cause scientists, politicians, and citizens to weigh the benefits and the drawbacks for the technologies carefully.

Genetic engineering also has a great effect on human health. Insulin is the peptide hormone that diabetics require. At one time, it could only be obtained from the pancreases of cattle and hogs. Insulin produced from these animals was available in limited supplies, and it was expensive. Furthermore, insulin from other animals was not very effective for some individuals because it was not similar enough to human insulin. By recombining the human insulin gene with bacterial genes, however, researchers have been able to produce human insulin in large bacterial fermentation systems. This process is an economical method for producing authentic human insulin (Figure E12.17).

Researchers currently are working on ways to treat certain human genetic disorders. They use recombinant DNA that has been constructed from harmless forms of viruses and functional copies of human genes. Introducing genetically engineered human cells into a human body for the purpose of curing a genetic defect is called **gene therapy**. The first successful attempt to accomplish gene therapy began on September 14, 1990. Genetically altered white blood cells were introduced into the circulatory system of a 4 year-old girl

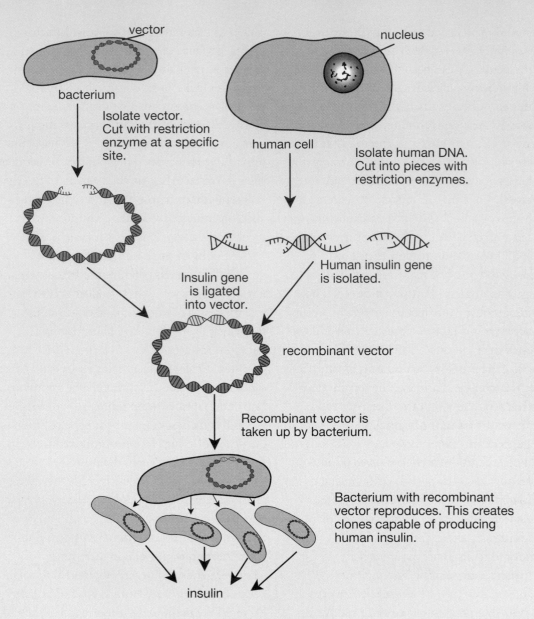

Figure E12.17 **Producing a recombinant DNA molecule containing the human insulin gene for expression in bacteria.**

named Ashanti De Silva. Ashanti was born with adenosine deaminase (ADA) deficiency. In this condition, an abnormal allele of the ADA gene fails to make a key protein. This key protein is required for the correct functioning of *T-lymphocytes*. These are cells that are critical to an individual's immune response. The absence of this protein meant that Ashanti, like other children who inherit ADA deficiency, could easily die of infections that would scarcely trouble other children.

Physicians treated Ashanti by genetically engineering some of her cells to produce the missing protein. First, they removed T-lymphocytes from her body. They then used genetic engineering techniques to insert copies of the normal allele of the ADA gene into them. Next, they allowed cells that started to use the inserted gene (thus producing the normal protein) to undergo mitosis and make many more functional cells. Finally, they inserted all of these genetically engineered cells back into Ashanti's body.

The scientists hoped that once back inside her body, those cells would continue to produce the normal protein. Thus, they would function normally to defend her body from disease. The engineered cells did, in fact, produce normal ADA. Ashanti's function improved. This procedure was repeated a dozen times over the next 2 years. The level of the normal ADA protein finally remained at 20–25 percent of that found in most people. That was enough to protect her. Today, Ashanti is a healthy, active teenager.

Despite the early promise of gene therapy, most such treatments are only in experimental stages of development. Like Ashanti De Silva, some individuals who have participated in gene therapy trials have experienced dramatic health improvements. However, most have shown only modest improvements. More than 300 gene therapy trials have been conducted. But, with the possible exception of one study whose participants are still toddlers, none have *cured* the underlying genetic disorder. Even those who have had dramatic health improvements require readministration of the normal gene. And the 1999 death of a participant in a gene therapy experiment has heightened awareness that gene therapy is not risk free. The experiment used a modified cold virus to insert a corrective gene into the patient's DNA. The modified virus caused an unusual but deadly immune response in the patient. This led to multiple organ failure and death.

Nevertheless, the potential promise and excitement of these techniques are causing significant activity in the pharmaceutical industry. Drug companies are investing billions of dollars into identifying genes associated with human disease. Discovering these genes may lead to the development of commercially produced gene products. It could also result in techniques for gene therapy that effectively treat a range of genetic disorders that are resistant to existing treatments.

As you might expect, gene therapy brings with it a whole series of ethical and legal questions. Some of the most troubling of those questions involve whether such techniques should be used to replace defective genes in a person's *reproductive* cells—her or his so-called *germ line*. Placing normal genes into a person's T-lymphocytes or lung cells (or other body cells) affects only these cells and the cells' offspring, should they divide. That type of gene therapy does not affect cells in the gonads. These cells produce the eggs or sperm that may carry the defective form of the gene.

On the other hand, replacing genes in a person's germ line is tinkering with that person's genetic legacy, as well as with the genetic legacy of the human species. Suppose that type of gene therapy is successful one day. The result will be a permanent change in genotype. And this change will affect all following generations produced from an individual who experienced the gene therapy.

Not surprisingly, the prospect of germ line gene therapy has triggered a great deal of controversy. Questions abound. For example, do children have a right to inherit an unmanipulated set of genes? Should they be allowed to inherit a set of "corrected" genes? Who will decide which genes need to be corrected and which genes do not? Say we discover the set of genes that control human height. Should parents be allowed to manipulate those genes in their germ lines in an effort to conceive children who will be shorter or taller than the parents' natural genetic legacy might dictate? What, after all, is "normal" or "preferred"? Who should decide, not only for people today, but for people who are yet unborn? These are difficult issues. The rapid growth in our understanding of the human genome and in our ability to manipulate DNA will only raise the stakes involved in resolving them. ◆

Landmark Discovery: New Technique Discovered While Driving

California (1983): A young scientist was driving at night to his cabin in northern California. He found his mind moving back and forth between the road and a problem he was dealing with in biochemistry. A tentative solution to his problem was soon replaced by a new problem. Suddenly, a flash of insight caused him to pull to the side of the road and stop. He awakened his passenger and excitedly explained to her that he had hit upon a solution. It was not a solution to his original problem, but to one of even greater significance. Kary Mullis, a scientist working for the Cetus Corporation, had just conceived of a simple method of producing nearly unlimited copies of a specific DNA sequence in a test tube.

Back at Cetus, Mullis asked a librarian to run a literature search on the enzyme DNA polymerase and its role, if any, in his idea of DNA amplification. Nothing relevant turned up. For the next several weeks, he described his idea to anyone who would listen. No one had heard of its ever being tried. No one saw any good reason why it would not work. For a year, he studied and refined his idea. In the spring of 1984, he presented a poster describing his idea at a scientific meeting. Joshua Lederberg, president of Rockefeller University and a Nobel Prize winner in 1946, expressed great interest in what he had proposed. After a long conversation, Dr. Lederberg saw the utter simplicity of the proposed idea. His response was, "Why didn't I think of that?" Mullis responded, "Nobody really knows why; surely I don't. I just ran into it one night."

What did Dr. Kary Mullis run into that spring night in northern California? It is a process called polymerase chain reaction (PCR). This technique revolutionized the way scientists analyze DNA and earned Mullis the 1993 Nobel Prize for Chemistry. Since the development of PCR, as little as a single molecule of DNA can be copied many times to provide sufficient amounts for sequence or mutation analysis. This technique is called **polymerase chain reaction**. It uses a DNA polymerase to produce exact copies of a DNA sequence. The term *chain reaction* refers to the fact that the DNA it produces becomes the template for additional DNA synthesis in the next cycle of reactions.

An automatic temperature-control device repeatedly warms and cools the reaction mixture. This device repeats the procedure shown in Figure E12.18 about 30–40 times. First, heating separates the double-stranded DNA molecules. Next, DNA polymerase acts at a lower temperature to synthesize matching strands for the single-stranded DNA. The cycle then repeats. The result of all this DNA synthesis is several million copies of the starting DNA.

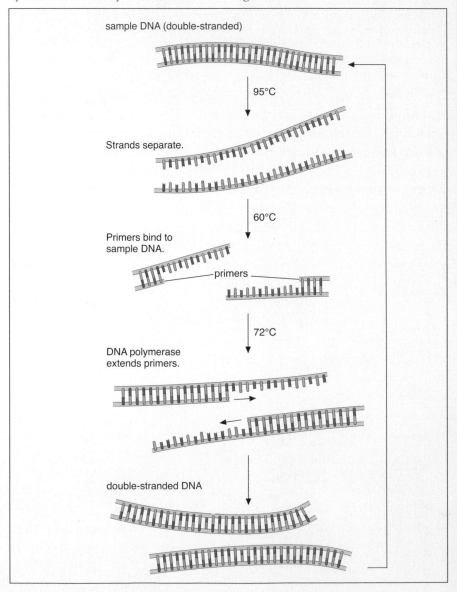

Figure E12.18 Polymerase chain reaction (PCR). Each cycle roughly doubles the number of DNA molecules.

Landmark Discovery: New Technique Discovered While Driving (continued)

Each cycle requires only 3–4 minutes. So the entire procedure can usually be completed in a few hours. The success of PCR requires use of DNA polymerase from *Thermus aquaticus*. This is a bacterium that lives in hot springs. Unlike the enzymes of most organisms, its DNA polymerase is stable at the high temperatures needed to separate double-stranded DNA. Even moderate heating destroys the secondary structure of most proteins. For example, think of the changes that you see in an egg when it is fried. The albumin protein that makes up most of the egg white quickly congeals into a rubbery mass well before the fat-rich yolk is cooked. In PCR, the heating separates the DNA. But this does not damage the DNA polymerase. The use of DNA polymerase from *Thermus aquaticus* in PCR is a good example of the practical application of biological knowledge.

How might PCR affect your life? It has accelerated the study of gene function, gene mapping, and evolution. In medicine, PCR is particularly useful in prenatal testing for genetic diseases. Other medical applications of PCR include identifying viruses, bacteria, and cancerous cells in human tissues. In forensic science, PCR has revolutionized the process of criminal identification. Remember the DNA fingerprinting that was used to identify the Romanov family described in *A Royal Tragedy*. This is one example of how PCR can be used to amplify a small sample of DNA enough to make analysis possible. Similar tests also can be used to exclude or implicate criminal suspects by amplifying DNA obtained from small samples of blood, semen, skin, or hair left at a crime scene.

During his midnight ride, Dr. Kary Mullis was wrestling with a biochemistry problem. He developed a remarkable solution. While it may sound like Dr. Mullis made a chance discovery, it is actually a good example of the creativity, imagination, and critical thinking that characterize most scientific discoveries. ◆

Informatics: Mapping and Sequencing the Human Genome

Informatics is the use of complex databases and electronic techniques to sort and analyze genetic information. Informatics has opened up a wide range of new research opportunities. Increasingly, the electronic management of information is becoming a central, indispensable feature of science. This is because research produces ever more data that must be accessible to scientists. The accurate storage and rapid retrieval of scientific data are nowhere more critical than in the Human Genome Project. The purpose of the Human Genome Project was to map and sequence the estimated 35,000 genes, containing approximately 3 billion nucleotide pairs of DNA, and store the information in electronic databases.

The Human Genome Project had two major objectives. The first was to develop detailed maps of the human genome and the genomes of several other well-studied organisms. These included a bacterium, yeast, nematode, fruit fly, mouse, and a rapidly growing plant with a small genome, *Arabidopsis thaliana*. Dr. Mullis's PCR technique was one of the key genetic techniques that sped the pace of research involved in mapping genomes. The second objective was to determine the complete nucleotide sequences of these genomes. But a written record of the human genome sequences would require the equivalent of 200 telephone books of 1,000 pages each. So, one important part of the project was to develop systems for electronically storing and managing databases.

The findings from the Human Genome Project have the potential to increase our understanding of human variation, development, gene regulation, and evolution. The knowledge gained will help advance the

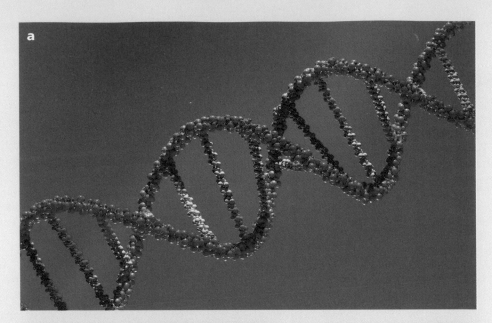

Figure E12.19 **(a)** False colors identify the different chemical structures that make up this model of a DNA molecule. **(b)** Researchers study the sequence of the nucleotides in DNA. One method for reading the sequences is by using a technique that converts the sequence of nucleotides into a series of bands on a piece of X-ray film. Knowing the nucleotide sequence of a gene allows the scientist to predict what kind of protein is coded for by the gene.

practice of medicine by uncovering new ways of diagnosing and treating inherited disorders. New technologies, especially those that help manage the enormous amounts of data generated by the Human Genome Project, will have applications far beyond the project. The development of electronic databases has been a great advantage to the Human Genome Project. But it also has raised important questions about using such information. ◆

Genetic Screening: A Dilemma for All of Us

Finding the gene for cystic fibrosis was a major breakthrough in biomedicine. There is new hope that research will produce a cure for the disorder. The *CF* gene can be detected through DNA analysis. DNA analysis could help identify people who carry the gene (heterozygotes). Once recognized, these people could be advised of the risk of having a child with CF. They could choose alternative methods of having a child such as adoption, artificial insemination, or in vitro fertilization and embryo transfer. Any gametes used in these methods could be screened for the *CF* gene. DNA analysis also permits the detection of the disorder in developing fetuses (homozygotes). The parents of a fetus diagnosed with CF could choose to abort the pregnancy or to carry it to term.

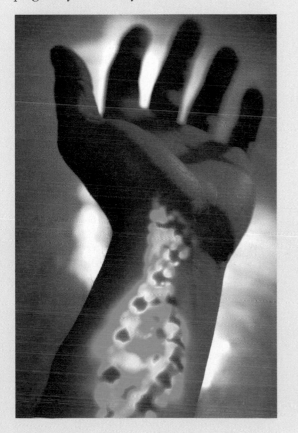

Genetic screening is the ability to screen an individual or a population for a variety of genetic disorders. This screening allows for early detection and prevention. It also raises many difficult questions about ethics and public policy. Dorothy Nelkin and Laurence Tancredi are sociologists who study the social impact of medicine. They agree that DNA analysis in genetic screening has shifted the focus of the health care system from looking for actual disease in individuals to looking for tendencies to develop disease. As a result, there is a danger that people who have no symptoms of disease may be labeled as disabled. These people may be discriminated against by health or life insurance companies. Potential employers, for example, may refuse to hire such individuals. They do not want to risk increased costs for medical benefits. They also do not want to spend time and money training an employee whose life expectancy might be limited.

Neil A. Holtzman, a pediatrician/geneticist at Johns Hopkins University raises another concern about DNA analysis. The tests may not always predict with certainty whether a person will develop a particular disorder. This is especially true for multifactorial disorders such as heart disease, cancer, and schizophrenia. These disorders are due to a complex interaction of genes and environmental conditions. Furthermore, says Holtzman, there are too few laboratories that can perform DNA analysis with precision and not enough trained genetic counselors to interpret the results.

Holtzman, Nelkin, and Tancredi recommend the development of new regulations to control how genetic screening is done and what is done with the results. Without regulation and greater public education about genetics, there is danger that some individuals may lose some control of their lives. Carried to extremes, some people might be forbidden to marry, to have children, or to do certain kinds of work.

The ethical, legal, and policy issues raised by DNA analysis and genetic screening must be considered along with the potential benefits to society. Approximately 5 percent (several million dollars per year) of the annual budget for the Human Genome Project supported research, discussion, and public education about the ethical, legal, and social implications of human genome research. Scientists, ethicists, philosophers, legislators, and a variety of other people are still involved in these discussions. Challenging and value-laden questions often accompany advances in science and technology and affect individuals, families, and society. ◆

Shaping the Future

Near the end of his book *The Firmament of Time,* the late paleoanthropologist and science philosopher Loren Eiseley described an interesting incident. While walking in the desert, he came upon a hen pheasant and a blacksnake locked in struggle. The bird evidently had seen the snake attempting to steal some of her eggs and attacked it. In defending itself, the snake had coiled itself around the bird. When Eiseley came upon them, the snake was being severely battered against the stones by the bird. But the bird was weakening rapidly as she struggled to free herself from the snake's coils.

Here is Eiseley's description of how he responded to this sight and the deep questions that were raised by his action.

I suppose I could have waited there to see what happened; . . . I suppose it would have been worth scientifically recording. But I could not stand that ceaseless, bloody pounding in the gravel . . . so . . . I unwound the serpent from the bird and let him hiss and wrap his battered coils around my arm. The bird, her wings flung out, rocked on her legs and gasped repeatedly. I moved away in order not to drive her further from her nest. Thus the serpent and I, two terrible and feared beings, passed quickly out of view. . . . Over the next ridge, where he could do no more damage, I let the snake, whose anger had subsided, slowly uncoil and slither from my arm. He flowed away into a little patch of bunch grass—aloof, forgetting, unaware of the journey he had made upon my wrist, which throbbed from his expert constriction. The bird had contended for birds against the oncoming future; the serpent writhing into the bunch of grass had contended just as desperately for serpents. And I, the apparition in that valley—for what had I contended?—I who contained the serpent and the bird and who read the past long written in their bodies (pages 174–175).

One aspect of Eiseley's story is of special concern for us here. Until the evolution of humans, all organisms on earth were roughly equal in the face of natural selection. The individual success or failure of each member of a species in one generation shaped the genetic legacy that gave rise to the next generation.

In humans, however, a species emerged that came to understand evolution and genetic

this may affect our own species. But human intervention has the power to affect the fate of many other species in addition to our own. Sometimes that intervention occurs through active genetic manipulation of domesticated organisms. Sometimes it happens merely as a by-product of our immense impact on the environments that support wild organisms. In either case, humans have become a major factor in determining the genetic futures of a huge range of other species. Today, that impact equals or even exceeds the force of natural selection itself.

But Eiseley suggests that this power, which comes to us through our large brains and conscious minds—the legacy of our own evolutionary history—carries with it a responsibility. It is the responsibility to employ those same conscious minds to examine what we do and to look beyond its immediate impact, as other species cannot. ◆

systems, and eventually began to reshape them consciously. We have looked briefly at how

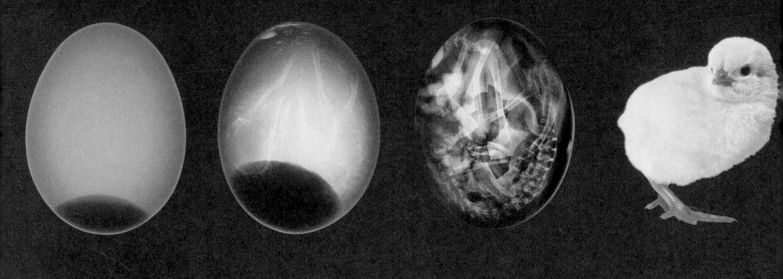

Development: Growth and Differentiation in Living Systems

In Unit 4, you learned about genetic processes that allow change in species from one generation to the next. In this unit, you will explore developmental processes that allow change within the lifetime of individual organisms. For instance, you will learn how changes in cells lead to changes in tissues, organs, and organisms. In Chapter 14, you will focus on changes in human growth and development from birth through old age. You also will explore human life stages in other cultures to learn how culture influences the expression of life stages.

In this unit, you will revisit your critter and participate in a multicultural fair. By the end of Unit 5, you should understand how

◆ development takes place from fertilization to death;

◆ physical development involves processes of growth and differentiation;

◆ humans grow and develop through various stages of life (these include physical, cognitive, emotional, and social stages); and

◆ culture influences the expression of those human life stages.

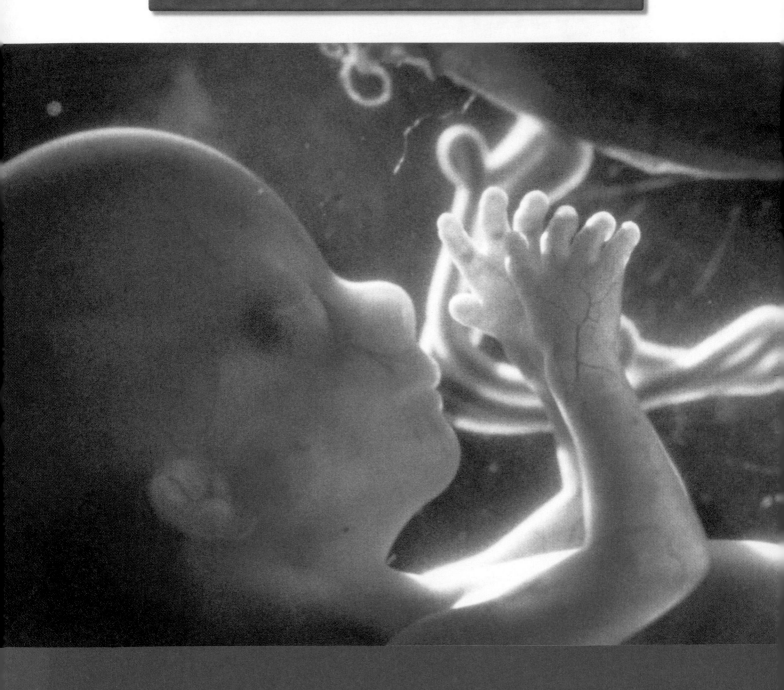

> "Be not afraid of growing slowly; be afraid only of standing still."
>
> *Chinese proverb*

Processes and Patterns of Development

People sometimes describe the processes of science as a simple set of steps that one can follow to generate scientific knowledge. Perhaps you have studied the so-called "scientific method." That description is so oversimplified that it is inaccurate. It is true that practicing scientists really do generate questions, test hypotheses, and form conclusions. However, they do not necessarily complete exactly those tasks in exactly that order. Instead, "doing science" is a highly creative, long-term search for answers to complicated and fascinating puzzles. Searching for answers is a dynamic process. It requires careful questioning, hypothesis-making, and concluding. Scientific searches also involve imagination, persistence, humor, and sometimes, luck.

How organisms grow and develop is one of life's fascinating puzzles. How is it that organisms change in precise and predictable ways from fertilized eggs to adults? In this chapter, you will consider what we know about the processes and patterns of development. You also will be invited to think about how scientists have gathered this knowledge. How might scientists extend their understanding to answer the questions about development that continue to puzzle us today.

ACTIVITIES

Engage	One Hundred Years of Questions
Explore	A Start in Development
Explain	
Explore	Processes That Generate Complexity
Explain	
Elaborate	Development Gone Awry
Evaluate	Evaluating Where We Stand

One Hundred Years of Questions

How do scientists think of the questions that they would like to investigate? Actually, finding questions to ask is the easy part of science. The hard part is expressing our questions in such a way that we can answer them.

Materials

DVD and player

PROCESS AND PROCEDURES

1. View the DVD segment "From Egg to Adult." What questions do those pairs of images raise in your mind? In your journal, record 2 questions about development that arouse your curiosity.

2. View the DVD segment "A Collection of Eggs: An Assortment of Adults." What questions do those images raise in your mind? In your journal, record 2 more questions that you find interesting.

Figure 13.1
Sea urchins develop from eggs. The eggs develop into a stage when they are called *larvae* (singular: larva) before becoming adults (see Figure E13.20).

Analysis

1. To see how some scientists have approached the study of development, read the story *Changes All Around*. Then join the class in a discussion of the following:

   a. Compare Roux's hot-needle experiment on a frog embryo to Driesch's experiment on sea urchin embryos. Indicate similarities and differences in each of the following aspects of their experiments:

   ◆ Experimental design

   ◆ Results

   ◆ Conclusions

   b. What was the specific question that Roux tried to answer? How was his question different from the question, How do organisms develop? Why was this difference important?

   c. What was Roux's contribution to the science of developmental biology?

2. Work individually. Compare the questions that you recorded in Process and Procedures steps 1 and 2 with the questions that scientists in the *Science* survey named as most interesting to them. How are your questions similar to those the scientists asked? How are they different? Record your answers in your journal.

3. Scientists still are asking and answering questions about development. What does that suggest about the processes of development? What does that suggest about the processes of science? Record your answers in your journal.

SCENARIO

Changes All Around

The fertilized frog egg has just started to develop. It has undergone one cell division. Under a microscope, it is clear that the two cells are in contact with one another. The scientist picks up a hot needle. With excruciating care, he pierces just one of the two cells. The other cell remains untouched. The pricked cell dies. The scientist continues his observations to see if the remaining cell will develop further or if it also will die. The year is 1888. The scientist, a German named Wilhelm Roux (pictured below), is in the process of making a dramatic step forward in the study of living systems.

Why was the killing of one cell such an important experiment? How did this affect biology? Scientists in the late19th century knew that vertebrates, such as frogs or humans, start life as a single cell, the fertilized egg. Scientists had proposed many ideas to try to explain how an embryo develops after fertilization. Some thought that a fertilized egg contained a tiny, fully formed—or preformed—organism that simply grew larger during development. Others thought that the structure of an organism formed as the embryo developed.

Roux, however, took a big step forward by doing more than just thinking about how development might take place. He asked the large question—How do organisms develop? He then identified a simpler, related question that he could test. This question was, Does each of the first two cells in an embryo contain all of the structures and information needed to grow into an organism. Or does each cell contain just half of the structures and information needed? (The second half of this question would be true if a fertilized ovum contained a tiny, fully formed or preformed organism.) Roux tested this question by performing the hot-needle experiment described above.

The results of Roux's hot-needle experiment were spectacular. As Roux described them: "[An] amazing thing happened; the one cell developed in many cases into a half-embryo generally normal in structure, with

small variations occurring only in the region of the immediate neighborhood of the treated half of the egg."*

In other words, the cell that survived gave rise only to the portions of the embryo that it would have produced if the experiment had not been done. Roux interpreted his results as evidence for preformed embryos.

As new evidence came to light, however, Roux's conclusion was challenged. In 1892, another scientist, Hans Driesch, conducted a similar experiment with a different design. First, Driesch used a different organism, a sea urchin. Second, Driesch actually separated the two cells and watched to see what would develop from each one. (Roux had killed one cell and left them both in place.) Driesch's results supported a view of development that was opposite to Roux's. Driesch observed that whole embryos developed from each of the separate cells. This evidence supported the idea that the organism forms during development, not that it is preformed.

Driesch was astonished with this observation. How could he account for his results? His first response was that sea urchin eggs are not frog eggs. Perhaps he simply was seeing a difference between the two types of organisms. Did his results actually mean that frogs and urchins develop in completely different ways? Because that answer did not seem satisfactory, he suggested that perhaps Roux had not really "isolated" the frog cells. Roux had killed one cell. But the dead cell remained in contact with the live one. Possibly the dead cell was exerting an influence on the development of the live cell. In fact, in 1910, a scientist named J. F. McClendon removed one cell of a two-cell frog embryo by sucking it up into a tiny eyedropper. Like Driesch, he isolated one cell of a two-cell embryo. He also found that the remaining cell developed into a normal, although small, embryo. This result also suggested that the structure of an embryo is formed as it develops.

---

*Wilhelm Roux wrote these words in 1888. They were translated by Hans Laufer and appeared in Shostak, S. (1991). *Embryology: An Introduction to Developmental Biology.* New York: HarperCollins Publishers, Inc.

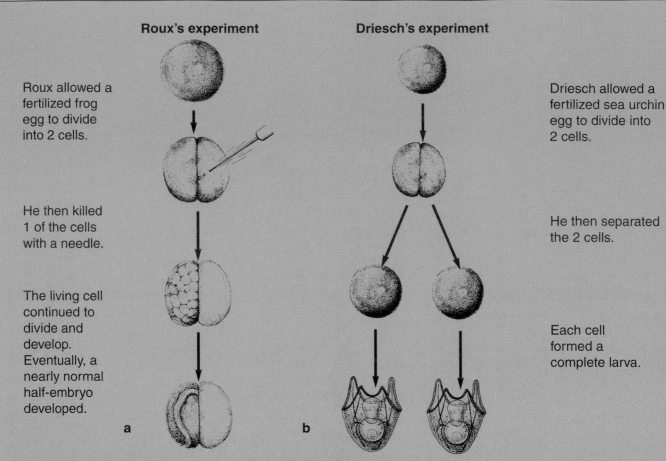

Roux's experiment

Roux allowed a fertilized frog egg to divide into 2 cells.

He then killed 1 of the cells with a needle.

The living cell continued to divide and develop. Eventually, a nearly normal half-embryo developed.

a

Driesch's experiment

Driesch allowed a fertilized sea urchin egg to divide into 2 cells.

He then separated the 2 cells.

Each cell formed a complete larva.

b

Figure 13.2   Early experiments in developmental biology.   **(a)** Roux killed one of the first two cells of a frog embryo. The remaining cell developed tissues corresponding to half of a normal frog embryo. The results would have been different if Roux had removed the dead cell.   **(b)** Driesch experimented with sea urchin eggs. He demonstrated that the presence of the dead cell influenced the development of the live cell.

Figure 13.2a illustrates Roux's historic experiment. Why do we remember it, despite Roux's incorrect conclusions? We remember it largely because it helped mark the beginning of the science of developmental biology. Roux's work and the work of other scientists of his time highlighted the importance of asking questions about development that we can answer by doing experiments. Sometimes the questions that we can answer are only parts of larger questions that we wonder about. We gain scientific knowledge from piecing together the answers to small questions. These answers in turn, shed light on more complicated questions.

In 1894, Roux helped start a scientific journal to communicate new discoveries and to air new discussions about development. Today, after more than 100 years of asking questions, performing experiments, and building answers, developmental biologists have a much better understanding of how a fertilized egg develops. We also have learned how many other aspects of development happen as well. Yet we still have unanswered questions. In 1994, 100 years after the establishment of Roux's journal, the publishers of *Science* magazine performed a survey. They asked scientists what questions about development were most interesting to them and what questions were most likely to be answered from experiments conducted during the 1990s. The top two questions that scientists named were these:

1. How are the body's tissues and organs formed?
2. What clues does development reveal about the process of evolution?

Today, scientists continue to explore these questions. As you read this chapter, they are devising new experiments and using new technologies to study those complex questions. New data emerge daily to help biologists find answers to the puzzles of development.

A Start in Development

Simple observation reveals changes in size and shape as a human baby grows to an adult (see Figure 13.3). The 19th-century scientists Roux and Driesch were able to watch the early development of a fertilized egg because the technology of microscopes improved their view. Today, more advanced microscopes and other technological tools, such as fiber optics and ultrasound, give scientists an even closer look at development.

Figure 13.3   Life stages.   What changes happen during the development that takes place before birth? What changes occur as organisms develop to maturity?

In this activity, you will use a series of DVD images to begin your study of development. As you do so, consider the question, How are the body's tissues and organs formed?

Materials   (per team of 2)

modeling clay
large sheet of paper
DVD and player (watch as a class)

PROCESS AND PROCEDURES

Part A   How Does Development Take Place?

The DVD images that you saw in the previous activity provided some basic information about development. However, the images did not reveal how much time each developmental change required. In fact, the time span that elapses between the stages of life (from fertilized ovum to adult) may be from weeks to years, depending on the organism. What happens during that time? The DVD segment "A Closer Look" will provide some clues. The images on that segment were filmed using a combination of technologies. These included fiber optics, high-resolution microscopes, and video recording equipment. Fiber optics allow tiny cameras to record images of hard-to-view areas, such as the uterus.

Topic: zygote and embryo
Go to: www.scilinks.org
Code: human3E550a

1. As you view the DVD segment "A Closer Look," think about the questions below. Record your observations and your answers to the questions in your journal.

   a. What types of changes do you observe in these images?

   b. How has technology expanded our ability to observe development? Compare the images in "A Closer Look" with the images in the DVD segment "From Egg to Adult" in the previous activity.

Topic: differentiation of cells during animal development
Go to: www.scilinks.org
Code: human3E550b

2. Developmental biologists use the terms *growth* and *differentiation*. These terms describe the fundamental processes that take place during development. Complete the following tasks in your journal:

   a. Explain the difference between *growth* and *differentiation*.

   b. List 4 specific examples from the DVD segment "A Closer Look" that show evidence of each of those processes taking place.

   Read the essay *The Long and Short of Development* on page 580. This important background information will help you formulate your answers.

PAGE 580

Part B   How Does Growth Take Place?

In Part A, you observed two basic processes involved in development. This part of the activity helps you explore one of those processes—growth.

1. Observe the cellular activity in the DVD segment "Cell Division" that your teacher presents.

   As you watch, try to determine what is happening to the cells involved. Think about how the events that you see relate to development.

2. Discuss the following with your class:

   a. Describe what you saw taking place in the DVD segment. What appeared to be happening to the cells?

   b. How do you think that cellular activity relates to the changes that take place as humans develop? Give 2 examples to support your answer.

c. Do you think that cell division (Figure 13.4) is an important aspect of the development of other organisms? Illustrate your answer with 2 examples.

3. Scientists refer to the cell division activity that you just observed as **mitosis**. Watch the DVD segment "Cell Division" again. Answer the following questions in your journal:

   a. What major cellular structures are most active during mitosis?

   b. What are the functions of the structures that you identified in step 3a?

   c. What happens to the chromosomes during mitosis? (Answer as specifically as you can.)

4. Work with your partner. Use the materials available, including the DVD and modeling clay, to construct a model of mitosis that shows the following:

   ◆ A starting cell with 2 pairs of chromosomes

   ◆ DNA synthesis

   ◆ The stages of mitosis

   ◆ The division process and cells formed as a result of mitosis

   To help you complete this task, read and use the information in the essay *The Cell Cycle and Growth Control* (page 582). You also may wish to view the DVD segment again. Compare the DVD segment with the diagrams in Figures E13.3 (mitosis) and E13.4 (cell cycle). This may help you follow the specific events of the cell cycle more easily.

5. Look at the *anaphase stage* of mitosis. What is important about the number and types of chromosomes that move to opposite ends of the cell? How does the genetic information in the 2 groups of chromosomes at each end of the cell compare with each other?

   Answer each question in your journal.

6. Think carefully about the specific manipulations you just completed with your clay models. In your journal, explain why is it important that

   ◆ chromosomes *duplicate* during mitosis,

   ◆ chromosomes *line up in single file* during metaphase of mitosis, and

   ◆ the duplicated chromosomes *separate* during anaphase of mitosis?

   Discuss the movement and distribution of the genetic material that take place during the stage identified in each question.

Analysis

One important skill that most successful scientists develop is recognizing disagreements between observations and conclusions. They also must be able to recognize the difference between the results of an experiment and an established scientific principle. Sometimes a contradiction shows that either the observation or the conclusion is wrong. In other cases, however, the contradiction is not real. In those cases, scientists may discover that there only appeared to be a contradiction. This is because they did not understand the bigger context of their experiment.

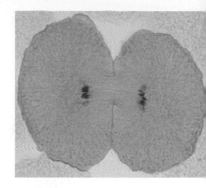

Figure 13.4   Cell division. The process of cell division produces offspring cells. When might be a time when your body's cells would need to produce offspring cells?

PAGE 582

Figure 13.5 Model of a cell with modeling clay chromosomes.

Topic: cell cycle and mitosis
Go to: www.scilinks.org
Code: human3E551

Read the following statements. Pay attention to any contradictions you find between them. Work individually to answer the questions after the statements in your journal. Then exchange journals with your partner. Let him or her write comments about your answers. After you have read and commented on each other's answers, retrieve your journal. Then rewrite your answers as necessary. Your teacher will collect your journal to assess your current understanding of development.

Examine these statements:

Statement 1: Growth takes place during development because of the mitotic division of cells.

Statement 2: Mitosis results in daughter cells that are genetically identical to each other and to the parent cell that divided.

Statement 3: During development, cells become both structurally and functionally different from one another.

1. To the best of your knowledge, is each of the above statements correct as written? Write a brief explanation for each statement to support your answers.

2. What contradiction do you see between statements 2 and 3? In other words, what is it about statement 2 that does not appear to be consistent with statement 3? Explain your answer.

3. Say you were a scientist who recognized that contradiction. Describe an experiment that you might attempt that explains the inconsistency. Answer specifically.

Explore
Explain

Processes That Generate Complexity

You have seen that the development of a multicellular organism involves the process of growth. But growth is only half of the story of development. **Differentiation,** the change in cells that happens during development, is the other half (see Figure 13.6).

Your body, for example, consists of trillions of cells. But those cells include hundreds of different types. Hold your hands up in front of you. Think about their complexity for a moment. Your fingers and thumbs are different lengths, yet their lengths match from one hand to the other. What about the skin, bone, and muscles that they are made of? These are packaged together in essentially identical and highly functional ways. There are hundreds of nerves in your hands. These nerves extend to your brain. Together, they form an extensive communications network that offers great sensitivity, precision, and coordination. Now consider the rest of your body: your heart, your brain, your kidneys, and even your big toes. Along with your hands, all of these complicated structures arose from the same single cell.

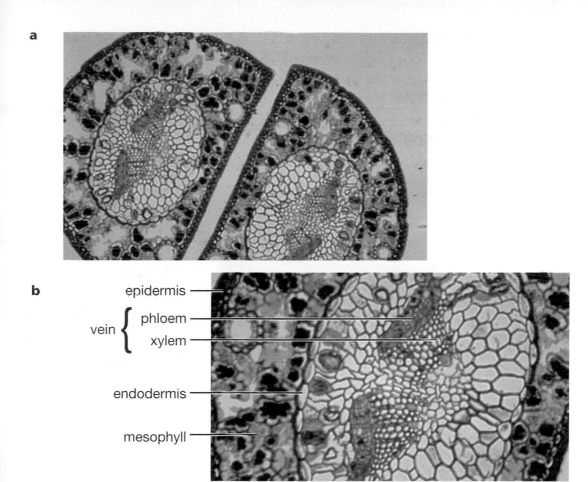

a

b

epidermis

vein { phloem
        xylem

endodermis

mesophyll

Figure 13.6 Differentiated tissues in plants. (a) How many different tissues can you see in this cross section of pine needles? (b) At higher magnification, even more detail is visible. Xylem and phloem function as support and transport tissues. Xylem permits water to move from the roots to the leaves. Phloem, on the other hand, conducts the carbohydrates produced as a result of photosynthesis from the leaves to the stem and roots.

In this activity, you will continue to examine development processes. As you work, consider the following questions: How are the body's tissues and organs formed? How can such a wide variety of tissues and organs develop from identical cellular origins?

Materials

DVD and player

PROCESS AND PROCEDURES

1. Observe the DVD segment "Cells, Cells, and More Cells." How do these images relate to the changes that take place as humans develop from a single-celled zygote to a mature person?

   As you watch the segment, compare the physical appearance of the cells within specific organisms. Think about what this tells you about development.

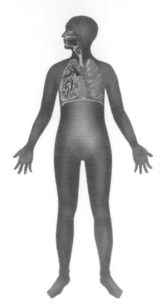

Figure 13.7
The trachea is commonly called the windpipe. It is part of the respiratory system.

PAGE 581   PAGE 582

2. Examine closely the series of frames that shows the low- and high-magnification views of the cross section through the trachea. The **trachea** is the tube that connects your nose and mouth to your lungs (see Figure 13.7). Discuss the following questions with your class:

   a. Describe some of the specialized cells that you see. How are they structurally different from each other?

   b. How do these cells compare with each other genetically?

   c. How do your answers in steps 2a and 2b relate to the process of differentiation?

3. Work with your partner. Examine the table in the need to know box Cell Types That Make Up the Human Trachea. Identify similarities and differences among the cell types listed. How does gene expression explain how genetically identical cells become structurally different? Be prepared to support your answer with specific examples from the table and to share your answer in a class discussion.

As you examine the information in the table, ask yourself whether the structural differences that you saw among these cells correlate with any molecular differences among them. Read the two essays *Coordinating Growth* (page 581) and *Differentiation and the Expression of Genetic Information* (page 582). These essays will help you learn more about the processes that lead to differentiation. Use your experiences with genetics from Chapter 12 and the information in the essays to complete the Analysis section.

NEED TO KNOW

CELL TYPES THAT MAKE UP THE HUMAN TRACHEA				
Type of cell	**Function**	**DNA**	**mRNA**	**Major proteins produced**
Goblet cell	Produces mucus	Identical to zygote	mRNA coding for proteins required for basic cell functioning; also much mRNA coding for proteoglycans and glycoproteins (complex protein-carbohydrate molecules)	Proteoglycans and glycoproteins, the major types of protein in mucus
Cartilage cell	Produces cartilage	Identical to zygote	mRNA coding for proteins required for basic cell functioning; also much mRNA coding for collagen	Collagen, the major protein in cartilage
Muscle cell	Contracts	Identical to zygote	mRNA coding for proteins required for basic cell functioning; also much mRNA coding for actin and myosin	Actin and myosin, the major proteins in muscle

Analysis

Review your work in this and the previous activity. Participate in a class discussion of the following:

1. Explain at a molecular level how genetically identical cells can differentiate into structurally and functionally diverse cells.

   Use specific examples from the table in the need to know box to support your answer.

2. How does a human develop from a fertilized egg into an adult?

3. To what extent do you feel that you understand the answer to question 2? List at least two areas of understanding that you would have to know more about to answer this question completely. Explain why that information would be important to explaining the puzzle of how growth and development take place.

Development Gone Awry

Elaborate

You have seen that the growth of cells and their differentiation into specialized tissues are highly regulated events. In this activity, you will investigate how sensitive that regulation is. You will also look at what can happen if errors occur during development. A human embryo, for example, can develop improperly if harmful environmental influences disrupt the regulation of growth or differentiation. Similarly, an embryo's growth and development can proceed incorrectly if its genetic plan contains mutations.

Developmental errors are not limited to the growing embryo. They can happen even after birth. For example, sometimes harmful changes in hormonal conditions alter the pattern of growth that normally would take place as an organism matures. Likewise, sometimes body cells stop responding properly to regulatory signals and grow unrestrained. This causes cancerous tumors. As you begin this activity, apply your understanding of the processes of human development. Consider situations in which human development has gone awry.

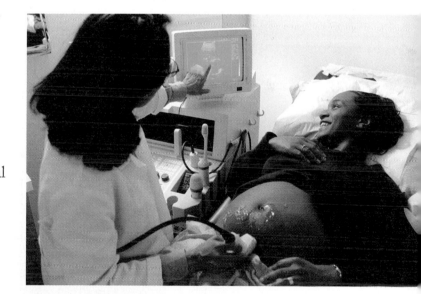

Figure 13.8 Early prenatal care helps to assure healthy development during gestation.

Materials (per person)

resource materials that include news articles, essays, and DVD material
video or audio equipment for recording and playing (optional)
DVD and player

PROCESS AND PROCEDURES

Imagine that you are a doctor who is handling a case that involves an error in development. Developmental errors fall into 2 general categories. These are birth defects and cancer. Follow the steps below to write a conversation in which you explain the disorder to your patient and describe what may be done about it. In this conversation, you (the doctor) will need to explain how normal developmental processes have been altered to produce the disorder.

Topic: genetic diseases/
genetic screening/
genetic counseling
Go to: www.scilinks.org
Code: human3E556

1. Work individually. Choose a disorder to be the topic of your script. Good ways to identify possible topics include the following:

   ◆ Find a news event that relates to either birth defects or cancer. Use this news coverage as the basis for your script. You may find interesting news bulletins on the Internet (be sure to select reputable sites), in newspapers, and in publications such as *Science News, Discover,* and *Harvard Health Letter.*

   ◆ Interview a person who has experienced a birth defect or cancer or someone who has had a family member with a birth defect or cancer.

   ◆ Use an idea that occurs to you as you review the resources listed in step 2.

2. Discuss your idea with your teacher. Ask him or her to approve your topic. Then collect information about the biology involved in the disorder from the available resources.

   It may help you to read through the criteria for a good script. These are listed in step 3. The criteria will help you decide what information you will need.

   Read and use the essays *Development and Birth Defects* (page 586) and *Cancer: Unregulated Growth* (page 589) as resources for this project. The DVD segment "Cancer in Humans" also contains important background information. The DVD

PAGE 586 **PAGE 589**

normal liver tissue   cancerous tissue

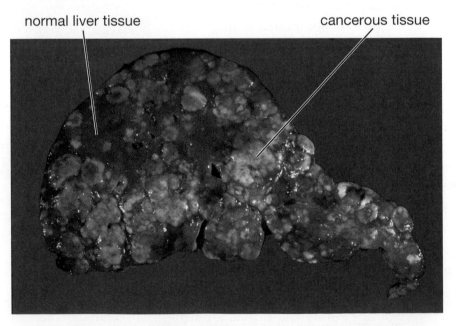

Figure 13.9   Liver cancer.   The extensive cancerous growths in this liver are the result of metastasis. The cancer began in the lungs.

images show cancerous growths in a variety of human tissues. They also show microscopic images of cancerous blood cells (leukemia), X-ray images of lung cancer before and after treatment, and MRI (magnetic resonance imaging) of brain tumors. For your project, use any other available resources as well.

Topic: cancer, cancer
genes (oncogenes)
Go to: www.scilinks.org
Code: human3E557

3. Develop your script of a conversation between a doctor (you) and a patient suffering from the disorder you chose in step 1. (The conversation may take place between the doctor and family members as well.)

You will know you have a good script when it does the following:

- Describes in detail the disorder you chose

- Explains the probable role (if any) of external (environmental) factors in producing the disorder

- Explains the probable role (if any) of genetic factors in producing the disorder

- Describes how and when (that is, in what way, and if known, through what specific events or mechanisms) growth and/or differentiation have been affected

- Describes the long-term effects of the disorder

- Mentions any treatments and their likelihood of working

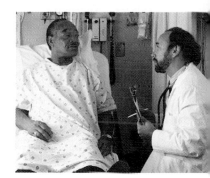

Assume that the patient or family members of the patient are just learning of the diagnosis and are struggling to deal with it. Your goal is to explain (a) what the disorder is, (b) how it came about, and (c) what can be done about it, if anything. Present the information in a way that meets the criteria listed above. Imagine what questions the patient or family members might ask and how the doctor would respond.

Your teacher will tell you if you are to submit your script in writing. You might enlist the help of other students and perform it for your class. Another option may be to record your script on video or audio.

Analysis

Your study should have convinced you that development involves the expression of a genetic plan within a set of environmental conditions. These conditions can influence and/or modify the plan's execution. Write a response in your journal to the following questions. Use your knowledge of development and the information in this activity about developmental errors. After you have written your answers, join the class in a discussion of this topic.

1. Do personal choices have a greater influence in determining an individual's risk of developing cancer or in causing a risk of birth defects? Explain your response.

2. Give three examples of developmental problems that scientists believe are largely or entirely genetic in origin.

3. Give three examples of developmental problems that scientists believe are largely or entirely environmental in origin.

4. Give three examples of developmental problems that scientists believe result from both genetic and environmental causes.

5. Is it possible for a person to make choices that could result in environmentally induced developmental errors? Explain and support your answer with an example.

Evaluate

Evaluating Where We Stand

How many arms and legs do humans have? Now, how many limbs do oak trees have? You can see from this simple comparison that different species show qualitative differences in their developmental patterns. The basic processes of development are essentially the same in all multicellular species, but the results vary greatly.

In this part of the activity, you will apply your knowledge of developmental processes and patterns to a new challenge. You will describe a developmental scheme for the critter that you discovered in Chapter 3. This will be your opportunity to show what you have learned up to this point. Keep in mind that how you apply your knowledge to explain your critter's processes of growth and development will help your teacher determine how much you have accomplished.

Materials (per person)

descriptions and diagrams of your critter from Chapter 10

PROCESS AND PROCEDURES

1. Describe in your journal what you have learned about how the body's tissues and organs are formed.

   Keep in mind that development involves more than just getting bigger.

2. If you took a snapshot of an outdoor scene, you would record a moment in the lifetime of a variety of organisms. Some of those organisms likely would be in different developmental stages. For example, you might see trees with bright red and orange leaves, adult animals foraging for food, and a caterpillar eating a leaf to build up its energy stores before changing into a moth. In the diversity captured by such a snapshot, you would see many different developmental stages and evidence of many different behaviors.

   Consider the developmental stages that you might see in various organisms. Choose 2 multicellular organisms that interest you. Identify as many significant developmental events or stages as you can that might take place in the lifetime of those organisms. Record them in your journal. Provide specific examples to illustrate your list.

Figure 13.10   Giant water bugs.   These male water bugs (*Abedus indentatus*) are caring for the eggs that will produce the next generation. What developmental stages will the offspring pass through before becoming adults?

Read the essay *Patterns of Development* on page 593 to help you with this step. As you generate your list, ask yourself when each event typically takes place and what each event or stage accomplishes for the organism. For example, what does puberty accomplish in the developmental pattern of humans? What does flowering accomplish in the developmental pattern of flowering plants?

PAGE 593

Analysis

1. Use your answers from step 2 in Process and Procedures to help you create a developmental pattern for your critter. Draw your critter in its various developmental stages. Label these stages with enough detail so that someone looking at the illustration will understand what is happening.

    Note: If your critter is single-celled, ask your teacher how to do this step.

2. Obtain a critter rubric from your teacher. Study the criteria. Participate in a class discussion about the criteria for this project.

3. On a page that you will include with your critter, write a detailed description of your critter's growth and development processes. Explain how your critter grows and develops through the stages that you drew and labeled. Where it is appropriate, explain how your critter's genetic plan interacts with environmental conditions to direct and regulate development.

    Review the essays, particular activities, and notes in your journal to meet the goals outlined in the need to know box Project Goals: Growth and Development in Your Critter.

NEED TO KNOW

Project Goals: Growth and Development in Your Critter

1. Your critter project should describe the basic processes of development.

   Show your understanding by

   a. identifying growth and differentiation as key processes of development,

   b. describing what these processes do and how they work (use specific examples)

   c. applying those concepts to a description of your critter's development.

2. Your critter project also should describe patterns in developmental biology.

   Show your knowledge by

   a. identifying key developmental steps in the critter's life span and comparing them to the steps of another species, and

   b. recognizing that the developmental steps in the critter's life involve much more than just increasing in size.

3. In addition, your critter project should explain how developmental processes can malfunction.

   Show your understanding by

   a. identifying the major developmental problems that affect your critter's species, and

   b. explaining the developmental causes of those problems.

4. Creatively apply your knowledge of development to a new situation (your critter).

   Show your creativity in this area by

   a. thinking of an interesting and logical way that your critter undergoes development, and

   b. presenting your ideas in a clear and interesting manner.

5. Finally, your critter project should describe how scientific study is done.

   Show your understanding by

   a. explaining why certain questions may be of interest to scientists for many years, and

   b. describing the process scientists use to find answers to complex questions.

Further Challenges

At the beginning of this chapter, you read about two questions regarding development that were of particular interest to scientists in 1994. The first question (How are the body's tissues and organs formed?) is basically the same question that earlier developmental biologists asked. It is possible that early scientists also wondered about the second question (What clues does development reveal about the

A View of Life

Can you imagine what it would be like to have experienced all of the stages of life? With a healthy lifestyle, the chances of a young person living an active life extending seven or more decades are much greater today than they were several generations ago. In this activity, you will have an opportunity to have an elderly guest visit your class and answer some interview questions that you and your teammates develop. This will give you a look back in time from the point of view of someone who has experienced most of life's stages. The type of interview you will be doing is an *autobiographical oral history*. That is the most personal type of interview. It should be relaxed and free-ranging.

PROCESS AND PROCEDURES

Part A   Interview Preparation

1. Assemble into your team of 4 from the activity *Growing Up—What Does That Mean?*

2. Refer to the class project that you completed in the previous activity. Make a list of any additional information that would help you construct a more complete representation of the life stages.

   Think about the insights that an interview could provide. What insights were not apparent from your observations in the previous activity? For example, you collected information about various phases of life. But you learned little about experiencing all of them.

3. Develop at least 5 interview questions for your guest. Use your list from step 2, along with the need to know box Guidelines for Interviews.

You also might find the questions in step 2 of the Analysis helpful as you develop your interview questions.

NEED TO KNOW

Guidelines for Interviews

A primary goal for an interviewer is to create a suitable environment in which to carry out the interview. You should make the guest feel comfortable, and the interviewers should be active listeners. The following tips might help you conduct a successful interview:

1. A good interviewer is not the star of the show; the guest is. The objective is to get the guest to tell his or her story.

2. Ask questions that give the guest an opportunity to tell stories.

   For example, What was the most exciting time of your life? is a better question than, Did you have an exciting life?

3. Ask only one question at a time. Keep the questions brief.

4. Do not begin with controversial or sensitive questions. Save those for later when the guest warms up to the class.

5. Allow plenty of time for your guest to reflect on and to respond to your questions. Be patient. Allow your guest to pause before answering.

6. Allow time at the end of the interview for the guest to add whatever he or she would like.

4. Order your questions with respect to importance (1 = what you feel is most important).

5. Have a representative from your team record your 1st question on the chalkboard or flip chart.

If there is already a question that is similar to yours, go to the next question on your list.

6. Continue to record questions in this manner until your class has about 15 questions listed.

With your class, suggest improvements for clarifying the wording or eliminating repetitive questions.

Part B   The Interview

1. Choose a spokesperson from your team. As your teacher calls on your team, have that person pose 1 of the prepared questions to the guest.

2. You may pose other questions that your guest's responses might raise. Your teacher will invite these questions periodically throughout the interview.

3. In your journal, record the major ideas from your guest's responses.

You will have access to a tape recording of the interview. This will allow you to review the responses and add detail to your notes. Make sure that you collect word-for-word quotes as *data* to support your inferences.

Analysis

Revisit the project that your class developed for the activity *Growing Up—What Does That Mean?* Then complete step 1 as a team and step 2 individually.

1. Determine what new information emerged from the interview. Add it to your class project.

2. Use the information from the interview to respond to the following in your journal:

   a. How did the guest's culture influence his or her growth and development?

   Explain how a different cultural setting might have had a different impact on this person.

   b. Provide examples of how technological change during the individual's lifetime influenced her or his development at each life stage.

Life-Span Development: Examining the Contexts

You have investigated how people develop through the major phases of life on their dramatic journey from birth to old age. Where we are along that journey frequently determines how we see those stages. By completing the previous activities in this chapter, you have had an opportunity to broaden your perspective through observation, an interview, and some analysis. In this activity, you will further develop your understanding of human life stages. You will prepare for and participate in a debate about the relative contributions that a genetic plan and the environment make to each individual.

PROCESS AND PROCEDURES

1. With your teammates, discuss the following 2 questions. Decide which question your team would like to explore.

   a. How much of the variation that we see in individuals can be attributed to their specific genetic plans?

PAGE 604

PAGE 607

PAGE 608

b. How much of the variation that we see in individuals can be attributed to their environment?

2. In your journal, begin to develop an answer to your question by outlining significant information. Also, record related questions that come to mind.

Use the following essays as resources to help you complete this step. They will add to what you already know and what you have learned in this program.

Physical Growth Influences Mental Growth (page 604)

Physical Growth Influences Social and Emotional Growth (page 607)

All Phases of Life Require Self-Maintenance (page 608)

3. Join with the other teams that selected the same question as your team. Prepare for a class discussion of the 2 questions from step 1.

   a. Choose a recorder for your new team.

   b. Summarize what you already know.

   Take turns adding new information to the team's collection of information. Make sure that you can support each statement. You may want to record your ideas on a flip chart.

   c. Make a list of other information that you would like to have. Explore the resources that your teacher has available to determine whether you can answer your questions.

   d. Think about what the other group might say and how you might respond.

4. Participate in a class debate.

   As the debate progresses, record notes and questions in your journal.

Analysis

With your classmates, discuss the findings from the debate. Then, individually, write a short essay in your journal that compares and combines the two sets of responses. Briefly summarize the responses to each question. Relate how heredity and environment interact to make us who we are.

Elaborate

Evaluate

Cultural Diversity in the Human Life Span

In this activity, you will explore life stages in another culture. In doing so, you will elaborate on what you have learned in this chapter. Each team will explore a different culture. You will then create a display and a presentation for a multicultural fair that will take place as part of the Unit 5 evaluate. At this fair, you and your classmates will display what you have learned about growing up and living in another culture. You also will present some feature of that culture for the rest of the class.

After you have studied a culture, you will evaluate your understanding of human development over a life span. You will do this by reflecting on the similarities and differences in the process of development when it takes place in different cultures. You also will explain the characteristics of biological development that permit those similarities and differences.

PROCESS AND PROCEDURES

1. To prepare for the multicultural fair, do the following:

    a. Think about the cultural setting in which you might want to explore human life stages.

    Your teacher will have a list of suggestions as well as some resources for you to look through to help you choose.

    b. Join with other classmates who have chosen to explore the same culture. Share with them your reasons for being interested in this particular group of people.

    Use the information in the essay *Culture: The Great Shaper of Life* on page 610 as a resource to help set the stage for your study.

    PAGE 610

2. Begin your study of another culture.

    a. Look through the resources that your teacher has as well as additional resources that you might want to find.

    b. Divide the responsibility of reading and reviewing the resources in order to develop a general overview of the culture.

    You may want to find additional resources of your own. Remember, you are not limited to books and magazines. You may want to look for Internet sites, films, videos, music, or art. You may even know someone from the culture you have chosen who might be willing to share some ideas with you.

    c. Share what you have learned so far. Exchange resources if you wish.

3. Develop a specific design for your entry in the multicultural fair. Refer to the guidelines in the following need to know box.

Remember, your job is not just to learn about the life stages in another culture, but to teach your classmates about them as well.

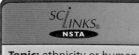
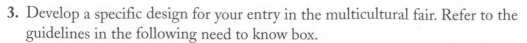

Guidelines for Creating Your Entry for the Multicultural Fair

Your entry for the fair should include a combination of visual displays and written support material. You may want to include an audio portion as well. Displays may be arranged in your booth in any way that you want within the boundaries that your teacher establishes. You also will need to create or develop some type of presentation that includes all team members.

As you create your entry, you should do the following:

1. Provide an overview of the culture that you studied. Include where this group of people lives or lived and a description of their way of life.

2. Present information about one of the following life stages:

    ♦ Infancy and childhood

    ♦ Adolescence

    ♦ Adulthood

    ♦ Old age

    a. Describe the physical and social setting that is predominant at this life stage.

        ♦ Who is around the individuals at this stage? What do the individuals do at this stage?

    b. Describe the cultural practices for individuals at this stage.

        ♦ What is expected of the individual at this stage?

    c. Describe the cultural values surrounding this stage.

        ♦ How are individuals in this stage perceived?

3. Explore some aspect of cognitive development that seems particularly significant in the culture that you are studying. (For example, in American culture, the point at which a child begins to speak is considered significant.) Explain why you think this particular cognitive development is highly valued. Describe the underlying biology that allows for this aspect of development.

4. Choose and complete one of the following:

    a. Describe the different forms of cultural expression that seem to be significant during any life stage—for example, music, art, dance, mythology, religion, or dress.

4. Obtain a rubric for the multicultural fair entry from your teacher. Participate in a class discussion about the criteria that your teacher will use to assess your entry and knowledge.

5. Design and prepare your entry for the fair.

   Be as creative as you want, but remember to follow the guidelines provided. Remember, your entry provides the evidence for all that you have learned in this chapter.

6. Practice the presentation portion of your entry.

   You may want to schedule additional practice time outside of class. You will participate in the fair as both visitor and exhibitor during the Unit 5 assessment.

Analysis

After you have completed step 5, record in your journal your reflections on the following questions. Work individually.

1. Imagine that you are a young woman or man living in the culture that you have just studied. Write two or three paragraphs that describe how she or he might view your American culture. Which aspects of your life experience would seem similar to her or his experiences? Which aspects would seem different?

2. What have you learned about biological development in humans that may help explain both these similarities and differences?

The Long and Short of Development

That nasty pimple finally disappeared, but you're coming down with a cold. You've gained 2 inches in height in the last 6 months. Surely you have noticed constant changes taking place in your body. Many of these changes are short-term internal adjustments that ensure homeostatic balance. Homeostatic changes tend to be relatively rapid and reversible. They happen in seconds, minutes, or hours. They allow conditions in our bodies to remain within narrowly defined limits.

Other changes take place at a slower pace and across a longer period of time. These changes are not directly involved in maintaining homeostasis. They are not rapid or easily reversed. Instead, they are relatively slow and generally permanent. This change process is called **development**. It begins at fertilization and ends at death.

Some developmental changes are dramatic, such as the formation of a beating heart in a 4-week-old human embryo. Continued changes in body size and proportion, thinking ability, and coordination take place in a growing child. Even more complex physical and emotional changes occur during puberty. Everyday changes, such as the replacement of skin and blood cells, seem less dramatic. Less welcome changes include those in physical appearance as we approach old age. All of these changes are important and natural aspects of the developmental process.

Development takes place in all multicellular organisms. Frog eggs turn into tadpoles that grow larger, lose their tails, and become frogs. Trees grow larger and develop branching limb and root systems (Figure E13.1). As humans, rats,

Figure E13.1 **Development in piñon pine tree (*Pinus edulis*).** What evidence of development do you see in these photos?

Figure E13.2 Pig embryos. These images of pig embryos show many common features of mammalian development. The embryos show increasing development from left to right.

chimpanzees, and other mammals grow older, their hair (or fur) turns gray, and their skin becomes less elastic.

The two most important changes in the early stages of development are **growth** and **differentiation**. Growth involves an increase in size of the organism due to an increase in the number of cells. Differentiation involves changes in the structure and function of cells within the organism. In most organisms that reproduce sexually, the fertilized ovum (the zygote) grows into a multicellular embryo through cell division. As the embryo continues to grow, specialized parts begin to appear as cells differentiate. A newborn baby—a precisely formed organism—consists of skin, nerve, liver, and blood cells located in specific places. Each cell type performs distinct and important functions. Figure E13.2 illustrates some of the stages that take place during early mammalian development.

Growth and differentiation continue after the embryonic period (that is, after

birth or hatching). These processes enable a child's body to grow and change. In addition, they maintain and repair body systems that become damaged through accidents or illness. In later life, the developmental process of **senescence**, or aging, becomes important. Developmental biologists recognize that aging leads to a progressive and irreversible loss of function. However, they do not have a complete understanding of the precise processes of aging. They generally agree that aging is genetically controlled. For example, scientists have identified a gene in fruit flies that appears to limit their life spans. Development can truly be defined as a set of changes that takes place continually from fertilization to death.

The central questions of development include, How does developmental change take place in organisms? and, How are developmental changes related to evolution and biological diversity? ◆

The Cell Cycle and Growth Control

Have you ever wondered why beetles are small and whales are large? At hatching or birth, both are smaller than their parents. Yet each grows to a size similar to their parents. What determines their growth and final size?

Because nearly all organisms grow during their lifetimes, growth is regarded as an important developmental process. Understanding development requires that we understand growth. In multicellular organisms, growth takes place primarily through an increase in the *number* of cells, not through an increase in the *size* of cells. Why? Diffusion and osmosis are the processes of cellular transport. These processes place upper limits on how large cells can become. These physical limitations have influenced development in a way that favors *more* cells rather than *larger* cells. As a result, an increase in the size of an embryo reflects an increase in the number of cells that compose it.

Simple observation of your own body suggests that growth is a highly regulated process. Think, for example, of the changes in size and proportion that already have taken place in your body. In most cases, growth takes place according to a predictable schedule. With some minor exceptions, that growth takes place evenly from one side of the body to the other. The production of new cells also allows for the replacement of cells that become damaged or die during the normal events of life. Such replacement activity also is precisely controlled.

Before we consider how cell production is controlled during development, we must look at how cell division happens. This process of cell division produces offspring cells that are genetically identical to each other and to the parent cell. Cell division almost always includes the process of **mitosis**, which is the precise distribution of genetic material to offspring cells. Figure E13.3 illustrates this process. The chromosomes duplicate before mitosis. During the four phases of mitosis, the duplicated chromosomes condense, line up, and separate into two newly formed offspring cells. Other parts of the cell also are distributed between these offspring cells during cell division. The result of mitosis and cell division is two cells. Each contains a copy of the same genetic information and the same types of subcellular compartments that were contained in the parent cell.

As shown in Figure E13.4, mitosis is only a small fraction of the **cell cycle**, or life cycle, of a typical cell. Mitosis takes place during the *M phase* of the cell cycle. The bulk of a cell's life is spent in a phase between cell divisions. During most of this nondividing interphase, the cell functions in the way it was intended. The cell also synthesizes the RNA, protein, and other macromolecules needed for cell division during this phase of the cell cycle. Most importantly, DNA replicates during interphase. It doubles the cell's genetic material. The cell must produce sufficient cytoplasm and genetic material to distribute to the two offspring cells produced by mitosis and cell division.

If a population of cells does not divide, growth can occur only by a limited increase in cell size. Adipose (fat-storing) tissues are an example of that kind of cell population. Once your body produces a basic number of fat cells, these cells do not multiply in number. However they can become larger by incorporating more fatty substances.

In the cells of most tissues, controlling growth means controlling the occurrence and rate of mitosis. Two major levels of control regulate mitosis. The first level, called *internal control*, involves substances inside the cell. These critical substances regulate the timing of the specific phases of the cell cycle. That regulation is necessary. Or, for example, a cell

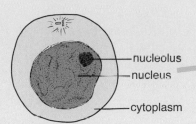

nucleolus
nucleus
cytoplasm

a

During **interphase** materials required for
the next cell division are synthesized
(Interphase is a long and active phase
of the cell cycle.) For example, DNA
and chromosomes are duplicated
in the nucleus. Cell structures such as
mitochondria are made in the cytoplasm.
The cell grows.

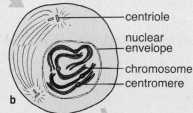

b

centriole
nuclear
envelope
chromosome
centromere

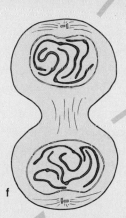

f

During **telophase**, the chromosomes
approach the opposite ends of the cell
and group together. A new nuclear
envelope is synthesized around the
chromosomes. The cytoplasm begins to
divide. A new cell membrane forms.
(In plant cells, a new cell wall is laid down
between the two new cells.) The new
cells enter interphase.

As **prophase** begins, the long thin
chromosomes coil and become shorter
and thicker. Each chromosome now
appears as a doubled structure joined at
a centromere. The centrioles were duplicated
during interphase. They now begin to move
to opposite ends of the cell. (In plant cells,
there are no centrioles. But the events of mitosis
otherwise take place as described here.)

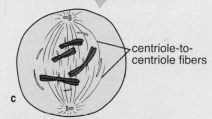

c

centriole-to-
centriole fibers

Later in prophase, the nuclear envelope
breaks down. The chromosomes contract
to their shortest lengths. Cytoplasmic fibers
stretch from centriole to centriole. They also
stretch from each doubled chromosome to
both centrioles.

e

The doubled chromosomes
separate during **anaphase**. The
new chromosomes are pushed
and pulled to opposite ends of
the cell by the cytoplasmic fibers.

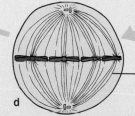

d

centromere-to-centriole fibers

During **metaphase**, the doubled
chromosomes line up along the
middle of the cell. Cytoplasmic
fibers now are attached to each
doubled chromosome at the
centromere.

Figure E13.3 The phases of mitosis. How does mitosis compare with meiosis?
(Meiosis is the process of cell division that precedes the formation of gametes.)

could enter mitosis before it replicated its DNA. If that happened, there would not be a full set of chromosomes in each offspring cell. Both offspring cells would die as a result.

A second level of control involves environmental factors. These external signals trigger internal events in the cell. These internal events initiate or suppress the events of the cell cycle. One example of external control is *contact inhibition*. This causes cells to stop dividing. Contact inhibition takes place when cells reach a certain population density or degree of crowding (Figure E13.5). This happens even though nutrients may be plentiful in the environment. Contact inhibition prevents overcrowding of cells within a particular organ or area of the body. Sometimes this inhibition must be relaxed to allow healing. When your skin is cut, the cells at the edge of the wound begin to divide and slowly cover the bare spot. Once the open wound is repaired, however, cell division and cell movement stops again. Contact inhibition is an important example of growth control. Problems arise when this control is lost. A cell that suffers mutations in the genes that regulate contact inhibition may divide without regard to external signals. Eventually, a tumor forms.

The actions of hormones represent another form of external growth control. Recall that hormones are produced by one set

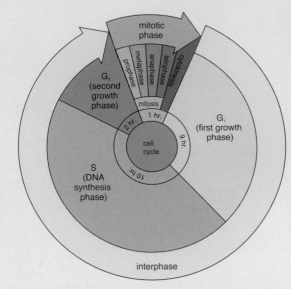

Figure E13.4   The cell cycle. The times given for each phase represent the approximate times for a liver cell grown in the lab.

of cells. But hormones exert their effects on other cells, often in distant locations of the body. For example, growth hormone coordinates the proportional growth of the body. As its name suggests, growth hormone stimulates cells to divide. An excess of growth hormone before puberty results in gigantism. Likewise, a lack of growth hormone produces dwarfism. The most obvious effects of growth hormone show in the long bones of the limbs. But it affects growth all over the body. ◆

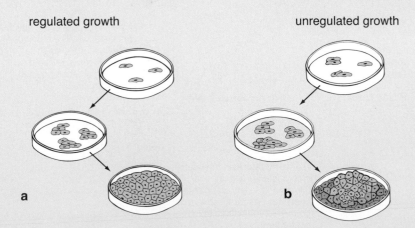

Figure E13.5   Contact inhibition.   (a) Cells experiencing normal growth regulation stop dividing when they make contact with other cells. **(b)** Cells that have lost this regulation will continue to divide, piling up on one another.

Coordinating Growth

Imagine engineers and mechanics replacing the engines, wings, and cockpit of an airliner *while the plane is airborne*. As difficult and absurd as that may seem, controlling the growth of a living organism is like that. Internal and external controls on growth operate during every phase of an organism's development. During the embryonic period, rapid cell division produces millions of offspring cells. These cells slowly give shape and substance to an embryo's arms, legs, and internal organs. This growth must be coordinated constantly. This is because an embryo is not like a machine, which does not work until all of its parts are in place. Instead, an embryo functions from the very moment that it exists. And it keeps functioning even as it constantly changes. In some ways, controlling an embryo's growth is like remodeling an airplane as it flies.

Coordinating growth requires some complex events as an organism develops. For example, because an embryo's cells are alive, they need a regular supply of oxygen and nutrients. Chicken eggs contain a special set of blood vessels that lie just under the shell. These blood vessels also surround and penetrate the yolk. The blood vessels connect to the developing circulatory system of the growing embryo. They carry oxygen that is absorbed across the shell. They also carry nutrients that are absorbed from the yolk into the body of the embryo where they are needed (see Figure E13.6). The umbilical cord and the placenta serve similar functions in the human embryo.

As an embryo's tissues and organs grow and take shape, its circulatory system also grows and changes. This process is a good illustration of the interaction between internal and external growth controls. Scientists have found that different types of cells reproduce when different sets of proteins are present in the cellular environment. When the local concentration of these proteins, or growth factors, rises, cells that were not dividing now begin to divide. For example, the brain of a vertebrate embryo begins to develop. The new brain cells secrete a specific growth factor. This external growth signal promotes internal changes in cells at the tips of nearby blood vessels. These blood vessel cells undergo rapid cell division and grow toward the source of the growth factors. They build a circulatory network to support the new brain tissue. Scientists have discovered a whole set of growth factors that work during embryonic development and after birth. Typically, these substances have powerful effects even at low concentrations. In addition, these effects are specific to the cells that release the factor and to the tissue that responds.

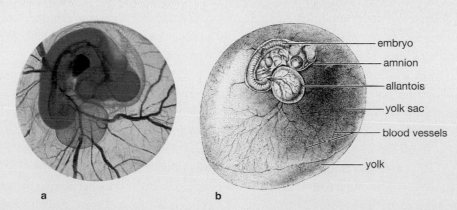

a   b

embryo
amnion
allantois
yolk sac
blood vessels
yolk

Figure E13.6 Which structures are involved in transporting oxygen and nutrients to the embryo, and wastes out of the embryo?

This constant remodeling, balancing, and regulation of growth continues throughout life. Look again at Figure 13.3. Notice how large the newborn's head is in proportion to its arms and legs. Then compare the proportions of the newborn with your own (or those of the adolescent in the same figure).

Clearly, your arms and legs *must* have grown much faster than your head and torso. And even after we have achieved our full growth, our cells still divide in a controlled manner. This means that cells lost through normal wear and tear or through injury are replaced at an appropriate rate. If too little division takes place, injuries go unrepaired. If too much division takes place, a tumor can develop. Scientists still do not understand all of the mechanisms involved in the control of cell division. Yet it is becoming increasingly clear that proper regulation happens only when both internal and external mechanisms work together in a coordinated fashion. ◆

Differentiation and the Expression of Genetic Information

Early research into developmental events involved painstaking observations of many types of developing organisms. These observations revealed that all embryos of a particular species go through apparently identical stages in the same sequence. Specific tissues and organs become visible and then functional at specific times. Scientists concluded that developmental changes must be under precise control. We can make the same observation about development later in life. Although people vary in exactly *when* they reach various stages of life (puberty, for example), most of us go through every stage in the same sequence.

These observations raise a question. How are the processes of development regulated and coordinated? In the case of humans, the union of the ovum and the sperm eventually gives rise to an adult made up of trillions of cells. An adult's body continues to change and develop until death. What is it that affects how, where, and when each part of our body develops as it does?

Part of the answer to this question rests in our chromosomes. The original 46 chromosomes that were present in the zygote (23 from the ovum and 23 from the sperm) contained all of the basic instructions needed to produce a complete human. In other words, the basic information by which all cells grow and differentiate is located in the zygote's DNA. Through mitosis, this information is distributed to each offspring cell.

All of the developing cells in the body contain all of the instructions for producing a complete human. However, this does not explain how cells become *different parts* of that human during development. Some cells, for example, become long and ridged as they develop. They build extended filaments of protein that allow them to contract (muscle cells). Other cells secrete digestive enzymes that help reduce a turkey sandwich and a piece of fruit into useful nutrients (pancreatic cells). Still other cells become flat and scaly. They produce the pigment responsible for skin color (skin cells).

Knowing that nearly all of the cells in the body contain the same DNA does not explain how any particular differentiated cell tends to remain that same type of cell. Most cells continue to produce proteins and display functions that are characteristic of that cell type. We don't have to worry that our heart cells suddenly will start growing hair or that our skin cells will start oozing digestive enzymes. Instead, these cells likely will spend their entire lives working as they always have.

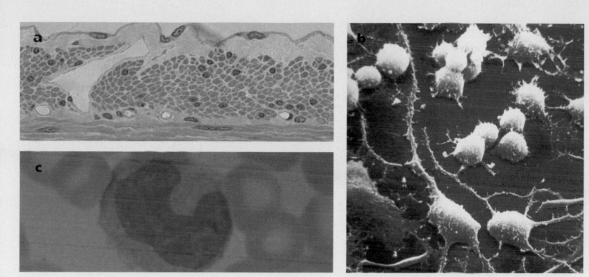

Figure E13.7 Different cells, same DNA.   (a) Smooth muscle cells (160×). The nearly circular structures near the top of the image are smooth muscle cells in cross section. The long cells at the bottom are in longitudinal section. **(b)** Nerve cells (2,500×). The long cell structure extending toward the top of the photo from the cell body is an axon. The shorter structures extending downward are dendrites. **(c)** Blood cells (710×). White blood cells such as this monocyte are part of the immune system. What differences do you see among the cells illustrated?

Figure E13.7 shows several types of human cells. If all of these cells have the same genetic information, why do so many different and stable cell types form? Why are we not 6-foot-tall livers. Why do we never become 4-foot-wide brains? The general answer to these questions is that different cell types use different parts of their genetic material.

Although most body cells receive exactly the same genes, *environmental influences* both inside and outside the cell cause certain genes to turn on and others to turn off. A gene turns on or becomes active when it is transcribed into messenger RNA for protein synthesis. A gene remains or becomes inactive when it is not transcribed. The particular pattern of on and off genes determines cellular differentiation.

As differentiation proceeds, cells use a more narrow range of genes. Therefore, they produce a more narrow range of products and perform more specialized functions. Under normal circumstances, a mature skin cell will never send an electrical signal to the brain the way a nerve cell does. The genes

required to accomplish that function are not active in the skin cell. Instead of generating electrical signals, the skin cell displays different functions (such as pigmentation) that are encoded by a different set of genes. These different functions are consistent with the environmental influences that have affected the cell's development.

A great deal of research has focused on understanding the mechanisms that turn sets of genes on and off. Scientists wondered how these patterns remained stable across time. Most of the earliest embryologists focused on *describing* development. Eventually, scientists began investigating *how* cells went about differentiating. One of the ways researchers tried to answer their questions was to manipulate nonhuman embryos. Embryos were shaken, poked at, turned upside down, and treated with chemicals to see how these actions would affect development. The experiments of Wilhelm Roux and Hans Driesch provide good examples of this type of *experimental* embryology. The knowledge that scientists have accumulated through

more than 100 years of such studies is beginning to answer the central question of differentiation: Why don't all cells with the same DNA do the same thing?

One explanation for this question is that the environments *inside* these cells differ. The internal makeup of a cell influences the pattern of gene expression. For example, there may be a substance in one area of a cell's cytoplasm. As a result of cell division, this substance ends up in one offspring cell and not the other. The substance may change the activity of the genes in the cell that received it. Another explanation is that something *outside* the cells differs. A substance secreted by one cell may affect a neighboring cell's pattern of gene expression. In either case, influences from inside or outside the cell may affect the pattern of its gene expression and lead to its specific differentiation.

Experimental results from a wide variety of organisms and laboratories have provided evidence for *both* explanations. In some species, molecules that can regulate gene expression are located in different portions of the zygote's cytoplasm. The division of this cytoplasm into offspring cells distributes these molecules into some cells but not into others. As these molecules begin to influence gene activity, the cells that received them follow one path of development. The cells that did not receive them follow another path. Figure E13.8 illustrates how this mechanism of differentiation may take place.

In other cases, substances released by one group of cells can cause a neighboring group of cells to differentiate in a particular way. Figure E13.9 illustrates this example of outside influence on differentiation. Scientists call this type of outside influence **induction**. Notice the presence of inducing tissue in the outpocketing of the brain. This causes cells that would have become skin tissue to become eye tissue instead. The development of all human organs and systems, including sweat glands, teeth, and limbs, involves induction.

Development requires a sophisticated system of genetic instructions and controls. What happens when these genetic instructions or control systems change? Usually, the result is a change in the phenotype of the organism. Across many generations, changes in phenotype within a population can lead to the evolution of a new species. ◆

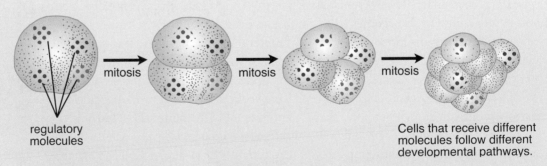

regulatory molecules

mitosis

mitosis

mitosis

Cells that receive different molecules follow different developmental pathways.

Figure E13.8 Cytoplasmic regulation. Regulatory molecules are unequally divided during the development of some organisms. This can lead to different developmental fates for different cells.

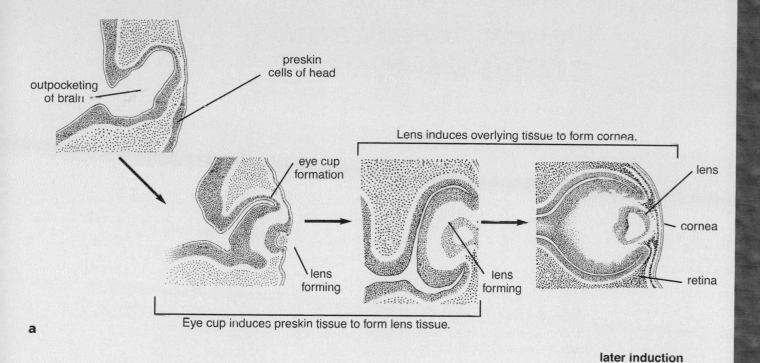

preskin cells of head

outpocketing of brain

Lens induces overlying tissue to form cornea.

eye cup formation

lens

cornea

lens forming

lens forming

retina

Eye cup induces preskin tissue to form lens tissue.

a

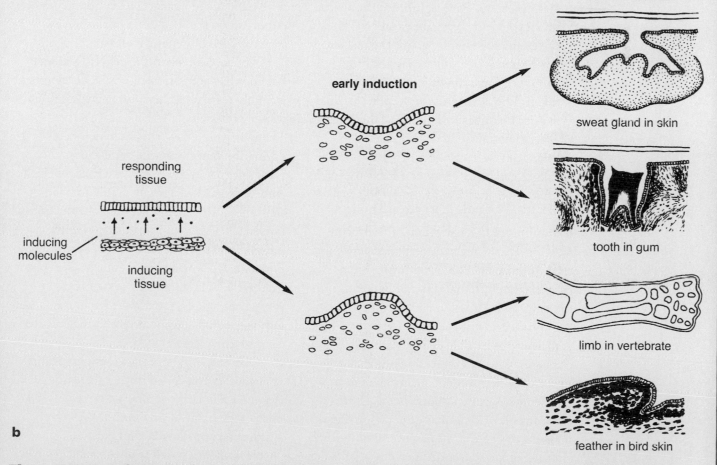

later induction

early induction

responding tissue

inducing molecules

inducing tissue

sweat gland in skin

tooth in gum

limb in vertebrate

feather in bird skin

b

Figure E13.9 Induction.   (a) In the early development of a human's eye, an outpocketing of the brain called the eye cup causes early skin cells of the head to become the lens of the eye. The lens, in turn, causes skin cells to become a cornea. (b) Regulatory molecules released by the inducing tissue can affect the responding tissue in different ways.

Development and Birth Defects

The parents wait while the doctor examines their daughter immediately after she is born. The mother is physically exhausted from hours of labor. The father is mentally exhausted from the tension of waiting and supporting her efforts. They both eagerly wait to hold their baby. The doctor smiles and hands the child to the mother. Everything seems to be fine.

Not all delivery room scenarios go so smoothly. Despite the highly regulated and precise expression of the genetic instructions for development, sometimes things go wrong. Each year about 3 percent of all babies born in the United States have significant problems. Many of these are developmental problems. Often couples feel guilty about the challenges their newborns face. They may ask their doctors if they did anything to cause the problem. The doctor may not always be able to answer that question. But in some cases, the specific source of a developmental problem can be determined. Developmental problems can be categorized into two general groups: those that result from errors in the genetic plan and those that result from disruptions in the expression of that plan.

In the first category, certain mutations exist in the DNA inherited from either parent. (Rarely, mutations can happen in the embryo itself.) These mutations can disrupt the growth and differentiation of the embryonic cells. This disruption may result in permanent and even life-threatening changes in the offspring. Indeed, many changes in development cause a spontaneous abortion (miscarriage). Sometimes, the miscarriage happens before the woman even knows that she is pregnant. Up to 20 percent of all pregnancies may end in miscarriage. Other disruptions allow the embryo to develop full term in spite of the developmental errors.

Such a baby may have physical, mental, or both types of challenges.

Exposure to a mutagenic agent such as radiation can disrupt development in an embryo by causing changes in the DNA (see Figure E13.10). When your dental assistant makes an X-ray of your teeth, he or she covers the rest of your body with a leaded apron. Though it's quite small, the radiation level of a dental X-ray presents a risk, especially to pregnant women. However, radiation damage to the DNA of developing ova and sperm threatens the future offspring of both men and women.

In the second category, developmental errors can be the result of a disruption in the *expression* of genetic material. A disruption can happen even when the genetic material does not have mutations. Because development is highly regulated, there are many points at which a misstep could have lasting effects. The major organ systems become established during the first 3 months of development. Early pregnancy, therefore, is a time when the embryo is particularly vulnerable to toxic substances. Exposure to certain chemicals can interrupt tissues from forming properly. Normally, the uterus and placenta provide protection for the growing embryo (see Figure E13.11). However, some toxic substances and even pathogens that enter the mother's blood supply can reach the embryo through the placenta.

One of the most tragic examples of this vulnerability happened during the early 1960s. An unusually large number of extremely malformed babies were born in Western Europe, Japan, Canada, and Australia. Medical scientists determined that all of the mothers had taken a mild sedative known as thalidomide. Thalidomide had been prescribed to help control nausea due to

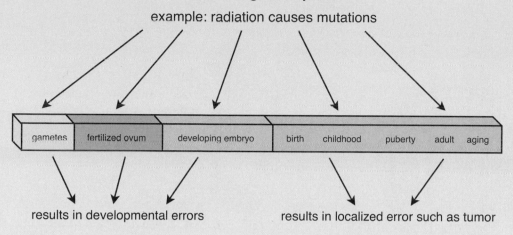

errors in genetic plans

example: radiation causes mutations

| gametes | fertilized ovum | developing embryo | birth | childhood | puberty | adult | aging |

results in developmental errors   results in localized error such as tumor

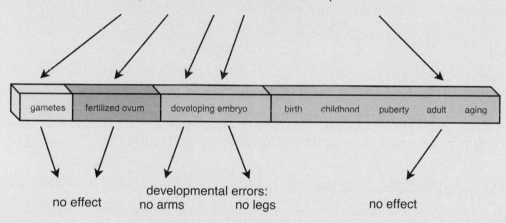

errors in expression of genetic plans

example: thalidomide causes developmental errors

| gametes | fertilized ovum | developing embryo | birth | childhood | puberty | adult | aging |

no effect

developmental errors:
no arms   no legs   no effect

Figure E13.10 **Developmental stages at which errors can take place.** Developing humans are vulnerable to developmental problems at different times and in different ways. Notice that changes may arise from a combination of genetic and environmental factors. Errors can be alterations in the genetic plan for development (in a gamete or in a developing embryo). Or errors can be disruptions in the expression of that plan.

pregnancy. The drug had produced almost no side effects in the mothers. Its devastating effects on the embryo happened when the drug was taken between the third and fifth weeks of pregnancy. Even a single dose of thalidomide taken during the third week of pregnancy resulted in improperly formed or missing arms in the children. As shown in Figure E13.12a, exposure during the fourth week caused malformed or missing legs.

Other abnormalities were mapped to other periods of development. By the time doctors realized the effects of thalidomide on development, many children had already been born with serious problems.

In the United States, the Food and Drug Administration (FDA) did not approve the use of thalidomide for pregnant women. Frances O. Kelsey, a medical officer at the FDA, examined the results of clinical trials on the

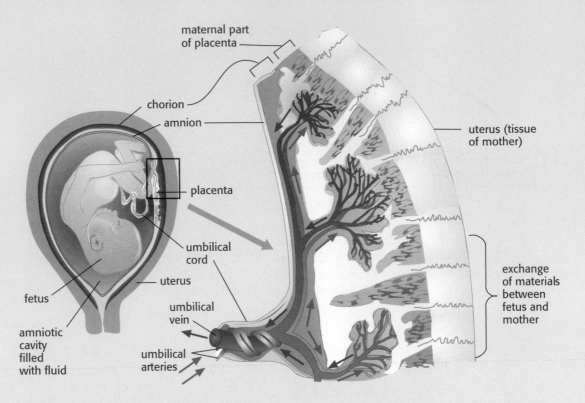

Figure E13.11 **Developing embryo in uterus.** Part of the placenta is enlarged to show the circulation of the mother and the fetus. The two systems do not mix. But nutrients and gases are exchanged. They cross the membranes that separate the maternal blood supply in the uterus and capillaries that deliver blood to the fetus.

Labels on figure:
- maternal part of placenta
- chorion
- amnion
- placenta
- umbilical cord
- uterus
- umbilical vein
- fetus
- amniotic cavity filled with fluid
- umbilical arteries
- uterus (tissue of mother)
- exchange of materials between fetus and mother

use of the drug. She decided that there had not been enough testing to conclude that thalidomide did not cause birth defects. She refused to approve this drug for pregnant women. As a result, few families in the United States experienced the tragedy of children born with severe limb defects.

This tragic example demonstrates that a developing embryo is not fully protected by the uterus and placenta. More commonly used drugs also can do serious harm to the developing embryo. Some nonprescription drugs such as aspirin may increase risk of miscarriage. Diet pills that contain dextroamphetamine have been implicated as a possible cause of birth defects when taken at particular stages of pregnancy.

A mother's exposure to cigarette smoke and alcohol damages a developing embryo.

Among mothers who smoke, the effect of nicotine on blood circulation results in generally weakened infants with low birth weights. The developing brain is particularly sensitive to damage from alcohol. Amounts of alcohol that an adult can tolerate with limited damage can have an extreme effect on the embryo. Scientists do not know for certain whether there is a minimum amount of alcohol that the mother can drink without harming the baby. Even limited drinking, however, appears to contribute to low birth weight and to an increased risk of birth defects and mental retardation. Many women choose to give up alcohol during pregnancy to protect their unborn children. Damage to a child caused by the mother's alcohol consumption is called fetal alcohol syndrome (FAS). Children who have FAS usually have low birth weights and

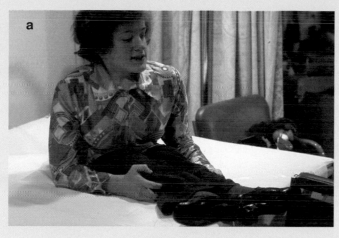
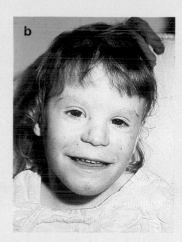

Figure E13.12 (a) **The effects of thalidomide on leg development.** (b) **Small child affected by fetal alcohol syndrome.** Facial abnormalities and mental retardation are typical of children damaged in utero by alcohol.

flattened faces with thin upper lips (see Figure E13.12b). They also exhibit a range of mental, behavioral, and developmental problems. These may include mental retardation, hyperactivity, and developmental delays. FAS is the leading known cause of mental retardation in the United States.

You have seen that environmental hazards threaten the health of a newborn in several ways. They may mutate genes in the gametes of the parents or interfere with the expression of normal genes prior to birth. Some of these errors are beyond the control of the parents. Others are due to their lifestyle choices. ◆

Cancer: Unregulated Growth

A pediatrician invites two parents into her office to discuss the physical examination she has just made of their 7-month-old daughter. The child looks pale and is terribly weak. She has a fever, and the doctor can feel an enlarged spleen.

The doctor tells the parents that the baby will have to be hospitalized for tests to determine which of several possibilities explains their daughter's condition. As they sit down, the mother looks the doctor squarely in the eyes and asks, "Is leukemia the worst thing it could be?"

"No," the doctor replies. "Leukemia is the best thing it could be."

The parents are shocked because they are old enough to remember a time when leukemia, like almost any cancer, meant certain death. However, they are reassured to learn that many

forms of childhood leukemia now can be treated. In fact, the likelihood of success for these treatments is relatively high.

When the tests are done, the diagnosis comes back: their daughter Lauren does have leukemia. Fortunately, the pediatrician also specializes in treating cancer. The doctor treats Lauren with chemotherapy to control the growth of cancerous blood cells.

As you might guess from her photograph (see Figure E13.13), Lauren is now a healthy and energetic 7-year-old, free of leukemia. Now her parents worry about whether she is careful while riding her bicycle or hiking in the mountains.

Figure E13.13 Lauren, a leukemia survivor, is now a healthy, energetic child.

Certainly, pregnancy represents a particularly vulnerable period for development. However, developmental errors can happen throughout life. **Cancer**, one such condition, occurs most often in mature adults. It may happen in many different tissues. Some of the more familiar forms of cancer include skin cancer, breast cancer, prostate cancer, lung cancer, and leukemia. The name "cancer" comes from the Latin word for crab. Many years ago, physicians noticed that cancerous growths were often shaped like crabs. The growths had leglike appendages extending from a central mass. Cancer results from cells that have lost some or all of their differentiated characteristics and grow uncontrollably. Cancerous cells are not inhibited from dividing by contact with other cells (contact inhibition) as normal cells would be. They pile up on one another, forming a tumor.

Scavenger cells of the immune system often destroy these abnormal, or *transformed* cells. However, some transformed cells escape the immune system's defenses. Those cells can grow into a tumor. A tumor may be benign or malignant. *Benign* tumors remain localized in one area surrounded by connective tissue. The cells of *malignant* tumors release enzymes that enable them to invade other tissues. Figure E13.14 illustrates how cancer cells can spread from one part of the body to another. This process is called **metastasis**. It can result in the production of new tumors and damage to many organs.

For many years, scientists and physicians have tried to understand the causes of cancer and find effective ways to treat it. Some scientists conduct basic research. That is, they do research studies that explore the cellular and biochemical mechanisms that cause malignancy. Other scientists carry out applied research. They use the knowledge gained from basic research to search for new treatments and preventive measures. Through the combination of basic and applied research,

we now have both a better understanding of the causes of cancer and better methods for treating it.

In 1911, a young scientist named Peyton Rous performed an experiment to investigate the cause of cancerous transformations. He

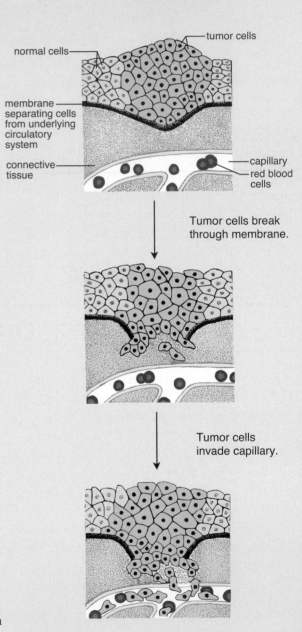

metastasis

normal cells — tumor cells

membrane separating cells from underlying circulatory system

connective tissue

capillary
red blood cells

Tumor cells break through membrane.

Tumor cells invade capillary.

Figure E13.14 Metastasis involves the dangerous spread of cancer cells from a localized tumor to new areas in the body.

crushed cancerous cells from a chicken tumor and filtered the material. The filtered liquid produced tumors in healthy chickens. Today, we know that the liquid contained a virus called *Rous sarcoma virus* (refer to Figure E13.15). This virus can infect animal cells and transform them into cancer cells. It took more than 40 years for the scientific community to fully accept this idea. During that time, many other cancer-causing viruses were identified. (Most viruses do not cause cancer in animals. For example, the influenza virus does not cause cancer.) Fifty years after publishing his work, Rous was awarded a Nobel Prize.

Genetic and biochemical experiments in the 1970s and 1980s led scientists to discover an unexpected connection between normal cells and viruses that cause cancer. Strangely enough, genes within many cancer-causing viruses nearly match normal genes found in animal DNA. Furthermore, many of the nearly matching animal genes code for necessary regulatory proteins. Regulatory proteins affect normal cell growth and adhesion (see Figure E13.16). The viral forms of those genes are called **oncogenes**. These genes are slightly different, causing them to be abnormally active. That results in abnormal growth or altered adhesion of the host cell. Normal cellular genes for growth regulation may also be mutated. This causes them to be abnormally active. That also can result in a normal cell transforming into a cancer cell.

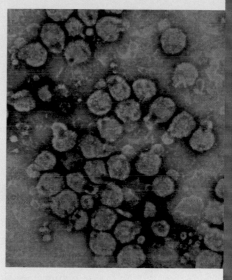

Figure E13.15 *Rous sarcoma viruses (85,000×).*

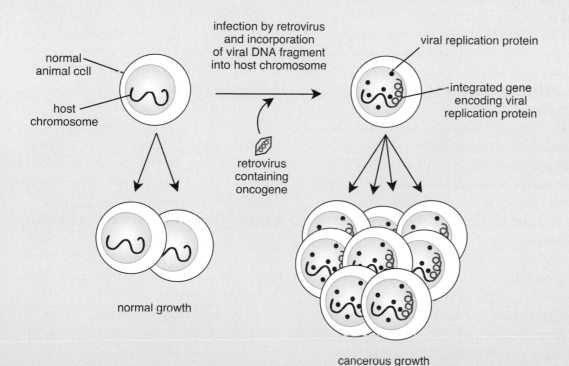

Figure E13.16 Cancer can result from alterations in normal genes whose products regulate cell growth. It can also result from infection by certain viruses. Cancer-causing genes are called oncogenes. These genes can originate from changes in normal cellular genes. They can also enter the cell from an invading retrovirus. How might evolution explain the similarity between the DNA sequences of viral oncogenes and normal regulatory genes?

A number of mutant genes have been identified that appear to play a role in human cancer. For example, researchers identified a mutation in a gene on chromosome 17 (BRCA1) and another on chromosome 13 (BRCA2). Both of these mutations increase the risk of breast and ovarian cancer in women. (BRCA1 and 2 stand for BReast CAncer gene 1 and 2.) One clue helped researchers identify these mutant genes. That clue was finding that breast cancer occurred among close relatives in several families. This suggested a genetic basis for susceptibility to this cancer. Researchers discovered that the product of the normal BRCA1 and 2 genes helps to suppress cell growth. Altered genes release this brake on cell growth. The researchers also discovered that both men and women have these genes. Because of this, either the mother or the father can pass down these mutated genes. They also noted, however, that only about one in 10 breast cancer cases involves inherited, altered genes. This means that 90 percent of all breast cancers are *not* due to mutant genes. Furthermore, some inherited breast cancer involves inherited genes other than BRCA1 or BRCA2.

Genetic testing for BRCA1 and BRCA2 requires a simple blood sample. Genetic testing raises many questions, however. Who should be tested? Should insurance cover the cost of the test? Should the insurance company then be entitled to know the results? How will the person react to the knowledge that she has inherited the gene? Inheriting the altered BRCA1 or 2 genes does not guarantee that the disease will occur. Rather, these altered genes increase the *possibility* of developing cancer. One, or more likely several, additional mutations may be needed for cancer to occur. A healthy immune system may also offset the development of cancer.

A similar sequence of mutations is probably required to cause cancer in a person who has not inherited a mutated gene.

Cigarette smoke, for example, contains several compounds that greatly increase the risk of cancer. Nicotine and other compounds produce cancer-causing mutations in cellular DNA. In addition, tar and other components of cigarette smoke impair the action of the immune system in the lungs and the esophagus. If the immune system can no longer destroy transformed cells effectively, the risk of developing cancer increases. Sunbathing exposes skin cells to UV radiation, which damages DNA. Mutations to the genes that control the cell cycle may result in skin cancer.

As science builds an understanding of the mechanisms that underlie cancer, our culture's view of cancer has changed. People now understand the need to avoid behaviors that either damage the immune system or increase the risk of transforming cells. Using sunblock helps avoid damaging UV radiation and limits the risk of skin cancer. The choice not to smoke greatly reduces the risk of lung cancer (as well as heart disease and emphysema).

Not all forms of cancer can be avoided. Advancements in medical technology, however, have helped make cancer a treatable, and in some cases, a curable disease. One treatment involves removing the cancerous tissue surgically. The success of this treatment relies on early detection, while a tumor is still localized. Technologies such as magnetic resonance imaging (MRI), mammography (Figure E13.17), and ultrasound offer nonsurgical methods of searching for tumors while they are still small. Low-tech methods such as breast self-exams also are valuable for early detection. Finding a small breast tumor early increases survival rates to nearly 90 percent. Late detection drops survival rates to about 10 percent.

Other approaches for treating cancer rely on therapies that attack and kill cancer cells. Unfortunately, it is difficult to limit the damage caused by these therapies to just the cancer cells. The challenge of these therapies is to kill more cancer cells than healthy ones. Radiation therapy does this by precisely targeting the cancerous tissue. Chemotherapy uses toxic chemicals that specifically kill dividing cells. This strategy relies on the fact that cancer cells divide more often than most normal cells. Some exceptions are normal cells that divide rapidly, such as hair follicle cells and the cells that line the intestinal tract. This explains why patients who undergo chemotherapy frequently lose their hair and experience nausea and vomiting. The immune system also may be impaired temporarily by chemotherapy. Researchers continue to search for therapies that *specifically* target cancer cells. ◆

Figure E13.17 Mammography is a type of X-ray technology. It is used to detect breast cancer. Do you know of other technologies that help to detect or treat cancer?

Patterns of Development

Think of development as a series of important events that take place during the life of an organism. Some of these events happen in the lives of almost all multicellular organisms. For example, development in all sexually reproducing organisms begins with fertilization and ends with death. Development also typically involves both growth and differentiation. These processes produce a multicellular organism that looks quite different from the fertilized ovum from which it began.

Other developmental events take place only in *some* organisms. In fact, a remarkable number of developmental plans exist among multicellular organisms. Some organisms, such as trees, never completely stop growing. Biologists say that these organisms have indeterminate growth. Other organisms, like humans, stop growing at some point during their lives. (At least, we stop getting *taller*.) These organisms demonstrate determinate growth.

Consider the spectacular growth of the giant sequoia. These huge trees begin life as tiny seeds that weigh less than 1/5,000 of an ounce. Successful seedlings grow rapidly. Young sequoias, at about 100 years of age, begin producing seeds. At this age, they are about the size of typical pine trees. Healthy sequoias normally attain their full heights at about 1,000 years. They would grow even taller except that they tend to lose their growing tips to lightning. Even so, the 2,500-year-old General Sherman tree at Sequoia National Park continues to produce cones, seeds, new wood, leaves, and branches each year. The amount of new mass produced each year by this tree (and others like it) equals the wood of a tree 18 meters (59 feet) tall and 0.5 meters (about $1\frac{1}{2}$ feet) in diameter! Other types of trees, and even nonwoody plants such as tomatoes and cucumbers, demonstrate a similar, if not so spectacular, pattern of continued growth.

Plants show indeterminate growth. They do this because, unlike most animals, they retain groups of undifferentiated cells (meristems) for as long as they live. Meristems act like permanent embryonic cells. Cell division in meristems near the tips of shoots and roots produces a constant supply of new cells. These cells then differentiate into new branches and roots. Meristem tissue can be removed from a plant to produce a clone. Figure E13.18 illustrates development in a growing plant.

Some animals continue to increase in size for as long as they live. (Examples include many types of invertebrates, most types of fish, and some mammals.) This growth, however, usually slows greatly once the animals attain sexual maturity. Most animals, including birds and most mammals, grow to a defined size.

Metamorphosis is another example of a developmental plan that takes place only in some organisms. Organisms that undergo metamorphosis start life with one body plan.

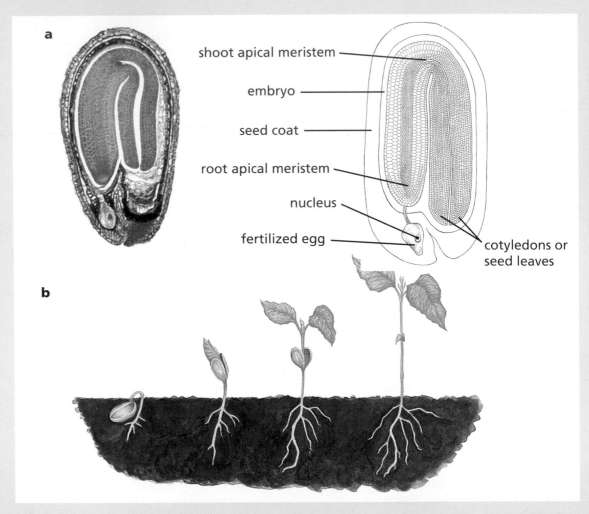

Figure E13.18   Development in a flowering plant.   (a) When pollen grains, which contain sperm cells, come into contact with the female reproductive organs of a flower, fertilization of an egg cell can take place. The zygote then grows and develops into an embryo. In a seed (as shown here), the embryo has temporarily stopped developing. Seeds are well adapted for survival. Many can survive being eaten and eliminated. (b) Under favorable environmental conditions, a seed can germinate. When this happens, development resumes. A new plant develops from the embryo. A root develops from the root apical meristem in the embryo. The cotyledons then help provide food for the plant until the leaves develop.

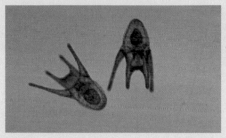
a larvae

metamorphosis

b adult

Figure E13.19 Sea urchin metamorphosis. (**a**) Sea urchin larvae (150×) before metamorphosis (**b**) Adult sea urchin (8–20 centimeters [3–8 inches] across)

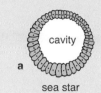
cavity

a

sea star

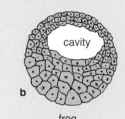
cavity

b

frog

cavity

c

bird

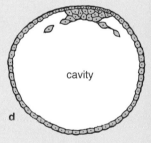
cavity

d

mammal

Then, at a particular stage in their life cycles, develop a quite different plan. In most cases, metamorphosis from the first plan (for example, a caterpillar) to the second plan (a butterfly) takes place before the organism has reached sexual maturity. In vertebrates, metamorphosis occurs in several species of amphibians, such as frogs. Metamorphosis also takes place in a number of invertebrates, such as insects and echinoderms (see the sea urchins in Figure E13.19).

Sexual maturity is an especially important event in development. Under the pressures of natural selection, the final test of any organism's developmental scheme is how well it assures the organism's reproductive success. This is the perpetuation of its genes. From the time that an organism originates as a zygote until it reaches reproductive maturity, selection acts on the sequence of its developmental events. Developmental patterns that ensure survival and sexual maturity are maintained. In contrast, developmental plans that do not assure reproduction are not maintained. In this way, the developmental patterns of species respond to the forces of evolution just as any other characteristic might.

Not surprisingly, the diversity in developmental plans that we see among different organisms mirrors the diversity we see among the organisms themselves. This observation brings us to the second of the scientists' questions about development:

What clues does development reveal about the process of evolution?

We have already begun to answer this question. We have seen that all development involves the basic processes of growth and differentiation. This uniformity in basic developmental processes reflects the evolutionary relatedness of all types of life. There are, however, other evolutionary patterns that we can identify. For example, the earliest rounds of cell division in many different types of animals give rise to embryos of the same basic form. This form consists of cells grouped around an internal cavity. As Figure E13.20 shows, the exact shape and structure of this cavity varies with the species. In more closely related animals, such as all vertebrates, subsequent developmental stages also show some similarities. In closely related vertebrates, such as mammals, the developmental similarities are even more obvious.

Such observations suggest a general developmental plan for all vertebrate embryos. Distinguishing features in the different classes of vertebrates result from modifications of this plan. Exactly what types of modifications are possible in a developmental scheme? How might these changes result in a changed phenotype or perhaps a new species? Can such changes ever lead to valuable differences that might continue through reproduction?

Figure E13.20 Developmental patterns. The similarity of this early developmental phase among diverse organisms reflects an evolutionary connection. Which organism would you expect to most resemble the early developmental phases of a salamander? Why?

Figure E13.21 Changes in timing can lead to quite different results in different developing systems. **(a)** In cold regions, tiger salamanders never receive the developmental signal that triggers metamorphosis. Thus, the salamander retains its aquatic larval form as it sexually matures. **(b)** In warm regions, tiger salamanders produce a hormone that triggers metamorphosis before sexual maturity is reached. This causes the salamander to transform into a land-dwelling organism.

One way to answer those questions is to look for evidence. Can the same process, occurring in slightly different ways, lead to changes in structures? One particularly important change that often takes place in development is a change in the *timing* of developmental events.

A much-studied example of this is the tiger salamander, *Ambystoma tigrinum*. Throughout warmer regions of this tiger salamander's range, individuals pass their early lives as aquatic larvae. They have external gills and flattened tails for swimming. When these organisms undergo metamorphosis, they become burrowing land animals. They have lungs and rounded tails. The organisms become sexually mature only after these metamorphic events. In colder regions, the same tiger salamanders have adapted to live permanently in streams and lakes.

Tiger salamanders reach sexual maturity and adult size even though they never undergo metamorphosis. This fact represents a major evolutionary change (see Figure E13.21). This might seem to be a major developmental alteration requiring many genetic differences.

However, the actual change turns out to be quite simple. Take the tiger salamanders that live in warmer regions. Metamorphosis is triggered by a surge of thyroid hormone that takes place before the organisms reach sexual maturity. For tiger salamanders that live in colder regions, however, the cold environment prevents production of thyroid hormone in the amounts required to stimulate metamorphosis. This means that the animals simply continue to grow in size until they become sexually mature. As a result, these tiger salamanders retain gills and other adaptations of the larvae. They remain aquatic organisms throughout their lives.

A single environmental signal that affects the developmental path of an organism represents a significant evolutionary force. In the case of *Ambystoma tigrinum*, developmental flexibility allows it to adapt to a specific environment. In other organisms, developmental pathways are fixed. The life cycle of the Mexican salamander, *Ambystoma mexicanum*, illustrates a fixed developmental pathway. These salamanders never undergo metamorphosis in nature. Indeed, they live their entire lives in the larval form. There are many physical similarities between the tiger salamander and the Mexican salamander, however. These similarities suggest that evolutionary change from one species to another may proceed through changes that alter the course of development. ◆

Human Development 101

Personal Journal Entry: 21 October

I am just about to begin observations for my human development class. I am both excited and apprehensive. I am already tired of reading the textbook and am really excited about getting to observe. It will be a great way to learn. So why am I apprehensive? I guess maybe it's because I won't be observing plants or protozoans as I'm used to doing in my biology classes. I'll be observing *people!*

My professor has been great about helping us get ready. She has explained to us all of the important things to keep in mind. I think it's interesting that public ethical standards for working with children were established only after World War II. Officials discovered the unethical and inhumane experiments that Nazi physicians had conducted on both children and adults. Because of this, administrators developed the first written guidelines to protect people who participate in research projects. Then, in the late 1960s, government officials in the United States established their own set of specific guidelines to protect human subjects. And in 1982, the American Psychological Association published a set of ethical standards for conducting research with children.

I think the first important issue is respect for all participants. All participation must be completely voluntary. This means that if people do not want us to observe them or to include them in a study, then we must respect their wishes. Also, the participants can decide to drop out of the project at any time. And with children, it's important to remember that even if the parents have given permission, if the child does not want to participate, we must respect the wishes of the child—not just the parent. It seems obvious that you especially shouldn't do anything that would harm a participant physically or emotionally.

I remember that the ethical guidelines also say we must explain the purpose of our research or observations to the participants. Also, the information that we obtain is confidential. This means that we should never discuss personal information about a participant with anyone outside the project. When social scientists publish

When making observations, a complete, detailed written record is essential.

research papers, they never disclose the participants' identities.

The participants also have the right to ask questions about the observations or the research. It's important to remember that they may want to know the results. It's critical to remember that the rights of the participants come before the rights of the researcher.

O.K. I think I'm ready for my first day of observations.

Personal Journal Entry: 28 October

Well, I thought I was ready, but I wasn't. I was supposed to make observations of cognitive growth and development. But I didn't even remember what that meant. So, I went back to my notebook from class and read through my notes. I found out that *cognitive growth* refers to the changes that take place as we age in how we learn and process information. *Cognition* involves perceiving, remembering, imagining, and reasoning. It makes sense that we get better at that as we grow older. My cognitive skills are better now than when I was 5. They were better at 5 than when I was 5 months old.

So, what exactly do I look for to find examples of cognitive growth? Maybe I need to ask the children to do something, like solve a problem or do a puzzle. Maybe I could just ask certain questions. Let's see, what are some ideas?

For the youngest children

Ask them to point to things of specific colors.

Ask them to point to pictures of different animals.

For children a little older

Ask them to write something or draw something.

Listen to how well they use language, such as how long their sentences are, and stuff like that.

For children in late childhood

Ask them to solve simple math problems.

Listen to their sentences and their use of language.

Ask them to read.

For adolescents

Ask them to discuss some book they just read or a movie they just saw.

Ask them to solve a puzzle like Tangoes.

Ask them to solve a more difficult math problem.

For adults

Ask them to discuss a book or a movie.

Ask them to describe what they do in their jobs.

For the elderly

Ask them what they remember about their families.

Ask them about the people in the photographs around the room.

Ask them to play a board game or card game.

A special note on children

I remember a neat activity about the idea of conservation. First, you hold a tall, narrow container of water. Then, with the children watching, you pour the water into a shallow cake pan or something like that. You ask the children which one had more water. Young children will say that the tall, narrow container had more water in it. But at some point in their cognitive growth, their abstract thinking improves, and the children will realize that the amount of water is the same. I think that is so cool.

Goal: Maybe tomorrow I can try to find out at what age that happens. Complete, clear notes will be important. Maybe I will revise my forms so they are easier to use.

Personal Journal Entry: 29 October

Observing physical development is sort of straightforward. I mean, you actually can watch people do things. I asked the kids if I could measure how tall everyone is. They thought it was great and enjoyed helping me. Sometimes they were even a little bit competitive about who would get to help. (This is when I realized that, although I thought I was recording data about physical development, my partner was recording a lot of stuff about social and emotional behavior. That was great. We didn't even have that planned! It helps to be ready for anything.) Our professor explained that when we observe adolescents, we should measure only height, not weight, because adolescence is a time when people generally are very sensitive about their weight.

Even though I thought observing physical development was more straightforward, I realized that I wasn't getting a very detailed picture. It would be great to be able to observe the kids on the playground. Maybe tomorrow I will ask them to skip and see who can do it and who can't. I should ask my mom how old I was when I started to skip.

Personal Journal Entry: 3 November

I just noticed that my notes on emotional growth and development aren't as complete as I would like them to be. This type of development is a hard thing to observe. Is what I think someone is feeling really what the person is feeling? Or am I misinterpreting her or him? This is hard. I need to try to separate what I see and hear from what I think it means. I need to separate the *observation* from the *interpretation.* My professor has reminded me to place brackets in my notes around any phrases that represent interpretations.

Should I ask or just observe? Maybe I could ask them to explain to me what emotions like anger, excitement, and love mean. This is not the same as *observing* the emotions, and would give me some different information.

Social growth is pretty easy to observe with children in groups. As I was watching a group of children, it was easy to separate the sociable ones from the reserved ones. But again, I tried to write down my observation, not my interpretation. I could observe how many children were willing to share toys, how often they would make eye contact with others, and how much time they preferred to play alone.

It's really important what size group you are observing. If you don't have a large enough group (at least three), then you really limit the amount of social interaction that happens. But if the group is too large (more than six or seven), then it is too hard to keep track of everybody.

Social behavior will be harder to observe in adolescents and adults. They have more self-awareness. They also are more concerned about how others will perceive them. For these reasons, they are more cautious in their interactions. How can I find out about their social growth? What questions can I ask? Maybe I can ask them to estimate how much time they spend each week (outside of school and work) by themselves, and with one, two, or more than two other people.

O.K. It looks like I have a place to start again. Observing is fun, but harder than I thought. ◆

Growing Up through Life's Phases

Learning to ride a bicycle, watching a baby take her first steps, helping a grandfather walk with his cane. Through experiences of your own and those around you, you have learned that life proceeds through phases. Each phase can be characterized by certain biological changes and experiences. Virtually every human culture seems to recognize benchmarks in life. Such benchmarks include learning to walk, learning to talk, going through puberty, selecting a mate, having children, and growing old. Let's look more closely at these benchmarks and their associated phases of life.

Infancy includes roughly the first year of life. Most languages have one or more special words for individuals of this age. In English, we say *baby*; in French, *bébé*. The Trobriand Islanders near New Guinea say *wayway* until an infant crawls and then *pwapwawa* until the child begins walking. During the first year of life, an enormous number of physical and mental changes take place very quickly. Baby teeth begin to erupt. Control of movements and handling of objects improves markedly. Physical growth takes place rapidly: a baby normally weighs three times its birth weight by the end of the first year.

Figure E14.1 shows the average age at which a number of physical actions first appear. It is important to recognize that these are just average ages. Many first-time parents become needlessly upset if their infant fails to reach these milestones "on schedule." In all societies, cultural practices influence the development of sitting and walking. As shown in Figure E14.2, infants in the United States

often walk by the time they are 1 year old. Among the Aka in Africa, however, infants tend to walk several months before their first

Average age in months	Physical activity
12	walks alone but may prefer crawling
11	stands alone, climbs stairs
10	walks with support
9	pulls self up, sidesteps along furniture
8	grasps in effort to pull self up
7	crawls, sits alone
6	sits unsupported up to half an hour
5	rolls over, moves by rocking and twisting
4	controls hands, rolls from side to side
3	controls head, bats at objects
2	vocalizes, grasps voluntarily
1	moves arms and legs reflexively
0	suckles, lifts head briefly

Figure E14.1 Physical activities during the first year of life. This chart presents guidelines for the average ages at which infants can perform various activities during the first year of life. The age at which specific children can do each activity will vary.

Figure E14.2 In the United States, an infant's first unassisted steps usually happen at about 1 year.

birthdays. These infants receive more physical stimulation and direct training for sitting and walking. Among the Ache in South America, however, family members hold infants almost constantly. Infants in this culture do not begin walking until they are 22–24 months old.

From birth to age 2, growth of the brain and the accompanying mental development are rapid. The brain grows to 80 percent of its adult size by the end of the second year. An important aspect of brain development is the infant's awareness of the people with whom he or she is in regular contact. This interaction results in *attachment*, the development of close emotional ties to the parent or regular caregiver. Just as the cultural setting affects the age when babies begin walking, it also influences the way in which attachment takes place.

In 1988, a group of researchers studied parenting patterns in five different cultures. Figure E14.3 demonstrates some of the differences they found between a group of Gusii parents in Kenya and a group of Boston parents in the United States. Gusii mothers,

like mothers in many developing societies, are primarily concerned with the physical survival of their young. By holding them and keeping them close, the mothers help keep their children safe. In addition, the Gusii believe that children cannot understand language until they are close to 2 years old. Therefore, they rarely talk to their babies. Even during conversations, the Gusii generally do not look at each other. They avert their gaze when talking with someone. Similarly, Gusii mothers make very little eye contact with their babies. In Boston, on the other hand, infants spend more time in infant seats and playpens than in their mothers' arms. This practice may reflect the mothers' need for independence during the day and perhaps also the value of teaching independence to their young. Boston parents, however, provide more visual and motor stimulation for their babies. They make frequent eye contact with the babies, play special music for them, and read to them.

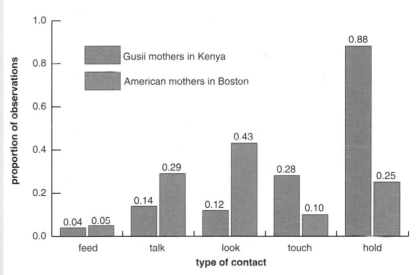

Source: Data from Richman, A. et al. (1988). Maternal behavior to infants in five cultures. In R.A. LeVine et al. (eds.). *Parental Behavior in Diverse Societies: New Directions for Child Development.* San Francisco: Jossey-Bass.

Figure E14.3 Interacting with infants. The way parents interact with their infants reflects greater cultural patterns.

Childhood is the next phase of life. Most human societies use one or more specific terms to refer to individuals in this period of life as well. English-speaking people say *child*. Trobriand Islanders say *gwadi*. The French say *enfant*. The Ainu people of Northern Japan say *ki yakka pirika*, which means "it eats with adults now." During the decade or so of childhood, physical growth continues at a moderate pace, with a growth spurt just before adolescence. The first permanent teeth usually erupt during the fifth to seventh years. During childhood, the skull grows mostly within bones of the facial region, as illustrated in Figure E14.4.

Other important changes also take place. Physical coordination and language skills improve. This happens both through deliberate teaching by adults and through less formal practices. For example, physical games and verbal activities, such as telling or listening to jokes and stories, contribute to this development. In the United States,

parents engage in a lot of face-to-face interactions and conversations with their young children. (The graph in Figure E14.3 illustrates this point.) Young children in such settings are likely to begin talking and interacting socially earlier than in cultures where these practices are less common.

A growing child continues to develop her or his own unique identity and personality. The child discovers personal likes and dislikes in everything from foods to hobbies to academic studies. A healthy child makes steady progress in the development of personal judgment and an internal sense of what *is* or *is not* appropriate behavior toward others.

Studies by child-development specialists have shown that, across cultures, the type of economic activity that predominates in a society influences its child-rearing values and practices. For example, in hunting-and-gathering societies, adults work independently much of the time. Such societies value

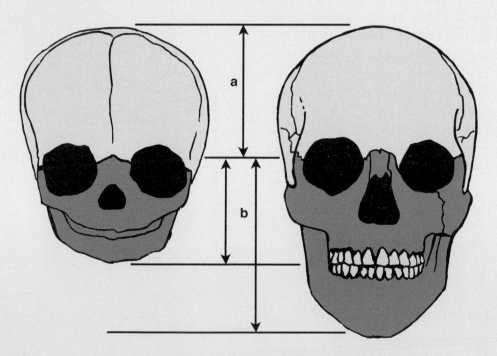

Figure E14.4 Facial development in childhood.   The heights of the cranium in the infant and the adult are indicated by distance **a**. Distance **b** indicates the length of the bones of the facial region. It is clear that after infancy, most of the growth of the skull takes place in the facial bones, especially the jaw bones.

self-reliance and autonomy. Parents exercise little control over their children and rarely punish them. In agriculturally based societies, however, adults work under close supervision. These societies value conformity and obedience. In these societies, parents demonstrate a more restrictive and controlling child-rearing style.

When puberty occurs, childhood ends and the period called *adolescence* begins. Most human societies recognize adolescence as a distinct milestone. Secondary sexual characteristics appear. These include the appearance of hair in the pubic region and under the arms. In females, the pelvic area broadens and breasts develop. In males, the shoulders broaden, facial hair grows, and the voice deepens. In early adolescence, girls generally are taller than boys due to a growth spurt just before puberty. However, by the end of adolescence, males are, on average, 5 inches taller than females.

The arrival and length of puberty vary widely among individuals. Puberty, primarily under hormonal control, also can be influenced by socioeconomic conditions and nutrition. As adolescents are experiencing the obvious changes associated with the onset of sexual development, a number of other physical alterations take place. These are summarized in Figure E14.5.

Mental capacity changes as well. Thinking skills improve. This includes the ability to deal with abstract concepts and to engage in critical thinking. In the United States, this development often accompanies an interest in challenging the statements and rules of adult authority figures, including parents. Many individuals have a strong desire to gain social acceptance from their peer group by presenting the "right" appearance and behavior. Adolescents struggle with striking a balance between questioning and conformity. This balancing act is perhaps the most difficult part of adolescence for every generation. But it marks a key step in the development of each person's individual identity.

Adulthood begins when individuals reach their maximum physical stature, usually in the later teens. Adulthood does not mark the end of development, however. For most people, social, emotional, and cognitive development

PHYSICAL DEVELOPMENT IN ADOLESCENTS

Boys	Age span	Girls	Age span
Beginning of growth spurt; growth of scrotum, testes, and penis; sparse, light-colored, slightly curled pubic hair	11–13	Beginning of growth spurt, breasts and nipples elevated (breast buds); sparse, light-colored, slightly curled pubic hair	10–11
Maximum physical growth; deepening of voice, maturation of scrotum, testes, and penis; ejaculation of semen; sparse facial hair; pubic hair darker, denser, and more curled	13–16	Maximum physical growth; deepening of voice; further breast enlargement; rapid growth of uterus, vagina, and ovaries; vaginal secretion acidic; menstruation begins; pubic hair darker, denser, and more curled	11–14
Slowdown or cessation of physical growth; further deepening of voice; penis adult size; darkening of scrotum; increased body and facial hair; adult-type pubic hair	16–18	Slowdown or cessation of physical growth; breasts adult size; clitoris mature; adult-type pubic hair	14–16

Figure E14.5   Physical development in adolescents.

continues long after physical growth ceases. Key events that take place during the adult lives of many individuals include developing a long-term pair bond with another individual. Adults learn and practice a skill that allows them to support themselves financially. Many adults create a new household, produce children, and parent those children through all the stages of development. Each of these activities clearly calls for the development of many social and cognitive skills that individuals can acquire only gradually as they practice them. In traditional societies, people often engage in the same occupation throughout their adult life and establish their family near their relatives. In contemporary Western societies, however, people often change their homes, occupations, and even family affiliations well into their adult years.

Biologically, the adult years represent the period of aging. The aging process begins when adults are in their 20s. Aging involves a slow deterioration of all the body's systems. Muscles slowly lose strength and mass. Skin becomes less resilient. Cuts heal more slowly. Bones and tendons gradually become more brittle. The peak performance of major organ systems declines. For people whose physical gifts allow them to become professional athletes in vigorous sports, these changes usually compel retirement from top-level competition by age 40. For most people, however, the changes of aging are so slow and gradual that they can maintain much the same level of activity from their 20s through their 40s or 50s. ◆

Physical Growth Influences Mental Growth

Physically, humans are animals possessing the same basic biological functions and organs as their primate relatives. Humans also are highly social creatures. Because of this, growth and development in humans is not just a physical process. It is also a cognitive, social, and emotional one. The capacity of humans for cognitive growth has a clear biological basis. Because the human birth canal would not be big enough to accommodate a baby's head if its brain were full-sized, human brains continue to grow after birth. This allows humans to acquire the capacity for a more complex cognition and learned behavior than they would have otherwise.

The frontal lobes of the cerebrum grow rapidly around age 2, with another increase between ages 5 and 7. Growth of the cerebrum accompanies a growth spurt in the circumference of the head. An insulating myelin sheath develops around neurons in the cerebrum by age 7. This sheath speeds neural transmission between different parts of the brain. By this age, children's brains generally have developed a level of complexity comparable to that of adults' brains.

Genetic or developmental disorders and physical accidents can delay or permanently limit a child's capacity for mental growth. Shaken-baby syndrome illustrates how an injury can cause brain damage. Shaken-baby syndrome can take place when someone severely shakes an infant. The brain injury often results in permanent retardation or even death. At the other end of life, conditions such as Alzheimer's disease, stroke, or injuries can lead to the deterioration of mental abilities.

Cognitive growth refers to the increase in an individual's ability to construct a mental picture of the external world and to understand the relationships of objects within it. Cognitive growth appears to parallel the physical growth of the brain. Most

COGNITIVE STAGES DEVELOPED BY PIAGET

Cognitive stage	Description
Sensorimotor	**0–2 years:** infants learn through direct experience; do not understand things that exist outside their own actions
Preoperational	**2–7 years:** children develop the ability to use symbols, but have difficulty understanding multiple classification systems; sometime between 5–7 years, a qualitative improvement occurs in the child's ability to organize information logically and coordinate information from several sources
Concrete Operational	**7–12 years:** by age 7–8, most children can reason about objects and events that they can perceive; this stage is characterized by the ability to solve problems involving cause and effect, ordering, multiple classification, and numbers
Formal Operational	**12+ years:** adolescents begin to think logically about abstract or imagined concepts

Source: Fogel, L. and G. Melson (1998). *Child Development: Individual, Family, and Society.* St. Paul, MN: West Publishing Company.

Figure E14.6 Cognitive stages developed by Piaget.

developmental psychologists agree that the brain develops in stages. Not surprisingly, they hold different opinions about the precise stages in the process.

As an example, Jean Piaget made significant contributions in the field of developmental psychology. Trained as a biologist in Switzerland, Piaget later became interested in human development. He suggested that all complex forms of knowing develop through the interaction between the individual and the environment. He divided childhood into a series of stages defined by the type of knowing that the child uses, as summarized in Figure E14.6.

Language development illustrates cognitive growth in children. Language development requires more than merely acquiring a larger vocabulary. Evidence suggests that language development proceeds by a similar series of steps in children of many different cultures. At around 1 year, infants begin to utter single words. Most of these are nouns that simply identify things the infant sees. These nouns can represent names,

questions, or demands, depending on the intonation, as in "toy," "toy?" or "TOY!" Between 18 and 24 months, children proceed to the stage of two-word utterances. These allow them to make a surprising variety of statements, such as "book here," "sit chair," "allgone milk," and "MY ball." (This is a favorite remark concerning many different things in the infant's world.) Three-word sentences follow shortly. These allow the child to express more complex ideas or demands such as "Daddy read book." As language acquisition continues, children begin to learn the particular grammatical rules of their own language. Children in all cultures generally follow a similar sequence. In English, for example, children learn at a young age that they can form a question by inverting the word order, as in "Can he walk on the road?" instead of "He can walk on the road." It takes longer, however, to be able to form a question that begins with a question word. So children will continue to say, "Why he can walk on the road?" for some time after they learn the basic rule.

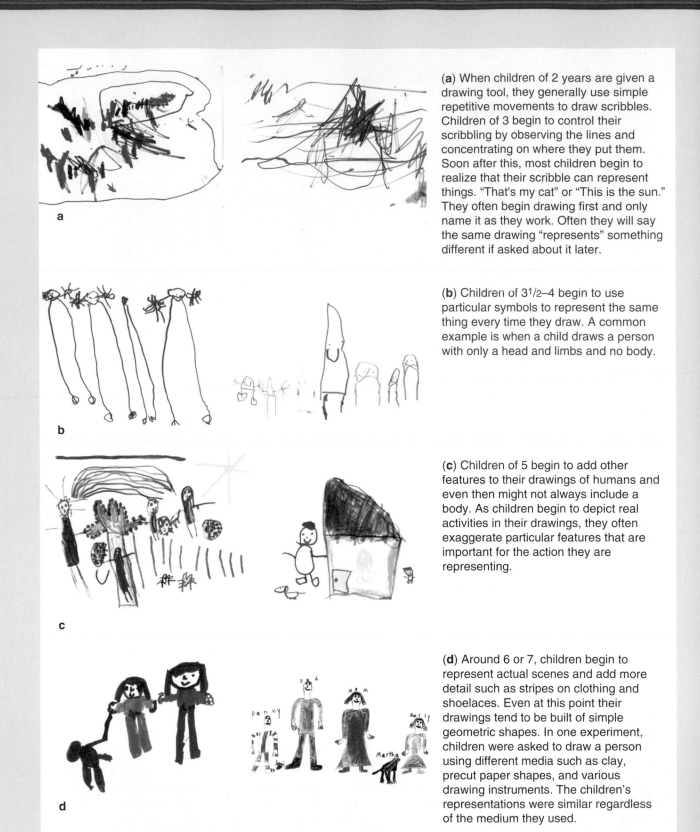

(a) When children of 2 years are given a drawing tool, they generally use simple repetitive movements to draw scribbles. Children of 3 begin to control their scribbling by observing the lines and concentrating on where they put them. Soon after this, most children begin to realize that their scribble can represent things. "That's my cat" or "This is the sun." They often begin drawing first and only name it as they work. Often they will say the same drawing "represents" something different if asked about it later.

(b) Children of 3½–4 begin to use particular symbols to represent the same thing every time they draw. A common example is when a child draws a person with only a head and limbs and no body.

(c) Children of 5 begin to add other features to their drawings of humans and even then might not always include a body. As children begin to depict real activities in their drawings, they often exaggerate particular features that are important for the action they are representing.

(d) Around 6 or 7, children begin to represent actual scenes and add more detail such as stripes on clothing and shoelaces. Even at this point their drawings tend to be built of simple geometric shapes. In one experiment, children were asked to draw a person using different media such as clay, precut paper shapes, and various drawing instruments. The children's representations were similar regardless of the medium they used.

Figure E14.7 Drawings by children of different ages.

Interestingly, the developing human brain appears to be able to acquire language most easily very early in life. Young children who live in bilingual situations appear to acquire multiple languages with relative ease. Teens and adults experience more difficulty in learning a new language. Even highly intelligent people who learn a second language in adulthood almost never gain the same ease and fluency of a language as those who learn it as children. Moreover, studies on the rare cases of children who were separated from other people throughout childhood and not exposed to language suggest that they never can develop complex language skills.

Cognitive growth also can be expressed as visual development. We can observe this through the artwork that children produce at different ages, as illustrated in Figure E14.7. ◆

Physical Growth Influences Social and Emotional Growth

The social growth of humans, the best understood type of mental development, becomes more complex from infancy to maturity. Psychologists often describe social growth as a process in which individuals gradually move from seeing others only in terms of their own wants and needs to seeing themselves as defined by give-and-take relationships with others. Social growth has a physical basis, however. Humans who suffer from impairments in physical development of the brain frequently cannot develop mature social skills. For example, the consumption of alcoholic beverages during pregnancy disrupts fetal brain growth, resulting in fetal alcohol syndrome. The normal convolutions of the brain may fail to develop. Affected children frequently cannot develop mature social skills or other types of advanced mental functions.

Bonding—or its absence—with parents and other family members characterizes the first social interactions in an infant's life. As children grow, their social contacts reach beyond the family to include playmates and other adults (refer to Figure E14.8). As they reach maturity, most individuals develop an extensive circle of friends and acquaintances. The circle includes teachers and other authority figures. Through these interactions, individuals acquire appropriate social skills. These social skills include not only a desire to please and help relatives and friends, but also a sense of social responsibility toward all people.

Interestingly, evidence indicates that a specific portion of the human brain governs responsible behavior. Individuals who experience accidents that damage only a region located in the frontal lobes sometimes

Figure E14.8 Play is so central to the life of a young child that the years from 2 through 5 are often referred to as the play years.

retain normal reasoning powers. But they lose all sense of social responsibility and appropriate behavior toward others. Phineas Gage, an engineer who lived in the 1800s, experienced such a tragic accident. While at work, a metal rod shot through the frontal lobes of his brain (refer back to Figure E1.5). Although he survived and could take care of himself, the once friendly, dependable worker became irresponsible and foul-mouthed.

Like cognitive and social growth, emotional growth in humans has a biological basis and takes place progressively as a child's brain matures. Mental retardation may delay or limit emotional growth. Affected individuals may become physically mature, but remain somewhat childlike in their emotional development. Moreover, older individuals affected by disorders such as Alzheimer's disease frequently undergo emotional regression and become childlike.

Emotional growth normally begins in a child's relationship with his or her parents or caregivers and gradually extends to a wider circle of individuals. With successful emotional growth, a child learns to express negative feelings in a nondestructive manner. The child learns to accept that some of his or her wishes and desires cannot be satisfied immediately— or at all. A key point in the process of emotional growth takes place at puberty. This is when individuals begin to experience the very powerful drives and emotions connected with sex. Adolescents learn to control sexual behavior in order to maintain personal health and social acceptance. For some young people, the realization that their sexual orientation is different from most of those around them further complicates their lives. Because this often happens at the age when the desire to be like one's peers is at its peak, such young people experience additional hardships. ◆

All Phases of Life Require Self-Maintenance

Both our physical and mental capacities have a biological basis. As a result, our ability to develop and sustain them requires self-maintenance. Self-maintenance includes physical fitness. Anyone who has participated in sports has discovered that the body's ability to perform increases with training, practice, and a good diet. Furthermore, anyone who has interrupted a regular routine of training and healthy diet has found that performance level drops off when fitness declines. In recent years, we have learned that regular exercise and a healthful diet improve the body's ability to carry on even routine activities throughout life.

An individual's environment influences whether that individual reaches her or his genetic potential. Environmental influences are especially influential during periods when the body and brain are growing and developing. We already have noted that mothers who drink even small amounts of alcohol while they are pregnant may have a child who is affected by fetal alcohol syndrome. Many other agents—including tobacco and certain prescription and illicit drugs—also can affect a developing fetus unfavorably.

Once born, growing children also are at risk. Some children who go through periods of severe starvation, particularly those whose diets lack protein, never reach full physical or mental growth, even if food is plentiful thereafter. In fact, even far less severe situations can affect the attainment of biological potential. One study found that, during middle childhood, the average heights of Nigerian boys from wealthy families were significantly greater than those from poor families. Likewise, the average height of the population of Japan increased throughout the 20th century as many people adopted a diet richer in protein.

Evidence indicates that the social environment also may affect the development of mental capacities such as emotional and social development. Babies who are orphaned and placed in impersonal institutions experience little social stimulation. Researchers who studied these babies found that their physical needs were met, but attendants had little time to cuddle or talk to the babies. These infants did not thrive or develop as well as babies given comparable physical care, but more attention. In fact, children who spend their entire childhoods in such situations often appear to be stunted in their emotional and social growth. Studies suggest that many of them are never able to form normal relationships in later life.

Clearly, the environment influences an individual's potential. Of course, an individual's genetic makeup also influences her or his potential. Researchers have studied identical twins who were raised together and those who were raised apart. Identical twins have virtually the same genetic makeup. You might expect that identical twins, even those raised apart, would demonstrate a high degree of similarity in various traits. Based on research with identical twins, scientists now think that physical characteristics, intellectual abilities, and personality traits are all influenced by genetics. However, the impact of genes on physical characteristics is stronger. Creativity and social attitudes seem to be more influenced by environmental factors than genetic ones. Both genes and the environment are influential during the entire life span. It seems, however, that environmental influences have a greater impact at earlier stages of development. But these influences become somewhat less important as individuals age.

Once the body and brain mature, maintaining them requires effort. Individuals need to stay physically and mentally active, eat balanced meals, and avoid activities or behaviors that accelerate degenerative changes. While in their teens or 20s, individuals sometimes make lifestyle choices and acquire habits that damage their bodies' tissues. These choices include mental and physical inactivity, heavy drinking, smoking, drug abuse, excessive exposure to the sun, and eating large quantities of fatty foods. The bodies of teenagers and young adults may tolerate some of these activities without showing many obvious ill effects. Over time, however, any of these behaviors may cause cumulative damage to one or more organ systems. This damage will negatively affect the individuals' quality of life.

Many of the changes once thought to be unavoidable aspects of old age can be slowed or even reversed. Programs of regular exercise and good nutrition can slow the weakening of joints, bones, and muscles, and the resulting loss of mobility. These programs also strengthen the immune system, thus lowering susceptibility to disease. Moderate exercise and attention to good nutrition should be lifelong priorities for everyone, as illustrated by the seniors exercising in Figure E14.9.

Interestingly, evidence suggests that mental capacities also may benefit from continued mental exercise throughout life. A number of psychological studies have demonstrated that people who continue to challenge their minds retain a much higher ability for dealing with new information and adjusting to new situations and challenges as they age. Two activities that are known to improve general mental abilities are playing bridge and learning a foreign language.

A common theme of most aspects of self-maintenance emerges. Self-maintenance is at least partially under the conscious control of the individuals themselves. Of course, a fetus or a young child must rely on the care and judgment of the adults responsible for her or him. As individuals approach maturity,

Figure E14.9 Seniors exercising.
Exercising throughout life provides both physical and psychological benefits.

however, they are expected to take responsibility for making intelligent decisions about maintaining their mental and physical health. ◆

Culture: The Great Shaper of Life

Personal Journal Entry: 5 April

Well, I'm getting the hang of observing humans. I think I probably make the best observations with infants and young children and then with older adults. I think it is probably hardest to observe people closest to my own age. I find myself comparing my own thinking and behaviors with theirs too much, and forget to focus on them.

I just got a letter from Malcolm, a friend who is in graduate school in California. He has an even bigger challenge. He is studying anthropology and is doing some field work in New Guinea and the surrounding area. He was describing to me how hard it is to study people from another culture. He says that when you are just beginning to learn about another culture, it is natural to fill in the gaps in your understanding with what is familiar from your own culture. He points out, however, that by doing so, you often develop an inaccurate picture of the culture you are trying to learn about.

I remember from my anthropology course last semester that it is important to try to put your own cultural values aside. You need to learn about another culture from the perspective of how certain behaviors and attitudes work within that other culture—to whatever extent that is possible. Of course, this is tricky. But Malcolm explained in his letter how cool it is to learn not just about the differences, but that, in spite of those differences, humans from all over the earth have many things in common.

I also remember learning about the work of Urie Bronfenbrenner. In 1979, he proposed an ecological approach to the study of development (see Figure E14.10). Bronfenbrenner points out that an individual is embedded in a set of nested environments. The environments influence each other, and together influence the development of an individual.

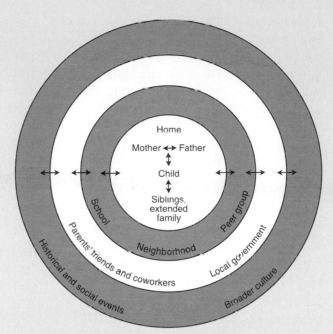

Source. Kopp, C. and J. Krakow (1982), *Child Development in the Social Context.* Addison-Wesley Publishing Company, Inc.

Figure E14.10 This diagram represents a simplified version of Urie Bronfenbrenner's ecological approach to development. As a child develops, she or he is influenced by each of these environments.

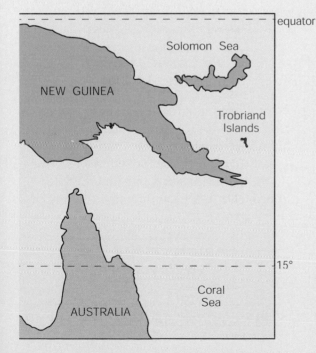

Figure E14.11 The Trobriand Islands. The Trobriands are a group of small islands off the east coast of New Guinea.

Personal Journal Entry: 15 May

I just got another letter from Malcolm. He now is spending time with the modern-day Trobriand Islanders (see Figure E14.11). That reminded me of the traditional Trobriand society that we had studied in our class, so I sent him the following copy of my notes from class last semester.

Anthropology 220 11 November

Trobriand Islanders

In general, traditional societies are societies that have not been influenced by the modern or Western cultures around them. Because we live in an extremely mobile world, most traditional cultures have had contact with modern cultures. But the timing and the extent of this contact have varied.

In traditional Trobriand society, children were usually weaned from breast-feeding by the time they were 2. They usually were weaned by being sent to sleep with their father or their maternal grandmother. When the children turned 4 or 5, they began to spend time with a children's group that had quite a bit of independence. They stayed with this group until puberty. On any given day, the children might remain with their parents or go with their group as they chose.

When the children stayed at home, the parents gave the children miniature tools and showed them how to plant crops and do other adult work. When the boys reached 6, their maternal uncles (their mothers' brothers) took more and more charge over their training. After the boys reached puberty, they still ate at home, but began sleeping in special bachelors' huts with several other boys their own age. This also was the time when the boys began to participate in the regular occupations of adult men.

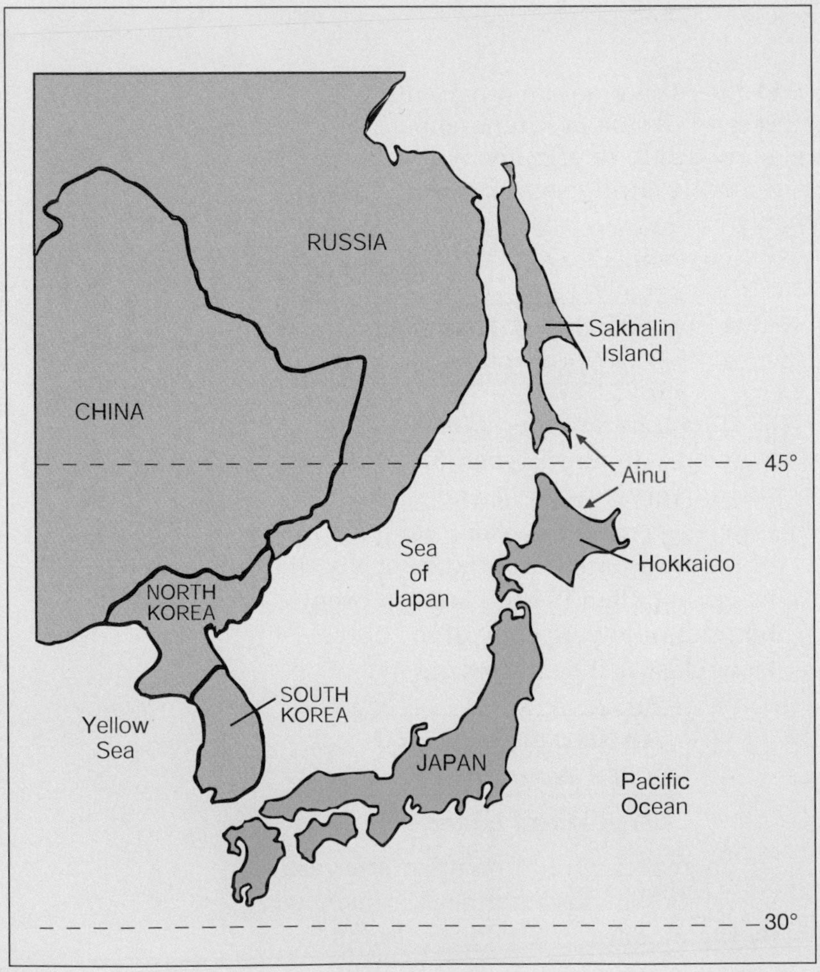

After girls reached puberty, they often joined their boyfriends in the bachelors' huts at night, but could still sleep at home whenever they wanted. At this time, they began to do more adult women's work in the home.

After several years of informal relationships, a pair of adolescents would form a long-term relationship and begin to appear together in public. This act was a signal that they were ready to marry. If both young people consented, the family would build them a hut of their own near a maternal uncle of the boy, and the couple would begin adult life together.

In cases of divorce, which were usually at the woman's request, all of the children would stay with their mother. In this society, grandparents had little to do with the training of children, and respect for elders was not highly valued.

Personal Journal Entry: 16 May

As I was looking through the notes from my class to send to Malcolm, I came across notes about other cultures as well. I read through them and again was struck by the different ways in which people approach life. The following is a copy of those notes.

Anthropology 220
18 November

Ainu—People of Northern Japan

The Ainu were a traditional hunting and fishing people who lived in small coastal settlements in far northern Japan (see Figure E14.12). Mothers often

Figure E14.12 The Ainu lived in small coastal settlements in far northern Japan and on the southern tip of Sakhalin Island.

breast-fed their children until the age of 4 or 5, and families traced their descent through the female side.

Small children played with carved fish, toy boats, and other toys that resembled objects that they would use later when they became adults. Older boys played with miniature hunting weapons, and girls played with dolls. Both girls and boys lived at home during childhood. Usually, the grandparents would instruct the children in the proper behavior and the duties expected of people in Ainu society. One of the most important behaviors was respect for elders.

When boys were about 5, they were allowed to watch the men prepare for fishing expeditions. At about 12 or 13, they began going out in the ocean with the adult men. When boys turned 15, they started wearing their hair as the adult men did. They began to let it grow long and grew a mustache and beard as well. Girls began learning household chores when they turned 5 or 6. At 13, the girls began to receive facial tattoos. A few years later, when the tattoos were complete (see Figure E14.13), they put on adult women's clothing. (The Ainu believed that tattoos in conspicuous places would keep evil spirits at bay.)

Young couples usually courted with little involvement of their parents and usually married by the time they were 16 or 17. When a child was born, both the new father and new mother would spend a period of time at home and would not engage in their usual activities. Either partner could end the marriage if she or he wanted. If this happened, the daughters would live with their mother, and the sons would live with their father.

Gusii—People of Kenya

Among the traditional Gusii of Kenya (see Figure E14.14 for location), people lived in farming homesteads as extended families. Usually one man was the head of

Figure E14.13 When Ainu girls began to mature, they started receiving tattoos. The Ainu believed that the tattoos would keep evil spirits away.

these extended families. The family might include his wives and their children as well as his married sons and their wives and children. People traced their descent entirely through the male line.

Generally, children were weaned when their mother became pregnant again, which might be anywhere from 1 to 3 years. Children stayed close to home and had duties to perform. As soon as they turned 5, the girls began to take care of the infants, and the young boys helped with the cattle. Both girls and boys worked in the fields from the time they were about 6 or 7 years old.

The grandparents generally were friendly and good-humored. But the children's own father was a strong authority figure whom the children both respected and feared. When the boys turned 7 or 8, they began living in a separate children's house on the homestead.

Girls were formally initiated into womanhood when they were only 8 or 9, as soon as they began to show a strong

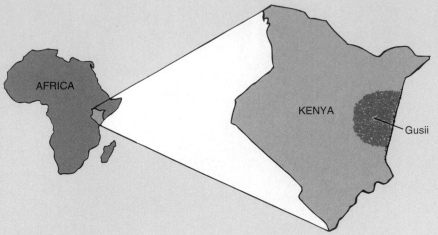

Figure E14.14   The Gusii of Kenya.

interest in women's duties. Boys were formally initiated into manhood when they were between 10 and 12. After special initiation ceremonies, there would be a period of seclusion and then a formal public appearance. At this point, the boys and girls would be welcomed as adult members of society.

After a few years of brief relationships, a young man would choose a girl as a prospective wife. He would send someone to inquire about her background. This person also would find out the formal price (in cattle) that her family would expect in return for her hand in marriage. If everyone agreed and the young man's family had paid the price, the groom and his family would come and take the bride to his home. It was a tradition that the bride would pretend to put up a fight rather than go willingly.

After a girl was married, she would remain with her new husband for a month. But then she would return to her father's home for about 2 months. During this time, she could request that the marriage be dissolved if she were truly unhappy. She also might leave her husband later, especially if she did not become pregnant within a year or so. In all cases, the children from a marriage legally belonged to the father.

The Amish in America

The Amish are a present-day traditional culture that exists in North America side by side with modern American culture (refer to Figure E14.15). The Amish are of Swiss and German descent and speak both English and a particular dialect of German. They refer to all members of the modern American culture as "the English."

They reject many aspects of the dominant culture and prefer simplicity. In general, Amish people avoid any use of electric power other than some batteries they use in the home. They travel in horse-drawn buggies and do not own or operate automobiles. (However, they will hire or accept rides in cars and buses when necessary.) They farm using horse-powered cultivating methods or else are carpenters or craftspeople.

Amish children dress almost as miniature adults as soon as they are old enough to be out of diapers (see Figure E14.16). They are regarded with great affection by the adults. Children are encouraged to play but also to be responsible for many chores around the farmstead.

At around 5, the children begin formal schooling. In the United States, the Supreme Court has recognized the right of the Amish to run and administer their own system of schools. These are staffed by Amish teachers. These teachers are usually young women who are not yet married.

The children study English, practical arithmetic, High German (which is necessary to read their religious books), geography, basic science, and several

Figure E14.15 Amish communities like this one in Lancaster County, Pennsylvania, exist throughout North America.

other subjects. The goal of all of their studies is to provide the children with the knowledge that they will need to function successfully in Amish society and to deal with the surrounding culture.

The Amish consider their society a community of equals and they frown on pride. In school, then, they expect the bright students who finish their lessons quickly to help the slower schoolmates

Figure E14.16 At a very young age, Amish children are dressed in styles similar to the adults.

with their work so that the whole group can advance together. The Amish believe that formal education should end with the eighth grade to avoid the possibility of the children becoming too worldly.

When Amish children are not in school, they spend time playing and learning about the skills of adult life. It is not unusual to see a young Amish boy of 10 driving a five-horse hitch of big draft animals and plowing a field by himself. And Amish girls of the same age are expected to handle a big garden or care for a group of younger children.

When their formal education is over, Amish youngsters work full time at home where they learn agricultural skills. The Amish believe that a person must be a mature adult, usually in his or her early 20s, in order to freely choose to accept formal baptism into the Amish community. (Formal baptism means a commitment to completely reject the forbidden aspects of the outside culture.) Therefore, young people between 16 and 22 have more freedom to experiment with the outside culture than either young children or baptized adults. This period is described by a Germanic term that roughly translates as "running-around-time." Young Amish men often spruce up their buggies in ways that would never be tolerated later and may dress in clothes like those of the "English" teenagers. These young men often work at town jobs in construction. Some may even own a car, which they generally keep somewhere other than at home.

Girls often make and wear brightly colored dresses that would be completely unacceptable at other ages. They may hold jobs as restaurant workers or store clerks. Groups of young people or courting couples may travel into cities to attend films, sporting events, or even dances. Their elders are aware of what is going on but, in general, regard it as a necessary period in the young people's

development. Those who finally decide not to receive baptism, but instead join the mainstream culture, usually remain on good terms with their families and often return to visit. Those who accept baptism but later decide to leave, however, are shunned (avoided).

When young Amish people marry, they take up a lifestyle like their parents and raise a family of their own. Amish elders are highly respected and generally turn over the responsibility of running the farm when the youngest child is old enough to take over. At this time, the elders move from the main house into a small one that is located nearby. They take an active role in raising and teaching their grandchildren and are always on hand to lend advice and help around the farm.

Personal Journal Entry: 19 May

Because I have been making observations of humans and learning about many related aspects of human growth and development, it has been interesting to read over my notes from anthropology. It has been clear to me that fundamental aspects of human biology are responsible for both similarities and differences in the way humans develop. It now is becoming clear to me that all human cultures have developed ways of responding to developmental milestones and the processes involved as humans develop. But, because different cultures have unique environments and histories, they respond to the stages of development in diverse ways. ◆

UNIT 6

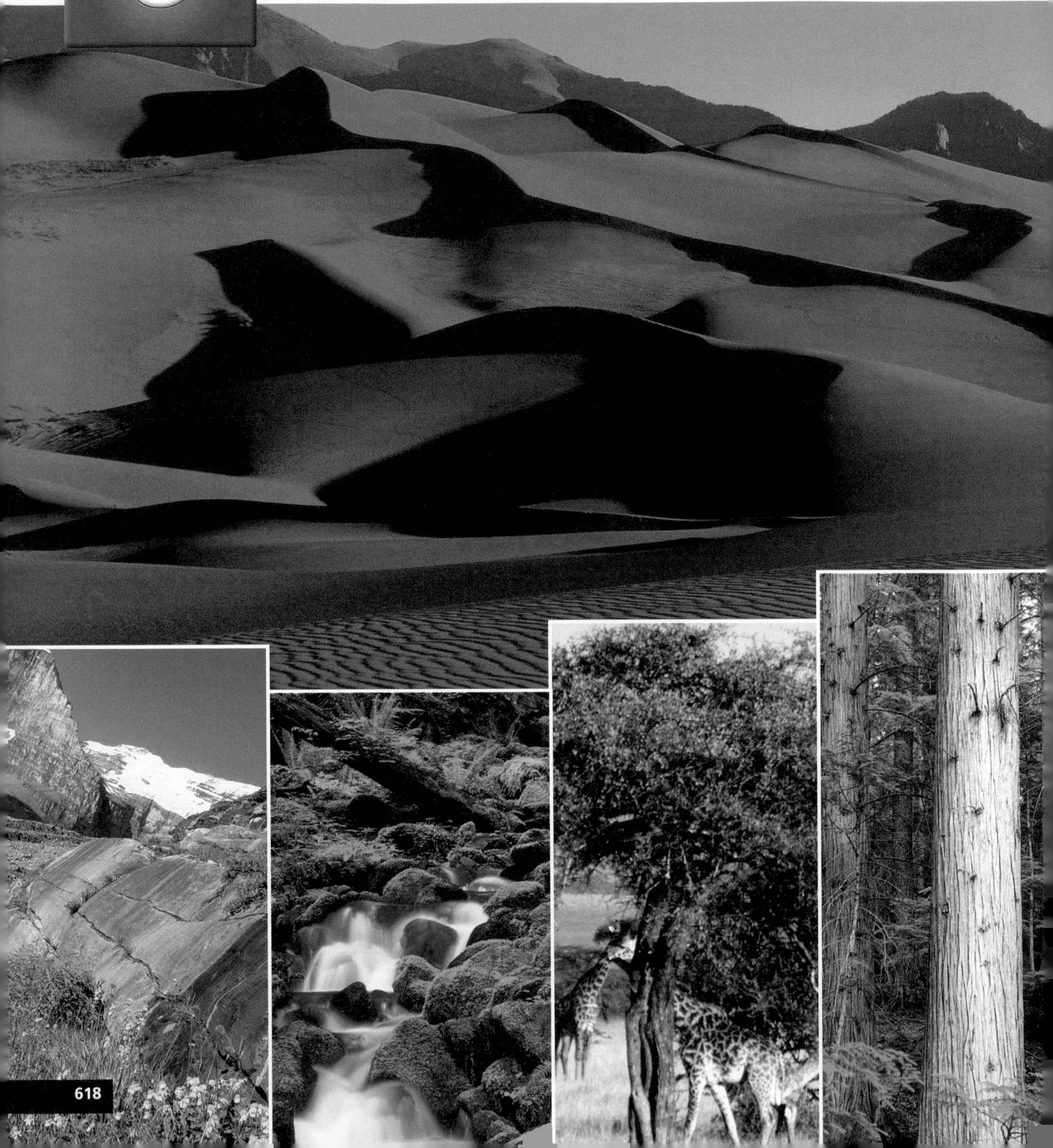

Ecology: Interaction and Interdependence in Living Systems

What happens when developers cut down the trees along a riverbank? The trees are gone, you say. But what effect does the loss of these trees have on the river's ecosystem? How has a web of dependence been altered? In this unit, you will explore the concepts of interaction and interdependence in living systems. You will also investigate the issue of human influence in the biosphere.

By the end of this unit, you should understand that

- a community of organisms interacts with the abiotic environment to form ecosystems,
- ecosystems are complex, but it is possible to analyze them,
- population size is affected by carrying capacity,
- ecosystems can be modified by human actions, and
- human actions follow from decisions.

You also will continue to design and conduct experiments, evaluate explanations, and explore the relationship between public policy and scientific investigation.

> "We do not inherit this land from our ancestors; we borrow it from our children."
>
> *Haida Indian saying*

Interdependence among Organisms in the Biosphere

Chapter 15

Life in Havasu Canyon. Life in a forest. Life on a bustling city street. Life in the oceans. Life in a refugee camp in Africa. Life on a farm in rural Ohio. How do the organisms within each of these settings depend on one another for survival? How can such interdependence be described? What factors influence their interdependence?

In this chapter, you will learn about the interdependence of organisms in various ecosystems within the biosphere. First, you will seek evidence of communities and interactions in your own school yard or neighborhood. Next, you will study interactions in ecosystems throughout the world. You will further explore ecosystems by considering the types of resources that exist in them. You will then analyze the influences those resources have on communities of organisms. To apply your understanding of communities and resources, you will analyze patterns of population growth in a real group of people who lived on an island off the coast of South America. Finally, you will evaluate your understanding by describing how your critter will use resources and interact with other organisms in a particular ecosystem.

ACTIVITIES

Engage	Observing the World around Us
Explore	
Explore	Interactions in the World around Us
Explain	The Pasture Story
Elaborate	Mystery on Easter Island
Evaluate	Critters and Interdependence

Observing the World around Us

Imagine crawling out of bed in the morning. You flip on a light and your CD player and stroll to the bathroom as your CD player plays in the background. For breakfast you eat a bowl of cornflakes. It's an especially cold morning, so you fix yourself some hot chocolate. The television is blaring with news of an overnight fire in the nearby national forest. It's getting late. So you pack your lunch, fill the bird feeder outside your window, and rush off to catch the bus.

The interactions in that scenario are typical for some teenagers. In this activity, you will make observations and consider what interactions you see in the natural world.

PROCESS AND PROCEDURES

Go outside as your teacher directs. In your journal, record the following observations and answers to the questions:

1. Look carefully at the organisms around you. How many different types of organisms do you see? Look for 2 or more organisms that are interacting with each other.

2. Use your drawing skills to create a quick, 2-minute drawing of 2 or more interacting organisms that capture your attention. Add labels or a brief explanation for the interaction.

3. Close your eyes. Spend a few minutes listening for sounds made by living organisms. Write a brief description for how 1 organism used sound to interact with other organisms.

4. Focus on the smells of the natural world. How many different odors can you detect? What might be the function of the odors you smell? Write a brief description for how 1 odor you smelled may be evidence for an organism interacting with other organisms in its community.

5. Name and describe or draw 2 different organisms around you that are likely prey for other organisms. Explain how taste might influence how an organism interacts with potential predators.

6. Name and describe or draw 2 different organisms that have a distinguishing texture. Write a brief description for how each texture may encourage or discourage other organisms to touch it.

7. Name and describe or draw 1 organism that you observe to be living in isolation from other organisms.

Analysis

1. Think about the organism you observed and recorded in step 7. Explain whether you think it requires any interactions with other organisms to survive.

2. During this activity, do you think that you overlooked any major groups of organisms? Explain your answer.

Interactions in the World around Us

Why might an ecologist study a certain area? There are a variety of reasons. Say you were an ecologist studying the area in this chapter's engage activity. You would attempt to describe and understand the interrelationships that exist between organisms and their environment. First, you would gather information about the organisms and their environment. Then, you might compare this area to different regions to look for similarities, differences, and patterns. Finally, you would try to explain the patterns you observed. You might run experiments to test your hypotheses.

In this activity, you will practice thinking like an ecologist. You will look for patterns and explanations for the interactions you observed in the engage activity. You also will have the opportunity to compare your observations with a series of DVD images from around the world that represent a wide variety of interactions in many different settings.

Figure 15.1 Some ecologists analyze the complexity of an ecosystem by concentrating on the changes in quantity and quality of one particular component of the ecosystem.

Materials

DVD and player (watch as a team)

PROCESS AND PROCEDURES

1. With your partner, discuss the observations you recorded during the engage activity. Consider the following. Be prepared to share your ideas with the rest of your class.

   a. What types of interactions did you see between organisms where only 1 organism appeared to benefit from the interaction? What types of interactions seemed to benefit all organisms involved?

   b. Give examples of odors that lead to interactions between organisms. Explain whether your examples attract or discourage interactions.

   c. Name and describe interactions that are influenced by taste and sound.

   d. Name at least 5 populations and 3 nonliving components that are part of the area where you made your observations.

   e. Compare and discuss your answers to the engage Analysis questions.

2. Participate in a class discussion about your observations and answers as your teacher directs.

   As you share ideas with your classmates, consider how you might describe the ecosystem where you made your observations.

3. In your journal, use your own words to write a definition for the term *ecosystem*.

4. Obtain a copymaster with 4 tasks. Record the assigned examples from the DVD segment "Images from around the World."

   In your journal, make a simple table to help you take brief notes about examples you see in the DVD while you watch (see Figure 15.2).

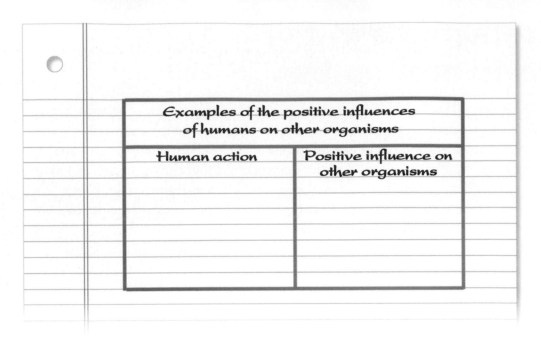

Figure 15.2 Sample table for a sample task.

5. Watch the DVD segment. Pay particular attention to interactions that involve humans. Provide examples of the influences assigned on your task cards.

   Briefly, record examples in your table.

6. Discuss your DVD observations with your partner. Prepare to share your examples with the rest of your class.

   How many different ecosystems did you and your partner recognize?

7. Participate in a class discussion. Focus on identifying the interactions in the ecosystems shown in the DVD segment.

Analysis

Topic: biosphere
Go to: www.scilinks.org
Code: human3E624

1. Read the scenario *Early Morning Reflections* on page 625. Think about the interactivity examples from that reading, your observations from the engage activity, and the images and in the DVD. Write one or two logical conclusions that you can make from those examples about the interactions taking place in the world.

2. The term **biosphere** refers to the portion of the earth where organisms naturally live. It begins in the lower atmosphere and extends deep into the earth's crust. Do you think that humans have more or less influence on the biosphere than other organisms? Explain your response.

3. Do you think that humans have a responsibility to monitor how they influence the biosphere? Explain your response.

SCENARIO

Early Morning Reflections

Dear Senator Wilks,

I just returned from an interesting stay at a ranch in northern Nevada. I would like to share with you some reflections about my visit to your part of the state.

The landscape of northern Nevada is spacious and stark. Yet there is still something splendid about the place. I spent the weekend with my good friend and his family at their ranch on the Marys River floodplain. I was inspired by their down-to-earth approach to life and genuine concern for the fragile river ecosystem that is part of their vast 7,000 acre ranch.

Marys River winds its way through the ranch. As my friend showed me around, I noticed a group of willow trees lining the riverbank. But farther upriver and downriver, there were almost no willows. I wondered why this was. When I asked, I saw a faint smirk cross my friend's face, followed by a touch of sadness. He told me that back in the '70s, many of the farmers along the river began cutting down the willows because they thought they sucked up too much water. They thought that by cutting down the willows, they would increase their crop yields. My friend explained that it may have worked that way for a while, but there were unintended consequences when the river flooded. It flooded in 1983 and 1984, after the willows along the river on most farms had been long gone. My friend's family never cut the willows, and their ranch had the least damage of any along the river. Others, where the willows were cut, had great damage. The willows, along with the native hay meadow vegetation, helped stabilize the riverbanks and the floodplain soils. Together they reduced erosion and other flood damage. But my friend said there was even more to the story. To show me what he meant, he took me down to the riverbank.

The variety of lush vegetation that I saw in addition to the willows amazed me. I tried to figure out why there was so much vegetation there. I saw beaver dams built across the river at various places and although I didn't see any beaver, I did see two otters.

Soon my friend began to fill in between the lines. He explained that the willows and other vegetation along the river provide material with which the beavers can build their dams. With the dams in place, the water becomes somewhat deeper just upriver from the dam. The amount of groundwater increases in these areas as well. This additional water is what supports the lush vegetation. As he talked, I made mental notes of all the evidence I saw. My friend explained that the willows and other overhanging plants also shade the river so that it stays cooler. This keeps the level of oxygen higher.

I started nodding my head. I was beginning to get the picture. Willows for shade. More oxygen in the water. Deeper water levels. With these things, the river could support more life, including aquatic plants and fish. This affects the entire food chain to the level of the beaver (an herbivore) and the otter (an omnivore that loves fish).

Without the willows, the ranchers lost out during the spring floods. But the beaver also lost out because without willows there was no material for building dams. Without the dams and the shade from vegetation, the river was too shallow and warm to support much aquatic life either. So the fish lost out. Without the fish, the otter lost out too because it had almost nothing to eat.

The river environment surrounding this ranch is quite barren, especially to the west. But my friend and his family have been stewards of the river and the land—and their stretch of the river is fertile and beautiful. I would like to encourage you to consider how the government can reward and encourage good stewardship.

Sincerely,
Jada Cameron

The Pasture Story

In the previous activity, you studied some of the complex interactions that take place in a variety of ecosystems. One organism's actions influence those of another. Populations influence each other as well. Humans influence other humans, other species, and the nonliving components of the ecosystems where we live. In some situations, we feel that we can control the influence that other humans have on our lives. In most situations, the decisions made by other people in our communities have significant influence on our lives. In this activity, you will study a dramatization of farmers grazing cows on a shared pasture. This will help you think about the factors that influence how individuals share resources.

Materials

The Commons CD (1 per team)
computers with CD-ROM drives (1 per team)
Copymaster *Pasture Profits* (2 per team for each simulation run)

PROCESS AND PROCEDURES

1. Work in teams as your teacher directs. View the video "The Pasture Story" on *The Commons* CD.

2. With your teammates, discuss what happened in the video and why.

3. Go to the "Pasture Profits" simulation on *The Commons* CD. Work with your teammates to assume the role of a dairy farmer who, along with another dairy farmer, grazes cows on a commonly owned pasture.

   Divide your team into 2 groups. Have each group make the decisions for 1 of the dairy farmers. Read the opening screens of the simulation carefully. Follow the instructions provided.

4. Print individual and summary reports at the end of each simulation round. Graph the 4 sets of data on the summary report onto the Copymaster *Pasture Profits*.

   Follow your teacher's instructions to try 1 or more management options for the pasture. Work with your group to graph the results from each simulation run.

5. Analyze your graphs with your teammates. Discuss the following questions:

   a. Which management option scenario(s) protected the pasture?

   b. What is the relationship between the amount of food available per cow and the number of cows?

   c. What is the relationship between the amount of food available and production of milk per cow?

d. The maximum number of cows that the pasture can support without destroying its ability to renew itself is called its **carrying capacity**. Using your graphs, determine the carrying capacity for cows on the simulated pasture.

> You may want to look at other teams' graphs for additional information.

e. For each different management option available in the simulation, explain what, if any, change takes place in the carrying capacity.

6. Read the background information provided in "The Abundant Earth" on the enrichment level of *The Commons* CD (see Figure 15.3). In your own words, explain what a natural resource is. Record your explanation in your journal.

7. Participate in a class discussion of steps 5 and 6 as your teacher directs.

Analysis

With your team, consider the following questions. Record your answers in your journal.

1. List three examples of resources in the modern world that humans use like the commonly owned pasture in the video. Explain how people manage each example.

2. Write a paragraph that summarizes the challenges you and your teammates faced in maximizing personal profits on a pasture owned in common. In your summary, include a response to this question: Is it easier to make decisions about how to best manage the pasture if you know what the rate of resource consumption and carrying capacity are for the pasture?

3. Explain the difference between biotic and abiotic resources.

4. Are renewable resources more likely to be biotic or abiotic? Explain your answer.

5. What is the relationship between resources and carrying capacity in a particular ecosystem?

6. In what ways is the simulation "Pasture Profits" a realistic model of a pasture owned and used in common? In what ways is it unrealistic?

> Record and explain at least two realistic and two unrealistic aspects of the model.

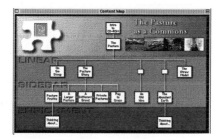

Topic: carrying capacity
Go to: www.scilinks.org
Code: human3E627

Figure 15.3 Navigating in *The Commons* CD. Bring up the content map for the segment being used. (The *up arrow* in the lower right corner of the screen loads the content map.) Click on any piece of the puzzle in the content map to jump to that part of the CD.

Mystery on Easter Island

Elaborate

Islands are intriguing ecosystems to study because they are somewhat isolated. Isolation makes the island's resources easier to measure. It is especially interesting to study the patterns of population growth for land animals that are confined to an island. Such is the case for a human population who lived on Easter Island from AD 500 to the present. This activity will give you an opportunity to examine the mystery that surrounds Easter Island. You will study data about the history of its human populations and reflect on some of the interactions that took place in that ecosystem.

THE MYSTERY

Noted writer Jared Diamond called Easter Island "the world's most isolated scrap of habitable land." Easter Island is located in the Pacific Ocean, more than 3,218 kilometers (2,000 miles) west of South America. The island has an area of about 166 square kilometers (64 square miles). Its subtropical location gives it a mild climate. And its volcanic origin provides fertile soil.

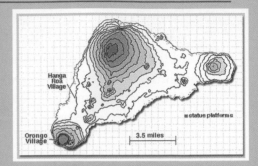

Figure 15.4 Easter Island is located more than 3,218 kilometers (2,000 miles) west of South America. It is roughly triangular, with sides of 18, 18, and 24 kilometers (11, 11, and 15 miles). How would you calculate the surface area of Easter Island?

Despite its mild climate and fertile soil, when Europeans first reached the island in 1722, their first impression was of a barren wasteland. The island was without a single tree or bush more than 3 meters (10 feet) tall. There were no native animals larger than insects. The people had no real source of firewood to warm themselves. Chickens were their only domestic animals. Yet, the evidence indicates that at one time in its history the island offered abundant food and building materials. This was when the first Polynesian colonists arrived, some 1,400 years earlier. So what happened?

The first colonizers traveled to the island in double canoes. They arrived at the roughly triangular island in approximately AD 450 (see Figure 15.4). When these first colonists came to the island, it was covered by a forest dominated by a now-extinct species of giant palm tree (see Figure 15.5). These abundant palm trees were an important resource for the colonists. In fact, ancient Easter Islanders created rock art showing images of palm trees and other important island resources such as birds, fish, turtles, and dolphins (see Figure 15.6).

Figure 15.5 This Chilean palm is similar to the now-extinct species of giant palm that was abundant when colonizers first moved to Easter Island.

Figure 15.6 Petroglyphs at Orongo.

The giant palm is similar in appearance to the Chilean wine palm. We can look at the Chilean palm and make inferences about the characteristics of the Easter Island palm. The Chilean wine palm is one of the largest palms in the world. It stands more than 20 meters (about 65 feet) tall and has a trunk diameter of 1 meter (about 3 feet) or more. The trunk has a characteristic bulge, and the large leaves are featherlike. South Americans use the palm sap to make honey and wine.

What happened to the population of colonizers on Easter Island? Why did the giant palms that once covered the island become extinct? Visitors to Easter Island have been asking these and many other questions about the mysterious island for hundreds of years. For some questions, we can only speculate answers. However, evidence from archaeological digs and inferences based on population studies provide important clues for uncovering Easter Island's history.

Materials

The Commons CD (1 per team)
computers with CD-ROM drives (1 per team)

PROCESS AND PROCEDURES

1. With your teammates, study the graph in Figure 15.7. Answer questions a–j.

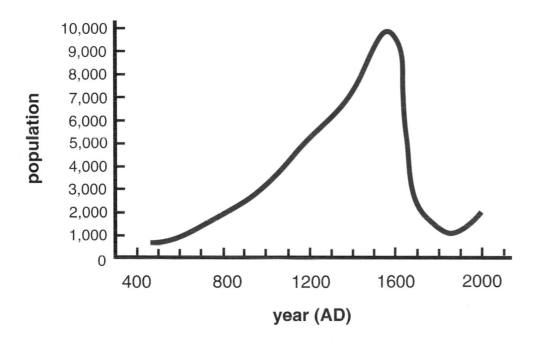

Population Growth on Easter Island

Figure 15.7 Population growth for the first Easter Island colonizers.
Researchers Paul Bahn and John Flenley used historical studies and population formulas to infer population graphs for Easter Island during its first settlement.

a. What was the approximate size of the colonizing population in the year 450?

b. What was the size of the population in the year 850?

c. What was the difference in the number of people between 450 and 850?

d. What was the average annual increase in the number of people between 450 and 850?

e. What was the difference in population size between the years 850 and 1250?

f. What was the average annual increase in the number of people between 850 and 1250?

g. What was the average annual increase in the number of people between 1250 and 1600?

h. During which 1 of the following 3 periods was the increase in the human population greatest: 450–850, 850–1250, or 1250–1600?

i. What was the greatest number of people found on Easter Island between 450 and 2000? In approximately what year did this happen?

j. By the mid 1700s, only 2,000 Easter Islanders were still alive. The population continued to decline to approximately 100 people during the next century. This was due in part to the slave trade and epidemics brought by Europeans. What is the average annual decrease in the number of people between 1600 and 1950?

2. Refer to the vegetation charts and information in Figure 15.8. Write a brief description of the Easter Island ecosystem. Include at least 3 examples of biotic and 3 examples of abiotic resources that likely influenced the colonizing population.

3. At one time in history, hundreds of giant stone statues overlooked the Easter Island landscape. Hundreds more were being carved in quarries, moved along roads, or waiting to be erected. Ruins of these monoliths remain on the island today.

Study the "Easter Island" segment on *The Commons* CD. You will learn more about the islanders, the mysterious statues, the land, and the vegetation.

4. Discuss with your partner the changes that took place on Easter Island after colonization. In your journal, write 1 or 2 paragraphs that summarize the changes in vegetation on Easter Island between 950 and 1980. Explain what you think caused those changes.

Consider the interactions and interdependence that took place between the people as well as between humans and the shared biotic and abiotic resources.

5. Participate in a class discussion of steps 1–4.

Topic: population
Go to: www.scilinks.org
Code: human3E630

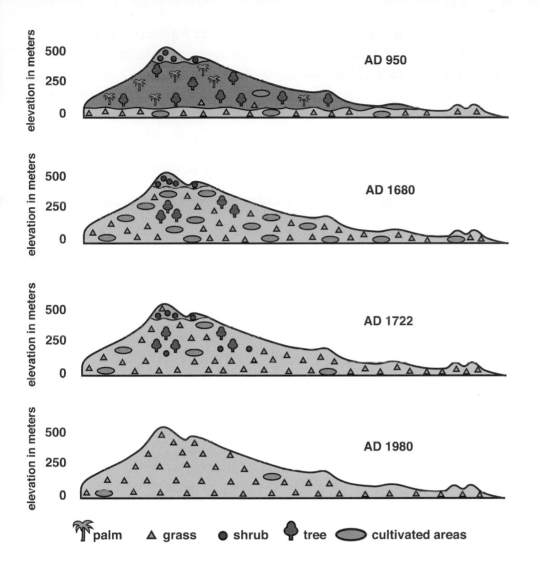

Figure 15.8 Easter Island vegetation distribution between AD 950 and AD 1980. Biologists study ancient pollen and spore samples to determine the historical vegetation distribution.

palm ▲ **grass** ● **shrub** 🌳 **tree** ⬭ **cultivated areas**

Analysis

Read the essay *Interdependence Involves Limiting Factors and Carrying Capacity* (page 650). Use it as a resource for the following questions: **PAGE 650**

1. Think about the growth in human population between 1000 and 1600. Compare that with the rate of growth during the first years that the colonizers were on the island. What might account for this large increase?

2. What factor or factors finally limited the growth of the human population? What other factors might limit the growth of a population? Give at least three specific examples.

3. Work with a partner to redraw the population growth graph in Figure 15.7. Color-code your graph so that each significant trend in the rate of growth is a different color.

   Create a legend that shows what type of growth rate happened during each different-colored period.

Figure 15.9 These monoliths (called *moai*) were carved with stone tools from compacted and hardened volcanic ash. They stand up to 11 meters (about 35 feet) tall and weigh up to 77 metric tons (85 short tons).

4. The maximum number of people that the island can support without destroying its ability to renew itself is called its carrying capacity. Add a line to your graph that shows where you think the island's carrying capacity for people was when the colonizers first landed on Easter Island. Label this line *initial carrying capacity*. Why did you draw your line there?

5. What evidence is there that the number of people on the island exceeded its carrying capacity?

6. Add another line to your graph. Show where you think the island's carrying capacity for people was after 1690. Label this line *later carrying capacity*. Why did you draw your line there?

   Write your explanation in your journal.

7. What does this study tell you about unchecked population growth?

8. Think about the relationship between the island's population size and resources-available-per-individual. How is that similar to the relationship between the number of cows and the common pasture from the previous activity? What do each of these relationships demonstrate?

Evaluate

Critters and Interdependence

It's time to evaluate what you have learned about interdependence among living organisms and the complex interactions that take place in communities and ecosystems. You will work in teams to create a story that describes interactions among various organisms and resources in a particular habitat. Those organisms will include your critter, other classmates' critters, humans, and other native organisms.

Materials   (per team, size will vary)

pencil and paper   descriptions and diagrams of your critter
colored pencils and markers   DVD and player (watch as a class)

Topic: ecosystem
Go to: www.scilinks.org
Code: human3E632

PROCESS AND PROCEDURES

Part A   Resources and Ecosystems

1. Watch the DVD segment "Ecosystems of the Earth." In your journal, record the name of each ecosystem. List at least 4 significant factors presently found there.

   Remember, include both biotic and abiotic factors.

2. Participate in a class discussion that your teacher guides. You will summarize the interactions and resources that characterize each of the ecosystems depicted in the DVD.

   Think about the main ideas of this chapter and how they relate to those ecosystems.

Part B   Critters in Ecosystems

1. Join with classmates who had the same habitat card as you in the activity *First Encounter with the Critter* in Chapter 3. Introduce your new teammates to your critter.

    Be sure to describe all the features of your critter in detail. Respond to any questions that your teammates might have.

2. Imagine that you, your teammates, and each teammate's critter are living together in the assigned habitat from Chapter 3. Consider what interactions might take place between the different populations.

3. With your team, hold a brainstorming session to generate ideas about the following:

    ◆ Possible interactions among the organisms that inhabit this ecosystem

    ◆ The biotic and abiotic resources that might exist

    ◆ The interdependence that might exist

    ◆ Adaptations that might evolve

    ◆ How humans from a variety of cultures might interact with other organisms in this environment

4. Obtain a rubric for this critter story from your teacher. Discuss the criteria with your teammates.

    Ask your teacher to clarify any questions that come up during your discussion that your team cannot answer fully.

5. Individually, write a story that features some of the ideas that your team suggested. Make sure it follows the criteria outlined in the rubric.

    Remember, your teacher will assess what you have learned from this chapter by reading your story.

Analysis

Reflect on the process you used to think about and write your story. Participate in a class discussion of the following questions:

1. What was the most challenging part of writing your story? Explain.

2. Which of the major concepts in this chapter did you have the most difficulty incorporating into the story? Explain.

3. You wrote about the interactions and interdependence of your organism with other organisms. You also wrote about the limiting factors at work and the carrying capacity of the environment. Which was easier to write about? Explain why.

4. What adaptations did you consider adding to your organism? Explain why you did or did not add them.

> Enjoy present pleasures in such a way as not to injure future ones.
>
> *Seneca (3 BC – AD 65)*

Decision Making in a Complex World

What do you think about when you look at this picture? From space, the earth might seem so large that human influence on the planet is minuscule. But don't be fooled. In this course, you have explored the tremendous diversity of life on earth. By now you probably appreciate that a vast number of interactions connect living organisms. Think about the interactions and interdependence among living organisms and between those organisms and the environment. These connections make possible the evolutionary processes that characterize the earth's biodiversity. Unfortunately, the complexity of these interactions makes it difficult for humans to predict how their actions will affect other organisms and the environment.

In this chapter, you will investigate decision making in a complex world. You will analyze some consequences of human actions on ecosystem interactions and resource distribution.

ACTIVITIES

Engage	Tri-Lakes: Asking Questions
Explore	Tri-Lakes: The Investigation
Explain	The Gulf of Maine
Elaborate	Are There Limits?
Evaluate	Tri-Lakes: Public Policy

Tri-Lakes: Asking Questions

Engage

If you are cold, you can probably identify the cause of your discomfort pretty easily. Perhaps your clothes aren't well suited to the weather. Maybe a cold wind is blowing around a leaky door on to your feet. If a baby cries, you can often figure out the problem by feeding, changing, or holding the infant until he or she stops crying. When a computer crashes, you may go through a series of steps to determine the cause and make necessary repairs.

These are examples of situations where figuring out the cause of a given problem is relatively straightforward. You engage in that type of troubleshooting every day. Many situations that affect your life, however, are much more complex. What about determining the causes for diseases or changes in the earth's atmosphere, for example? These situations involve many possible interacting influences. When researchers study complex systems, they must identify the many parts of the system. They must then try to limit the study to a few that can be managed or controlled.

You will practice these skills in this activity about the Tri-Lakes region. The Tri-Lakes situation is a model. It is not real. But it is similar to the situations faced in many communities. Residents around Lake Erie have successfully revitalized one of the Great Lakes that many thought was dead due to industrial pollution. The citizens of Sweden, Canada, Germany, and the northern United States have been studying the acidification of lakes in their countries. In some places, professional and citizen scientists have been able to reverse what some thought was an irreversible course of events leading to dead lakes. The types of questions raised by the Tri-Lakes Association could be asked in any community about many science and technology issues.

Figure 16.1 Tri-Lakes is a fictional lake system, but there are many lakes similar to it in the world.

PROCESS AND PROCEDURES

PAGE 653

1. Listen to or read to yourself the letter from the Tri-Lakes Association on page 637.

2. Read the essay *Systems Analysis* on page 653. Consider your own approach to investigating the Tri-Lakes system.

   You will be trying to answer the questions asked by the Tri-Lakes Association regarding the Tri-Lakes system. As you read the essay, think about the steps you will take to answer those questions.

3. In your journal, create a list of at least 10 biotic and abiotic components in the Tri-Lakes ecological system.

   As you create your list, think about which components are most likely to affect the bass population positively or negatively.

4. Work with your partner to compare your lists and your ideas about which components might be important in determining the bass population size.

   Focus on particular topics or components that you think may be key to understanding the Tri-Lakes situation.

Analysis

For the next two activities, you will be working on the Tri-Lakes problem. You will think of questions, search for answers, and draw logical conclusions. As questions occur to you, be sure to record them in your journal. Leave space to add any possible explanations you may develop as you gather information.

SCENARIO

The Problem at Tri-Lakes
TRI-LAKES ASSOCIATION

Dear Biology Students at Tri-Lakes High:

The members of the Tri-Lakes Association are very concerned about a confusing problem we have in the Tri-Lakes region. In general, the fishing is good. But people are not catching as many bass as they did years ago. As a result, our reputation as the bass-fishing capital of the world is suffering. Reservations at local resorts are down by 25 percent. This has had disturbing financial consequences for our area.

I know that the biology classes at Tri-Lakes have kept records on the water quality of the lakes for many years. The members of the association have noticed something about the change in the number of fish being caught. This change seems to have happened along with, or as a result of, a number of other changes around the area. We hope that your ties to the lake and your scientific abilities will help us determine what is happening (or at least what questions we need to study).

The members of the association have made the following observations. We hope this information helps.

- Microorganisms such as Daphnia and Gammarus are less common in the lake.

- The lake is greener for more of the year than it used to be.

- The perch seem smaller and less colorful than in previous years. They also congregate in the hollows of discarded cinder blocks and hover in one place for a long time.

In addition to those observations, I am sending some data packets with information gathered from local papers and lake study records. These packets contain information that the association members pulled together in an attempt to understand what might be happening to our region. Some of the data may look familiar. We pulled some information from your annual report to the association. We hope that this combination of local, national, and historical data will provide enough clues for you to identify our problem(s) so that we can begin working on solutions.

Our next association meeting is in 2 weeks. We look forward to hearing from you at that time. Because many of you and your families are involved in the fishing and resort industries, I am sure you understand the seriousness of this situation. I eagerly await your response.

Sincerely,

Chris Tackle

Chris Tackle
President, Tri-Lakes Association

1. In your journal, record the Tri-Lakes questions that you can identify at this point based on your discussion of the components.

    Use information from Chris Tackle's letter and your own knowledge to come up with logical questions about the Tri-Lakes issue. Record each question as precisely as possible. After you have written at least two questions on your own, discuss them with your partner. Add any additional questions that come to mind.

2. Write a brief paragraph in your journal that describes your prediction or tentative explanation for what you think may be causing the Tri-Lakes problems.

    Remember, these are early ideas that are based on minimal evidence. You likely will revise your ideas as you gather more information.

Explore

Tri-Lakes: The Investigation

Think about the essay you read on systems analysis. One of the essential steps before analyzing any complex system is that the scientist must understand as much as possible about the initial behavior of the system. As an ecologist studying the Tri-Lakes system, you will collect as much pertinent information as possible from a variety of sources. In this activity, you will review written resources about the Tri-Lakes region in a way similar to the research process that an ecologist would undertake. After reviewing the current news and data about Tri-Lakes, you will conduct an investigation to learn about the effects of altering components in that system. Imagine yourself as an ecologist. You lower various probes into the water, sample water quality at different places and depths, and observe system components as you investigate the lake's ecosystem. Remember, keep asking questions and thinking critically.

Materials   (per team of 2)

safety goggles
data packet
glass stirring rods
dropping pipets
10-mL graduated cylinders
watch glasses
beaker labeled *Culture Water*
petri dish
nonmercury thermometers or thermisters
beaker labeled *Used Culture*
forceps
hand lenses or stereomicroscopes
vinegar in dropping bottles
pH strips or pH probe ware
microorganisms such as *Daphnia* or *Gammarus*
hot water

PROCESS AND PROCEDURES

The process of answering questions scientifically requires a scientist to gather as much information or data as possible. This information may come from several sources. It may be other scientists' written records, general informational articles,or it may be firsthand observations. In this activity, you will use a variety of methods to gather information.

1. Pick up a data packet from your teacher.

   Each data packet contains information sheets.

2. Review the titles listed in the need to know box. Choose the information sheets most likely to be helpful to you.

3. Divide the work in half. Study your half of the packet; your partner will study the other half. As you read, take notes and record questions you have about the information.

NEED TO KNOW

Information Sheets

Study the information sheets that you decide are likely to help solve the mystery at Tri-Lakes. You also can use other available resources.

1. Tri-Lakes Advertisement
2. *Tri-Lakes Tribune* Article, January 29, 1996
3. *Tri-Lakes Tribune* Article, June 17, 2000
4. Location of Tri-Lakes Resorts
5. Zone Map of the Average Temperature
6. Largemouth Bass
7. Yellow Perch
8. Total Number of Fish Caught Annually, 1982–2002
9. Number of Largemouth Bass and Yellow Perch Caught Annually, 1982–2002
10. Average Length of Fish Caught Compared with Legal Limit
11. Table of Dissolved Oxygen and pH for Tri-Lakes, 1982–2002
12. Algae and Cyanobacteria
13. *Daphnia*
14. *Gammarus*
15. Pesticides
16. Acid Precipitation

You do not have to read everything in the data packet. Compare the titles of the information sheets with the questions you raised. Which information sheets are likely to be helpful for answering your question? Sort through the large quantities of information critically to find the important pieces. This is a valuable scientific skill.

4. When you are finished studying the packet, meet with your partner and share what you have learned. Exchange information and learn things that might help answer a question you have raised. Add that information to your journal.

At the end of this activity, you will rate yourself and your partner on how well you taught each other about your information sheets.

5. In your journal, review your initial ideas about the Tri-Lakes problem from the Analysis in the engage activity. Revise or add to your explanation to reflect your current understanding.

NEED TO KNOW

Helpful Background Information

pH is a measure of how acidic a solution is. The pH scale goes from 0 to 14. The lower the number, the more acidic the solution is.

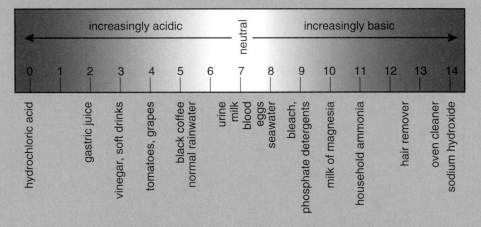

increasingly acidic — neutral — increasingly basic

0   1   2   3   4   5   6   7   8   9   10   11   12   13   14

hydrochloric acid · gastric juice · vinegar, soft drinks · tomatoes, grapes · black coffee / normal rainwater · urine · milk · blood · eggs · seawater · bleach, phosphate detergents · milk of magnesia · household ammonia · hair remover · oven cleaner · sodium hydroxide

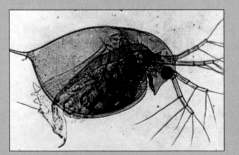

Daphnia. Can you find the heart, gut, and brood pouch on your *Daphnia*? *Daphnia* are about 1 mm (about 0.04 inches) long.

Gammarus. *Gammarus* are about 4 mm (about 0.16 inches) long. What features are easier to see because the photograph is enlarged?

You must gather as much information as possible if you are going to apply a limited system analysis to Tri-Lakes. A limited system analysis involves your interpretation of how the system will react when any of its components are altered. For the Tri-Lakes system, it is important to understand the microorganisms that Chris Tackle mentioned. The next steps in this activity will help you learn more about them.

6. Identify a question about the microorganisms that you hope to answer by experimentation. Record this question in your journal if it is different from the questions you already recorded.

7. Write in your journal a procedure to use to gather data about your question. After you have written the procedure, ask your teacher to approve it.

The following protocols provide 2 examples of methods for studying the microorganisms *Daphnia* and *Gammarus*. Don't forget, a protocol is not a replacement for your own experiment. However, it may provide a valuable technique for you to incorporate into your work.

PROTOCOL

Protocol 1: Microorganisms and pH

SAFETY: Put on your safety goggles.

1. Place about 15 mL of culture water in a watch glass.
2. Use the dropping pipet to carefully transfer 2 or 3 microorganisms from the culture to the watch glass.
3. Observe the microorganisms with a hand lens or stereomicroscope long enough to determine their behavior.
4. Record this behavior in your journal.
5. Measure the pH of the water in the watch glass. Record this value in your journal but not in your table.
6. Use the dropper to add 1 drop of vinegar at a time. This will gradually change the pH of the water by 0.5 pH units. Stir the water after each drop of vinegar. Wait 30 seconds before adding the next drop. With pH strips or a pH probe, measure the pH each time you stir in 1 drop of vinegar.

CAUTION: Vinegar is a *mild irritant.* Avoid eye contact. If contact occurs, flush affected area with water for 15 minutes. Call the teacher.

Warning

Safety Goggles

7. Record observations. Look for changes in the microorganisms' behaviors.
8. Continue observing the microorganisms for 1 minute after the last addition of vinegar. Record your observations in your journal.
9. Transfer the microorganisms to the container labeled *Used Culture* when you are finished.

Warning

PROTOCOL

Safety Goggles

Protocol 2: Microorganisms and Temperature

SAFETY: Put on your safety goggles.

1. Place about 10 mL of culture water in a watch glass.
2. Use the dropping pipet to carefully transfer 2 or 3 microorganisms from the culture to the watch glass.
3. Observe the microorganisms with a hand lens or stereomicroscope long enough to determine their behavior.
4. Record this behavior in your journal.
5. Measure the temperature of the water in the watch glass.
6. Gradually add hot water to the watch glass. Stop when the temperature is 2°C different from the starting temperature.

   You may need to remove some water.

7. Observe the microorganisms for 1 minute. Record your observations in your journal.
8. Repeat steps 5–7 until you have changed the temperature of the water 10°C from its starting temperature.
9. Transfer the microorganisms to the container labeled *Used Culture* when you are finished.

8. In your journal, create a data table to organize and record your experimental data and observations.

9. Conduct your experiment. Record your observations, data, and results in your journal. Consider which, if any, of the questions you wrote may be answered by your results. Record how the evidence you obtained through experimentation supported or contradicted your explanation from step 5.

10. Follow your teacher's directions and visit other teams. Ask what they have learned from the data packet and their experiments.

Analysis

1. Use the information you gathered during this activity to develop an explanation for at least three of the questions in your journal. Write at least one paragraph for each of your explanations in your journal and include each question.

   Include specific evidence that supports each explanation that you write. Draw evidence from the data packet as well as from your experimental results. You may need to reread some pieces from the data packet to do this.

2. Rate your team on how well you taught each other about the packet of information. Use a scale of 1 = not very well, to 5 = very well. Record your rating and two sentences of justification in your journal.

The Gulf of Maine

The ocean is a common resource owned by everyone. Is it limitless? You just finished investigating a fictional lake system, Tri-Lakes. What similar complex interactions exist in real aquatic systems on the earth?

In this activity, you will look into the situation humans face managing the resources of the Gulf of Maine (see Figure 16.2). This activity will help you to better understand the types of issues faced by all people involved in making decisions about the Gulf of Maine. You will assume the role of one of the various stakeholders involved with that resource. Using *The Commons* CD, you will research management options and participate in a debate about them. How should we manage the Gulf of Maine fisheries? Your answer may depend on your point of view. Many individuals depend on or work with the fisheries. These include fishing-boat owners, fisheries scientists, marine biologists, resource economists, and policymakers.

You will act as one of the stakeholders involved with the Gulf of Maine. You will discuss which three management options to implement for the fisheries. You need to prepare for the role play by studying the files in *BioSeeker*, a simulated Internet browser on the CD. After you have explored those files, you may wish to learn more about the Gulf of Maine by completing a real Internet search.

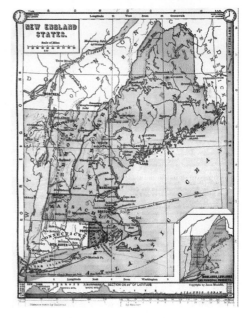

Figure 16.2   The Gulf of Maine.

Materials

The Commons CD (1 per team)
computers with CD-ROM drives (1 per team)
Copymaster *Thinking about the Gulf* (1 per student)
Copymaster *Gulf of Maine Occupational Sketches* (1 per team)

PROCESS AND PROCEDURES

1. Follow your teacher's directions for determining which role your team will assume in the upcoming role play.

    Your team will assume one of the following roles: large-fishing-boat owners, small-fishing-boat owners, resource economists, marine biologists, fisheries scientists, or policymakers.

2. With your team, view the videos on *The Commons*. Begin with "The Fisheries" and continue through to the "Surfing the Gulf" activity.

    View the sidebar *Historical Timeline* to see how the Gulf of Maine has changed over time.

3. Discuss the following questions with the members of your team:

   a. What is the controversy surrounding the Gulf of Maine fisheries?

   b. Who has a stake in the health of the fisheries?

4. Search *BioSeeker* (found in "Surfing the Gulf"). Look for information about 3 of the options that exist for managing the fisheries in the Gulf of Maine. Use the keyword searches and the organizations' Web sites that are listed to gather information about management options.

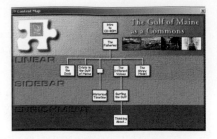

Figure 16.3 The content map for "The Gulf of Maine as a Commons" appears when you click on the picture of the dock in the upper right corner of the program's content map.

   Your challenge is to decide which of the 3 options is best *from the perspective of your assigned role.* Identify the files that will be most useful, and take notes about key information. Remember, in *BioSeeker* the Web sites are fictitious. But you can search real Web sites about those issues on the Internet, as well.

5. Discuss the management options with the members of your team. Create a table to help you organize your discussion. Include a brief description of each option. Then identify the advantages and disadvantages of each. During your discussion, consider the following questions:

   a. Who benefits from the option? Who doesn't?

   b. Who manages the option? How difficult is it to manage?

   c. What data support the option? What assumptions is the option based on? Are the assumptions correct?

   d. What short- and long-term effects is the option likely to have on the fish population? on the economy? on people's lives?

6. Read the information provided on the Copymaster *Gulf of Maine Occupational Sketches.* Begin to think about which management option is best from the perspective of your assumed role.

7. Work as a team to conduct a new search in *BioSeeker.* Prepare for a class discussion on the best management option for the Gulf of Maine fisheries.

   Concentrate on locating information and building arguments that support the management option that benefits your "occupation."

8. Choose a representative from your team as your teacher directs. That person will present a brief explanation (3 to 4 minutes) to the class for the option your team has chosen.

   Be sure to provide relevant data and logical arguments. Be ready as a team to answer questions and respond to comments from classmates representing the same or other roles. Also be ready to ask questions of your classmates as they present the results of their analyses.

Analysis

1. Participate in a class discussion. Vote on the best management option for the Gulf of Maine fisheries.

   Vote as an individual, not as a team or as a representative of your earlier role.

2. Record your vote in your journal. Write a paragraph explaining your choice.

3. With your teammates, discuss what general principles you saw in the Gulf of Maine example that apply to all of earth's resources. In your journal, record the three strongest ideas your team discussed. Explain each briefly.

4. Compare the Gulf of Maine ecosystem to the fictional Tri-Lakes ecosystem. How are those systems similar? How are they different?

Topic: technology and human culture
Go to: www.scilinks.org
Code: human3E645

Are There Limits?

Elaborate

Is the quality of life on earth improving or getting worse? There are two schools of thought. One group is labeled by the popular press as "doomsters." These scholars believe that increasing human population size and resource-consuming lifestyles are depleting the world's limited resources. They believe that this threatens the quality of the environment and jeopardizes the present and future quality of life for the world's people. Therefore, doomsters believe that people everywhere must take immediate action. We must address our population and resource problems to ensure a high quality of life for future generations.

The second group of scholars is known in the press as "boomsters." They don't believe that increasing human population size and resource-consuming lifestyles are threatening our existence. Boomsters believe that the material lives of people and the quality of the environment are generally improving. They contend that human creativity and technology will continue to make the world a better place.

In this activity, you will hear from a well-known boomster, Julian Simon, and a well-known doomster, Paul Ehrlich. Both will express their basic positions on whether the earth has limits. You will have the opportunity to examine your own views and take a closer look at two important components of our earth's complex system: human population growth and human resource consumption.

Materials

The Commons CD (1 per team)
computers with CD-ROM drives (1 per team)

PROCESS AND PROCEDURES

Part A Humans in the World System

1. With your teammates, begin *The Commons* CD at "The World." Watch the video "Are There Limits?" (see Figure 16.4).

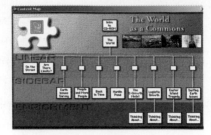

Figure 16.4 Go to the content map for "The World as a Commons." Begin with "The World."

2. Discuss the following questions with your teammates. Record your own answers in your journal.

   a. What is the central question discussed in the video?

   b. What is the major difference between the views expressed by Julian Simon and Paul Ehrlich?

3. Take the *Earth Issues Survey* individually. Consider your results. Write a paragraph in your journal explaining whether you tend to agree more with Julian Simon or Paul Ehrlich.

   Include specific examples from the video that you agree or disagree with. You may review the video if needed.

4. With your teammates, watch the animation "People and More People."

5. Discuss the following questions with your teammates:

   a. What relationship between time and human population growth did you notice?

   b. What relationship between space and human population growth did you notice?

   c. When did you see major changes in population size or in its distribution?

   d. Does the greatest increase in population take place at a time that corresponds to any historical events that you know about?

   You may want to view *The Commons* CD section "Back in Time" to see major historical events in human history.

   e. Did the animation give you any new insights about human population growth? Did it raise any questions about environmental issues?

   f. Is there any sense in which the animation gives a false picture of what is really happening?

6. Participate in a class discussion of the questions from step 5.

7. Read the essay *Environmental Ethics and You* (page 654). Add a brief description of your environmental ethics views to your *Earth Issues Survey* summary.

Topic: human populaton growth
Go to: www.scilinks.org
Code: human3E646

PAGE 654

Part B Exponential Growth

Growth rates are one aspect of ecosystems that must be understood to analyze the impact that changing population sizes have on the system. One type of growth found in populations is exponential growth. You may have heard of exponential growth in a math class. In this part of the activity, you will study what exponential growth looks like. You will learn about factors that influence when and at what rate it happens.

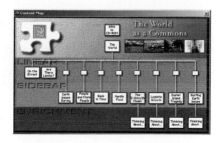

Figure 16.5 The "E-Growth Model" is a sidebar section of "The World as a Commons."

1. With your teammates, study and run "The E-Growth Model" section and the "Hardin Pond" simulation on *The Commons* CD (see Figure 16.5).

2. How does the example of Hardin Pond relate to the human population growth that you saw in "People and More People"?

3. Complete the following questions as a team. Read and use the essays *Growing, Growing, Grown* (page 656) and *Endless Interactions* (page 658) as resources. Record your answers in your journal.

PAGE 656   **PAGE 658**

   a. How do differences in the starting size of a population affect population growth? How do differences in the number of offspring produced per parent seed affect population growth?

   b. How would increasing the time between reproduction events affect population growth?

SCI**LINKS**
NSTA

Topic: niche
Go to: www.scilinks.org
Code: human3E647

   c. How would decreasing the time between reproduction events affect population growth?

   d. In what ways is this simulation of population growth on Hardin Pond realistic? How is it unrealistic?

   Use concepts from the essays and *The Commons* CD to explain your answers. Include specific examples of types of growth and interactions.

Part C Logistic Growth

If exponential growth is one of the basic principles of population growth, then why isn't the earth covered with flies, elephants, or sunflowers? To explore that question further, we study logistic growth.

1. View the "Logistic Growth" animation on *The Commons* CD with your team. Discuss the differences and similarities between exponential and logistic growth.

2. In your journal, explain how resource consumption and interactions differ in exponential and logistic growth.

Analysis

1. Think about what you have learned in this activity and about the information you have recorded in your journal. Explain whether you think there is the potential for a human population problem. Give specific examples of interactions and components in the earth system to explain your answer.

2. Say that half of the nations in the world reduced their growth rate to zero. Would that change the type of population growth humans are experiencing on a global level? Why or why not?

3. In what ways is the earth system as a whole similar to an island ecosystem such as Easter Island? Use specific examples of resource consumption and interactions to explain your answer.

Tri-Lakes: Public Policy

Figure 16.6 Lakes like the one described in the Tri-Lakes scenario are complex systems that are affected by many human decisions.

The sheer number of humans on earth complicates our interactions with the environment. To preserve the environment, we must consider many economic and political aspects to gain support for public policies. Situations such as those of Tri-Lakes or the Gulf of Maine involve complex interactions between all people involved. These interactions are in addition to interactions between humans and resources in the ecosystem.

In this evaluate, you will combine the results of all the system analyses from this unit to construct a more complex, and more accurate, examination of the Tri-Lakes system. You will describe how the components in the Tri-Lakes system interact under normal conditions. Then you will analyze the changes that have taken place and the policy decisions you think must be made. From this activity, you and your teacher will evaluate what you have learned about interactions and interdependence in living systems.

PROCESS AND PROCEDURES

1. Develop a response to the letter from the Tri-Lakes Association. Obtain a rubric for the letter from your teacher. Discuss the criteria with your partner before writing your response.

2. Exchange letters with another person as your teacher directs. Analyze the letter you received according to the rubric.

3. Provide the person whose letter you analyzed with at least 3 specific comments about their letter.

   Your feedback should be a mix of statements. Provide positive statments that indicate the strengths of the letter. Other statements should identify weak areas that need to be revised.

4. Revise your letter to reflect the feedback that you received.

5. Share your letter with your teacher and class as your teacher directs.

6. Participate in a class discussion. Talk about the changes in particular components that likely affected the Tri-Lakes ecosystem and the recommendations for public policies to address the problems.

7. In your journal, briefly summarize the difference between an explanation based on a single, limited analysis and one based on a combination of related analyses. Explain how this difference should affect the way you interpret scientific studies that are reported in the news.

8. Write a general statement that assesses our ability to predict the consequences of introducing new, humanmade components into the environment. Provide reasons that support your statement.

Interdependence Involves Limiting Factors and Carrying Capacity

Newspaper articles worldwide report that famines continue to occur in Africa and that new animals are being added to the endangered species list. What are the causes of these events? Are they caused by human mismanagement, or do some happen naturally?

Scientists agree that we can find some of the answers by studying the concepts of limiting factors and carrying capacity.

A **limiting factor** is anything that can slow, or limit, the growth of a population. The combination of limiting factors in a given habitat influences the carrying capacity of that habitat. **Carrying capacity** is the maximum population of a particular species that the habitat can support.

The carrying capacity of an environment is not necessarily fixed. It changes as environmental conditions change. The limiting factors that influence the carrying capacity may be biotic (living), or abiotic (nonliving), or both. Biotic factors include food supply and other organisms. Abiotic factors include space, raw materials, and climate.

Climate is the prevailing weather conditions in a given area through long periods of time. Weather conditions result from abiotic limiting factors that affect all organisms. These weather factors include temperature, sunlight intensity, precipitation (rainfall, snowfall, and fog), humidity (amount of moisture in the air), and wind. Although you can measure each factor alone, each affects the others. Together they affect the population size of organisms living in the area. Climate and particular weather conditions can affect the population's size directly. They do this by presenting optimal conditions for various plants to grow and reproduce or by presenting conditions that are adverse to growth and reproduction. The abundance or lack of certain plants translates into an abundant or limited food supply for a chain of other organisms. In this way, climate and vegetation help determine the carrying capacity of a particular environment for various organisms. (See Figure E15.1 for an example.)

You might be asking yourself, How can temperature be a factor that limits the size of a population? In the northern part of the

Figure E15.1 The snowy owl (*Nyctea scandiaca*) inhabits Arctic tundra regions and in winter is always searching for food in this sparse environment. When the winter food supply is especially limited, the snowy owl can be seen as far south as Colorado.

United States, the first heavy frost of autumn kills almost all adult mosquitoes. When the population of insects drops, the population of organisms that feed on mosquitoes is affected. In this example, the limiting factor of temperature affects the mosquito population directly by killing most of them. By limiting other organisms' food supply, however, temperature also affects the carrying capacity of the winter environment for those organisms.

The same type of interactions take place between various wildflower populations and the insects that pollinate them. As temperatures drop in the autumn, the wildflowers die. The insects then either die, become dormant, or migrate. In both cases, temperature has caused limited population growth for a period of time.

Water is a requirement of all living organisms. Thus, it is a limiting factor in every ecosystem in the biosphere. Almost all chemical reactions that organisms carry out to stay alive take place in water. Water molecules themselves are a part of many chemical reactions. A few organisms can survive by becoming inactive when there is no water. But most organisms die. Because water is essential for all living organisms, it is a limiting factor that influences the carrying capacity of

virtually every ecosystem. Look at Figure E15.2. Water limits the carrying capacity of a savanna in East Africa and consequently limits the distribution of the organisms.

Because of other weather conditions, rain and snow alone may not ensure that an environment has enough water. Wind increases the rate of water evaporation. Low humidity in the desert also results in an increased evaporation rate. Thus, high rates of evaporation can affect the survival of certain organisms, even when the precipitation is adequate. In some cases, a high rate of evaporation together with low rainfall may permit only plants with special features to survive. This situation severely limits the carrying capacity of the desert. For example, desert plants often have thick, succulent stems

Figure E15.2   Water is a limiting factor in the savanna in East Africa. Here only grasses and scattered trees can grow. These plants, in turn, support grazing animals. The grazing animals move on when the rainfall in particular locations decreases.

Figure E15.3   Desert organisms have adaptations that enable them to survive despite the scarcity of water. The fleshy stems of this saguaro cactus (*Carnegiea gigantea*) store water. The plant's extensive shallow root system increases its access to rainwater.

that can store water. They also have extensive root systems that can absorb large quantities of water during infrequent rainfalls (see Figure E15.3). Some animals, such as the kangaroo rat, can survive without drinking water. They use the water that is released during cellular respiration and produce a nearly solid urine.

Light also can be a limiting factor. The penetration of light into the ocean determines the depth to which photosynthetic organisms can grow. This is generally not beyond the depth of 180 meters (590 feet). If silt or algae growth reduces the water clarity in a pond or lake, plant growth is limited. In dense rain forests, the tallest trees spread their leaves and take most of the light. The ground below them is shaded. This prevents other plants from reaching great heights. Light affects animals indirectly. The amount of light influences the number of plants that can grow. This then influences the carrying capacity of the environment.

Space is another abiotic limiting factor for populations. Every individual needs living space. Some organisms, however, need more space than others. For example, individual corn plants grow well when they are planted close together. A mountain lion, on the other hand, usually requires many square kilometers to find enough food to sustain itself. You may remember that the higher a given organism is on the energy pyramid, the fewer of them the environment can support. Therefore, the amount of space needed by all organisms at trophic levels above the producers is linked primarily to a biotic factor—the availability of food energy.

The available space is affected by population density. **Population density** is the number of individuals in relation to the space the population occupies. For example, consider an experiment at the University of Wisconsin, which is illustrated in Figure E15.4. Researchers gave mice in cages more food than they needed each day. As the mice reproduced, the density of the population increased, and the cages became very crowded. Some female mice stopped taking care of their nests and young. Mice continued to be born, but many newborn mice died from neglect. Eventually, the death rate of the young mice reached 100 percent. This kept the population density from increasing further.

In a similar experiment, conducted in England, the death rate of young mice was not affected. Instead, the birthrate declined almost to zero. In this experiment, the extremely low birthrate kept the population density from increasing. Space, as a limiting factor, affects all living populations and the carrying capacity of particular ecosystems for those populations. ◆

Figure E15.4 **(a)** In one population experiment, researchers provided mice with more than enough food. **(b)** As a result, the population grew dramatically. Space then became a limiting factor that resulted in a high death rate among young mice.

Systems Analysis

Some situations arise that are so complex that predictions seem at best unreliable and at worst impossible. When that happens, scientists turn to a method of analysis called systems analysis. In systems analysis, scientists try to understand enough about the interactions of complex situations so that they can reliably predict the effect that certain changes will have on the system.

Weather provides an example of a complex system that is relatively easy to understand in the short term. For example, dark black clouds usually lead to rain. The interactions that produce weather are so complex, however, that it is nearly impossible to understand or predict weather across large distances or times (see Figure E16.1). Ecosystems are examples of complex systems. Ecosystems are made up of living organisms and nonliving elements in an environment.

The first step in analyzing any complex phenomenon is to identify the components of the system under study. The **components**, or collection of *things*, that make up an ecological system include living (biotic) as well as nonliving (abiotic) things. For example, an ecologist might describe a pond in terms of its biotic components. These would be its microscopic organisms, plant life, and fish. She also might describe the pond in terms of its abiotic components. These would be the pH of the pond water, the nutrient and oxygen levels, and the depth of sunlight penetration. These components also include elements outside of the pond. Thus, the pond system is not isolated from the world around it. In this case, the pond's pH is influenced by the pH of rainwater and the pH of anything that might wash into the pond. The nutrients are determined by the amount and type of food that washes or falls into the pond and the types of organisms that decay there. And the penetration of sunlight is affected by the

amount of shading the pond receives (for instance, is it surrounded by large trees?) and the stillness of the water. All of these components influence and define the system.

Once the components of a system are identified, most scientists try to make the system more manageable by *limiting* the number of components that are included in the analysis. For instance, our pond ecologist might organize her analysis to include only the effects of several different nutrients on the number and size of perch in the pond. The scientist who sets such a structure knows that outside factors, such as pH and sunlight, also influence the fish. However, she might choose not to take those into consideration because they further complicate an already complex study.

Limiting the number of components is necessary because it focuses the scientist's

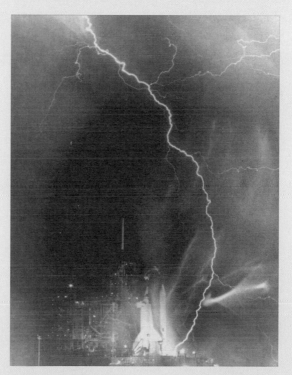

Figure E16.1 Predicting the weather can be difficult because it involves a complex system.

thinking on a particular area of interest. Developing and testing hypotheses is much easier when the focus of the investigation is narrow. Unfortunately, using a limited structure somewhat reduces the accuracy of the analysis. Most systems analysts try to organize their system in a way that is simple enough to be manageable and complex enough to be accurate.

The last essential step before beginning any analysis of a complex system is that the scientist understands as much as possible about the initial behavior of the system. If the initial behavior of the system is not understood, then it is difficult to interpret how the system will react when one of its components is altered. In the pond example, say the ecologist does not already know that perch populations decline each fall. (This happens because a particular nutrient that they require becomes scarce.) In that case, she might mistakenly attribute the decline to a recent change in pH. (In fact, the pH change might influence the perch population. But this effect may be small compared with the annual fluctuations caused by varying nutrient levels.)

Once a limited analysis is complete, scientists may try to combine the results of several analyses. This way, they can construct a more complex, and more accurate, understanding of the whole system.

From this brief description of systems analysis, you can see that it is important to know as much as possible about the behavior of a system before attempting to analyze the effect that *changes* in particular components might have on it. For this reason, ecologists collect large amounts of data in an attempt to understand how one structured set of interactions affects another. Despite this effort, ecologists realize that they never will have all of the information necessary to make an error-free prediction. To compensate for this limitation, many ecologists choose to be conservative in their prediction. They generally assume that intervening in ecosystems will result in some unpredictable consequences. ◆

Figure E16.2 A lake or pond is a good example of a complex system that interacts with the world outside of it.

Environmental Ethics and You

Environmental ethics is a branch of ethical study that considers how people *ought* to relate to the natural world. The different ethical perspectives people have about humanity's relationship to nature are based on different values, beliefs, and attitudes. People's values, beliefs, and attitudes about nature are formed by a variety of influences including the overarching values and attitudes of their culture. People's attitudes about nature also are influenced by their personal experiences, the people they talk to, and the books they read. These values taken together influence how people behave toward the environment. This has a major impact on the state of the natural world around us.

Following are brief descriptions of two rather distinctive ethics. How similar or different is your personal environmental ethic from the two views described here? What factors have influenced your environmental ethic? What other environmental ethical models are you aware of?

The human-centered environmental ethic. People who support a human-centered environmental ethic take the position that humans should dominate the natural world because they are fundamentally different from all other life-forms and are somehow superior to or separate from nature. From this perspective, nonhuman life-forms are commodities that have no value other than their usefulness to humankind. People holding this ethic tend to view the earth primarily as a collection of natural resources that humans can use to promote economic growth and prosperity. People who support this position also think that the earth is vast and has many resources in unlimited or abundant supply. They point out that human history has been characterized by continual progress and that, through technology, people find solutions to all problems (including those of resource depletion and pollution), and progress continues.

The deep ecology environmental ethic. The deep ecology ethic is a life-centered ethic. People who support this position think that all life-forms on earth have intrinsic value regardless of their usefulness to humankind. From this perspective, humans have no right to reduce the earth's biological richness and diversity except to satisfy fundamental needs. People who support this position think that the earth's resources are in limited supply and that these resources are for all life-forms, not just for humans. The deep ecology ethic takes the position that both human and nonhuman life will continue to flourish only if humans greatly reduce their rate of population growth. People who hold this position think that human interference in the nonhuman world has been excessive and human impact must be minimized. From this perspective, people must make economic, technological, and ideological changes that promote a sustainable lifestyle rather than one that seeks the highest standard of living. ◆

Human-centered ethic

Deep ecology ethic

Figure E16.3 The Florida Everglades was established as a national park in 1934 to preserve the plants and animals that are part of this unique wetland environment. The influence of humans, however, has caused disruptions in the ecosystem. People who have different viewpoints about the environment have different ideas about how a unique environment such as the Everglades should be managed. What is your point of view? Do you view this with a human-centered or a deep ecology environmental ethic?

Growing, Growing, Grown

Just look around. You can observe plenty of evidence that populations grow. The guppies in your fish tank have more guppies, the songbirds in your yard have young each spring, and the stray cats in the neighborhood seem to have a litter of kittens every couple of months. But have you ever thought about how populations grow?

In 1798, after years of thinking about this question, Thomas Malthus (pictured in Figure E16.4) reported that in ideal conditions, populations tend to grow exponentially. In **exponential growth**, both the total population size and the rate of increase rise steadily across time. Charles Darwin later wrote in his book *On the Origin of Species* (1859) that, "There is no exception to the rule that every organic being naturally increases at so high a rate, that, if not destroyed, the earth would soon be covered by the progeny of a single pair." Biologists discovered that *any* population growing exponentially can potentially approach an infinite size in a relatively short amount of time *if* provided with necessary resources such as food, water, space, and protection from other organisms.

When populations grow exponentially, the population growth curve takes on a J-shaped appearance. This is due to the continuous increase of a larger and larger population size (see Figure E16.5). You can observe this principle of population growth when you examine a fast-breeding species such as the common housefly or a slow-breeding species such as the elephant. Biologist L. O. Howard discovered that, if the environmental conditions were ideal, a housefly population beginning with just one adult female could increase to more than

Figure E16.4 Thomas Malthus was an English economist who lived from 1766 until 1834. He gave serious thought to how populations grow.

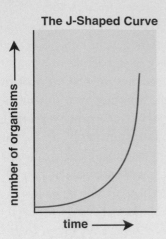

The J-Shaped Curve

number of organisms →

time →

Figure E16.5 The J-shaped curve is characteristic of populations that are growing exponentially.

5.5 *trillion* flies in several generations or just *1 year* (refer to Figure E16.6). Even the rather slow-breeding elephant has the capacity for explosive population growth. Charles Darwin calculated that an elephant population of just two elephants (a single breeding pair) could grow to 19 *million* elephants in only 750 years.

PREDICTED POPULATION GROWTH OF THE COMMON HOUSEFLY IN ONE YEAR

Generation	Population size
1	120
2	7,200
3	432,000
4	25,920,000
5	1,555,200,000
6	93,312,000,000
7	5,598,720,000,000

Source: Data from Kormondy, E. J. (1984). *Concepts of Ecology, third edition.* Englewood Cliffs, NJ: Prentice Hall Publishers.

Figure E16.6 Predicted population growth of the common housefly in 1 year. This prediction is based on the following observations and assumptions. An average female fly lays 120 eggs at a time. About half of the eggs develop into females. There are seven generations in 1 year. Individual flies live for one generation.

Under ideal conditions, populations tend to increase in size exponentially (that is, 1, 2, 4, 8, 16, 32, 64, 128). In addition to realizing that, Thomas Malthus realized that the food supply tends to increase only arithmetically (for example, 1, 2, 3, 4, 5, 6, 7). Most of the world's organisms serve as the food supply for other organisms higher on the food chain. Because of this and other limiting factors such as space, populations generally do not continue to grow exponentially. When a food supply is limited, the environment's carrying capacity for the populations that feed on that food supply is reduced.

Technological advances in agriculture have helped food production generally keep pace with human population growth. Still, many scientists are concerned that a time will come when food production will not meet the requirements of the world's rapidly increasing human population. In other words, we will reach a point when the human population will exceed the carrying capacity of the earth.

In theory, populations could continue to grow exponentially if they are provided with ideal conditions and unlimited resources. In the real world, conditions are not ideal and resources are in limited supply. So we do not observe ongoing exponential growth. **Logistic growth** represents a pattern of population growth that scientists have observed in real populations in natural conditions. The logistic growth curve has the shape of a flattened S (see Figure E16.7), rather than the J-shape that is characteristic of exponential growth. In exponential growth, the population continues to increase across time. But in logistic growth, the population levels off at the carrying capacity of the environment.

The S-Shaped Curve

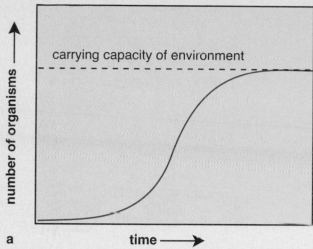

a

Population Growth of Paramecium

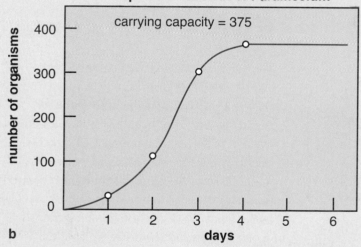

b

Source: From Gause, G. F. (1934). *The Struggle for Existence.* Baltimore: Williams and Wilkins.

Figure E16.7 (a) An idealized S-shaped growth curve. (b) Population growth curve for the single-celled organism _Paramecium_. Limiting factors force this population of organisms to level off.

Legend has it that the game of chess was invented by a mathematician who worked for an ancient king. The king was so delighted with the game that he asked the mathematician to name his own reward. He told the king that he was a humble man who wished a humble reward. He asked that a single grain of wheat be placed on the first square of the chessboard, two grains of wheat on the second square, four grains on the third square and so on, doubling the number of grains on each square until all 64 squares on the chessboard were filled. The king granted his request and ordered the Master of the Royal Granary to begin counting out the grains. But before the task was anywhere close to being finished, the king handed his kingdom over to the mathematician. ◆

Endless Interactions

You have just finished a delicious bowl of chicken soup for lunch. As you clean up, you wash out the bowl and throw away the can. A garbage truck will haul the can to the dump where it will lie among the trash. A female fly might lay her eggs in the can. Her offspring might fly from the dump, feed on some decayed food, and then rest on top of someone's peanut butter sandwich. Each of these interactions depends on the one before it. Most of the time, these interactions go unnoticed.

All populations, including human populations, interact with one another in a complex web of relationships. The set of interacting populations present at one time in one place is called a *community*. In your community, there may be dogs, cats, trees, weeds, and humans that interact. When you mow your lawn or your dog bites the mail carrier, for example, the interaction is very direct. Much of the time, however, interactions are indirect.

One type of direct interaction is a **predator/prey** interaction. In this, one type of organism (the predator) eats the other (the prey). The predator benefits from the

Figure E16.8 For food, this red-tailed hawk (*Buteo jamaicensis*) depends directly and indirectly on a number of organisms in its habitat. Note the rodent in its talons.

relationship, but the individual prey does not. An animal can spend its life as a predator and then abruptly become the prey. A snake, for example, may prey on ground squirrels and then become prey for a hawk. The snake depends on a large population of ground squirrels. The hawk, then, depends directly on the snake, and in this case, indirectly on the quantity of ground squirrels. The hawk, however, also may prey directly on the ground squirrels. The limiting factor in this case is the food supply. Although the individual ground squirrel does not benefit, the population of ground squirrels may benefit by being held in check by the snake population. There also might be a selective advantage to the ground squirrel population because the snakes would tend to prey on the slower, weaker squirrels. Consequently, the best-adapted ground squirrels would be more likely to escape becoming prey and thus would survive to reproduce.

Competition is another type of direct interaction. This type of interaction between organisms benefits neither one. Organisms compete for limiting factors, such as space, food, sunlight, nutrients, and water (see Figure E16.9). Competition among organisms may increase as a particular resource becomes scarce.

Figure E16.9 The melaleuca tree (*Melaleuca quinqueneruia*) was introduced to Florida from Australia. It has been overwhelming the cypress in the everglades.

When tadpoles live in densely packed areas, the competition increases for available space and food resources. As a result, these tadpoles remain tadpoles longer, they suffer higher death rates, and they develop into smaller frogs. In communities of wolves, competition leads to the establishment of social hierarchies. A high position in the pack gives the individual an advantage in terms of obtaining food, mates, shelter, and other resources. Individuals of any species that compete successfully can survive to reproduce and pass on their genetic material to future generations. In this way, populations adapt through time to changes in the environment.

Competition also can take place between different species. If the species' needs are similar and resources are scarce, then more competition will exist. In New Guinea, four species of pigeons rely on a particular fruit tree for their primary food source. The four types of pigeons differ in size, and the smaller pigeons have adapted to feed on the fruit of the lower branches.

An experiment involving paramecium demonstrates another example of this form of adaptation. Researchers placed two species of paramecium in the same test tube, which was filled with liquid food. The researchers formulated a hypothesis that one of the species would die out as a result of competition. In fact, both species survived and thrived. One species fed on the food that settled at the bottom of the tube. The other fed on the food suspended in the liquid. The two species of paramecium, as well as the four species of pigeons, occupied separate niches. The **niche** of an organism refers to its role in the community. This is what it eats, what organisms eat it, where it lives, and what indirect relationships it has with other organisms. As a result of occupying different niches, the two species could feed and

reproduce without interfering with each other even though they lived in the same place, or **habitat**.

Competition is not the only relationship that exists among populations of different species that live in the same habitat. Some different species of organisms live in direct, physical contact with one another. This relationship is called **symbiosis**. For example, certain species of fungi live on the roots of many plants. The fungi absorb nutrients from the soil and secrete an acid that makes the nutrients available to the plant. At the same time, the fungi are nourished by photosynthetic products from the plant. The fungi also absorb water and protect the plant against various pathogens in the soil. This type of symbiosis that benefits both organisms is called **mutualism**. Another example of mutualism is the interaction between a cow and a certain type of bacteria that live in its intestines. The cow benefits because the bacteria digest the cellulose in the plants that the cow eats. The bacteria benefit because the cow provides a steady supply of food.

A common form of symbiosis is **parasitism**. In parasitism, one organism (the parasite) lives on or in another organism (the host) and uses it as a food source. The host usually remains alive during the interaction. The parasites, however, may weaken a host to the extent that it becomes susceptible to disease or becomes an easier prey for predators. A leech, for example, clings to a turtle's skin and sucks its blood. Other parasitic microorganisms in the turtle absorb food directly from its blood. Interactions such as these eventually may weaken the turtle. In humans, tapeworms absorb food directly from the intestines, where they live.

Plants also may have parasites. Large microorganisms may have smaller parasitic microorganisms in them. Parasites may be

Figure E16.10 The mistletoe growing in this pine tree is a parasitic plant.

molds, microorganisms, and even other plants such as the mistletoe shown in Figure E16.10. All viruses are parasitic because they require a host to reproduce and acquire energy.

These examples illustrate a few of the many different types of interactions that take place among organisms. Some of these interactions, such as mutualistic relationships, are beneficial for both organisms. Other interactions are not as positive. These interactions result in some degree of harm to one member of the interacting pair, as in parasitic relationships. Each of these interactions is influenced by limiting factors such as light, temperature, food supply, and space. Because of these interactions, there is a web of interdependence among living things. ◆

"The important thing in science is not so much to obtain new facts as to discover new ways of thinking about them."

Sir William Bragg

662

Thinking like a Biologist

This final section in *BSCS Biology: A Human Approach* helps you evaluate what you have learned about biology and about the process of scientific thinking. Now that you have completed this course, we hope that you are better able to ask questions about the world around you and to reason scientifically to find answers. As you continue to learn and become an independent citizen, you will encounter many situations that are best understood when you think about the biology involved. Remembering the six unifying principles of biology that we used to organize this program may help you understand those situations.

In this Evaluate Section, we will revisit the six unifying principles. There are several opportunities to express your understanding of the principles. These include two scenarios based on actual events, a series of questions under the heading *Chapter Challenges,* and a portfolio that your teacher may assign as an additional or alternate activity.

ACTIVITIES

Part A	Recognizing Biology in Medicine
Part B	Chapter Challenges
Alternate	Building a Portfolio of Scientific Literacy

Recognizing Biology in Medicine — Part A

Each unit in this program focused on one of the six unifying principles that unite the biological sciences. Each principle illustrates a different aspect of biology. But remember, all of these principles act together in living systems. If you have learned the concepts associated with each principle, you now should be able to think about any biological topic in light of these principles. Doing so will help you understand the world from a biological point of view.

PROCESS AND PROCEDURES

1. Obtain a scoring rubric from your teacher. Study the requirements for completing this activity successfully.

   Discuss the rubric with your partner. Ask your teacher to answer any questions that you have about the project.

2. In your journal, identify each of the 6 unifying principles. Write a statement describing what each one means.

   The unifying principles of biology were the foundation for this course. They are in the title of each unit.

NEED TO KNOW

Unifying Principles of Biology

These principles should look very familiar by now. They have been the basis for organizing the ideas of this program.

Evolution: Patterns and Products of Change in Living Systems

Homeostasis: Maintaining Dynamic Equilibrium in Living Systems

Energy, Matter, and Organization: Relationships in Living Systems

Continuity: Reproduction and Inheritance in Living Systems

Development: Growth and Differentiation in Living Systems

Ecology: Interaction and Interdependence in Living Systems

3. Review both scenarios that follow. Choose one that you will use to complete the Analysis.

4. In a few sentences, describe 2 or more interesting things that you learned from reading the scenario.

Analysis

Write an essay of at least five pages that describes how each of the six unifying principles is evident in the scenario. Describe how the principles overlap and act together in this situation.

Remember, all six unifying principles are represented either directly or indirectly whenever you study living systems. Be sure to use specific examples from the scenario that you choose to illustrate each principle.

SCENARIO

Scenario 1 Iguanas and Aspirin, Shots and Antibiotics

"I hate going to the doctor. It's probably just a cold anyway," Miguel complained as he sat in the waiting room with his father.

"Oh come on, seeing the doctor isn't so bad," his father replied. "Besides, there's been a lot of flu going around, so I don't want to take any chances."

Just then the nurse called, "Miguel Hernandez, Dr. Chen can see you now."

Before seeing the doctor, Miguel was examined by a nurse who took some measurements and asked him a few questions. The nurse recorded these data for Miguel.

Patient	Miguel Hernandez
Temperature	38.3°C (101°F)
Blood pressure	122/80
Pulse	77 beats/min
Mass/weight	52.3 kg (115 lbs)
Comments	Complains of sore throat, headaches, lack of appetite

The doctor then examined Miguel. She looked in his throat and ears and listened to his heart and lungs as he breathed slowly. When finished, the doctor began to explain her analysis and treatment plan to Miguel.

"I suspect you have a *Streptococcus* bacterial infection. I'll give you a prescription for penicillin. But first we need to take a throat swab and blood sample for the lab. They'll grow bacteria from the swab on an agar plate and use antibiotic disks to test for resistance. They'll also check your blood for antibodies."

"How do you know it isn't just a cold?" Miguel asked.

"The rhinovirus that causes a common cold usually doesn't cause a fever. And you don't have congestion. Also, the spots on your throat look like a strep infection to me."

"Are you sure it's not the flu?" Miguel's dad asked. "Maybe he should have had a flu shot. He wasn't vaccinated for German measles either."

"Flu is caused by an infection of body cells by the influenza virus," Dr. Chen said. "It infects humans and some other animals such as ducks. Influenza does produce fever, but it also causes extreme body aches and many other symptoms that Miguel doesn't have. I don't think Miguel necessarily needs a flu shot; he's young and generally healthy. Vaccination against the rubella virus, which causes German measles, is probably a good idea for all youngsters, though the danger of infection is much lower than it used to be. Let me see if I can find those data . . . here we are. Look at these data showing a recent history of rubella cases.

"Rubella vaccination is most important, however, for girls because of the risk of infection later in life. If a pregnant woman gets rubella, it can seriously damage her developing fetus."

"Anyway, if it were the flu, the penicillin would wipe it out, right, Dr. Chen?" Miguel asked.

(continued)

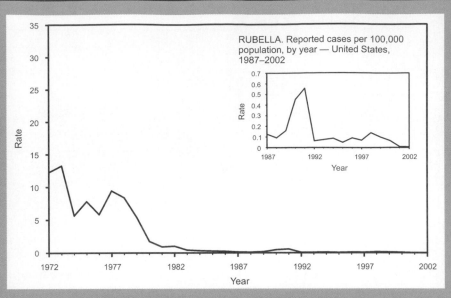

RUBELLA. Reported cases per 100,000 population, by year — United States, 1987–2002

Figure Ev.1 **Rubella occurrence in the United States.** A vaccine for rubella became available n the United States in 1969. Data show slight increases in the number of cases of rubella in 1990–1991 and again in 1998–1999. What might have caused these increases? Why hasn't rubella been eliminated completely?

Dr. Chen shook her head. "No, penicillin works by interfering with the production of the bacterial cell wall as the bacterial cells divide. Because viruses such as influenza live inside the host's cells, antibiotics don't affect them. Also, it's a bad idea to use antibiotics when they aren't needed. This is because some bacteria carry genes whose products make the bacteria resistant to the action of a particular antibiotic. Those resistant bacteria are usually only a tiny percentage of the population infecting you. Remember, you should always finish all of the antibiotics you are given when prescribed. If you stop taking them early, you could give resistant bacteria a chance to reproduce and repopulate your tissues."

"Should Miguel take aspirin or a cold medicine containing aspirin to reduce his fever?" Mr. Hernandez asked. "Is the fever bad for him?"

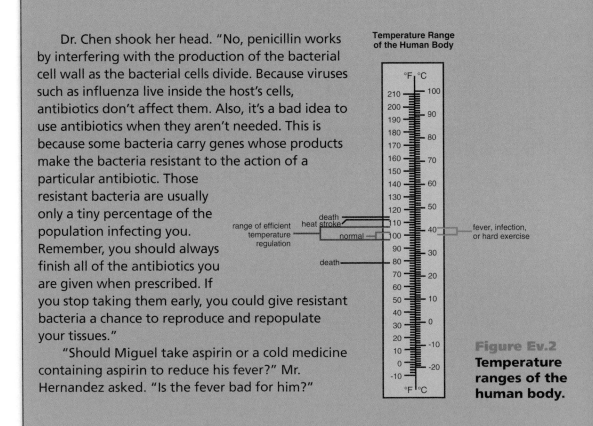

Temperature Range of the Human Body

Figure Ev.2 **Temperature ranges of the human body.**

Fever in Animals

Does fever act as a defense mechanism against disease? Several studies have shown that infections may last longer and be more severe when people are treated with drugs such as aspirin. Aspirin reduces fever. But it also blocks pain and reduces inflammation. Scientists have conducted experiments with animals to try to isolate the effects of fever. Rabbits treated with drugs that reduce fever are more likely to survive bacterial infections if an external heat source is applied to the animals.

In humans and other mammals, fever is produced when the chemical signals of infection cause the brain to increase the set point for body temperature. The rate of the body's metabolism increases. The organism shivers to warm its body, and blood vessels near the skin constrict, thus reducing heat loss. Fever may enhance the immune system's response. It also induces sleepiness and pain, so the victim is less active and saves energy for fighting the infection. When the infection is over, sweating occurs, and the body temperature returns to normal.

Some animals, such as reptiles, do not rely on metabolic warming to produce fever (see Figure Ev.3). They rely on behavioral changes to help adjust their body temperature. For example, they can move to warm or cool locations. In one study, scientists infected desert iguanas (*Dipsosaurus dorsalis*) with the bacteria *Aeromonas hydrophilia*. The iguanas moved to locations that increased their temperature above normal. When scientists prevented the infected iguanas from moving to the warmer, fever-inducing locations, the infections worsened.

Figure Ev.3
Reptiles, such as the iguana, do not produce fevers from metabolic warming. They rely on behavioral changes and interactions with the environment to regulate temperature.

"Well, it certainly makes him feel bad," Dr. Chen said. "But his fever is not a dangerous level." Dr. Chen pointed to a wall chart showing grades of temperature for humans.

"As long as his fever is at a reasonable level and appears to be caused by an infection instead of a head injury or overheating, it won't hurt him. Aspirin and over-the-counter cold and flu medicines that contain aspirin can be effective in reducing fevers. But they shouldn't be given to children or teenagers who have flulike symptoms. Aspirin is associated with increasing the risk for Reye syndrome when it is given to children or teenagers who have fever-causing viral infections such as chicken pox or influenza. Reye syndrome affects the blood and liver, and can trigger life-threatening pressure on the brain.

"In Miguel's case today, it's difficult to say whether it's helpful or harmful to lower his fever. Fever may be helping to fight his infection. Read this interesting research report." Dr. Chen showed the account of Fever in Animals to Miguel and his father:

"What about the old saying, starve a fever, feed a cold?" Mr. Hernandez asked.

"Well, I wouldn't recommend starving, but don't force too much food. Do drink lots of juices and water to keep hydrated. You use energy to produce the fever. But you have some body stores of glycogen and fat to use for energy. You may suffer from diarrhea as the antibiotic kills off the bacteria that normally live in your intestines. If so, you can eat yogurt, which contains lactobacillus cultures, or take tablets containing normal intestinal bacteria to stop the diarrhea. Those bacteria also help keep the growth rate of pathogens low by competing or resources."

SCENARIO

Scenario 2   Cystic Fibrosis and Cholera

Most harmful genetic disorders are quite rare among human populations. In many cases, the most serious mutations never show up. This is because the changes are so harmful that the embryo does not survive during early development. So it may seem surprising that cystic fibrosis (CF) is much more common than many other serious genetic disorders. CF is an inherited disease that causes severe problems with the gas exchange and digestive systems. People with CF experience chronic coughs, lung infections, pneumonia, and digestion difficulties. Those problems generally become worse as patients become older. Approximately 25 percent of all CF patients survive into their 30s, although new treatments may help extend their lifetimes.

Why has the mutant gene for CF remained in certain populations at a relatively high frequency? One possibility is that it provides some advantage in addition to the problems it causes. Scientists examined the mechanism by which the CF mutation causes disease. They looked for the possibility that it also could cause beneficial effects. One way to investigate that was to consider what

happens in heterozygotes, people who carry only one copy of the CF allele (and so do not have any disease symptoms). The pedigree, or family tree, in Figure Ev.4 shows a possible inheritance pattern of CF.

This is what the scientists found. Cystic fibrosis is caused by mutations in the gene for a protein. This protein is known as the cystic fibrosis transmembrane conductance regulator protein, or CFTR protein. This protein normally has 1,480 amino acids and is found in the membranes of lung and intestinal cells. The normal form of the CFTR protein is a *transport protein*. It acts as a gate in certain membranes, similar to a gate that allows people to go in and out of a stadium. That protein controls the exchange of chloride ions across the membranes of cells in the gas exchange and digestive systems (Figure Ev.5).

In patients with cystic fibrosis, the protein is altered and does not function properly. For example, one particular mutation causes the deletion of just one amino acid. This is the phenylalanine at position 508 in the amino acid sequence of the CFTR protein. This mutation, called △F508, takes place in 75 percent of all CF cases.

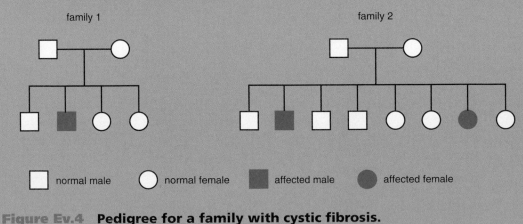

Figure Ev.4   Pedigree for a family with cystic fibrosis.

The CF allele results in only a small change in the amino acid sequence of the CFTR protein. But it has a large effect on the protein's ability to function. Mutant versions of CFTR protein cannot regulate the exchange of chloride ions. The loss of chloride ion regulation means that the regulation of water balance is lost as well. This is because the concentration of chloride ions outside of the cell affects the amount of water moving into or out of the cell. (This movement takes place by the process of osmosis.) As a result, thick mucous secretions build up outside the cells of the gas exchange and digestive systems in people with CF. These are people who are homozygous for the CF allele.

Mucus in the digestive ducts of the pancreas interferes with the release of certain digestive enzymes, as shown in Figure Ev.6. Mucus in the lungs interferes with breathing and makes people with CF more vulnerable to lung infection. That susceptibility occurs because the immune system cells cannot pass through the mucus. Normally, these cells destroy

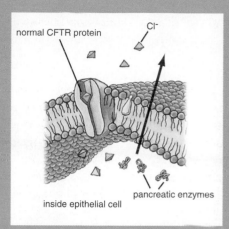

Figure Ev.5 Normal CFTR protein regulates chloride ion flow across the membrane. This indirectly affects the secretion of pancreatic enzymes.

Figure Ev.6 The effect of cystic fibrosis on the pancreas. Mutant CFTR protein interferes with Cl– movement across the membrane. This, in turn, interferes with water movement across the membrane. Pancreatic enzymes get stuck in mucus that builds up outside the cell.

harmful invaders. Without the help of the immune system, even relatively minor infections can become quite serious.

You may wonder, along with many scientists, how such a harmful allele could continue in some human populations. Evidence obtained from studies of another disease, cholera, suggests a possible reason why CF continues to be relatively common today. Cholera is an infectious disease spread by bacteria that infect the intestines. The disease causes severe diarrhea that, in humans, often leads to death if medical treatment is not available. Individuals who are heterozygous for the CF allele may be more likely to survive cholera than those individuals who are homozygous normal for the CFTR gene.

The first step in understanding the possible relationship between CF and cholera was to consider what causes cholera's symptoms. The invading pathogen is the bacterium *Vibrio cholera*. It produces a toxin called cholera toxin, CT. This toxin interferes with the normal CFTR protein. The toxin CT causes the normal CFTR protein to

(*continued*)

change its regulatory activity and secrete too much chloride ion and water from intestinal cells. That change causes diarrhea and dehydration in otherwise healthy mice (and humans).

Once the cause of cholera's symptoms was understood, scientists set up a model using mice that had mutant CFTR genes and that could be infected with cholera. With that model, the scientists tested how mice that are heterozygous for the CF allele would react to cholera. Such heterozygous mice have only half as much normal CFTR protein as homozygous normal mice. The heterozygous mice had less normal-functioning regulatory protein. This is because they only had one allele for normal CFTR. The other allele produces nonfunctional (mutant) CFTR. This difference is illustrated by the data shown in Figure Ev.7.

When infected with the cholera pathogen, the heterozygous mice secrete only half as much fluid (diarrhea) as normal (non-CF) mice. Their diarrhea is less severe than normal mice, as shown in Figure Ev.7b. The mice that are heterozygous for CF do not become as sick from cholera as do mice lacking the mutant CF allele.

The scientists concluded that their data supported the hypothesis that the presence of the CF allele may increase the ability to survive cholera. They also concluded that these data suggest that the high incidence of CF in certain human populations may be related to an increased resistance to cholera. They submitted a report of their experiments to the journal *Science*. Their report was reviewed by a panel of scientists who decided that their results and conclusions were worthy of publication. As a result, the science and medical community had access to this new information.

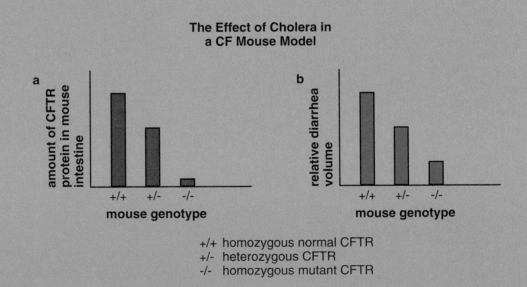

The Effect of Cholera in a CF Mouse Model

+/+ homozygous normal CFTR
+/- heterozygous CFTR
-/- homozygous mutant CFTR

Figure Ev.7 **The effects of cholera in relation to the presence of the CF allele.** (a) This figure shows the amount of CFTR protein in normal mice, mice with one copy of the CF allele (heterozygotes), and mice with two copies of the CF allele (homozygotes). (b) This figure shows how these groups of mice react to having cholera.

Chapter Challenges

In this section, you will find at least one challenging question or problem for each chapter in the program. You can use these questions to test your understanding of the specific ideas in the chapters you studied. Keep in mind that although a question may be listed under a particular chapter heading, you can respond by including material from other chapters.

Unit 1 Evolution: Patterns and Products of Change in Living Systems

Chapter 1 The Human Animal

1. Long before humans developed ways to write their languages, they passed on information about their lives and the world around them by telling stories, drawing pictures, acting out plays, dancing, or singing. As the collection of information grew, people needed very good memories to pass along all the information.

    a. How have written language and modern electronic communication altered the way information is stored and transmitted?

    b. Explain how you think these changes may have affected human cultures.

Figure Ev.8   There are many ways to transmit information.

Chapter 2 Evolution: Change across Time

1. Describe two examples of how evolution is happening today.

2. How does technology play a role in helping scientists collect evidence of biological change across long periods of time?

3. Scientists have hypothesized that modern whales are descended from land mammals that moved into the water environment between 50 to 60 million years ago. In 1994, scientists found two exciting fossil discoveries, both whalelike creatures with legs.

Occurrence (in millions of years ago)	Appearance*	Name	Year of discovery	Description*
55		*Mesonychid*	prior to 1989	Hyena-like land mammal 4 long legs Slender tail
50		*Ambulocetus*	1989	Land and sea mammal 4 short legs with feet No tail fluke but probably swam like an otter
46		*Rodhocetus*	1994	Whalelike sea mammal Legs shorter than *Ambulocetus* May have been able to move awkwardly on land Strong tail for swimming
40		*Prozeuglodon*	1994	15-foot long aquatic mammal Tiny 6-inch hind legs that could not support weight on land Tail fluke for swimming

* Based on fossils of skeleton

Source: From Zimmer, C. (January 1995). Back to the sea. *Discover*, 82–84.

Figure Ev.9   New fossil evidence for whale ancestors reveals a link to land-based mammals.

a. Look at the data presented in Figure Ev.9. Explain how this information supports an evolutionary explanation for the origin of modern whales from an ancestor that lived on land and had legs.

Chapter 3 Products of Evolution: Unity and Diversity

1. Develop a reasonable scientific explanation for this statement: Birds are related to dinosaurs.

2. The Nature Conservancy is an example of a conservation organization that seeks to protect land from human development. How could the activities of an organization such as this have an effect on biological diversity? Give specific examples using this organization or a similar one.

Unit 2 Homeostasis: Maintaining Dynamic Equilibrium in Living Systems

Chapter 4 The Internal Environment of Organisms

1. An astronaut in space depends on a space vehicle or a space suit to create an environment that can support his or her life. The data in the need to know box show the average daily dietary and metabolic needs of an astronaut in space.

NEED TO KNOW

An Astronaut's Daily Dietary and Metabolic Needs

What do these data tell you about an astronaut's needs?

Input	Amount needed per day
Oxygen	0.84 kg/day
Food solids	0.62 kg/day
Dietary water (includes drinking water and water in food)	2.77 kg/day
Water for washing and food preparation	25.26 kg/day

Source: From Wieland, P. O. (1994). *Designing for Human Presence in Space: An Introduction to Environmental Control and Life Support Systems* (NASA Reference Publication 1324). Alabama: George C. Marshall Space Flight Center.

a. Make a table that shows the types of output that each astronaut would produce given the input shown. (You do not need to use numerical values, but you can identify what types of waste will be produced.)

b. Consider the output you listed in your chart. What technological adaptations would be necessary to maintain a healthy and clean living environment in the space vehicle? How does your answer relate to the concepts of this chapter?

Chapter 5 Maintaining Balance in Organisms

1. What role does the brain have in maintaining the body's balance of temperature, water, gas exchange, and blood pressure?

Chapter 6 Human Homeostasis: Health and Disease

1. A human body is continuously subjected to changes in its external environment. Use one or two examples to explain why these changes normally do not cause problems for the body. Under what circumstances can homeostasis become disrupted?

2. How do AIDS and autoimmune diseases keep the body from maintaining a healthy condition?

Unit 3 Energy, Matter, and Organization: Relationships in Living Systems

Chapter 7 Performance and Fitness

1. Have you ever watched someone race-walk? The unusual twisting motion of the hips makes it look as if it would be so much easier for the racers to pick up their feet and run. What is the difference between running and walking? Humans, like many other vertebrates including horses, dogs, cats, and deer, have different ways of moving their legs for locomotion. If you ever have ridden a horse, you know that the jarring bounce you feel when the horse trots is very different from a gallop or a canter. Use the data displayed in Figure Ev.10 to answer the questions below.

   a. At a speed of 5 km/hour (about 3 miles per hour), is running or walking more energy efficient? Is the same true at 8 km/hour (about 5 miles per hour)? Explain how the data in Figure Ev.10 support your answers.

   b. During very fast running, above 16 km/hour (10 miles per hour), most people are exercising anaerobically. If this is the case, would the type of data measured in Figure Ev.10 be an appropriate way to determine their energy efficiency? Explain your answer.

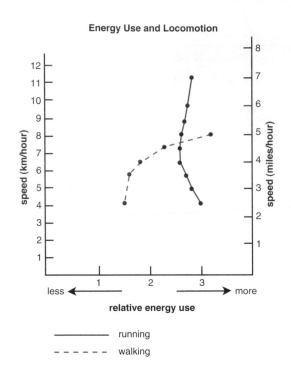

Energy Use and Locomotion

——————— running

– – – – – – walking

Source: From McNeill, A. R. (1992). *Exploring Biomechanics: Animals in Motion.* New York: Scientific American Library.

Figure Ev.10 **Energy use in different modes of human locomotion.** These data are based on measurements of oxygen consumption of the person running or walking.

Chapter 8 The Cellular Basis of Activity

1. Metabolism includes the series of chemical reactions that break down macromolecules. These include glycolysis, fermentation, and aerobic respiration. It also includes the reactions that build up macromolecules, such as protein synthesis or (in plants and certain prokaryotes) photosynthesis.

   a. Can both types of reactions happen in the same cells of the same organism? Explain your answer.

   b. Show how your answer to question 1a relates to activity in a living system.

2. To grow and develop, a seed must germinate (sprout) as the embryonic plant begins to grow. Germination requires water. For example, lettuce seeds germinate in about 48 hours after being soaked in water. Germination also may be sensitive to light. Some seeds require light to germinate. In other species, light inhibits germination.

   a. Design and carry out an experiment to test whether light affects the germination of common garden seeds. You will need to use seeds that germinate quickly, such as Grand Rapids lettuce seeds.

   b. Report your results and conclusions. Include a possible explanation of why the seeds you selected behaved as they did.

c. Explain the sources of energy and matter for a germinating seed *before* the sprout emerges and leaves grow. Do the same for *after* the sprout is aboveground and the leaves are open.

Chapter 9 The Cycling of Matter and the Flow of Energy in Communities

1. Explain the flow of energy in a compost pile. What happens to the matter? What is the connection between the flow of energy and the changes in the matter?

2. Identify a population of organisms that lives in your community. Draw or construct a food web that shows the connections among the organisms in that population. Include a discussion of what happens to the energy as you move to higher trophic levels. Illustrate those relationships.

Unit 4 Continuity: Reproduction and Inheritance in Living Systems

Chapter 10 Reproduction in Humans and Other Organisms

1. Use the population data shown in Figure Ev.11 to answer the following questions:

   a. Explain how birthrate and death rate work together to determine both continuity and size of a population of organisms.

   b. What other factors contribute to the size of a population of organisms? How?

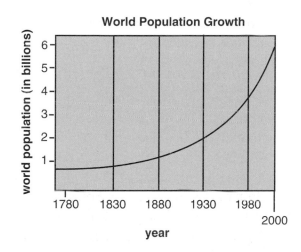

World Population Growth

world population (in billions)

year

- Starting in the year AD 1, it took more than 1,500 years for the population size to double.
- Starting in the year 1900, it took about 75 years for the population size to double.
- In 1980, the number of babies that died in their first year of life was one-fourth the number that died in 1940.

Figure Ev.11 How does reproductive success affect population size?

2. The behavior of animals such as crickets plays an important role in reproductive success. Read this short description from *Science* magazine about the results of a research project that used a robot model of a cricket.

NEED TO KNOW

Modeling Behavior

A psychologist in the United Kingdom, Barbara Webb, used a robot cricket to model the way crickets use call songs to find mates. Webb had hypothesized that a cricket's complex behavior of moving toward a calling mate may result from simple reflexes that could be mimicked in a robot cricket that had sound sensors.

 The robot was programmed to respond to a specific set of syllables from a recording of a male cricket's song. When this recording was played, the robot moved toward the speakers. When the syllables of the recorded cricket song were altered, the robot became "confused." And when key syllables were separated between two speakers, the robot went to a spot halfway between the speakers before "choosing" one and heading toward it.

Figure Ev.12   Modeling behavior of even relatively simple organisms such as crickets has proven difficult. Why do you think this is so?

    a. Explain how these results relate to what you know about mating behavior in animals, including humans.

  3. Say you were to invent two new types of contraceptives, one hormonal and the other physical. What would they be and how would they work?

Chapter 11 Continuity of Information through Inheritance

  1. In the laboratory, scientists can use enzymes to remove the cell walls from plant cells in growing tissue. This produces protoplasts. Protoplasts then can be placed on a growth medium in a petri dish. If the medium contains the proper mixture of plant hormones, a single isolated protoplast can divide and eventually produce a whole plant.

    a. What does this observation tell you about the genetic material of a plant cell?

    b. How does genetic material affect continuity in sexually reproducing organisms? in asexually reproducing organisms?

Chapter 12 Gene Action

  1. How is the molecular structure of genetic information important to the replication and expression of genes? In your response, describe the similarities and differences among the following molecular processes: replication, transcription, and translation.

2. How is it possible that a change in a single nucleotide of a gene can produce a mutant protein? Will such a change in a nucleotide always produce a mutant protein? Explain.

Unit 5 Development: Growth and Differentiation in Living Systems

Chapter 13 Processes and Patterns of Development

1. Plants and animals adjust to environmental changes in many ways. Read the following brief description of several adaptations to change. Then complete the task below.

NEED TO KNOW

Adaptations to Change

We are bothered much less by flying insects, such as flies and mosquitoes, in the winter than in the summer. What happens to those insects in the winter months? There are regions where winters are very cold and the land often is covered by snow or lakes are frozen over. Here organisms display a wide variety of adaptations that help them survive the harsh conditions. For example, the sap in broad-leafed deciduous trees, such as maple, apple, and oak, withdraws into the roots and trunk. Leaves fall off and new ones grow in the spring. Animals may migrate, as do many birds. They may slow their activity and enter a prolonged sleep (as do bears and skunks). Or they may enter a dormant state of hibernation (as do ground squirrels). In this state, metabolic activity and body temperature drop significantly.

Adult insects have hard exoskeletons. Their bodies are filled with bloodlike liquid in which their organs are suspended. Insects cannot easily regulate body temperature and can be damaged by freezing. With their small size, migration is difficult. Monarch butterflies, however, manage to use this strategy successfully. Some insects bury themselves in a protected place. But most insects in harsh climates survive winter in an immature developmental stage. Those species lay eggs prior to cold seasons, and then the adults die. The eggs, larvae, or pupae spend the winter in a protected spot. They become active and continue their development in the spring.

Figure Ev.13
Crown gall on (a) tomato plant and (b) laurel tree.

Use either deciduous trees or insects as an example. Describe how their pattern of development represents an adaptation for extreme seasonal differences in temperature.

2. A tumorous disease of tomato and tobacco plants known as crown gall can result from the action of a bacterium, called *Agrobacterium tumefaciens*. This bacterium infects a wound on the plant stem (see Figure Ev.13). Those bacteria contain copies of a DNA plasmid with special genes that can transform the growth regulation of plant cells. The bacterial genes incorporate into the plant's genetic material. Here those genes direct plant cells to make unusual amino acids that are useless to the plant but serve as food for the

bacteria. A mass of undifferentiated tissue at the infected site soon grows into a tumor.

Describe how that bacteria-induced tumor compares with cancer in humans. How is the tumor different from cancer?

Chapter 14 The Human Life Span

1. People go through the same life stages. Each generation, however, does so at a different time in history. A high school student named Rachel was 15 years old in 2003. Her parents were 15 in 1974. They listened to music by the Beatles and the Rolling Stones recorded on large vinyl records. Rachel's grandparents were 15 in 1949, shortly after World War II. They liked to dance to a big band sound and listen to shows on the radio.

   a. Make a table that compares the physical biology and the cultural setting for a single life stage of three generations. For example, your chart could include you, your parents at your age, and your grandparents at your age. (If you prefer not to use your own family, use a family that you know about or have read about.) You can use any life stage as long as you have information that corresponds to each generation.

   b. Make two columns. Label one *Physical Biology* and the other *Cultural Setting*. Under each column, describe the characteristics that apply to each of your individuals.

   c. Write a few sentences that describe the differences in the life stage of the various individuals according to the historical setting in which they take place.

Unit 6 Ecology: Interaction and Interdependence in Living Systems

Chapter 15 Interdependence among Organisms in the Biosphere

1. An instrument aboard NASA's *Nimbus-7* satellite records data from the surface water of the Atlantic Ocean off the U.S. coast. This instrument is called a Coastal Zone Color Scanner, or CZCS. It measures infrared radiation and concentrations of chlorophyll pigments. The pattern of radiation corresponds to water temperature. The patterns of both radiation and chlorophyll correspond to currents and tidal mixing. The highest concentrations of chlorophyll pigments are found near the shore. The lower concentrations are found in the relatively unmixed waters of the warm Gulf Stream current.

   To answer the following questions about interdependence, keep in mind that some places in the ocean have high concentrations of phytoplankton. Phytoplankton are photosynthetic microorganisms that drift with ocean currents. (You also may find it useful to review the discussion of photosynthesis in Chapter 8.)

a. The CZCS instrument on board the *Nimbus-7* can take measurements only from the surface water of the ocean. Is this where you would expect to find phytoplankton? Explain the basis for your answer.

b. How could the *Nimbus-7* data be useful for managing commercial fisheries?

2. Population growth rates are easy to see on graphs. They typically have a characteristic shape that reflects the involvement of limiting factors. Use your knowledge of these types of graphs to complete the following task:

a. Draw a graph that illustrates the growth of any population of organisms over a period of at least 10 generations.

You can pick a general type of organism such as insects for your graph.

b. Label your graph. Make sure the reader can tell how many generations have passed and what type of organism is represented.

c. Pick three distinct points on different parts of your graphed line. Label them A, B, C. Describe what is happening to the population at points A, B, and C.

Include a discussion of limiting factors to help explain your answer.

d. What point on the graph represents the carrying capacity for your population? Explain.

Chapter 16 Decision Making in a Complex World

1. A panel of lawmakers has met to consider zoning for 200 acres of land near a large forest that currently includes wetlands and a meadow. One development company wants to build a shopping center and apartments on most of this land. Another company proposes building a manufacturing plant there. Conservation groups want to protect the wetlands. Various specialists have provided reports that mention the following observations about natural land and human development:

◆ Nitrogen acts as a fertilizer for leafy parts of plants and for some microorganisms. Too much of this fertilizer causes plants to grow large tops and insufficient roots.

◆ Forests may help protect the world from global warming by converting carbon dioxide to plant mass by way of photosynthesis.

◆ Acid rain results from certain air pollutants produced by industrial processes. Its effects on living systems are complex.

◆ Nitrogen cycling is the conversion of atmospheric nitrogen into nitrogen that living organisms can use. In this process, nitrogen-fixing bacteria convert nitrogen gas, N_2, into chemical forms that biological systems can use (such as ammonium, nitrates, and nitrites). When an organism dies, different microorganisms (called denitrifying bacteria) decompose the organism's body. This releases some of its nitrogen back into nonbiological systems. Many denitrifying bacteria live in boggy wetland environments.

The panel is ready to make a decision, but now a new finding is presented.

NEED TO KNOW

NITRATES

In a study in Germany, where acid rain is a serious problem, scientists used radioisotope labels to trace nitrates leaving a forest through runoff water. Figure Ev.14 shows what happened to the nitrates in three stands of trees. For a control, the scientists compared their results with a tropical forest undisturbed by human habitation.

If nitrates move through soil without being taken up by living systems, then plants are deprived of the benefits of nitrogen. In addition, the free nitrates can remove other important nutrients that plants need, such as calcium and magnesium. The soil left behind is acidic enough to harm tree roots and kill microorganisms. In these conditions, old trees may die and young trees grow very slowly and may be stunted.

Relationship between Forest Health and Air Pollution

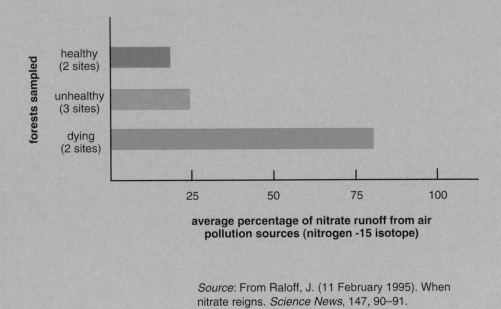

Source: From Raloff, J. (11 February 1995). When nitrate reigns. *Science News*, 147, 90–91.

Figure Ev.14   Tracking nitrate pollution.

Your task is to discuss the following:

a. How do the data in Figure Ev.14 support the concerns of scientists who claim that acid rain and excessive nitrates from pollution cause damage to trees?

b. List all of the possible biological and nonbiological consequences of developing the land. Then list the consequences of not developing the land.

c. Think about the findings reported in Figure Ev.14 and those from the earlier reports. How might these findings influence the panel's decision about how or whether the land in question should be developed?

d. What would you decide to do? Why?

Building a Portfolio of Scientific Literacy

In this activity, you will prepare a portfolio that shows your qualifications to be a scientifically literate citizen. To fill the job, you need to be able to reason, use evidence to support your ideas, and think conceptually about biology. That means you need more than just facts about biology. You must demonstrate that you understand those facts and how to use them. You will choose samples of your work from throughout the year. You may want to improve some of those samples to accurately show your progress. In addition, you may create new work to make your presentation the best show of your success.

PROCESS AND PROCEDURES

1. Obtain a rubric for the portfolio from your teacher. Read the rubric carefully. Discuss the criteria with your partner.

   Ask your teacher any questions about the project that you or your partner cannot answer from the rubric.

2. Review the chapters. Record in your journal what you think the main concepts are from each chapter. Do this by making a table. Create one column for the titles of the chapters in each unit. Add a second column to record the main concepts or ideas from each chapter.

3. Let your teacher review your table of concepts before you prepare your portfolio.

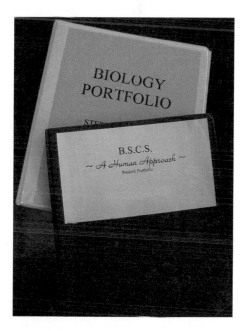

4. Look over your work for each chapter. Select the examples you think will make up the best portfolio for your interview as a scientifically literate citizen. Follow the criteria in the rubric for selecting work.

   a. Decide how to display your samples of work to make a portfolio for your interview.

   b. Find an example of work to illustrate the key concept(s) of each chapter. Use examples of your work just as they are. Or make corrections or additions if you think you understand the concepts and the particular activity better than when you did it.

      Remember, you can use additional resources to help you improve an existing activity. Use the essays, your journal, your teammates, or outside references.

   c. If you are missing good examples of work from some chapters, add new work to your portfolio. Choose at least one chapter question to answer from the collection of questions in the *Chapter Challenges*.

      You can put this new work in the portfolio along with the samples of your previous work.

5. Prepare a caption for each example in the portfolio. Each caption should include the information explained in the portfolio rubric.

Include a caption for all work in the portfolio, both existing work and new work.

Analysis

1. When you think your portfolio is complete, take time to look through it. Decide if you would get the job as a scientifically literate citizen. Be sure that you have organized your portfolio so that any reader can easily find and understand your work examples.

2. Have your portfolio reviewed as your teacher directs.

3. Revise your portfolio based on your self-evaluation and feedback that you receive.

APPENDIX A
Laboratory Safety

The laboratory has the potential to be either a safe place or a dangerous place. The difference depends on how well you know and follow safe laboratory practices. It is important that you read the information here and learn how to recognize and avoid potentially hazardous situations. Basic rules for working safely in the laboratory include the following:

1. Be prepared. Study the assigned activity before you come to class. Resolve any questions about the procedures before you begin to work.

2. Be organized. Arrange the materials you need for the activity in an orderly way.

3. Maintain a clean, open work area. This area should be free of anything except those materials you need for the assigned activity. Store books, backpacks, and purses out of the way. Keep laboratory materials away from the edge of the work surface.

4. Tie back long hair and remove dangling jewelry. Roll up long sleeves and tuck long neckties into shirts. Do not wear loose-fitting sleeves or open-toed shoes in the laboratory.

5. Wear safety goggles and a lab apron whenever you work with chemicals, hot liquids, lab burners, hot plates, or apparatuses that could break or shatter. Wear protective gloves when working with preserved specimens, toxic and corrosive chemicals, or when otherwise directed to do so.

6. Never wear contact lenses while conducting any experiment involving chemicals. If you must wear them (by a physician's order), inform your teacher *before* conducting any experiment involving chemicals.

7. Never use direct or reflected sunlight to illuminate your microscope or any other optical device. Direct or reflected sunlight can cause serious damage to your retinas.

8. Keep your hands away from the sharp or pointed ends of equipment, such as scalpels, dissecting needles, or scissors.

9. Observe all cautions in the procedural steps of the activities. **CAUTION** and **WARNING** are signal words used in the text and on labeled chemicals or reagents. These words tell you about the potential for harm and/or injury. They remind you to observe specific safety practices. ***Always read and follow these statements.*** They are meant to help keep you and your fellow students safe.

CAUTION statements advise you that the material or procedure has *some potential risk* of harm or injury if directions are not followed.

WARNING statements advise you that the material or procedure has a *moderate risk* of harm or injury if directions are not followed.

10. Become familiar with the caution symbols identified in the need to know box.

NEED TO KNOW

Caution

Safety Symbols Used in This Program

Caution

The caution symbol alerts you to procedures or materials that may be harmful if directions are not followed properly. You may encounter the following common hazards during this course:

sharp object

Sharp objects can cause injury, either a cut or a puncture. Handle all sharp objects with caution. Use them only as your teacher instructs you. Do not use them for any purpose other than the one intended. If you do get a cut or puncture wound, call your teacher and get first aid.

irritant

An irritant is any substance that, on contact, can cause reddening of living tissue. Wear safety goggles, lab apron, and protective gloves when handling any irritating chemical. In case of contact, flush the affected area with soap and water for at least 15 minutes. Call your teacher. Remove contaminated clothing.

reactive

These chemicals are capable of reacting with any other substance, including water. They can cause a violent reaction. **Do not** mix a reactive chemical with any other substance, including water, unless directed to do so by your teacher. Wear your safety goggles, lab apron, and protective gloves.

corrosive

A corrosive substance injures or destroys body tissue on contact by direct chemical action. When handling any corrosive substance, wear safety goggles, lab apron, and protective gloves. In case of contact with a corrosive material, immediately flush the affected area with water. Call your teacher.

biohazard

Any biological substance that can cause infection through exposure is a biohazard. Before handling any material so labeled, review your teacher's specific instructions. **Do not** handle in any manner other than as instructed. Wear safety goggles, lab apron, and protective gloves. Any contact with a biohazard should be reported to your teacher immediately.

Safety goggles

Safety goggles are for eye protection. Wear goggles whenever you see this symbol. If you wear glasses, be sure the goggles fit comfortably over them. In case of splashes into your eyes, flush your eyes (including under the lid) at an eyewash station for 15–20 minutes. If you wear contact lenses, remove them *immediately* and flush your eyes as directed. Call your teacher.

Safety Goggles

NEED TO KNOW

Safety Symbols Used in This Program

Lab apron

A lab apron is intended to protect your clothing. Whenever you see this symbol, put on your apron and tie it securely behind you. If you spill any substance on your clothing, call your teacher.

Lab Apron

Gloves

Wear gloves when you see this symbol or whenever your teacher directs you to do so. Wear them when using *any* chemical or reagent solution. Do not wear your gloves for an extended period of time.

Lab Gloves

Flammable

A flammable substance is any material capable of igniting under certain conditions. Do not bring flammable materials into contact with open flames or near heat sources unless instructed to do so by your teacher. Remember that flammable liquids give off vapors that can be ignited by a nearby heat source. Should a fire occur, *do not* attempt to extinguish it yourself. Call your teacher. Wear safety goggles, lab apron, and protective gloves whenever you handle a flammable substance.

Flammable!

Poison

Poisons can cause injury by direct action within a body system through direct contact with skin, inhalation, ingestion, or penetration. Always wear safety goggles, lab apron, and protective gloves when handling any material with this label. If you have any preexisting injuries to your skin, inform your teacher before you handle any poison. In case of contact, call your teacher immediately.

Poison!

11. Never put anything in your mouth. Never touch or taste substances in the laboratory unless your teacher specifically instructs you to do so.

12. Never smell substances in the laboratory without specific instructions from your teacher. Even then, do not inhale fumes directly. Wave the air above the substance toward your nose and sniff carefully.

13. Never eat, drink, chew gum, or apply cosmetics in the laboratory. Do not store food or beverages in the lab area.

14. Know the location of all safety equipment. Learn how to use each piece of equipment.

15. If you witness an unsafe incident, an accident, or a chemical spill, report it to your teacher immediately.

16. Use materials only from containers labeled with the name of the chemical and the precautions to be used. Become familiar with the safety precautions for each chemical by reading the label before use.

17. To dilute acid with water, *always add the acid to the water*.

18. Never return unused chemicals to the stock bottles. Do not put any object into a chemical bottle, except the dropper with which it may be equipped.

19. Clean up thoroughly. Dispose of chemicals. Wash used glassware and instruments according to the teacher's instructions. Clean tables and sinks. Put away all equipment and supplies. Make sure all water, gas jets, burners, and electrical appliances are turned off. Return all laboratory materials and equipment to their proper places.

20. Wash your hands thoroughly after handling any living organisms or hazardous material. Do this *before* leaving the laboratory.

21. Never perform unauthorized experiments. Do only those experiments your teacher approves.

22. Never work alone in the laboratory. Never work without your teacher's supervision.

23. Approach laboratory work with maturity. Never run, push, or engage in horseplay or practical jokes of any type in the laboratory. Use laboratory materials and equipment only as directed.

In addition to observing these general safety precautions, you need to know about some specific categories of safety. Before you do any laboratory work, familiarize yourself with the following precautions.

Heat

1. Use only the heat source specified in the activity.

2. Never allow flammable materials such as alcohol near a flame or any other source of ignition.

3. When heating a substance in a test tube, point the mouth of the tube away from other students and you.

4. Never leave a lighted lab burner, hot plate, or any other hot objects unattended.

5. Never reach over an exposed flame or other heat source.

6. Use tongs, test tube clamps, insulated gloves, or potholders to handle hot equipment.

Glassware

1. Never use cracked or chipped glassware.

2. Use caution and proper equipment when handling hot glassware. Remember, hot glass looks the same as cool glass.

3. Make sure glassware is clean before you use it and when you store it.

4. To put glass tubing into a rubber stopper, moisten the tubing and the stopper. Protect your hands with a heavy cloth when you insert or remove glass tubing from a rubber stopper. Never force or twist the tubing.

5. Immediately sweep up broken glassware. Discard it in a special, labeled container for broken glass. ***Never pick up broken glass with your fingers.***

Electrical Equipment and Other Apparatuses

1. Before you begin any work, learn how to use each piece of apparatus safely and correctly in order to obtain accurate scientific information.

2. Never use equipment with frayed insulation or loose or broken wires.

3. Make sure the area in and around the electrical equipment is dry and free of flammable materials. Never touch electrical equipment with wet hands.

4. Turn off all power switches before plugging an appliance into an outlet. Never jerk wires from outlets or pull appliance plugs out by the wire.

Living and Preserved Specimens

1. Be sure that specimens for dissection are properly mounted and supported. Do not cut a specimen while holding it in your hand.

2. Wash your work surface with a disinfectant solution both before and after using live microorganisms.

3. Always wash your hands with soap and water after working with live or preserved specimens.

4. Care for animals humanely. General rules for their care are listed below.

   a. Always follow carefully your teacher's instructions about the care of laboratory animals.

   b. Keep the animals in a suitable, escape-proof container in a location where they will not be disturbed constantly.

   c. Keep the containers clean. Clean cages of small birds and mammals daily. Provide proper ventilation, light, and temperature.

   d. Provide water at all times.

   e. Feed regularly, depending on the animals' needs.

   f. Treat laboratory animals gently and with kindness in all situations.

   g. If you are responsible for the regular care of any animals, be sure to make arrangements for their care during weekends, holidays, and vacations.

   h. Your teacher will provide a suitable method to dispose of or release animals, if it becomes necessary.

5. Many plants or plant parts are poisonous. Work only with the plants your teacher specifies. Never put any plant or plant parts in your mouth.

6. Handle plants carefully and gently. Most plants must have light, soil, and water, although the specific requirements differ.

7. Wear the following personal protective equipment when handling or dissecting preserved specimens: safety goggles, lab apron, and plastic gloves.

Accident Procedures

1. Report **all** accidents, incidents, and injuries, and all breakage and spills, no matter how minor, to your teacher.

2. If a chemical spills on your skin or clothing, wash it off immediately with plenty of water. Have a classmate notify your teacher immediately.

3. If a chemical gets in your eyes or on your face, wash immediately at the eyewash fountain with plenty of water. Flush your eyes for at least 15 minutes, including under each eyelid. Have a classmate notify your teacher immediately.

4. If a chemical spills on the floor or work surface, do not clean it up yourself. Notify your teacher immediately.

5. If a thermometer breaks, do not touch the broken pieces with your bare hands. Notify your teacher immediately.

6. In case of a lab table fire, notify your teacher immediately. In case of a clothing fire, drop to the floor and roll. Use a fire blanket if one is available. Have a classmate notify your teacher immediately.

7. Report to your teacher all cuts and abrasions received in the laboratory, no matter how small.

Chemical Safety

All chemicals are hazardous in some way. A hazardous chemical is defined as a substance that is likely to cause injury. Chemicals can be placed in four hazard categories: flammable, toxic, corrosive, and reactive.

In the laboratory investigations for this course, we have made every effort to minimize the use of dangerous materials. However, many "less hazardous" chemicals can cause injury if not handled properly. The following information will help you become aware of the types of chemical hazards that exist and of how you can reduce the risk of injury when using chemicals. Before you work with any chemical, be sure to review safety rules 1–23 described at the beginning of this appendix.

Flammable substances. Flammable substances are solids, liquids, or gases that will burn. The process of burning involves three interrelated components—fuel (any substance capable of burning), oxidizer (often air or a specific chemical), and ignition source (a spark, flame, or heat). The three components are represented in the diagram of a fire triangle in Figure A.1. For burning to take place, all three components (sides) of the fire

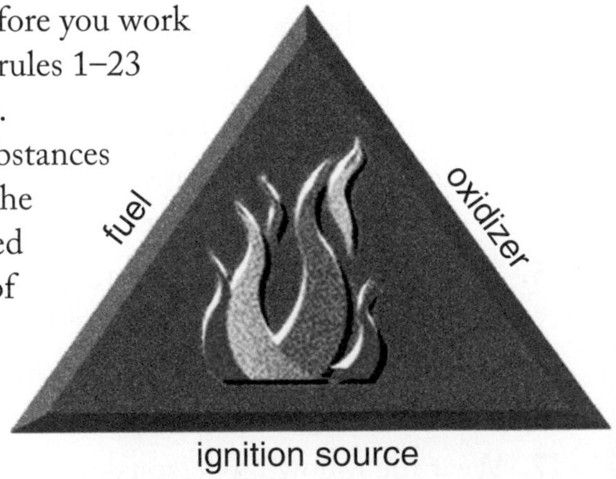

Figure A.1 The fire triangle. To control a fire, one must remove or make inaccessible at least one side of the fire triangle.

triangle must be present. To control fire hazard, one must remove, or otherwise make inaccessible, at least one side of the fire triangle.

Flammable chemicals should not be used in the presence of ignition sources, such as lab burners, hot plates, and sparks from electrical equipment or static electricity. Containers of flammables should be closed when not in use. Sufficient ventilation in the laboratory will help to keep the concentration of flammable vapors to a minimum.

Toxic substances. Most of the chemicals you encounter in a laboratory are toxic, or poisonous to life. The degree of toxicity depends on the properties of the specific substance, its concentration, the type of exposure, and other variables. The effects of a toxic substance can range from minor discomfort to serious illness or death. Exposure to toxic substances can occur through ingestion, skin contact, or inhalation of toxic vapors. Wearing a lab apron, safety goggles, and plastic gloves is an important precautionary measure when using toxic chemicals. A clean work area, prompt spill cleanup, and good ventilation also are important.

Corrosive substances. Corrosive chemicals are solids, liquids, or gases that by direct chemical action either destroy living tissue or cause permanent changes in the tissue. Corrosive substances can destroy eye and respiratory-tract tissues. The consequences of mishandling a corrosive substance can be impaired sight or permanent blindness, severe disfigurement, permanent severe breathing difficulties, and even death. As with toxic substances, wear a lab apron, safety goggles, and plastic gloves when handling corrosive chemicals to help prevent contact with your skin or eyes. Immediately wash off splashes on your skin or eyes while a classmate notifies the teacher.

Reactive substances. Under certain conditions, reactive chemicals promote violent reactions. A chemical may explode spontaneously or when it is mechanically disturbed. Reactive chemicals also include those that react rapidly when mixed with another chemical, releasing a large amount of energy. Keep chemicals separate from each other unless they are being combined according to specific instructions in an activity. Heed any other cautions your teacher may give you.

APPENDIX B

NEED TO KNOW

Techniques

Technique 1   Journals

You will use a journal on a regular basis in this program. Scientific journals have many purposes. They provide a place to record data, take notes, reflect on your progress, or respond to questions. This journal will become your permanent record of your work. You will refer to it often during discussions and assessments. The more complete your journal is, the more valuable it will be for you.

Your journal should be a spiral notebook or a hardcover book that is permanently bound. (Do not use a loose-leaf notebook or a spiral notebook with perforated pages that tear out.) A notebook with square-grid pages (graph paper) will make any graphing that you do much easier.

The following sections describe the major ways in which you will use your journal in this program.

Recording Data

Science depends on accurate data. No one—not even the original observer—can trust the accuracy of confusing, vague, or incomplete data. Scientific record-keeping is the process by which you maintain neat, organized, and accurate records of your observations and data. Use a pen to record data. Although your interpretation of data may change, *the original data are a permanent record.*

Keep records in a diary form. Record the date at the beginning of each entry. Keep the records of each activity separate. Be brief but to the point when recording data in words. It may not be necessary to use complete sentences, but single words seldom are descriptive enough to represent accurately what you have observed or done.

Sometimes the easiest way to record data is to draw an illustration. Such drawings need not be works of art. But they should be accurate representations of what you have observed. Keep the drawings simple. Use a hard pencil, and include clearly written labels. Often the easiest way to record numerical data is in the form of a table. When you record data numerically for counts or measurements, include the units of measurements you used, for example, degrees Celsius or centimeters.

Do not record your data on other papers and then copy the data into your journal. Doing so may increase neatness, but it will decrease accuracy. Your journal is your book. Blots and stains are a normal circumstance of field and laboratory work.

You will do much of your laboratory work as a member of a team. Your journal, therefore, will contain data that other team members have contributed. Keep track of the source of observations by circling (or recording in a different color) the data that others reported.

Responding to Questions

When you answer discussion or Analysis questions, record the date and activity title. Then number each response. You also may find it useful to record the questions. Sometimes you will respond to questions individually and sometimes with your team. Indicate whether your responses are your own or your team's. As you are writing your responses, practice writing in complete sentences; this will help you when you synthesize and present ideas. After each answer that you write, leave blank space where you can add questions or comments that arise as your understanding grows.

Taking Notes

Always begin with the date. Then record the source of information. Often, this is a person or a book, but it could be a video, Internet site, or a computer program. When recording notes, change lines for each new idea. Try to group related ideas under broad headings that will help you remember the important ideas and how they are connected. Write down more than you think you will need. It is hard to make sense of a few words when you look back at them later. Include diagrams and charts to clarify ideas.

It is often valuable to take notes during team discussions and class discussions as well as when your teacher is presenting ideas or instructions. In addition, taking notes in your journal as you read helps you better absorb the written information.

You can use the information in your journal to prepare for discussions or to review what you have learned. At times, you also will use the information that you have recorded in your journal to complete assessment activities.

Keeping Track of Your Questions

Often, as you read or work through an activity, a question will come to mind or you will find that you are confused about something. If you cannot talk with your teammates or your teacher right away, jot down your question or confusion in your journal so that you will remember to ask about it when you have the opportunity. You also may use this technique to record questions that you want to answer yourself.

Keeping Track of Your Responsibilities

Because you will use your journal every day in science class, it is a good place to record your class assignments and responsibilities. Each day, you may want to record these in red in the upper corner of your journal page.

Using Your Journal during Assessment

At times throughout this program, you will use your journal during assessments. These include both ongoing assessments, such as class discussions and team presentations, and more formal, end-of-unit assessments. Your teacher will collect your journal periodically to assess your progress. Using a journal for assessment will be a rewarding experience if your entries are complete, detailed, and well organized. Remember, make it easy for someone else reading your journal to understand what you have recorded. Using blank space to separate activities, notes, and data will make your journal easier to assess. It will provide space for you to add new information if needed. Keep this in mind as you make entries in your journal.

Technique 2   Graphing

Graphs are visual representations of numerical data. They help us see patterns that we might not see if we looked at numbers alone. Graphs make it easy to see at a glance what happened in an experiment. We also can use the patterns we observe in graphs to predict future changes or events.

Different graphs serve different purposes. For example, a line graph is a good way to show the relationship between two sets of numbers. Figure B.1 shows a line graph that relates the number of days and the number of individuals in a laboratory population of microorganisms. A bar graph (also called a histogram) is a good way to show the distribution of measurements among a particular group of objects. Figure B.2 shows a bar graph of shoe sizes among the girls in a high school biology class.

A graph has two major lines. One runs horizontally, and one runs vertically on the page. These lines are called the *axes* (singular: axis). The horizontal line is the *x*-axis. The vertical line is the *y*-axis. The point at which these two lines meet is the place where the graph begins.

Both axes include a sequence of numbers called a *number scale*. The numbers on the *x*-axis read from left to right. Those on the *y*-axis read from bottom to top. The number scale is not necessarily the same on both axes. Look at Figure B.1. The number scale on the *x*-axis reads from 0 to 30; in Figure B.2, the scale reads from 5 to 9. What is the number scale on the *y*-axis of each graph?

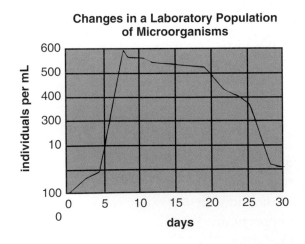

Figure B.1   Line graph.

Graphs should be labeled to help the reader understand them. Look again at Figures B.1 and B.2. Each axis is labeled to explain to the reader what the numbers represent. And each graph has a title that describes the relationship that the graph displays.

Making a graph involves several important steps. The steps in Part A will help you draw any line graph. The steps in Part B will help you draw any bar graph.

Materials (per person)

2 sheets of graph paper
ruler

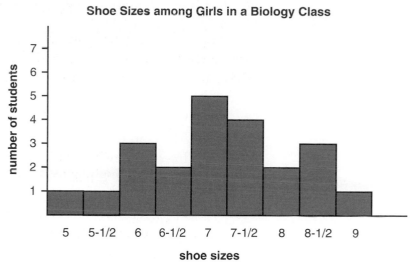

Figure B.2   Bar graph.

PROCESS AND PROCEDURES

Part A   Line Graphs

1. Review the data in Figure B.3.

   Before you can make a graph using data that you have collected, you need to organize your data into a data table. For this practice in graphing, you will use the data in Figure B.3.

2. Draw the *x*-axis and the *y*-axis for the graph.

   Use a ruler and graph paper so that your lines will be straight and perpendicular (see Figure B.4a).

3. Identify what information will go on the *x*-axis and what information will go on the *y*-axis.

   Information on the *x*-axis is usually constant in nature. This might be items such as dates, numbers, miles, and sizes. Information on the *y*-axis is variable in nature. This could be the number of mice caught, the number of people of a certain height, or the number of butterflies captured.

4. Label each axis of the graph using the headings in the data table.

5. Set up the number scales on each axis.

   Allow space on each axis for all the numbers that are included in the data table (see Figure B.4b). (A number scale does not have to start with the number 1. But the numbers do need to be spaced in equal increments.)

NUMBER OF MICE CAUGHT IN A FIELD	
Day	Number of mice caught per 100 traps per night
0	25
30	45
60	38
90	30
120	20
150	14
180	13
210	8
240	7
270	11
300	4
330	13

Figure B.3   Table showing the number of mice caught.

6. Give your graph a descriptive title.

7. Plot the data on your graph by doing the following:

    a. Read one row of data from the data table, for example, day 0 and 25 mice caught.

    b. Find the number on the *x*-axis where the piece of corresponding data fits (for example, 0).

    c. Move up from the number on the *x*-axis to the place on the *y*-axis where the corresponding piece of data fits (for example, 25).

    d. Draw a dot, called a *data point*, at that place.

    e. Repeat steps a–d for all the pieces of data in the data table.

        Figure B.4c illustrates 5 data points. Can you determine where the remaining data points go?

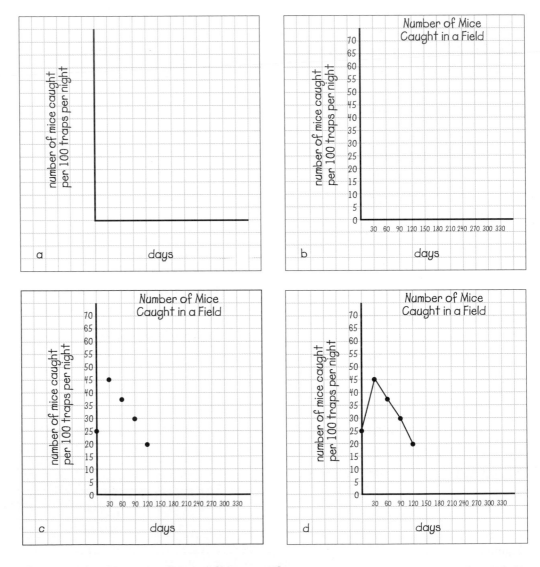

Figure B.4 **How to draw a line graph.**

8. Draw a smooth line from left to right that connects the data points. This should help you see the relationship between the data points.

In this case, the line illustrates how the number of mice caught changed throughout the year. See Figure B.4d.

Part B Bar Graphs

1. Review the data in Figure B.5.
2. Draw the x- and y-axes for the graph.
3. Decide which information goes on each axis (refer to Figure B.6a).
4. Label each axis. Use the headings in the data table.
5. Decide on the number scales or labels for each axis. Position the numbers on the x-axis so that you can draw bars in the spaces between the lines. Place the numbers on the vertical axis next to the lines so that you can end a bar between two numbers, if necessary.

Figure B.6b will help you with this step.

6. Add a title to your graph.
7. Plot the data by following these steps:
   a. Read 1 row of data from the data table, for example, year 1900 and population size 90.
   b. Find the label for the corresponding piece of data on the x-axis of the graph (for example, 1900).
   c. Move up the column above the label to the appropriate number for that piece of data on the y-axis (for example, 90).
   d. Draw a horizontal line at that number to make the top of the bar.
   e. Color in the bar from that line down to the x-axis.
   f. Repeat steps a–e for all the pieces of data in the data table (see Figure B.6c).

POPULATION OF HEATH HENS, MARTHA'S VINEYARD, MA

Year	Population size
1900	90
1905	45
1910	280
1915	2,010
1920	550
1925	40
1930	10

Figure B.5 Table showing the population of heath hens.

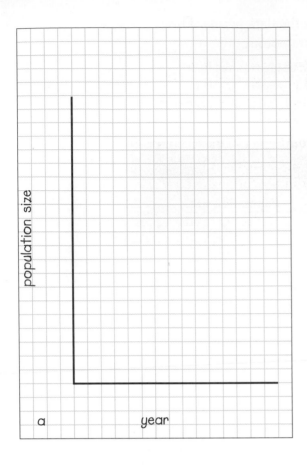

a

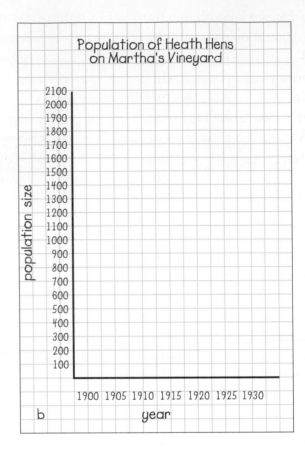

b

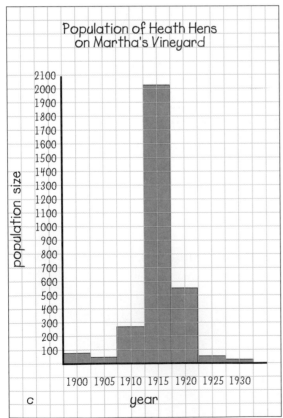

c

Figure B.6 **How to draw a bar graph.**

Technique 3   Measurement

Scientists measure things according to the *Système Internationale d'Unités* (International System of Units), more commonly referred to as "SI." SI is a modification of the older metric system. It was used first in France and now is the common system of measurement throughout the world.

Among the basic units of SI measurement are the meter (length), the kilogram (mass), the Kelvin (temperature), and the second (time). All other SI units are derived from these four. Some of these units are described in the following sections. You will use some of these units in your laboratory work.

Length

1 kilometer (km) = 1,000 meters = 10^3 m
1 hectometer (hm) = 100 meters = 10^2 m
1 dekameter (dkm) = 10 meters = 10^1 m
1 meter (m)
1 decimeter (dm) = 0.1 meter = 10^{-1} m
1 centimeter (cm) = 0.01 meter = 10^{-2} m
1 millimeter (mm) = 0.001 meter = 10^{-3} m
1 micrometer (μm) = 0.000001 meter = 10^{-6} m
1 nanometer (nm) = 0.000000001 meter = 10^{-9} m

The meter is the basic unit of length. Its increments increase or decrease by the power of 10. For example, measurements under microscopes often are made in micrometers, which is one-millionth of a meter. Still smaller measurements are made in nanometers. You might use nanometers to measure wavelengths of light that plants use in photosynthesis. The units of length you will use most frequently in the laboratory are centimeters (cm) and millimeters (mm).

Units of area are derived from units of length by multiplying two lengths. One hectometer squared is one measure that often is used in ecological studies. It commonly is called a hectare and equals 10,000 m^2. Measurements of area made in the laboratory most frequently are in centimeters squared (cm^2).

Mass

1 kilogram (kg) = 1,000 grams = 10^3 g
1 hectogram (hg) = 100 grams = 10^2 g
1 dekagram (dkg) = 10 grams = 10^1 g
1 gram (g)
1 decigram (dg) = 0.1 gram = 10^{-1} g
1 centigram (cg) = 0.01 gram = 10^{-2} g
1 milligram (mg) = 0.001 gram = 10^{-3} g
1 microgram (μg) = 0.000001 gram = 10^{-6} g
1 nanogram (ng) = 0.000000001 gram = 10^{-9} g

Like the meter, measurements of mass are based on the gram. The basic units of mass also increase or decrease by the power of 10. In the biology laboratory, measurements usually are made in kilograms, grams, centigrams, and milligrams.

Volume

1 kiloliter (kL) = 1,000 liters = 10^3 L
1 hectoliter (hL) = 100 liters = 10^2 L
1 dekaliter (dkL) = 10 liters = 10^1 L
1 liter (L)
1 deciliter (dL) = 0.1 liter = 10^{-1} L
1 centiliter (cL) = 0.01 liter = 10^{-2} L
1 milliliter (mL) = 0.001 liter = 10^{-3} L

SI units of volume are derived from units of length by multiplying length by width by height. One meter cubed (m^3) is the standard unit. Although not officially part of SI, liters are often used to measure the volume of liquids. There are 1,000 liters in one meter cubed (m^3), that is, 1 L = 0.001 m^3. One milliliter equals one centimeter cubed, that is 1 mL = 1 cm^3.

Because one meter cubed (m^3) is too large for practical use in the laboratory, we use centimeters cubed (cm^3). Volume measurements in the laboratory usually are made in glassware marked for milliliters and liters.

Temperature

Units of temperature that you will use in this course are degrees Celsius, which are equal to kelvins. On the Celsius scale, 0°C is the freezing point of water, and 100°C is the boiling point of water. Figure B.7 illustrates the Celsius scale alongside the Fahrenheit scale, which still is used in the United States. On the Fahrenheit scale, 32°F is the freezing point of water and 212°F is the boiling point of water. Figure B.7 is useful for converting from one scale to the other.

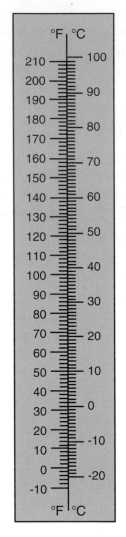

Figure B.7 A comparison of Fahrenheit and Celsius temperature scales.

Another type of measurement you will encounter is molarity (labeled with the letter *M*). Molarity measures the concentration of a dissolved substance in a solution. A high molarity indicates a high concentration. Some of the solutions that you will use in the activities are identified by their molarity.

If you wish to learn more about SI measurement, write to the U.S. Department of Commerce, National Institute of Standards and Technology (NIST), Washington, DC 20234.

Topic: SI measurement
Go to: www.scilinks.org
Code: human3E698

Technique 4   The Compound Microscope

The human eye cannot distinguish objects much smaller than 0.1 millimeter in diameter. The compound microscope is a technology often used in biology to extend vision. It allows observation of much smaller objects. The most commonly used compound microscope (pictured in Figure B.8) is monocular (that is, it has one eyepiece). Light reaches the eye after it has passed through the objects being examined. In this activity, you will learn how to use and care for a microscope.

Materials (per person or team of 2)

3 coverslips	3 microscope slides
100-mL beaker or small jar	dropping pipet
compound microscope	scissors
transparent metric ruler	lens paper
newspaper	water

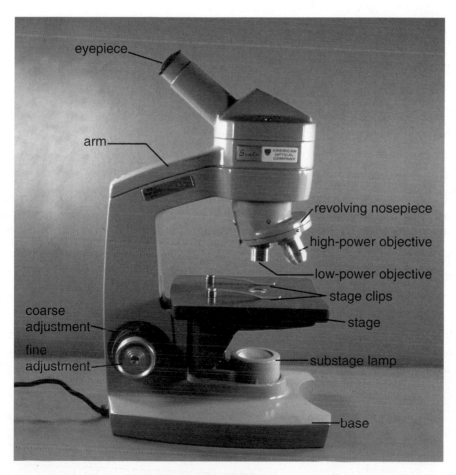

Figure B.8   Parts of a compound microscope.

PROCESS AND PROCEDURES

NEED TO KNOW

Care of the Microscope

1. The microscope is a precision instrument that requires proper care. Always carry the microscope with both hands. Put one hand under its base, the other on its arm.

2. Keep the microscope away from the edge of the table. If a lamp is attached to the microscope, keep its wire out of the way. Move everything not needed for microscope studies off your lab table.

3. Avoid tilting the microscope when using temporary slides made with water.

4. The lenses of the microscope cost almost as much as all the other parts put together. Never clean lenses with anything other than the lens paper designed for this task.

5. Always return the microscope to the low-power setting before putting it away. The high-power objective extends too close to the stage to be left in place safely.

Part A   Setting Up the Microscope

1. Rotate the low-power objective into place if it is not already there. When you change from one objective to another, you will hear the objective click into position.

2. Move the mirror so that you obtain even illumination through the opening in the stage. Or turn on the substage lamp. Most microscopes are equipped with a diaphragm for regulating light intensity. Some materials are best viewed in dim light, others in bright light.

Warning

WARNING: Never use a microscope mirror to capture direct sunlight when illuminating objects under a microscope. The mirror concentrates light rays, which can permanently damage the retina of the eye. Always use indirect light.

3. Make sure the lenses are dry and free of fingerprints and debris. Wipe lenses with lens paper only.

Part B   Using the Microscope

1. In your journal, prepare a data table similar to the one in Figure B.9.

Object being viewed	Observations and comments
Letter *o*	
Letter *c*	
Letter *e* or *r*	
mm ruler	

Figure B.9   Microscopic observations.

2. Cut a lowercase letter *o* from a piece of newspaper. Place it right side up on a clean slide. With a dropping pipet, place 1 drop of water on the letter. This type of slide is called a wet mount.

3. Wait until the paper is soaked before adding a coverslip. Hold the coverslip at about a 45° angle with the bottom edge of the coverslip touching both the coverslip and the drop of water. Then, slowly lower the coverslip. Figure B.10 shows these first steps.

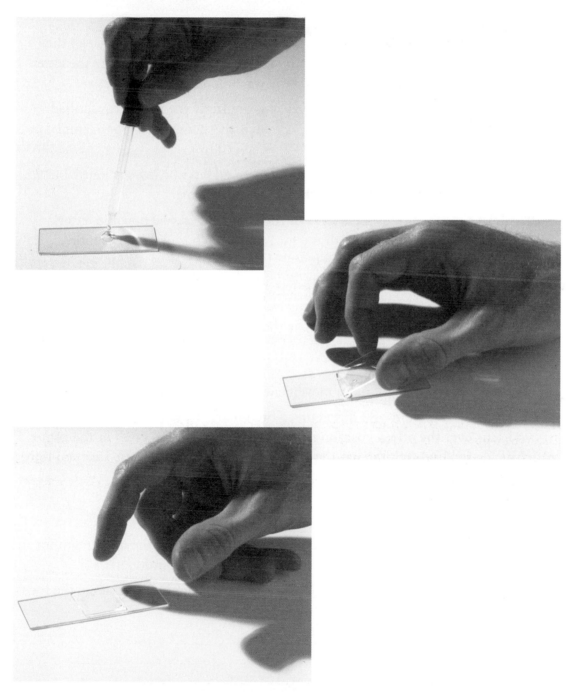

Figure B.10   Preparing a wet mount with a microscope slide and coverslip.

4. Place the slide on the microscope stage. Clamp it down with the stage clips. Move the slide so that the letter is in the middle of the hole in the stage. Use the coarse-adjustment knob to lower the low-power objective to the lowest position.

5. Look through the eyepiece. Use the coarse-adjustment knob to *raise* the objective slowly, until the letter *o* is in view.

6. If you cannot find the *o* on the first try, start the process again by repeating steps 4 and 5.

7. Once you have the *o* in view, use the fine-adjustment knob to sharpen the focus. Position the diaphragm for the best light. Compare the way the letter looks through the microscope with the way it looks to the naked eye.

8. To determine how magnified the view is, multiply the number inscribed on the eyepiece by the number on the objective being used. For example, eyepiece (10×) × objective (10×) = total (100×).

9. Follow the same procedure with a lowercase *c*. Describe in your journal how the letter appears when viewed through a microscope.

10. Make a wet mount of the letter *e* or the letter *r*. Describe how the letter appears when viewed through the microscope. What new information (not revealed by the letter *c*) is revealed by the *e* or *r*?

11. Look through the eyepiece at the letter as you use your thumbs and forefingers to move the slide slowly *away* from you. Which way does your view of the letter move? Move the slide to the right. Which way does the image move?

12. Make a pencil sketch of the letter as you see it under the microscope. Label the changes in image and in movement that take place under the microscope.

13. Make a wet mount of 2 different-colored hairs, 1 light and 1 dark. Cross 1 hair over the other. Position the slide so that the hairs cross in the center of the field. Sketch the hairs as they appear under low power. Then go to Part C.

Part C   Using High Power

1. With the crossed hairs centered under low power, adjust the diaphragm for the best light.

2. Turn the high-power objective into viewing position. Do *not* change the focus.

3. Sharpen the focus with the *fine-adjustment knob only. Do not focus under high power with the coarse-adjustment knob.* The high-power objective will touch the slide if it is in its lowest position. So you must not make large adjustments toward the slide. *Doing so can damage the objective and the slide by driving the objective into the slide.*

4. Readjust the diaphragm to get the best light. If you are not successful in finding the object under high power the first time, return to Part C, step 1. Repeat the entire procedure carefully.

5. Using the fine-adjustment knob, focus on the hairs at the point where they cross. Can you see both hairs sharply at the same focus level? How can you use the fine-adjustment knob to determine which hair is crossed over the other? Sketch the hairs as they appear under high power.

Part D   Measuring with a Microscope

1. Because objects examined with a microscope usually are small, biologists use units of length smaller than centimeters or millimeters to make microscopic measurements. One such unit is the micrometer. A micrometer is one-thousandth of a millimeter. The symbol for micrometer is μm. This is the Greek letter μ (called mu) followed by the letter *m*.

2. You can estimate the size of a microscopic object by comparing it with the size of the circular field of view. To determine the size of the field, place a transparent metric ruler on the stage. Use the low-power objective to obtain a clear image of the divisions on the ruler. Carefully move the ruler until its marked edge passes through the exact center of the field of view. Now, count the number of divisions that you can see in the field of view. The marks on the ruler will appear quite wide. One millimeter is the distance from the center of one mark to the center of the next. Record the diameter, in millimeters, of the low-power field of your microscope.

3. Remove the ruler. Replace it with the wet mount of the letter *e*. (If the mount has dried, lift the coverslip and add water.) Using low power, compare the height of the letter with the diameter of the field of view. Estimate as accurately as possible the actual height of the letter in millimeters.

Analysis

1. Summarize the differences between an image viewed through a microscope and the same image viewed with the naked eye.

2. When you view an object through the high-power objective, not all of the object may be in focus. Explain.

3. What is the relationship between magnification and the diameter of the field of view?

4. What is the diameter in micrometers of the low-power field of view of your microscope?

5. Calculate the diameter in micrometers of the high-power field. Use the following equations:

$$\frac{\text{magnification number of high-power objective}}{\text{magnification number of low-power objective}} = A$$

$$\frac{\text{diameter of low-power field of view}}{A} = \text{diameter of high-powered field of view}$$

For example, if the magnification of your low-power objective is 12× and that of your high-power is 48×, then A = 4. If the diameter of the low-power field of view is 1,600 μm, then the diameter of the high-power field of view is 1,600 ÷ 4, or 400 μm.

APPENDIX C
Supplementary Materials

Appendix 1
PROKARYOTES AND VIRUSES

Diseases Result from Interrelationships

1.1

Disease is a condition that interferes with an organism's ability to perform a vital function. An infectious disease involves a disease-causing agent, or **pathogen.** The disease results from the interaction between an organism, or **host,** and the pathogen. The pathogen infects the host. If the pathogen harms the host, symptoms of disease may appear.

How serious a disease becomes depends on the characteristics of both the host and the pathogen. The ability to cause disease is called **virulence.** The ability of an infected host to cope with a pathogen is called **resistance.** A pathogen with high virulence may cause death in a host with low resistance. A host with high resistance, however, may show only mild symptoms of the same disease. Sometimes, a moderately virulent pathogen may produce serious illness. During a famine, for example, more people die from disease than from starvation. This is because a poorly nourished host may have much less resistance than a well-fed host.

Although genetics does play a role in the ability of an organism to resist disease, much of an individual's resistance is acquired during the lifetime of the individual, rather than inherited. Resistance, whether acquired or inherited, is called **immunity.** When a pathogen infects a human host, the host produces proteins called **antibodies** that can help destroy the pathogen. In addition to antibodies, certain cells of the body's defense, or immune, system have a chemical memory. If the host survives the initial infection, these cells retain the ability to produce the same antibodies.If the same pathogen infects the host a second time, the host's body can act against it more rapidly, preventing symptoms from developing or reducing their severity.

Each type of antibody is effective against only the particular pathogen that brought about its production, or pathogens that are very similar. For example, a person can have chicken pox only once, because antibodies produced during the first infection usually prevent symptoms from developing after a second infection. These antibodies are not effective against measles, however. Because there are many types of pathogens that cause colds, immunity to one type does not confer immunity to all the others.

Many diseases can be prevented by **vaccines.** A vaccine contains only enough of the killed or weakened disease-causing agent to stimulate production of antibodies by the immune system, usually without producing symptoms of the disease. Memory cells keep later infections, by the same pathogen, from causing disease. Vaccines first were used by Edward Jenner, an English physician (see Figure A1.1).

Source: *BSCS Biology: An Ecological Approach, 10th Edition*

GUIDEPOST

What is the relationship between a pathogen and a disease?

Topic: bacteria
Go To: www.scilinks.org
Keyword: GV10E305

*SCi*LINKS
NSTA

Figure A1.1 ▲

The English physician Edward Jenner demonstrated in 1796 that by inoculating patients with a vaccine made of cowpox viruses he could protect them from the more serious disease of smallpox.

Figure A1.2 ▲

Fire blight is a disease of apples, pears, and related trees. It is caused by the bacterium *Erwinia amylovora*.

Disease may result from a variety of causes. The pathogens involved in infectious diseases may be viruses, or eubacteria or other organisms. For example, athlete's foot, ringworm, potato blight, and corn smut are caused by fungi. Protists cause malaria, African sleeping sickness, and amoebic dysentery. Many worms and insects cause diseases of plants and animals, and are important vectors, or carriers, of disease. Other diseases, such as scurvy, are the result of diet deficiencies; still others are a result of advancing age; and some, such as asthma, are brought on by reactions to substances or pollutants in the environment. Finally, some disorders, such as cystic fibrosis or Huntington disease, are hereditary.

 1.2 ▷ **Some Eubacteria Are Pathogens**

Although the vast majority of prokaryotes are beneficial or at least harmless to other organisms, some eubacteria are pathogenic. At the present time, however, no archaebacteria are known to cause disease.

Eubacterial diseases may be spread through water, food, or air. Many plant diseases are caused by eubacteria, and almost all types of plants are susceptible to one or more types of eubacterial disease. Fire blight, shown in Figure A1.2, is a common eubacterial disease that can destroy fruit trees. In Florida in 1984, an outbreak of a eubacterial disease called citrus canker led to the destruction of more than 4 million citrus seedlings in four months in an effort to halt the spread of the disease. Citrus canker is caused by one of more than 100 distinct varieties of the gram-negative eubacterium *Xanthomonas campestris*. Other varieties of this eubacterium cause diseases with similar symptoms in beans, cabbages, peaches, and other plants. Citrus canker is a continuing threat to the existence of the Florida citrus industry, an annual $8.5-billion business.

Eubacteria also cause human diseases such as cholera, leprosy, tetanus, eubacterial pneumonia, whooping cough, and diphtheria. Many eubacteria multiply in the human digestive tract and leave the body in the feces. If untreated feces enter the water supply, the eubacteria may enter another organism when it drinks the water. Waterborne diseases such as typhoid kill 6 million children each year worldwide. Most cases of food poisoning are due to eubacteria. In some cases, the eubacteria produce poisonous substances, or toxins, that are released in the food. These toxins can cause nausea, vomiting, and diarrhea within a few hours of ingestion. In the case of botulism, even a small amount of the toxin can be fatal. In other cases, eubacteria ingested with food multiply in the intestine, causing symptoms even several days after ingestion.

Many eubacteria are airborne. Whenever you open your mouth and exhale, you release droplets of moisture, each of which may contain one or two eubacteria. With a sneeze, you release many thousands of droplets at great speed. Droplets from a sneeze, visible in Figure A1.3, have been clocked at 200 miles an hour. Droplets from a cough travel at about half that speed. Each time you sneeze, you can expel from 10,000 to 100,000 individual eubacteria. The eubacteria travel through the air without being killed and may infect another person standing close to you.

Group A streptococcus (GAS) bacteria commonly infect people and cause a variety of health problems. Scientists believe that there are more than 120 different strains of GAS that each produces its own set of proteins. Some infections caused by GAS are minor, but some can be life-threatening. For example, some people may have been infected with the bacteria but don't have any illness or symptoms. These people can pass the infection to others;

Figure A1.3 ▲

Droplets from a sneeze carry disease causing agents through the air.

GAS infections are spread by direct contact with saliva or nasal mucus. One of the more common diseases caused by GAS is strep throat; people who have strep throat have a sore throat, white patches on their tonsils, swollen lymph nodes, fever, and headache. GAS can also cause minor skin infections. Medical experts estimate that more than 10 million mild GAS infections occur each year. These minor infections can normally be treated effectively with antibiotics. However, some GAS bacteria cause severe, or invasive, infections. Severe infections include infections of the bloodstream, streptococcal toxic shock syndrome (not the same illness that is associated with tampon use in menstruating females, although that disease is also caused by a bacterium), and necrotizing fasciitis (sometimes referred to as the flesh-eating disease). All of these severe infections can lead to shock, organ failure, and even death. Although illnesses such as the flesh-eating disease are scary because of their severe nature, they are fairly rare. Approximately 10,000 to 15,000 cases of invasive GAS diseases occur each year in the United States, compared with millions of cases of strep throat and minor skin infections caused by GAS. Scientists continue to learn more about how GAS bacteria cause such a wide range of diseases. In recent years, scientists have found that a strain of the GAS bacteria that cause rheumatic fever, the most common infectious cause of childhood heart disease, contains gene sequences that appear to come from bacteriophage, viruses that infect bacteria. The viral genetic sequences that were inserted into the bacterial DNA cause the bacteria to produce new toxic proteins. A strain of GAS without the viral genes does not cause rheumatic fever. Continuing scientific research will help scientists understand how GAS bacteria can cause such a wide variety of illnesses in humans.

Figure A1.4 ▲

Streptococcus mutans is a bacterium associated with tooth decay.

Even dental caries, or tooth decay, is an infection caused by eubacteria. The decay begins on the surfaces of the teeth in a biofilm known as dental plaque. This biofilm, which consists of large eubacteria in a complex sugar matrix (shown in Figure A1.4), builds up on unbrushed teeth and in crevices not reached by a toothbrush. Sugars and carbohydrates in the diet serve as food sources for the eubacteria (Streptococcus mutans) that are present in the mouth. The eubacteria break the sugars and carbohydrates down into simple sugars and produce lactic acid as a waste product. The acid then causes the tooth enamel to lose minerals, thus causing tooth decay. Fluoride makes the teeth more resistant to decay because it retards the loss of minerals, including calcium and phosphate, from the teeth. It also promotes the replacement of these minerals to help keep the teeth healthy.

1.3 ▷ Viruses Are Unusual Pathogens

What do AIDS, hepatitis, measles, mumps, influenza, colds, and polio have in common? These diseases all are caused by viruses such as those shown in Figure A1.5. A virus is an infectious agent that contains a nucleic acid (either DNA or RNA) and a protein coat. Viruses are so small that they can be seen only with an electron microscope. In fact, viruses can pass through most bacteriological filters. Viruses may play one of two roles when they enter a host cell. As agents of disease, viruses enter the host cells, disrupt their normal functioning, and sometimes kill them. As agents of heredity, viruses can enter cells and cause permanent, inheritable changes. Often, the role the virus plays depends on the host cell and environmental conditions.

Viruses differ from living things in several important ways. They are able to produce copies of themselves only inside a living organism. Outside

SC*LINKS*®
NSTA

Topic: virus
Go To: www.scilinks.org
Keyword: GV10E308

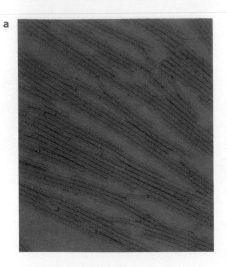
a

b

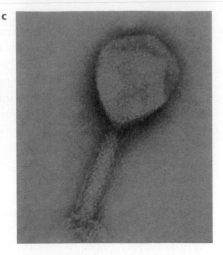
c

Figure A1.5 ▲

All viruses are pathogenic. Tobacco mosaic virus (a) causes a disease of plants (×185,000); adenovirus (b) causes respiratory illnesses in humans (×11,000); T4 bacteriophage (c) (×240,000) infects and kills bacterial cells.

Figure A1.6 ▲

TYMV (turnip yellow mosaic virus) in a young cabbage plant

the host cell, viruses neither reproduce, feed, nor grow. They have no metabolism of their own. They do not take in and use energy. They do not have cell parts. Some can be crystallized and survive for years in that state. Only when they enter the appropriate host cells can they resume reproduction. Viruses infect plants (see Figure A1.6). Viruses also infect bacteria, as shown in Figures A1.7 and A1.8. The virus first attaches to the host cell and then injects its viral DNA or RNA into the host cell. The viral nucleic acid takes over the machinery of the host cell (the proteins that replicate host DNA and that make host cell proteins). Viral proteins direct the host cell to make more viral protein and viral nucleic acid. The proteins and nucleic acids then are assembled into new virus particles, and the infected cell ruptures, releasing hundreds of newly made viruses. Each new virus has the ability to infect a single new host cell.

Usually, genetic information is stored in DNA, transcribed into mRNA, and then translated into protein. In many viruses, genetic information is stored as DNA. In some viruses, however, the viral genetic information actually is stored as RNA. Certain RNA viruses, known as retroviruses, must go through an additional step before they can reproduce. Retroviruses must make copies of DNA from their RNA, the reverse of the normal flow of stored information in biological systems. Like other viruses, a retrovirus binds to the surface of a host cell and injects its

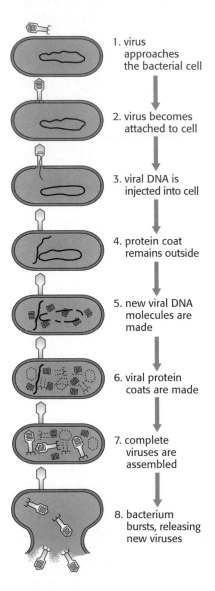

1. virus approaches the bacterial cell

2. virus becomes attached to cell

3. viral DNA is injected into cell

4. protein coat remains outside

5. new viral DNA molecules are made

6. viral protein coats are made

7. complete viruses are assembled

8. bacterium bursts, releasing new viruses

Figure A1.7 ▲

A bacterial virus (called a bacteriophage or simply, a phage) attacking a single eubacterium

a
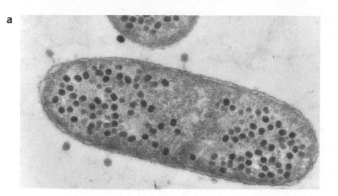
b
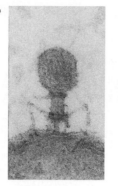

◀ **Figure A1.8**

The eubacterium *Escherichia coli* (a) with T4 phage viruses attached to the surface and inside (×50,000). T4 phage (b) attached to the eubAacterium after it has injected its DNA (×200,000).

RNA into the cell. Reverse transcriptase, a special enzyme associated with the RNA, allows the retrovirus to make a complementary DNA copy of its RNA (see Figure A1.9). The newly formed viral DNA then can be integrated into the host cell DNA, replicated at the same time, and transmitted to offspring cells. When the cell produces RNA from its own DNA, it also produces viral RNA, which becomes the source of new viral particles, thus continuing the infection.

Retroviruses are known to cause cancer in some animals and have been associated with certain types of cancers in humans. Human oncogenes have similarities to genes in these retroviruses; both can result in cancerous growth when they are somehow disturbed. The virus that causes AIDS is a retrovirus that attacks and kills certain cells of the immune system. Once these cells are killed, the immune system is unable to perform its normal function of defending the organism against disease.

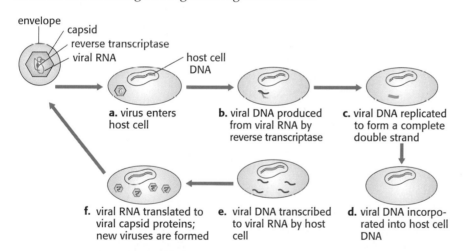

a. virus enters host cell
b. viral DNA produced from viral RNA by reverse transcriptase
c. viral DNA replicated to form a complete double strand
d. viral DNA incorporated into host cell DNA
e. viral DNA transcribed to viral RNA by host cell
f. viral RNA translated to viral capsid proteins; new viruses are formed

◀ **Figure A1.9**

Retroviruses are composed of an envelope (from the plasma membrane of a host cell), a protein coat, viral RNA, and the enzyme reverse transcriptase. Retroviruses use the enzyme reverse transcriptase to make a DNA copy of their RNA. The viral DNA then is incorporated into the host cell DNA, and the host cell directs production of new viruses.

CONCEPT REVIEW

1. Describe the interaction between host and pathogen that may result in disease.
2. Distinguish between infection and disease.
3. What is immunity? How can a vaccine bring about the development of immunity?
4. Describe, using examples, the major ways by which eubacterial diseases can be spread.
5. What is the role of eubacteria in dental caries?
6. What is the structure of a virus and how does it infect a host cell?
7. How does a virus direct the formation of other virus particles?
8. How does a retrovirus differ from a virus?

Contents

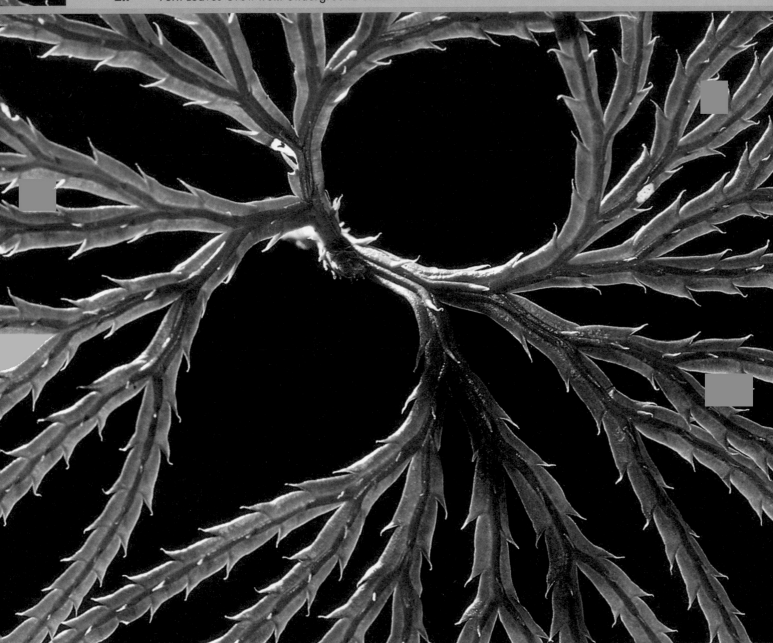

Source: *BSCS Biology: An Ecological Approach, 10th Edition*

EUKARYOTES:
Plants

Figure A2.1 ▲

The giant sequoias, *Sequoiadendron giganteum,* are the largest organisms in the world.

Several hundred million years ago, the land surface of the earth was barren. Life existed only in the water. One-celled algae colored the surface waters of the oceans shades of green. Some algae joined together into multicellular organisms and evolved a degree of cell specialization. These organisms probably were the ancestors of modern plants.

This chapter examines several of the characteristics that enabled plants to invade the land and describes a few examples of modern plants. Today, plants adapted to life on land are found in most habitats, from prairies to tundra and in the forests and deserts of the world. They come in the widest possible range of sizes. The largest organisms in the world are the giant redwoods in California, such as those shown in Figure A2.1. Some of these trees are more than 100 meters tall and 7 meters in diameter. From a simple multicellular green alga in the ancient sea to a giant California redwood tree with billions of cells, the differences in structure and function are tremendous. The evolution of such a complex land organism from a relatively unspecialized multicellular ancestor did not occur overnight. It took millions of years.

This is a curious-looking plant. What type of plant is it?

The Evolution
of Land Plants

2.1 ▷ Two Major Groups of Land Plants Evolved

What adaptations allowed plants to colonize land?

Most plants that we observe around us today are multicellular, photosynthetic organisms adapted primarily for life on land. The evolution of multicellular green algae that had some division of labor among their cells produced many adaptations that allowed plants to live in this environment. The oldest known plant fossils are simple, branched structures that had several important adaptations.

Because the climate on land may vary from hot to freezing and from wet to dry, water is the major limiting factor for any organism. On land, the only reliable source of water is underground, where it is too dark for photosynthesis. What possible advantages of living on land could overcome such a major disadvantage?

Without the presence of other organisms, plants that were able to tolerate the dry conditions that exist on land would have had little competition for food, minerals, living space, and the other necessities of life. Another advantage would have been the abundance of carbon dioxide and oxygen present in the air. A third advantage for these plants would have been increased light levels, because the air does not absorb as much light as water does. Finally, there would have been plenty of space, and minerals would have been readily available in the soil.

A multicellular alga tossed onto the shore would have had a better chance of surviving than would a one-celled alga. The outer cells of the organism could provide some protection against drying out for the inner cells, and the inner cells might have been efficient at photosynthesis. Other cells of the same organism might have specialized in collecting water or nutrients from the environment. The resulting division of labor would have enabled the alga to exploit the resources in its new environment. A specialized multicellular alga, the *Chara* in Figure A2.2, is a modern day

Figure A2.2 ▷

The multicellular green alga *Chara*. The fossil record of *Chara*-like algae extends back about 400 million years. Why is *Chara* considered to be a model of the ancestors of land plants?

example of plants that seem to have made this adjustment to land, living and reproducing on land where ocean spray and tides keep it moist.

There is ample evidence that two plant groups evolved from relatively complex multicellular green algae. The more complex group, which includes fossils of the oldest land plants, has many adaptations to life on land, including **vascular tissue**—cells joined into tubes that transport water and minerals throughout the body of the plant. These plants are called vascular plants. The less complex group, the **bryophytes,** are not aquatic, yet they possess few adaptations for life on land. This group includes the true mosses, hornworts, and liverworts. Bryophytes are called nonvascular plants because they do not have vascular tissue.

Vascular plants can be divided into two groups: those that produce seeds, and seedless plants such as ferns that reproduce with spores. Vascular plants that produce seeds can be divided further into two groups. One group is those, such as pine trees, that produce naked seeds in cones (the Cycadophyta, Ginkgophyta, and Coniferophyta). The second group is flowering plants (Anthophyta), which produce seeds enclosed in a fruit. Figure A2.3 represents an evolutionary history of plants.

Vascular Plants Have Adaptations That Conserve Water and Permit Gas Exchange

2.2

The success of plants on land depends largely on their ability to absorb and hold water. Structures that enable them to do so include roots, vascular tissue, and an outer covering that retards water loss.

Vascular plants such as ferns, conifers (cone-bearing plants), and flowering plants have well-developed root systems that penetrate into many parts of the soil. An extensive root system provides an efficient way to collect water and minerals from the soil and bring them to the main body of the plant. Rooted plants offer a good example of division of labor: The cells in the roots collect water and minerals, and the aboveground cells absorb sunlight and produce food through photosynthesis.

Tall plants require cells that can transport water from the roots to the leaves and cells that can support an upright body. Because vascular tissue serves both these functions, vascular plants can grow taller than bryophytes and thus capture more sunlight. Bryophytes never grow very tall because they lack an efficient water transport system.

In bryophytes, water can evaporate from the entire surface, so a moss plant, for example, dries out quickly. Vascular plants produce a waxy covering, or cuticle, that covers the plant body above the ground, reducing the amount of water that can evaporate from its surface. The **cuticle** is often thick on the leaves of plants living in dry places, such as the stonecrop in Figure A2.4. The covering does not prevent gas exchange with the environment because vascular plants have slitlike openings, or **stomates,** in the surface of their leaves. Stomates (Figure A2.5), found in the oldest fossil plants, permit carbon dioxide and oxygen to enter or leave the plant. Roots that absorb water, vascular tissue that supports the plant and conducts water, a cuticle that prevents evaporation, and stomates that permit gas exchange are characteristics that enable plants to live on land.

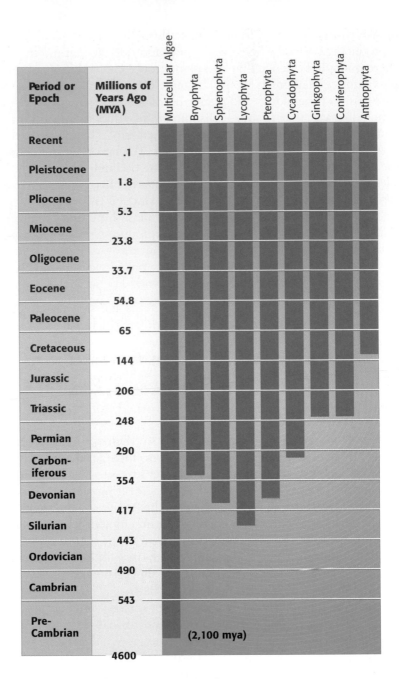

Figure A2.3 ▶

The evolutionary history of plants. What evidence was used to construct this history?

Period or Epoch	Millions of Years Ago (MYA)
Recent	.1
Pleistocene	1.8
Pliocene	5.3
Miocene	23.8
Oligocene	33.7
Eocene	54.8
Paleocene	65
Cretaceous	144
Jurassic	206
Triassic	248
Permian	290
Carbon-iferous	354
Devonian	417
Silurian	443
Ordovician	490
Cambrian	543
Pre-Cambrian	4600

(Columns: Multicellular Algae, Bryophyta, Sphenophyta, Lycophyta, Pterophyta, Cycadophyta, Ginkgophyta, Coniferophyta, Anthophyta)

(2,100 mya)

Figure A2.4 ▲

Plants such as this stonecrop (*Sedum adolphic*) have very thick cuticles. How are thick cuticles adaptive?

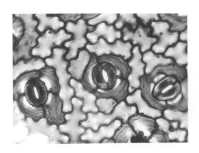

Figure A2.5 ▲

Stomates are found on the surface of a leaf.

2.3 ▷ Bryophytes Require Water for Reproduction

Reproductive adaptations also enabled plants to survive on land. Bryophytes are restricted to moist areas because their sperm are flagellated, as are those of animals and algae. For sexual reproduction to occur, the plants must be bathed in water so the sperm can swim to the egg. Thus, bryophytes reproduce sexually only where water sprays them or after they are wet with dew or rain. Like all sexually reproducing plants, bryophytes have a life cycle in which a haploid (*n*) phase alternates with a diploid (*2n*) phase. This type of life cycle is called **alternation of generations.**

The carpet of moss shown in Figure A2.6a actually is many individual plants. These small plants are haploid, and each is called a **gametophyte.** As the name implies, gametophytes produce gametes, usually in special structures near the tips of the plants. In wet conditions, sperm are produced

a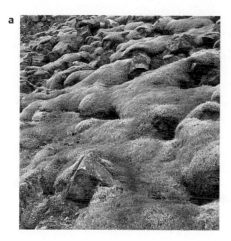
b

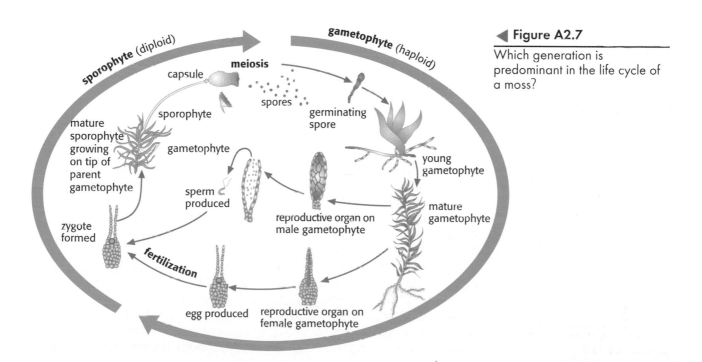

Figure A2.6

(a) Mosses thrive in moist conditions such as streambanks. (b) The whitish structures are sporophytes of the moss *Polytrichium,* growing from the female gametophyte plants.

in male gametophytes. The sperm swim in a film of water to the egg cell in the female gametophyte, where fertilization occurs and a diploid zygote is produced. In some species, both eggs and sperm are produced on the same gametophyte.

The zygote divides by mitosis and develops into a diploid embryo. Eventually, the embryo grows out of the female gametophyte into a stalklike structure, the **sporophyte.** The diploid sporophyte is visible above the small haploid individuals shown in Figure A2.6b. Meiosis occurs within the capsule at the end of the sporophyte, and haploid spores are formed. The capsule helps protect the spores. Once the spores are released, they are carried wherever wind or water transports them. Most spores fall onto unfavorable habitats and die. If a spore reaches a favorable environment, usually a moist soil surface, its wall can burst open. The cell within begins to divide by mitosis, producing long green threads that resemble the filaments of many aquatic algae. The gametophyte moss plant develops from these threads. When a spore germinates and grows into another gametophyte plant, the life cycle diagramed in Figure A2.7 is complete.

Figure A2.7

Which generation is predominant in the life cycle of a moss?

sporophyte (diploid)   **gametophyte** (haploid)

meiosis

capsule

spores

germinating spore

sporophyte

mature sporophyte growing on tip of parent gametophyte

gametophyte

young gametophyte

sperm produced

mature gametophyte

zygote formed

reproductive organ on male gametophyte

fertilization

egg produced

reproductive organ on female gametophyte

Figure A2.8 ▲

Scanning electron micrograph of pollen grains from dandelion (×2,500).

Topic: plant adaptations
Go To: www.scilinks.org
Keyword: GV10E338

SC*LINKS*®
NSTA

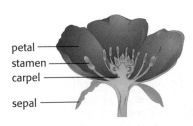

petal —
stamen —
carpel —
sepal —

Figure A2.9 ▲

The flower structure of a buttercup is shown in a cutaway diagram.

Flowering Plants Have Special Reproductive Adaptations

2.4

Unlike bryophytes and seedless vascular plants, which require water to be present for fertilization, seed plants produce special structures called **pollen grains** (Figure A2.8), in which nonflagellated sperm develop. The pollen grains may be blown by wind or may be carried by animals from one plant to another. This efficient means of transferring sperm to the egg under dry conditions is most highly developed in the flowering plants. Brightly colored or scented flowers attract a variety of animals, such as hummingbirds, bats, and insects. Many brightly colored flowers contain nectar that these animals drink and use as an energy source. As the animal drinks, it picks up pollen from one flower and carries it to another flower while searching for more nectar. Because seed plants are not restricted to moist conditions, sexual reproduction can occur whenever the sperm and egg are fully developed. Like bryophytes, flowering plants have a life cycle with alternation of generations, but the gametophyte generation of flowering plants is smaller and protected, at least while it is attached to the sporophyte generation.

Flowering plants are considered to be the most complex of the vascular plants. Their reproductive structures are found in flowers. A flower is actually a short branch bearing groups of specialized leaves. Some of these leaves may resemble ordinary leaves in many ways, but others are so different in structure that it is hard to think of them as leaves at all. If you closely examine a flower such as the buttercup illustrated in Figure A2.9, you will see a number of green, leaflike structures called **sepals** on the underside of the flower. Before the bud opens, the sepals cover and protect the other parts of the flower. The most conspicuous parts of a flower are the colorful petals. Although petals are often leaflike in shape, they are not usually green.

Just inside the circle of petals of a typical flower is a ring of male reproductive structures, the **stamens.** In the center of the flower is the **carpel,** the female reproductive organ. Although most plants have both male and female organs within the same flower, a few plants produce flowers with only female parts or only male parts. Stamens usually have an enlarged tip, the anther, whereas the carpel tip (the **stigma**) is more pointed. Despite their shape, however, both stamens and carpels are thought to be modified leaves that have been adapted for reproductive roles.

Figure A2.10 shows the relationship between reproductive structures and the life cycle of one type of flowering plant. At the base of the carpel is an enlarged portion, the ovary, that contains one or more small structures called **ovules.** Meiosis occurs in a special cell in each ovule, resulting in the formation of four haploid cells, the female spores. These spores do not separate from the sporophyte as they do in mosses. Instead, three of the spores disintegrate. The fourth spore divides three times by mitosis, forming eight nuclei. The nuclei, with their surrounding cytoplasm, form seven cells, one of which is the egg cell. (One of the cells contains two nuclei, the polar nuclei.) Figure A2.11a shows these seven cells, which constitute the female gametophyte.

In the stamens, cells in the anthers undergo meiosis, each giving rise to four haploid cells, the male spores. Each spore contains one haploid nucleus that divides by mitosis, forming two nuclei (see Figure A2.11b). A spore wall thickens around each nucleus, forming a pollen grain. A single

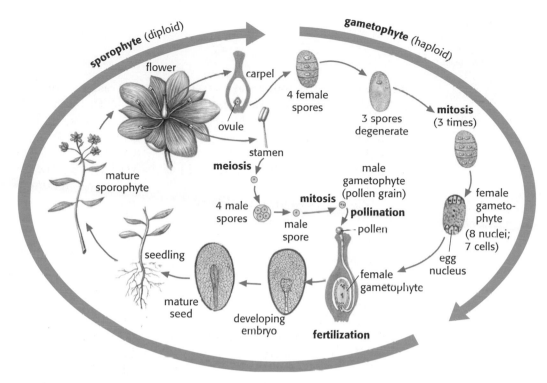

Figure A2.10 ▲

Which generation predominates in the life cycle of a flowering plant? The parts are drawn to different scales.

stamen may contain thousands of pollen grains. Each pollen grain is a single-celled male gametophyte containing two nuclei.

Pollination is the transfer of pollen from the stamens to the carpel, either within a flower, between flowers of the same plant, or between plants of the same species. The sticky stigma at the top of the carpel can trap pollen grains carried to it by wind, water, or a visiting animal. Only pollen grains from flowers of the same species are useful in fertilization.

The hard wall of the pollen grain protects the haploid cell until it lands on a stigma. Once there, a thin finger of tissue, the pollen tube, grows from the grain into the carpel. Within the pollen tube, one nucleus, the tube nucleus, leads the way. The other nucleus divides to form two sperm nuclei. The **pollen tube** grows down the carpel, transporting the sperm nuclei to the ovule. Fertilization occurs when one sperm nucleus unites with the egg, forming a zygote. This diploid cell gives rise to the embryo. The other sperm nucleus unites with the polar nuclei, leading to the formation of **endosperm,** a mass of food-storing cells that will later nourish the developing embryo. The endosperm is triploid: it has three sets of chromosomes, one set from the sperm and two from the polar nuclei. Figure A2.12 summarizes the stages of fertilization and embryo development in a flowering plant.

The life cycle of a flowering plant is similar to that of a moss in two ways. First, meiosis occurs just before spore formation. Second, there is alternation of generations between the sporophyte and gametophyte portions of the life cycle. There are, however, several differences. First, abundant surface water is not necessary for fertilization in flowering plants. Second, the gametophytes are smaller than the sporophytes. Third, the gametophyte that produces an egg and the spore that produces

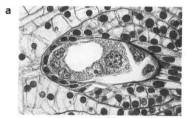

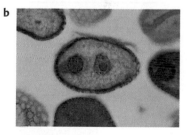

Figure A2.11 ▲

These two micrographs show the gametophytes of a lily. (a) We see the female gametophyte of a lily. This is a mature ovule ready to be fertilized; the egg nucleus is one of those on the left. (b) A pollen grain, the male gametophyte of a seed plant, is shown at the two-nucleate stage.

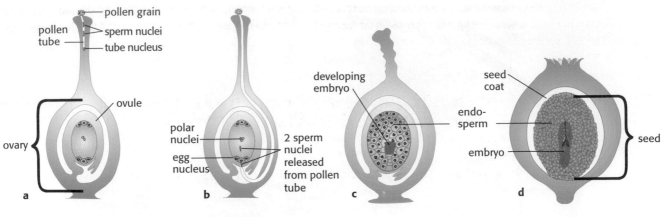

Figure A2.12 ▲

The events of pollination (a), fertilization (b), and development of the embryo (c) and seed (d) in a flowering plant are drawn here.

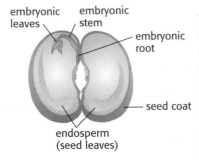

Figure A2.13 ▲

A bean seed, cut in half, shows the embryo and endosperm. The endosperm of the bean seed, as shown here, is found in structures known as the seed leaves.

Figure A2.14 ▶

The differences between mosses and land plants can be shown by diagraming the evolution and specialization in sporophytes and gametophytes.

the female gametophyte do not separate from the sporophyte plant. Thus, these structures are better protected from the environment than are their counterparts in an embryonic moss. Finally, the embryo (young sporophyte) grows for a short time, then becomes dormant. The embryo and its endosperm are surrounded by a protective coat formed from ovule tissues. This package is a **seed,** diagramed in Figure A2.13. The seed protects the young sporophyte, which remains dormant until environmental conditions are suitable for germination. Moss embryos, on the other hand, cannot tolerate dry conditions. Also, moss spores contain no embryos and only a small amount of food.

Land plants show a trend toward increasing specialization of the sporophyte and decreasing specialization of the gametophyte, as shown in Figure A2.14. Seed plants are more abundant and more diverse than mosses because of their adaptations to the changing environment on land. Cuticle,

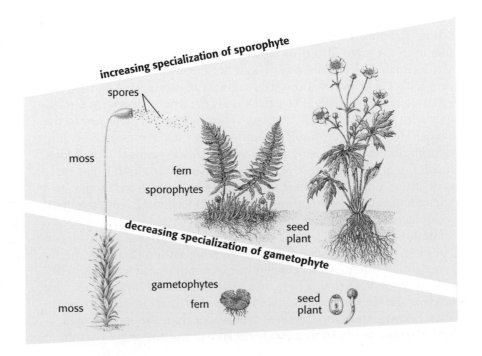

vascular tissue, root systems, sperm carried in pollen, spores protected on sporophytes, and embryos protected in seeds make flowering plants well suited to life on land.

CONCEPT REVIEW

1. Describe the limiting factors and advantages of life on land for the first land plants.
2. What types of adaptations were necessary for plants to live on land, and why were they important?
3. Briefly distinguish between the different types of land plants.
4. Compare and contrast gametophytes and sporophytes.
5. Compare and contrast the life cycles of bryophytes and flowering plants.
6. Explain the roles of the reproductive structures of flowering plants.
7. Describe the origin of the embryo, the endosperm, and the seed.

Bryophytes and Seedless Vascular Plants

2.5 Bryophytes Have No Roots, Stems, or Leaves

Most bryophytes (division **Bryophyta**) are relatively small. Few of them exceed 20 centimeters in height. Although they have structures resembling stems and leaves, these terms are not used in describing bryophytes because they lack the vascular tissue of other land plants. There are three classes of bryophytes: true mosses, the largest class; liverworts; and hornworts. Figure A2.15 shows several bryophytes.

GUIDEPOST

How do bryophytes and seedless vascular plants differ in structure and habitat?

a

b

c

Figure A2.15 ▲

These are examples of varieties of bryophytes: (a) moss, *Polytrichium*; (b) liverwort, *Marchantia polymorpha*; (c) hornwort, *Anthoceros punctatus*.

True mosses often grow in clumps or small clusters in rock crevices and on the shady side of trees. An individual moss plant from such a clump is simply an upright, green, stemlike stalk with threadlike structures called **rhizoids,** which perform the function of roots by aiding in absorption and helping to hold the plant in place. Many flat, green, leaflike structures are attached spirally along the stalk. Water and nutrients are absorbed throughout the body of the bryophyte, so most grow in fairly damp places, and a few grow in water. Under dry conditions, many mosses become dormant. When dormant, the life processes slow down, and the plant appears dead. Normal activities resume when the plant comes in contact with water. Because many bryophytes can photosynthesize in limited light, they often are found on the ground in forest ecosystems, where other plants cannot grow.

One important group of mosses is found in boggy places in the cold and temperate parts of the world. These plants, from the genus *Sphagnum*, form peat bogs—small lakes and ponds completely filled with living and dead mosses. Sphagnum produces a very acidic condition in the water that keeps decomposers such as bacteria and fungi from growing, thus allowing these plants to build up through time, layer on layer. People in Ireland and other countries cut blocks of peat, dry it, and use it for fuel or to build small enclosures. Dry peat absorbs water quickly and holds the water well, characteristics that make peat attractive to gardeners, who add it to their soil to lower the pH and to increase the water-holding capacity.

Liverworts and hornworts grow in very moist areas, such as on the banks of streams where water spray keeps the soil wet. Although bryophytes are less complex than vascular plants, there is no evidence that they are the ancestors of vascular plants. The fossil record for bryophytes is small. The earliest bryophyte fossils are about 350 million years old. By that time, vascular plants were already established on land. The first fossils of vascular plants appear 50–100 million years earlier in the fossil record.

2.6 ▷ Club Mosses and Horsetails Are Seedless Vascular Plants

The roots, stems, and leaves of vascular plants contain the vascular system through which water, sugar, and dissolved nutrients move from one place to another in the plant.

Rhynia major, shown in Figure A2.16, best represents the oldest land plants. *Rhynia* had an underground stem that probably anchored the plant and absorbed water. From this underground stem grew upright branched stems that had stomates. At the tips of the stems were sporangia, which split open to release thick-walled spores. A living relative of *Rhynia* is the whisk fern, *Psilotum*, shown in Figure A2.17.

The club mosses (division **Lycophyta**) are evergreen plants that seldom grow more than 40 centimeters tall. Although the word "moss" is a part of

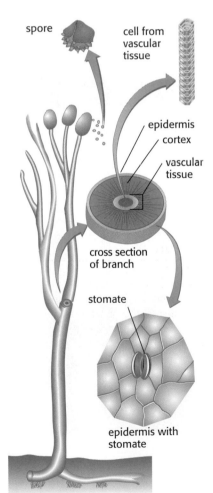

spore
cell from vascular tissue
epidermis
cortex
vascular tissue
cross section of branch
stomate
epidermis with stomate

◀ **Figure A2.16**

The extinct plant *Rhynia* is reconstructed here. It had no leaves or roots and stood about 30 centimeters high. Sporangia were produced at the tips of upper branches. The presence of stomates indicates that photosynthesis occurred in the branches. The cells of vascular tissue (upper right) were oblong and sometimes hollow. Thick-walled spores were produced in fours in the sporangia, an indication that the spores were produced by meiosis.

Figure A2.17
Note the sporangia along the stems of the whisk fern, *Psilotum*.

their name, they are not true mosses. Their branching, horizontal stems grow on the surface of the soil or just below it. The most noticeable part of a club moss plant is an upright branch growing from one of these stems (see the chapter-opening photo). Club mosses reproduce by spores, which are produced on modified, specialized leaves. In many species, these leaves form club-shaped cones at the tips of short, upright stems. The name "club moss" is derived from this feature. Club mosses are rather common in the eastern and northwestern United States and often are used to make Christmas wreaths. They rarely grow in the dry states of the Southwest.

Horsetails (division **Sphenophyta**) have hollow, jointed, upright branches that grow from horizontal underground stems. Their small, scale-like leaves grow in a circle around each stem joint. Spores are produced in conelike structures at the tips of some of the upright branches, such as those shown in Figure A2.18. In middle latitudes, horsetails rarely reach a height of two meters, but in the American tropics one species may grow several meters tall. They are found in moist places, such as along streams. Horsetails are harsh to the touch; their tissues contain silica, a compound

a

b

Figure A2.18
(a) Spores of *Equisetum* (horsetail) are produced in these conelike structures. The vegetative stage of *Equisetum* (b) is characterized by hollow, jointed, upright branches.

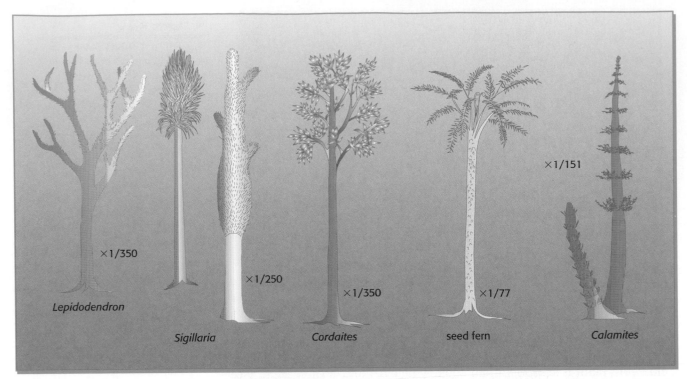

Figure A2.19 ▲

These are some examples of the trees of the Coal Age forests: *Lepidodendron* and *Sigillaria* were club mosses. *Cordaites* were primitive cone-bearing plants. The seed ferns have no living species. *Calamites* were horsetails.

present in sand. Because Native Americans and the pioneers scrubbed pots and pans with them, they are commonly called scouring rushes.

Relatives of the club mosses and horsetails can be traced back about 430 million years. During the Coal Age, about 300 million years ago, great parts of North America were covered by shallow swamps and seas. The warm and wet environment allowed plants to grow year round. Under these conditions, giant relatives of today's club mosses, horsetails, and ferns, as well as seed-producing plants, covered the land. Some of these plants were more than 20 meters tall (Figure A2.19). As they died, their large stems were covered with mud and soil before they completely decayed. A tremendous number of plants from the Coal Age were compressed over long periods of time and under high temperature and great pressure. Eventually, they became fossil fuels, mainly coal and some natural gas.

2.7 ▷ Fern Leaves Grow from Underground Stems

Ferns (division **Pterophyta**), like the club mosses and horsetails, reproduce by spores. At certain times of the year, small brown spots develop on the undersides of fern leaves, as shown in Figure A2.20. Each spot consists of a cluster of sporangia. Each sporangium produces a large number of spores, which are almost microscopic in size.

Figure A2.20 ▲

The dusty-looking spots on the underside of a licorice fern leaf, *Polypodium glycyrrhiza*, are sporangia.

a

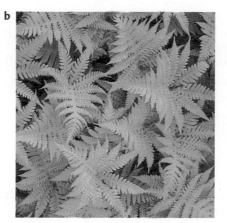
b

◀ **Figure A2.21**

You may never have seen a fern gametophyte (a), but you are probably familiar with the fern sporophyte (b).

When a sporangium is mature, it opens and the spores are thrown out into the air. Spores are very light and can be carried for incredible distances by wind. If a spore falls in a suitably moist place, it germinates and develops rapidly into a thin, green, heart-shaped plant that is rarely over one centimeter in diameter (see Figure A2.21a). This small gametophyte plant, which is completely different from the familiar fern with its large leaves, is seldom noticed in the woods. The gametophyte produces the sperm or eggs, or in some cases, both. Like the moss sperm, the flagellated fern sperm must swim in a film of water to fertilize the egg. The zygote produced by that fertilization eventually grows into the conspicuous spore-bearing fern plant that most people recognize. This large plant is the sporophyte generation of the fern, seen in Figure A2.21b.

The ferns native to most of the United States are shade-dwelling plants with underground roots and stems. From these stems, roots grow downward and new sets of upright leaves appear above the ground each spring. In Hawaii and elsewhere in the tropics, many species of ferns have stems that grow upright. These tree ferns may reach a height of 20 meters with leaves five meters long, as Figure A2.22 illustrates. Most fern species are found in the tropics, but many can be found in forest ecosystems around the world.

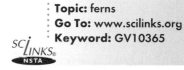
Topic: ferns
Go To: www.scilinks.org
Keyword: GV10365

SCI
LINKS®
NSTA

Figure A2.22 ▲

Tree ferns grow on the island of Sumatra.

CONCEPT REVIEW

1. How do bryophytes differ from vascular plants?
2. How does reproduction in seedless vascular plants differ from that in bryophytes?
3. What events must occur for a fern sporophyte to be produced from a gametophyte?
4. In what type of environment must ferns and horsetails grow in order to reproduce?

PIONEERS

Evolutionary Geologist

Dr. Geerat Vermeij (pronounced Ver May) is a paleontologist and a professor at the University of California, Davis. As a paleontologist, he studies life-forms from the ancient past by examining fossils. Dr. Vermeij specializes in the natural history of molluscs and their relationships with ancient predators. According to his research, molluscs have adapted to the presence of ever more efficient predators by developing progressively heavier and more protective shells. Dr. Vermeij feels that this reaction to natural enemies provides a better explanation of how molluscs evolved than the usual explanations based on climatic changes and other large-scale physical factors.

Dr. Vermeij was born in the Netherlands and raised in New Jersey. His proximity to the Atlantic seaboard allowed him to pursue his early interest in shell collecting. He has developed this interest through worldwide travel and extensive field study. He has traveled widely in the South Pacific, Central and North America, and Africa. His research on predatory patterns on molluscs has involved investigating shell geometry, breakage patterns, scarring, hole patterns, and evidence of repair following encounters with their marine enemies.

A graduate of Princeton and Yale Universities, Dr. Vermeij holds a particular distinction among paleontologists. He has been completely blind since age three and has never actually seen a single organism he has studied. Instead, he uses his fingers to feel the subtle features of the ancient marine creatures he investigates. His sense of touch is so refined that he often is able to identify molluscs to the subspecies based on the most

> According to his research, molluscs have adapted to the presence of ever more efficient predators by developing progressively heavier and more protective shells.

minor changes in the shapes, textures, and thickness of shells. Dr. Vermeij works closely with his wife and professional colleague, Dr. Edith Zipser, also of the University of California, Davis. Together, they have collected shells from their extensive travels and formulated their ideas on the evolutionary patterns of molluscs. Dr. Vermeij has risen above his physical restrictions and opposition from skeptical peers to be a premier-level paleontologist.

Seed Plants

2.8 ▷ Many Conifers Are Evergreens

Humans have used plants for food, clothing, shelter, and medicines. The conifers (division **Coniferophyta**) are woody vascular plants with seeds borne in cones. Conifers provide most of the paper pulp and much of the lumber used in home construction and furniture. They include pines, firs, spruces, and junipers, among many other species. Figure A2.23 shows several conifers and related plants.

Almost all conifers are trees or shrubs, and all are at least somewhat woody. Many have leaves that are like needles or scales, such as those in Figure A2.24, and most of these plants are evergreen. An evergreen tree or shrub appears green throughout the year because it always maintains most of its leaves. A few leaves die at different times of the year and drop to the ground. Although the number of conifer species is small, the number of individual conifers is enormous.

Many common conifers are well adapted to life in dry habitats. For example, although pine trees may grow where there is much snow, the snow is really frozen water and is not available for growth. In the spring, much of the snow evaporates, and the melted snow may run off into streams before it soaks into the soil. The leaves of pines are well adapted for growth in dry places. The long, narrow needles reduce the amount of water lost by evaporation. In addition, a pine needle often is covered by a thick, waxy cuticle that further reduces water loss.

Conifers reproduce by seeds that are attached to the upper surface of cone scales. A seed developing in a cone may be protected by the scales. If two scales are separated slightly, you can see the seed between them, as shown in Figure A2.25. Thus, the seeds in cones are not completely covered as they are in the fruits of flowering plants.

Topic: seed plants
Go To: www.scilinks.org
Keyword: GV10E367

How are seed plants adapted to life on land?

Figure A2.23 ▲

These are examples of conifers and related plants: (a) ponderosa pine, *Pinus ponderosa*; (b) cycad, *Dioon edule*; and (c) maidenhair tree, *Ginkgo biloba*. Seeds of these plants are not enclosed in tissues as are those of flowering plants.

a

b

Figure A2.24 ▲

Many conifer leaves are needlelike or scalelike. (a) The needles of Douglas fir, *Pseudotsuga menziesii,* are single and needlelike, while the leaves of juniper, *Juniperus chinensis pfitzerii,* (b) are scalelike.

Figure A2.25 ▶

The winged seed of this pine tree is tucked inside the scales of the pine cone.

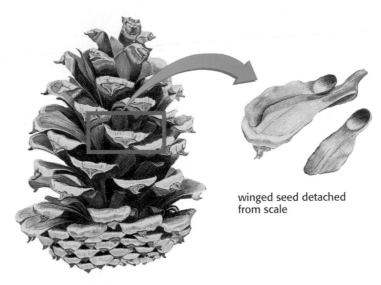

winged seed detached from scale

cone scale bearing seed on its upper surface

Conifer spores are of two types and are produced in different cones, illustrated in Figure A2.26. Typically, pollen develops from spores in the small male cone, and pollination occurs in the spring when the pollen is blown onto a female cone. The larger, more familiar female cones contain the ovules. Pollen grains, the male gametophytes, lodge in a sticky substance secreted by the ovule. Once lodged, the grains develop pollen tubes within which the sperm are formed. Within the ovule, the female gametophytes develop and produce eggs. Fertilization occurs approximately a year after pollination, and the seed requires an additional year to mature. Table A2.1 summarizes these events.

a

b

◄ **Figure A2.26**
These photographs show the difference between the male cone (a) and the female cone (b) of the piñon pine, *Pinus edulis.*

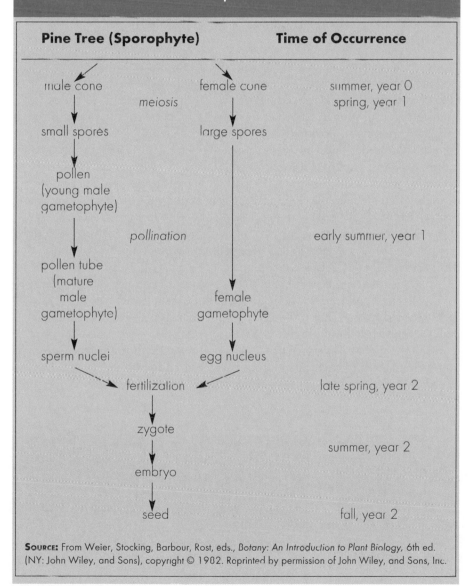

Table A2.1   Seed Development in a Pine

Pine Tree (Sporophyte)		Time of Occurrence
male cone	female cone	summer, year 0
meiosis		spring, year 1
small spores	large spores	
pollen (young male gametophyte)		
pollination		early summer, year 1
pollen tube (mature male gametophyte)	female gametophyte	
sperm nuclei	egg nucleus	
fertilization		late spring, year 2
zygote		
		summer, year 2
embryo		
seed		fall, year 2

Source: From Weier, Stocking, Barbour, Rost, eds., *Botany: An Introduction to Plant Biology,* 6th ed. (NY: John Wiley, and Sons), copyright © 1982. Reprinted by permission of John Wiley, and Sons, Inc.

Many Flowering Plants Have Special Pollinators

Flowers are the distinguishing feature of the most successful division in the plant kingdom, the **Anthophyta.** Although we commonly appreciate flowers for their beauty, their major role is in reproduction. When a flower opens, it reveals the reproductive structures, the stamens and carpels. Insects, birds, bats, or other animals that visit the flower may pick up pollen from the anther and carry it to the next flower they visit. When pollen is transferred from a flower of one plant to a flower of another in the same species, the process is called cross-pollination. The main pollinators of flowers are insects. Pollen also may be transported from flower to flower by wind. In some plants, the pollen falls on the stigma of the same flower. These flowers are self-pollinating. Many plants, however, have evolved devices that prevent self-pollination.

The sepals and petals are not directly involved in seed formation, so a flower can function without them. In fact, in a few plants a flower may consist of only a single stamen or a single carpel. Petals and their adaptations, however, usually play a major role in flower pollination. Much of the diversity among flowering plant species lies in their flowers (see Figure A2.27). This diversity usually is related to the way pollination occurs. If pollen is transferred from stamen to carpel by insects, the petals of the flower often are large and brightly colored, as in Figure A2.28a, and often have small glands that produce a sugar solution called **nectar.** These adaptations attract pollinating insects. On the other hand, flowers in which pollen is transferred by wind usually have small sepals and petals or none at all. These flowers often are located high on the plant, where they are accessible to wind currents and produce an abundance of pollen (Figure A2.28b). Their carpels commonly have large, long, or feathery structures at the tips, which are covered with a sticky fluid. These adaptations increase the likelihood that some pollen will stick to the carpels.

The great variety of flowers has come about, in part, by the coevolution of flowers and pollination agents. For example, hummingbirds have evolved with plants that produce large quantities of nectar. Research has shown that while hummingbirds do not have a good sense of smell, they can see the color red very well. Flowers pollinated by hummingbirds usually are well adapted to their pollinators, as you see in Figure A2.29. The columbine flowers shown in the illustration are red, have little or no scent,

a

b

c

d

Figure A2.27 ▲

Here are a few colorful examples of the diversity of flowers. (a) Indian paintbrush; (b) water lily; (c) elephantheads; and (d) bougainvillea.

Figure A2.28 ▲

Insect-pollinated flowers such as the aster in (a) usually are brightly colored. Wind-pollinated flowers often lack petals and sepals and produce an abundance of pollen. Shown in (b) is the male catkin of a willow, *Salix*. Note the many stamens.

and produce copious amounts of nectar. The nectar is found at the bottom of a long tube formed by the red petals, a shape that makes it difficult for other organisms to rob the flower of nectar.

Hummingbirds, however, have long beaks that can probe the flower and reach the nectar. The stamens stick out in such a position that the hummingbird's head is dusted with pollen when it visits these flowers. When the hummingbird flies to another flower of the same species, the tip of the carpel is in a perfect position to have pollen from the hummingbird's head scraped onto it. Thus, the flower is pollinated while the hummingbird drinks nectar. Interactions of this type, in which both organisms become uniquely adapted to each other, have helped shape the way flowering plants have evolved.

spurs of flower

Figure A2.29 ▲

The columbine and hummingbird are uniquely adapted to each other.

2.10 Flowering Plants Produce Fruits with Seeds

After pollination and fertilization, seeds begin to develop. The carpel (or carpels in a compound ovary), often with other parts of the flower, develops into a protective fruit around the seed, as shown in Figure A2.30. There may be many seeds in a fruit. Each seed began its development when an egg cell in one ovule was fertilized by a sperm from one pollen grain. In flowering plants, then, an embryo is protected within a seed, and seeds are protected within a fruit.

Part of the embryo in the seed consists of one or two modified leaves called **cotyledons.** Another part is a beginning of a root. Each seed also contains a supply of food that is used when the embryo starts to grow. The food may be stored in the endosperm, or it may be stored in the embryo itself, usually in the cotyledon (look back at Figure A2.13).

Beans and peas are examples of seeds. They are enclosed in protective pods, which are just one of many types of fruits. Each bean or pea contains a small embryo and a supply of stored food for its early development. The

entire bean or pea can act as food for humans. Beans and peas can be
germinated easily, and each embryo gives rise to a plant that, in turn, gives
rise to new flowers and fruits. Apples and oranges are examples of fruit that
contain a number of seeds. Under natural conditions, these fruits eventually decay, or are eaten by animals leaving their seeds behind to germinate
and give rise to the next generation.

Fruits show as much diversity as flowers, as indicated in Figure A2.31.
This diversity is related to the method of dispersal of the fruits and their
seeds, that is, how they are scattered from the parent plant. In
Investigation 2.3, you will observe some of the structures that aid in seed
dispersal. In many cases, part of the carpel becomes thick and fleshy, as in
the fruits of peach, plum, and tomato. Fleshy fruits, often red in color, may
be eaten by birds or mammals. The seeds in many such fruits have thick
coats that permit them to pass through an animal's digestive system
unharmed. They are dropped later at some distance from the parent plant.
Many fruits are not fleshy but have other adaptations that aid in scattering
their seeds. These fruits may have spines that catch on the fur of an animal
that brushes up against the plant. The fruit is carried from the plant and
later falls off or is brushed off by the animal. Many fruits and seeds are
lightweight and have special winglike projections that help them to be
carried away from the plant by wind. An entire plant, such as the tumbleweed, can be broken off near the ground and blown about by the wind. As
the tumbleweed bounces about, it drops its fruits (and the seeds within) all
along its path.

 2.11 ## Flowering Plants Are the Most Diverse Group of Land Plants

There is great diversity in the size of flowering plants and in the life span of
their shoots—the parts that appear above the ground. Many flowering
plants are trees. A tree bears leaves well above the ground where they are

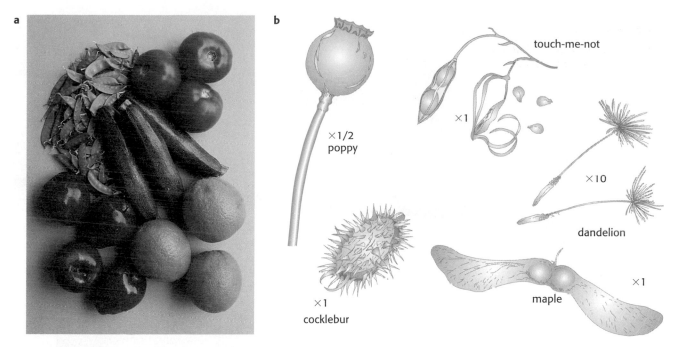

Figure A2.31 ▲

(a) Each edible fruit is a mature ovary containing the seeds of the plant. (b) Many fruits have structural adaptations for seed dispersal. Can you describe them?

likely to receive more light than do the leaves of shorter plants. Because of their size, trees can store large reserves of food in trunks and roots and can survive through bad years. Trees have relatively long life spans. A tree species may survive even if a year's seed crop is destroyed. Most species of flowering plants are not trees, however. Some, such as roses and raspberries, are woody shrubs. Others, such as ivy, grapes, and hundreds of tropical species, are woody vines that grow on rocks, walls, or other plants. Most, however, are neither trees, shrubs, nor vines. Instead, they are nonwoody, or **herbaceous,** plants such as those in Figure A2.32.

Flowering plants are divided into two large classes—the **monocots** and the **dicots.** In monocots, (monocotyledons), the embryo contains a single cotyledon. The monocots include grasses and grain-producing plants such as wheat, rice, and corn—the chief food plants of the world. The pasture grasses that feed cattle, another source of human food, are also monocots. Evidence suggests that human population could not have evolved to its present state without monocots.

The seeds of the dicots (dicotyledons) have two seed leaves. This class is larger than the monocot class. Most fruits and vegetables, such as carrots, lettuce, apples, and grapes, are dicots. In addition, the so-called hardwoods used in furniture, flooring, hockey sticks, and baseball bats come from dicot trees. Almost all shade trees are dicots, also. Figure A2.33 illustrates the major differences between monocots and dicots.

Figure A2.32 ▲

Herbaceous plants include marigolds, common garden flowers.

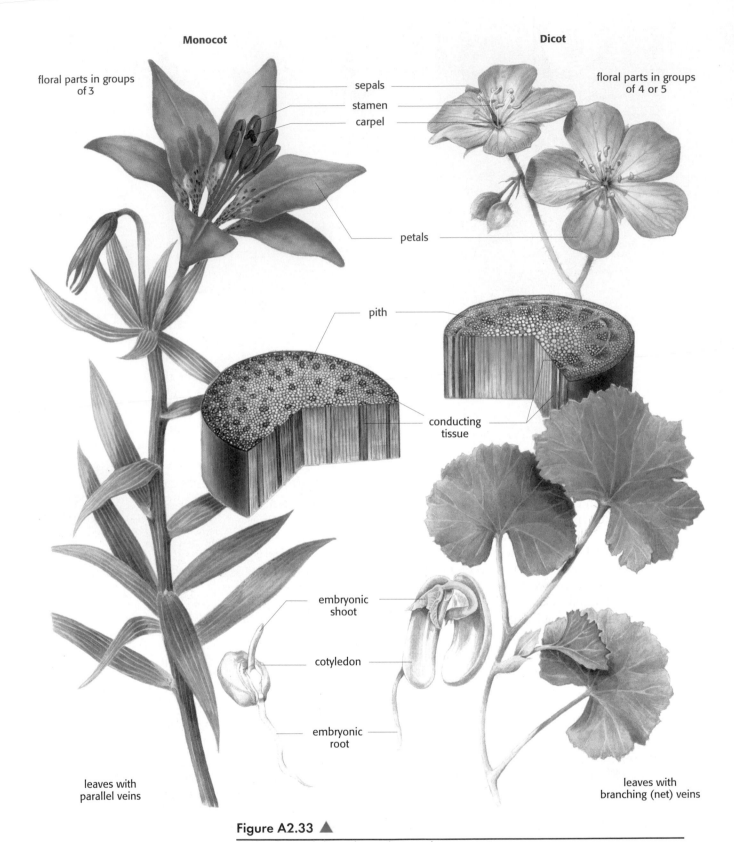

Monocot

floral parts in groups of 3

Dicot

floral parts in groups of 4 or 5

sepals

stamen

carpel

petals

pith

conducting tissue

embryonic shoot

cotyledon

embryonic root

leaves with parallel veins

leaves with branching (net) veins

Figure A2.33 ▲

Monocots and dicots have distinct characteristics.

BIOLOGY TODAY

▶ **Biological** Illustrator

Marjorie Leggit is a freelance biological illustrator. Biological illustrators illustrate reports, journal articles, and books prepared by researchers. Many illustrators work in natural history museums, painting and constructing the background scenery for different types of displays. These artists may recreate Alaskan ice floes to show off a group of polar bears or a South American hillside for a display of llamas. Marjorie's family is composed of writers, sculptors, painters, and woodcarvers, so an interest in art comes naturally to her. Her interest in science, Marj thinks, may have developed because she could do so much drawing in science classes.

Although a biological illustration course in college sparked her interest, Marjorie continued to study fine arts. After studying for a year in Europe, however, she realized she missed science and the technical art that goes with it. She returned to college and designed her own program of independent studies that led to a degree in scientific art. Her program included an internship at the Denver Museum of Natural History in Denver, Colorado. While searching for a full-time job after graduation, Marj illustrated a professor's botanical field guide. Her persistence was rewarded eventually with a position at the Field Museum of Natural History in Chicago, Illinois. Marj later returned to Denver.

Reestablishing her career there proved to be difficult because opportunities for biological illustration were far fewer than in very large cities where more research is conducted. For seven years, she worked at art-related jobs, including geological drafting and computer-aided graphics. Although she learned a whole new field of art, Marj was not satisfied with the direction of her career.

To keep in touch with the field of biological illustration, she contacted the Guild of Natural Science Illustrators (GNSI) in Washington, DC. Knowing Colorado had nothing similar, she founded the Colorado Chapter of GNSI and made friends with a group of local illustrators.

In 1986, Marj went into business for herself as a biological illustrator and graphic artist. She contacted old and new local clients as well as publishers throughout the country. She spent many hours researching the possibilities for assignments and marketing her skills. Marj did many of the illustrations used in this textbook, including Figure A2.33. To ensure accuracy in her work, Marj does a great deal of research and uses many references and photos. She consults extensively with authors when planning an illustration. It is essential that she understand the author's intent, what the illustration is meant to portray, and how it relates to the text and to other illustrations. Proper interpretation depends on good communication between author and artist. Marj strongly

believes that the hard work involved in creating illustrations has its rewards. At times the hours are long, the deadlines close to impossible, and the challenges seemingly insurmountable. However, she is doing exactly what she wants to be doing, full-time biological illustration.

1. How are conifers adapted to dry conditions?
2. How do conifers differ from flowering plants?
3. What role does flower color play in the reproduction of flowering plants?
4. How are fruits related to seed dispersal?
5. In what ways do monocots and dicots differ?

Summary

The ancestors of plants were probably multicellular algae. A multicellular organism has many advantages over a single cell, including size, division of labor, and ability to conserve water. Other adaptations that permit plants to absorb and hold water are roots, vascular tissue, and the cuticle. All plants have a life cycle that alternates between two different generations, a gametophyte and a sporophyte. In flowering plants, however, the egg cell (the gametophyte that produces the egg), and the spore that produces the gametophyte all remain protected in the flower. Mosses are nonvascular plants that lack roots, stems, and leaves. They possess some adaptations to life on land, but they still require a moist environment. Club mosses, horsetails, and ferns are seedless vascular plants, and many of their ancestors produced today's fossil fuels. Conifers and flowering plants are seed producing vascular plants, but flowering plants have a fruit that encloses their seeds. The great diversity of flowers and fruits is the result of the coevolution of plants and their agents of pollination or dispersal.

Applications

1. Which organisms in this chapter would you consider to be less complex? Which would you consider to be more complex? Explain your answer.

2. Why are nonvascular plants short?

3. The fossil record reveals that the diversity of flowering plants and the diversity of certain insect groups increased at the same time. How might you explain this?

4. Explain the following statement: The plant parts that furnish the greatest amount of human food are either seeds, roots, or underground stems.

Problems

1. Desert plants are land plants adapted to extremely dry conditions. What adaptations allow them to live with little water? Make a collection of desert plants or find out about them from a plant ecology text.

2. Fruits come in many sizes and shapes and with diverse appendages. Collect different fruits and try to identify their plants. Identify the methods of dispersal for the different fruits and their seeds.

3. Bring to the classroom different pieces of furniture, tools, sculptures, or other objects made from wood. What qualities of the wood make it useful for each object? Can you identify which tree provided the wood? Are some woods better than others for certain tasks?

4. Throughout history, plants have played religious and cultural roles in different societies. Many of these roles have been captured in paintings, sculptures, and tapestries. Find artwork that contains a plant or plants as an important part of the composition. What does the plant signify?

investigation 2.1

Increasingly Complex Characteristics

Biologists sometimes use pairs of terms such as "less complex" and "more complex" when discussing diversity among organisms. A species that has changed little from its ancestors is said to be less complex than organisms that differ greatly from their ancestors. Conversely, a species that has few of the characteristics of its ancestors is said to be more complex. After studying many types of evidence in the fossil record and in living organisms, scientists have reached fairly general agreement about which characteristics have been in existence for a long time and which are more recent. Table A2.3 is based on such studies. Because there may be many degrees of complexity, the terms "less complex" and "more complex" are not absolute, but they are useful for making the types of comparisons you will make in this investigation.

Materials (per team of 6)

stereomicroscope or
   10× hand lens
microscope slides
compound microscope
coverslips

10 labeled specimens of
   organisms of various
   kingdoms and divisions
data books
pens

Procedure

1. In your data book, prepare or tape in a table similar to Table A2.2, with enough lines for all 10 specimens.

2. Determine the complexity score for each of the labeled specimens. More-complex organisms such as plants are represented at each station as well as some less-complex organisms from other kingdoms. Start at the left of Table A2.3. Arrows from the starting point lead to two descriptions. Choose the one that fits the organism you are scoring.

Table A2.2

Name of Organism	Numerical Values of Choices Made	Total Complexity Score	Rank
1.			
2.			
etc.			

3. Proceed across Table A2.3 by following the arrows and choosing in each column the description that best fits each organism. Continue as far as the arrows go.

4. With each description there is a number. As you proceed, record the numbers of your chosen descriptions in the second column of your data table. The complexity score for the organism is the sum of all the numbers appearing after the descriptions you used in working through Table A2.3. The more alike two organisms are, the more alike their scores will be. The greater the difference between two organisms, the greater will be the difference in their scores. More-complex organisms, such as plants, will have high scores (maximum 26), and less-complex organisms, such as prokaryotes, will have low scores (minimum 3).

5. When you have the complexity score for each of the organisms, give the organism with the lowest score a rank of 1 and the organism with the highest score a rank of 10. Then rank the rest of the organisms according to their scores. Record the rankings in the column at the right side of your data table.

Discussion

1. Basing your conclusions on the way the complexity score key was designed, list some of the most important differences among the organisms you observed.

2. What are some of the less important differences?

3. Using the information in Table A2.3, list the characteristics you would expect to find in one of the less-complex organisms.

4. Do the same for one of the more-complex plants.

5. Evidence exists that today's land plants evolved from water-dwelling ancestors. Plants that live on land are in constant danger of drying out. Suggest how each of the following characteristics found in a more-complex plant would help the plant live on land: (1) roots; (2) stems that contain vascular tissues; (3) seeds; and (4) flowers.

Table A2.3 Key for Determining the Complexity Score for an Organism

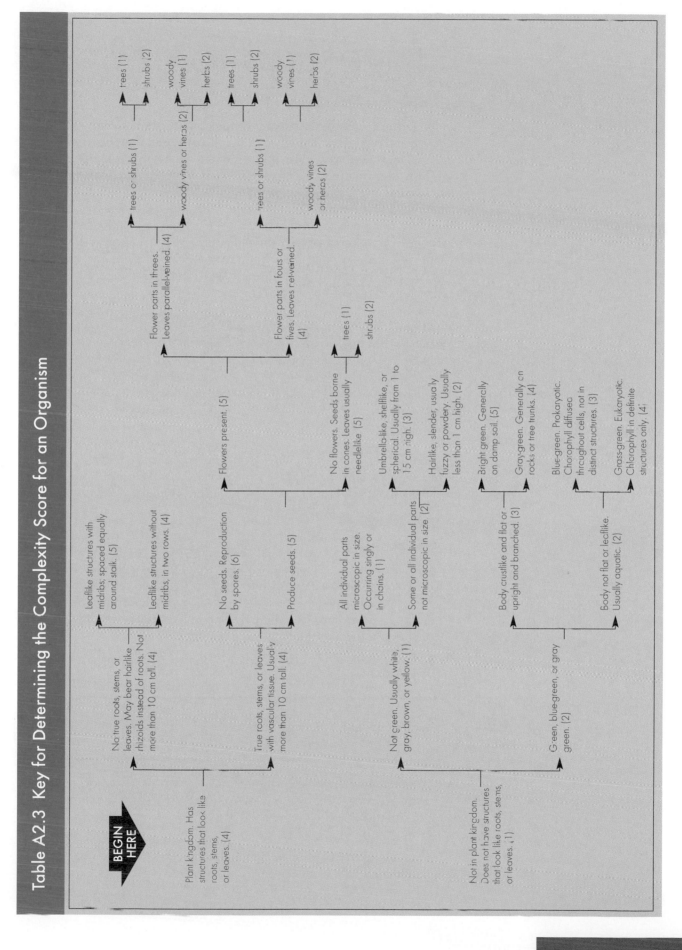

BEGIN HERE

Plant kingdom. Has structures that look like roots, stems, or leaves. (4)

No true roots, stems, or leaves. May bear hairlike rhizoids instead of roots. Not more than 10 cm tall. (4)

Leaflike structures with midribs; spaced equally around stalk. (5)

Leaflike structures without midribs, in two rows. (4)

True roots, stems, or leaves with vascular tissue. Usually more than 10 cm tall. (4)

No seeds. Reproduction by spores. (6)

Produce seeds. (5)

Flowers present. (5)

Flower parts in threes. Leaves parallel-veined. (4)

trees or shrubs (1)

woody vines or herbs (2)

Flower parts in fours or fives. Leaves retveaned. (4)

trees or shrubs (1)

woody vines or herbs (2)

trees (1)

shrubs (2)

woody vines (1)

herbs (2)

trees (1)

shrubs (2)

woody vines (1)

herbs (2)

No flowers. Seeds borne in cones. Leaves usually needlelike. (5)

trees (1)

shrubs (2)

Not in plant kingdom. Does not have structures that look like roots, stems, or leaves. (1)

Not green. Usually white, gray, brown, or yellow. (1)

All individual parts microscopic in size. Occurring singly or in chains. (1)

Some or all individual parts not microscopic in size. (2)

Umbrella-like, shelflike, or spherical. Usually from 1 to 15 cm high. (3)

Hairlike, slender, usually fuzzy or powdery. Usually less than 1 cm high. (2)

Green, blue-green, or gray green. (2)

Body crustlike and flat or upright and branched. (3)

Bright green. Generally on damp soil. (5)

Gray-green. Generally on rocks or tree trunks. (4)

Body not flat or leaflike. Usually aquatic. (2)

Blue-green. Prokaryotic. Chlorophyll diffused throughout cells, not in distinct structures. (3)

Grass-green. Eukaryotic. Chlorophyll in definite structures only. (4)

ⓘnvestigation 2.2

Reproductive Structures and Life Cycles

Although their reproductive organs differ, as do the environments in which they live and reproduce, the basic principles of sexual reproduction are the same in a moss, a flower, a bee, and a human. In this investigation, you will learn how the structures of a moss and a flower serve reproductive functions in their respective environments.

Mosses form mats on logs and on the forest floor, growing best in damp, shaded environments. Sporophytes grow out of the tops of the gametophytes and often look like hairs growing out of the mat of moss. Mosses cannot reproduce sexually unless they are wet. Flowering plants, on the other hand, are found in many different environments and climates. They need water to live but not to reproduce.

Materials *(per team of 2)*

compound microscope	fresh moss
stereomicroscope or 10× hand lens	prepared slide of moss male and female
3 microscope slides	reproductive organs
3 coverslips	gladiolus flower
dissecting needle	fresh bean or pea pod
scalpel	other simple flowers for comparison
forceps	modeling clay
15% sucrose solution	water in a dropping bottle
moss plant with sporophyte	petri dish with moistened cotton
prepared slide of filamentous stage	data books
of moss	pens

Procedure

Part A: Moss

1. Examine a moss plant with sporophyte attached. The sporophyte consists of a smooth stalk terminated by a little capsule. Separate the 2 generations by pulling the sporophyte stalk out of the leafy shoot of the gametophyte.

2. Using a dissecting needle, break open the capsule of the sporophyte into a drop of water on a slide.

Needles are sharp. Handle with care.

   Add a coverslip and examine under the low power of a compound microscope. What structures do you observe? How are these structures dispersed? How are they adapted for life on land?

3. Most moss spores germinate on damp soil and produce a filamentous stage that looks like a branching green alga. Examine a prepared slide of this stage.

4. The filamentous stage gives rise to the leafy shoot of the gametophyte. Using forceps, carefully remove a leafy shoot from the fresh moss. How does this shoot obtain water and nutrients for growth?

5. The reproductive organs of the gametophyte are at the upper end of the leafy shoot. Examine a prepared slide of these organs under the low power of a compound microscope. The male sex organs are saclike structures that produce large numbers of sperm cells. The female sex organs are flask-shaped and have long, twisted necks. An egg is formed within the base of the female organ. How does a sperm reach the egg? Would you expect to find moss plants growing where there was little or no water? Explain. The union of the egg and sperm results in a cell called the zygote. Where is the zygote formed? What grows from the zygote?

Part B: Flowers

6. Examine the outside parts of a gladiolus flower. The outermost whorl of floral parts may be green and leaflike. These green sepals protected the flower bud when it was young. In some flowers, such as lilies, the sepals look like an outer whorl of petals. Petals are usually large and colored and lie just inside the sepals. Both sepals and petals are attached to the enlarged end of a branch. These parts of the flower are not directly involved in sexual reproduction. What functions might petals have?

7. Strip away the sepals and petals to examine the reproductive structures. Around a central stalklike body are 5–10 delicate stalks, each ending in a small sac, or anther. Together, the stalks and the anthers form the male reproductive organs, or stamens. Thousands of pollen grains are produced in the anther. The number of stamens varies according to the type of flower. How many stamens are present in the flower you are using? How is pollen carried from the anthers to the female part of the flower?

8. If the anthers are mature, shake some of the pollen into a drop of 15% sucrose solution on a clean slide. Add a coverslip and examine with the low power of a compound microscope. What is the appearance of the pollen? How is the pollen adapted for dispersal?

9. Make another pollen preparation on a clean coverslip. Use modeling clay to make a 5-mm-high chamber, slightly smaller than the coverslip, on a clean slide. Add a small drop of water to the chamber and invert the pollen preparation over it. Examine after 15 minutes and again at the end of the lab period. What, if any, changes have occurred? (If no changes have occurred, store the slide in a covered petri dish containing a piece of cotton moistened with water and examine it the next day.)

10. The central stalk surrounded by the stamens is the female reproductive organ, or carpel. It is composed of an enlarged basal part, the ovary, above which is an elongated part, the style, ending in a stigma. How is the stigma adapted to trap the pollen grains and to provide a place for them to grow?

11. Use a scalpel to cut the ovary lengthwise.

Caution

Scalpels are sharp; handle with care.

Sharp
Object!

Using a hand lens or stereomicroscope, look at the cut surface. How many ovules can you see? Each ovule contains one egg. To what stage of the moss life cycle is the ovule comparable? How close to the egg can the pollen grain get? If the pollen grain cannot get to the egg, how do the sperm produced by the pollen reach it? To what stage of the moss life cycle is a pollen grain comparable?

12. The union of egg and sperm causes extensive changes in the female reproductive parts. Fertilization of the egg stimulates the growth of the ovary and the enclosed ovules. Carefully examine a fresh bean or pea pod. Open the pod to find the seeds. What part of the female reproductive apparatus is the pod of a bean or pea? What is the origin of a seed? If you plant ripe bean or pea seeds and water them, to what will they give rise? What can you conclude develops within a seed as a result of fertilization?

13. If time permits, examine other types of flowers. Compare the numbers of various parts and the ways the parts are arranged with respect to each other.

14. Wash your hands thoroughly before leaving the laboratory.

Discussion

1. In alternation of generations in a moss, which is the predominant, independent generation? Which is the less conspicuous generation?

2. Compare the life cycle of a moss (with alternation of generations) with your life cycle (with no alternation of generations).

3. Would you expect the most variation in flowering plants or in those reproducing by asexual means? Explain.

4. Compare and contrast the life cycle of a moss with that of a flowering plant.

5. Do flowering plants represent more or less adaptation to a land environment than mosses? Explain.

investigation 2.3

Fruits and Seeds

The survival of plants depends on their ability to reproduce. In seed producers, the most complex plants, reproductive ability is enhanced by mechanisms that protect and disperse the seeds (and fruits) so the seeds do not compete with the parent plants for nutrients, light, and water. Dispersal increases the likelihood that some seeds will not be eaten. In flowering plants, seeds are protected by the tissues of the mature ovary, or fruit. (Conifers, which lack an ovary, produce naked seeds on cone scales.)

In this investigation, you will try to determine how seeds of various fruits are dispersed. You also will use the fruits to make a dichotomous key, which can help you distinguish between objects by focusing on their similarities and differences.

Materials (per team of 3)
set of fruits
data books
pens

Procedure
Part A: Seed Dispersal

1. Blow gently at the fruits. What happens? Why? What parts of the fruits are important in allowing them to be wind-dispersed?

2. Gently rest the sleeve of your blouse or shirt on the fruits and then lift up your arm. Which fruits are lifted? What parts of these fruits are important in allowing them to be dispersed by animals?

3. Some fruits attract birds and other animals that eat the fruits but do not damage the seeds inside. What characteristics of the fruits might serve as attractants?

4. Some fruits contain a chemical that acts as a laxative. How might this function in seed dispersal? How might the contents of bird droppings assist in survival of the new seedlings?

Part B: Dichotomous Key

5. Design a dichotomous key using the fruits from Part A. Your dichotomous key should separate all the available fruits into individual categories. Assemble the fruits and review the characteristics you observed in Part A.

6. To form a dichotomous key, use characteristics that some fruits have and some do not, rather than characteristics that all share. For example, *fruits with spines* versus *fruits without spines* might be a good characteristic to use in building your key. On the other hand, *fruits that contain seeds* would not be a good characteristic because almost all fruits contain seeds.

7. To divide the fruits into 2 groups, choose one major characteristic not shared by all the fruits. Separate your fruits into 2 groups, one group that possesses the characteristic and another group that does not. In your data book, prepare a table similar to Table A2.3 but with the lines only, or tape in the table your teacher provides. Write the characteristic on the table as shown below:

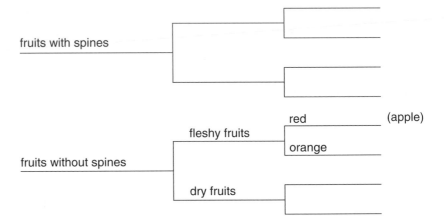

8. Focus on all the fruits in just 1 of your 2 groups. Choose another characteristic that separates those fruits into two groups. Write this characteristic in the second column of the key.

9. Continue to select characteristics and write them on the key until you have produced a key that separates all the fruits into individual categories. In other words, your key should split the fruits into smaller and smaller groups until each fruit is in a group by itself. Once this is done, place the name of the fruit (maple, ash, etc.) next to the appropriate line on the right side of the key.

10. Exchange keys with another team. See if you can follow their key and they can follow yours.

11. Wash your hands thoroughly before leaving the laboratory.

Discussion

1. What are some of the ways seeds/fruits are dispersed?

2. Describe how a dispersal mechanism that relies on the presence of other organisms might develop in a plant species.

3. What would happen to the distribution of plants that produce cockleburs if they lived on an island having no animals?

4. Explain how poplar trees might come to inhabit an island in the middle of a large lake.

5. What is the purpose of a dichotomous key?

6. What characteristics did you use to develop your dichotomous key? What characteristics did your class as a whole use?

7. Could you develop a dichotomous key for organisms that looked identical to each other? Explain.

The Body's Organization

We can think of the entire body as a large compartment that is physically separate from the outside environment. But your body also contains smaller compartments, with still smaller compartments inside of them. Let's examine the body's organization by looking at the structure of some of these compartments. We begin by considering the structure and significance of one of the body's smallest compartments—the cell.

The **cell** is the basic unit of structure and function in living things. All organisms are made of one or more cells. The exterior border of the cell is the **cell membrane**, a structure that separates the inside of the cell from the outside. The basic material within the cell is called **cytoplasm**, which consists of a complex mixture of water, salts, proteins, and other substances.

Suspended in the cytoplasm are numerous smaller compartments called **organelles**. Different types of organelles perform different functions in the cell. Chief among these is the **nucleus**, which contains the information required to operate the cell. Other important organelles include **mitochondria**, which provide most of the energy that powers activities within the cell.

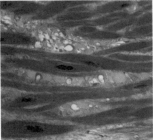

mitochondrion

cytoplasm

cell membrane

nucleus

epithelial cell

The human body contains several hundred different types of cells, such as muscle cells, nerve cells, liver cells, and blood cells. Different types of cells have different structures and functions.

A **tissue** is a group of similar cells that are organized together and perform a specific function. The human body contains four types of tissues. The cell in the drawing above is from epithelial tissue; the other three types are connective tissue, nerve tissue, and muscle tissue.

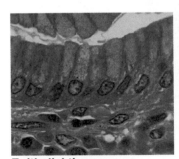

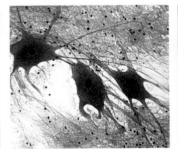

Epithelial tissue covers external and internal body surfaces. Examples of epithelial tissue include the skin and the linings of the digestive tract. Epithelial tissues protect the body's surfaces and produce secretions such as sweat and mucus.

Connective tissue binds, supports, and protects body structures. Connective tissue cells secrete nonliving material that forms a matrix. The matrix may be liquid (as in blood) or solid (as in bone and cartilage).

Nerve tissue is made up of nerve cells, or neurons, which are specialized to transmit nerve impulses (essentially information in the form of electrical signals) from one part of the body to another. The brain and spinal cord are made of nerve tissue.

Muscle tissue consists of cells that are able to contract in response to stimulation. Muscle tissue gives shape and support to the body and produces heat by shivering. It also helps move the whole body, as well as its individual parts.

Source: *BSCS, Biological Perspectives, 2nd Edition*

An **organ** is a group of tissues that are organized together to form a structural and functional unit. Every organ contains all four types of body tissue. Examples of organs include the heart, the kidney, and the stomach.

The tissues of an organ work together, bringing about the organ's function. For example, the stretching that occurs when food enters the stomach activates nerve tissue. The nerve tissue, in turn, stimulates epithelial tissue cells, which then secrete digestive substances that help break down the food. Contractions of muscle tissue cells mix food with digestive substances and move it into the next organ in the system. The connective tissue provides an elastic and supportive framework that holds all of the tissues together.

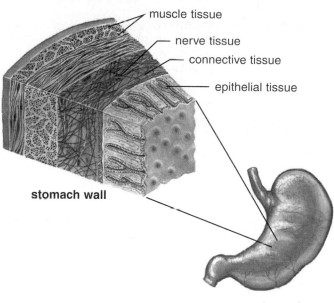

muscle tissue

nerve tissue

connective tissue

epithelial tissue

stomach wall

stomach

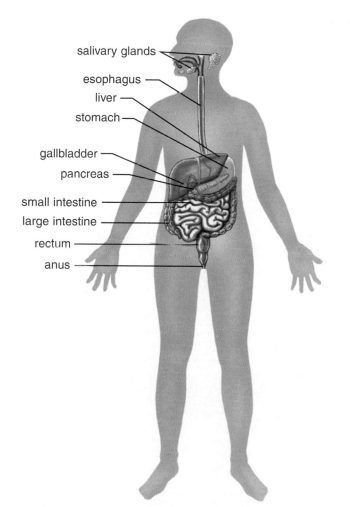

salivary glands

esophagus

liver

stomach

gallbladder

pancreas

small intestine

large intestine

rectum

anus

Groups of organs form **organ systems** that carry out major body activities such as circulation, gas exchange, and digestion. These activities are accomplished by the coordinated action of the organs that make up the system. The digestive system, for example, breaks down food into small molecules. This breakdown begins with mechanical and chemical processes in the mouth and continues with further chemical processes in the stomach and small intestine. Several organs in the digestive system contribute the chemicals needed for digestion. The nutrients that result are absorbed from the small intestine into the blood and transported by the circulatory system to all cells of the body.

Thinking about the structure of the body in this way should help you see that the function of a whole organism is the result of the coordinated action and interaction of all of its parts. For example, the function of a cell results from the coordinated action of its organelles, the function of a tissue results from the coordinated action of the cells that make it up, and so on. Thus, the function of the body results from the action and interaction of all of its parts.

Appendix 4

Phylogeny and the Evolution of Darwin's Finches

Process and Procedure

1. Read the following paragraphs about Darwin's finches. Check your understanding with a partner by sharing three key ideas from this reading.

   Generations of biologists since Darwin have wondered about the origin of Darwin's finches on the Galápagos Islands. Did they descend from a single ancestral species that colonized the islands in the distant past, or from different ancestors that colonized the islands at different times?

   In the past, biologists used anatomical and behavioral data to answer this question. The data were informative, but did not provide all the answers. Today, biologists use molecular data to learn more about the evolution of Darwin's finches. This example shows how new technologies help scientists answer old questions about the living world.

   By comparing the DNA of Darwin's finches to the DNA of bird species living in South and Central America, scientists have discovered that Darwin's finches form a single group of 14 closely related species. These finch species are more closely related to each other than to any other bird. The mainland species that is most closely related to Darwin's finches is the dull-colored grassquit. The finches and dull-colored grassquit likely evolved from the same ancestral species.

   The DNA data also suggest that Darwin's finches evolved from a single ancestral species that reached the Galápagos Islands from the mainland about 2.3 million years ago. The amount of genetic diversity among the finches suggests that they did not descend from a single pair, but a small flock of at least 40 individuals.

   Across time, individuals from this founding population spread to other islands and formed new populations. As natural selection began adapting these populations to their new island environments, they diversified into the different finch species we see today. This process of diversification from a single ancestor into several related species through natural selection is called *adaptive radiation*. The beak structure of each species has been adapted through natural selection for gathering its primary food. Study the beak structure and diet information provided in Figure A4.1.

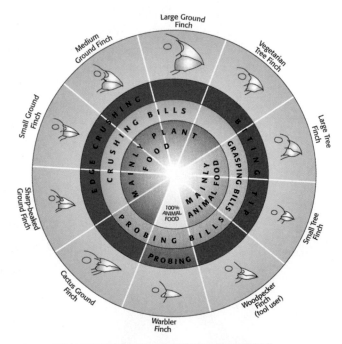

Figure A4.1 Beak structure and diet information

The evolutionary tree in Figure A4.2 shows the phylogeny and the evolutionary relationships among 13 of the 14 Darwin's finches and their closest non-finch relative (the dull-colored grassquit). Each branch point represents an ancestral species from which two or more lineages (lines of descent) evolved. The length of a horizontal line leading to a species indicates how genetically different the species is from other species.

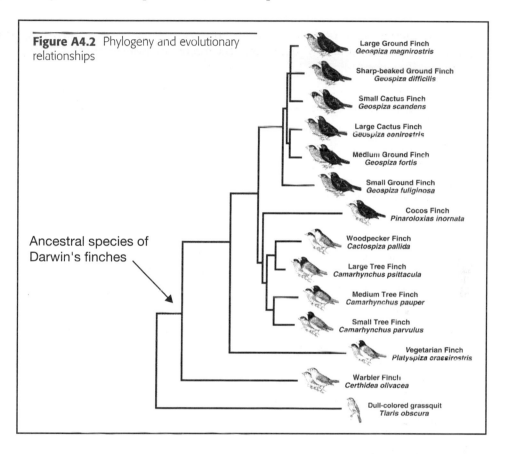

Figure A4.2 Phylogeny and evolutionary relationships

Large Ground Finch
Geospiza magnirostris

Sharp-beaked Ground Finch
Geospiza difficilis

Small Cactus Finch
Geospiza scandens

Large Cactus Finch
Geospiza conirostris

Medium Ground Finch
Geospiza fortis

Small Ground Finch
Geospiza fuliginosa

Cocos Finch
Pinaroloxias inornata

Woodpecker Finch
Cactospiza pallida

Large Tree Finch
Camarhynchus psittacula

Medium Tree Finch
Camarhynchus pauper

Small Tree Finch
Camarhynchus parvulus

Vegetarian Finch
Platyspiza crassirostris

Warbler Finch
Certhidea olivacea

Dull-colored grassquit
Tiaris obscura

Ancestral species of Darwin's finches

© Springer–Verlag Berlin Heidelberg 2002

2. When you are finished sharing ideas with your partner, work together to answer the Analysis Questions below. Record your best ideas in your student notebook.

Analysis Questions

1. What does the evolutionary tree suggest about the evolution of Darwin's finches?

2. How does this example illustrate phylogeny as a result of natural selection?

3. What does the beak structure and diet suggest about the feeding habits of the finches?

4. How might have these feeding habits developed?

Appendix 5

Analyzing Karyotypes

Process and Procedure

1. Read the following paragraphs about karyotypes.

    To produce a karyotype, chromosomes from a single cell are stained, photographed, and enlarged. The images of the individual chromosomes are cut out and arranged in a pattern showing pairs of numbered chromosomes and the pair of sex chromosomes. In humans, a normal karyotype shows 22 pairs of numbered chromosomes and a single pair of sex chromosomes (XX or XY).

    Unusual numbers of chromosomes in a karyotype are associated with genetic disorders. One of the most common genetic disorders caused by an extra copy of a chromosome is Down's syndrome. This disorder results when a child is born having three copies of chromosome 21.

2. Study the karyotype in Figure A5.1 of a normal male and in Figure A5.2, of a male with Down's syndrome. Locate and note the three copies of chromosome 21 in Figure A5.2.

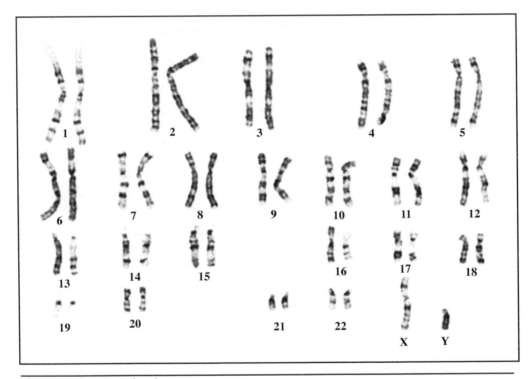

Figure A5.1 A normal male

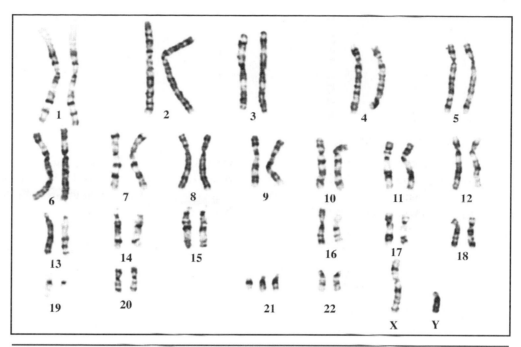

Figure A5.2 A male with Down syndrome

People with Down's syndrome display a number of symptoms including limited mental abilities, short stature, heart irregularities, and characteristic facial features. The severity of these symptoms varies among people with Down's syndrome.

3. Look at Figure A5.3, which is a karyotype of a normal female, and Figure A5.4, which is a karyotype of a female with Turner's syndrome, and answer the following question.

   a. Analyze the karyotypes in Figure A5.3 and A5.4 to determine the abnormality present in the Turner's syndrome karyotype. What did you discover?

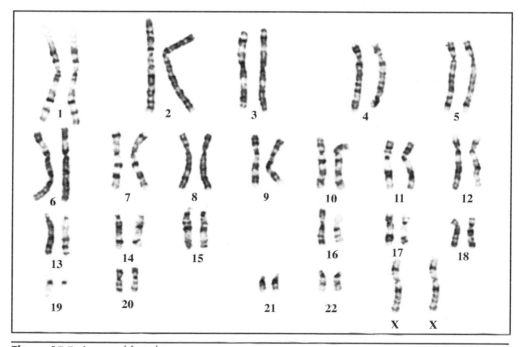

Figure A5.3 A normal female

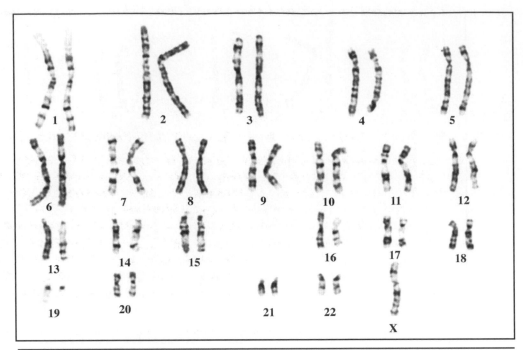

Figure A5.4 A female with Turner syndrome

Females with Turner's syndrome are of short stature, sexually underdeveloped, and infertile.

4. After considering all 4 figures, answer the analysis questions below.

Analysis Questions

Consider each of the following questions and record your answer in your student notebook.

1. How can human karyotypes be used to distinguish between males and females?

2. How can karyotypes be used to detect genetic disorders?

3. Can a karyotype be used to diagnose a genetic disorder caused by a mutation in a single gene? Why or why not?

Appendix 6

Exploring Commensalism

Process and Procedure

1. Read the following paragraph and share your understanding with a partner.

   Commensalism is a type of symbiosis where one organism benefits from the relationship and the other organism is unaffected. For example, many orchids use trees as surfaces upon which to grow. The trees are not harmed or helped by the orchids. The orchids however, benefit by growing near the top of the tree where they can collect more sunlight and rain. True commensalism is relatively rare in nature. Although it may be easy to conclude that one member of the pair is benefiting from the relationship, it can be difficult to prove that the other member of the pair is unaffected. Barnacles attach themselves to whales and benefit by being given a free ride to a new location. Presumably, the whales are not affected by this behavior. However, it can be argued that the presence of barnacles on a whale increases drag and causes the whale to expend extra energy while swimming.

2. After you have discussed your understanding with a partner, for each of the following examples, explain why the relationship is, or is not, an example of commensalism.

   a. A hermit crab living in an empty snail shell.

   b. Nitrogen-fixing bacteria living in nodules on the roots of a plant from the legume family.

   c. House mice living in a person's home.

GLOSSARY

A

active transport: The movement of a substance across a biological membrane against its concentration gradient with the help of energy input and specific transport proteins. Chapter 4, Unit 2 Essays

adaptation: In natural selection, a hereditary characteristic of some organisms in a population. The characteristic improves the organisms' chances for survival and reproduction in their environment compared with the chances of other organisms in the population. Chapter 2, Unit 1; Chapter 3, Unit 1

aerobic (eh ROH bik): Taking place or living in the presence of free or dissolved oxygen. Chapter 7, Unit 3 Essays

allele (al LEEL): One of two or more possible forms of a gene. Each affects the hereditary trait somewhat differently. Chapter 11, Unit 4 Essays

amylase (AM el ase): A digestive enzyme found in saliva. Chapter 7, Unit 3 Essays

anaerobic (an eh ROH bik): Taking place or living in conditions without free oxygen. Chapter 7, Unit 3 Essays

antibody: A blood protein produced in response to an antigen, with which it combines specifically. Antibodies block the ability of pathogens or foreign material to injure the body. Chapter 6, Unit 2

antibody-mediated response: Immune response in which B-cells produce antibodies to bind with and mark antigens for destruction by nonspecific defenses; initiated by helper T-cells. Chapter 6, Unit 2 Essays

antigen (AN tih jen): Any material, usually a protein, that is recognized as foreign and raises an immune response. Chapter 6, Unit 2

antihistamine (an tih HIST uh meen): A drug found in medicines used to counteract the histamine response. Chapter 6, Unit 2 Essays

artifact: Material remains, such as pieces of pottery, tools, and textiles, that are cultural evidence. Chapter 2, Unit 1

asexual reproduction: Any method of reproduction that requires only one parent or one parent cell. Chapter 10, Unit 4

atom: The smallest particle of an element. In turn, an atom is made of smaller particles that do not separately have the properties of the element. Chapter 2, Unit 1 Essays; Chapter 8, Unit 3 Essays

ATP (adenosine triphosphate [uh DEN oh seen try FOS fayt]): A compound that has three phosphate groups and is used by cells to store energy. Chapter 8, Unit 3 Essays

autoimmune disease: A response in which antibodies are produced to attack some of the body's own cells. Chapter 6, Unit 2 Essays

autosome (AW tow sowm): A chromosome that is not directly involved in determining sex. Chapter 11, Unit 4

autotroph (AW toh trohf): An organism able to make and store food, using sunlight or another nonliving energy source. Chapter 8, Unit 3

axon: A structure that extends out from a neuron and conducts impulses away from the cell body. Chapter 1, Unit 1 Essays

B

B-cell: A type of lymphocyte that develops in the bone marrow and later produces antibodies. Chapter 6, Unit 2

biomass: The dry weight of organic matter that makes up a group of organisms in a particular habitat. Chapter 9, Unit 3 Essays

biosphere (BY oh sfeer): The outer portion of the earth—air, water, and soil—where life is found. Chapter 15, Unit 6

biosynthesis (by oh SIN thuh sis): The process of putting together or building up the large molecules characteristic of a particular type of cell or tissue. Chapter 8, Unit 3

bipedal: Capable of walking erect on the hind limbs, freeing the hands for other uses. Chapter 1, Unit 1 Essays

bladder: Chapter 4, Unit 2 Essays

blood pressure: The fluid pressure created by heart contractions; allows blood to circulate. Chapter 5, Unit 2; Chapter 6, Unit 2

buffer: A solution of weak acids and bases that resists changes in its pH level when an acid or base is added to it. Chapter 5, Unit 2; Chapter 7, Unit 3

C

calorie: The amount of heat required to raise the temperature of one gram of water 1°C. Chapter 8, Unit 3

cancer: Malignancy arising from cells that are characterized by profound abnormalities in the plasma membrane and in the cytosol, and by abnormal growth and division. Chapter 13, Unit 5 Essays

carbon cycle: The chemical cycle in which carbon compounds made by some organisms (such as plants) are digested and decomposed by others. The carbon is released in small inorganic molecules that can be used again by more organisms to synthesize carbon compounds. Chapter 9, Unit 3

carbon fixation: Incorporating atmospheric carbon into carbohydrates through photosynthesis. Chapter 8, Unit 3 Essays

carrying capacity: The maximum population size that can be supported by the available resources of a given area. Chapter 15, Unit 6

cell cycle: An ordered sequence of events in the life of a dividing cell, composed of the M, G_1, S, and G_2 phases. Chapter 13, Unit 5 Essays

cell-mediated response: Immune response in which highly specialized lymphocytes circulate in the blood and lymphoid organs and attack and destroy cells that carry specific surface antigens. Chapter 6, Unit 2 Essays

cellular respiration (SEL yoo ler res pih RAY shun): The series of chemical reactions by which a living cell breaks down food molecules and obtains energy from them. Chapter 7, Unit 3 Essays; Chapter 8, Unit 3 Essays

cell wall: A nonliving covering around the plasma membrane of certain cells, as in plants, many algae, and some prokaryotes. In plants, the cell wall is constructed of cellulose and other materials. Chapter 4, Unit 2

chemical bond: The attraction between two atoms that results from the sharing or transfer of outer electrons from one atom to another. Chapter 8, Unit 3 Essays

chlorophyll (KLOR uh fil): The green pigments of plants and many microorganisms; converts light energy (via changes involving electrons) to chemical energy that is used in biological reactions. Chapter 8, Unit 3 Essays

chloroplast (KLOR oh plast): An organelle found only in plants and photosynthetic protists; contains chlorophyll, which absorbs the light energy used to drive photosynthesis. Chapter 8, Unit 3 Essays

chromosome (KROH moh sohm): A long, threadlike group of genes found in the nucleus of all eukaryotic cells and most visible during mitosis and meiosis; chromosomes consist of DNA and protein. Chapter 11, Unit 4 Essays

chromatography (KROM uh toh gra fee): Various techniques that scientists can use to separate mixtures of molecules based on their mass, charge, or ability to bind to other molecules. Unit 4 Essays

circulatory system: An organ system consisting of a muscular pump (heart), blood vessels, and blood itself; the means by which materials are transported to and from cells. In many animals, it also helps stabilize body temperature and pH. Chapter 4, Unit 2

class: The third largest grouping, after kingdom and phylum or division, in the biological classification system. Chapter 3, Unit 1 Essays

classification: An organizing process that focuses on the characteristics that different living systems share by virtue of their common ancestry. This places the millions of different types of life into large categories of similar organisms. Chapter 3, Unit 1

clitoris (KLI tor iss): An external reproductive organ of the female situated at the front of the vulva. It is homologous to the male penis. Chapter 10, Unit 4 Essays

clone: A population of identical cells or lineage of genetically identical individuals. Chapter 10, Unit 4

codon (KO don): The basic unit of the genetic code; a sequence of three adjacent nucleotides in DNA or mRNA. Chapter 12, Unit 4 Essays

cognitive psychologist: Engage Section

colony: Chapter 1, Unit 1 Essays

community: All the organisms that inhabit a particular area. Chapter 9, Unit 3; Chapter 15, Unit 6

competition: Interaction between members of the same population or of two or more populations to obtain a mutually required resource in limited supply. Chapter 2, Unit 1 Essays; Chapter 15, Unit 6

complement: Chapter 6, Unit 2

complementary base pairing: Predictable interactions between nitrogen bases on opposite strands of DNA and between DNA and RNA; consists of adenine-thymine and guanine-cytosine (adenine-uracil in RNA) base pairing. Chapter 12, Unit 4 Essays

components: The collection of things that makes up an ecological system, including biotic and abiotic factors. Chapter 16, Unit 6

concentration gradient: A difference in the concentration of certain molecules over a distance. Chapter 4, Unit 2 Essays

conditioning: Training that modifies a response so that it becomes associated with a stimulus different from the stimulus that originally caused it. Chapter 7, Unit 3

conservation of energy: Chapter 8, Unit 3 Essays

consumer: A heterotroph; an organism that feeds on other organisms or on their organic wastes. Chapter 9, Unit 3 Essays

continental drift: A hypothesis proposed in 1912 suggesting that the earth's landmasses had at one time been joined in a supercontinent that has broken up to form the present continents. Continental drift is now considered to be part of a broader theory of plate tectonics. Chapter 2, Unit 1 Essays

controlled experiment: Chapter 4, Unit 2

corpus callosum (KOR pus KAL o sum): A bundle of nerve fibers that connects the right and left hemispheres of the brain. Chapter 1, Unit 1 Essays

corpus luteum (KOR pus LOOT ee um): The structure that forms from the tissues of a ruptured ovarian follicle and secretes female hormones. Chapter 10, Unit 4 Essays

covalent (ko VAYL ent) bond: A chemical bond formed by two atoms sharing a pair of electrons. Chapter 8, Unit 3 Essays

cowpers (KAU perz) gland: Gland in the male reproductive system that produces an alkaline mucus. This mucus is secreted before ejaculation to protect sperm from the acidic vagina. Chapter 10, Unit 4 essays

crossing over: During prophase I of meiosis, it is the breakage and exchange of corresponding segments of chromosome pairs at one or more sites along their length. This results in genetic recombination. Chapter 11, Unit 4

cultural adaptation: An adaptation to new pressures or situations resulting from cultural innovation. Chapter 2, Unit 1

cultural evolution: Chapter 1, Unit 1 Essays

culture: A system of learned behaviors, symbols, customs, beliefs, institutions, artifacts, and technology characteristic of a group and transmitted by its members to their offspring. Chapter 1, Unit 1 Essays

D

decomposer: An organism that lives on decaying organic material, from which it obtains energy and its own raw materials for life. Chapter 9, Unit 3

deletion mutation: Mutation that results when replication enzymes mistakenly skip a base. The new DNA strand forms missing a base. Chapter 12, Unit 4 Essays

dendrite: A structure that extends out from a neuron and transmits impulses toward the cell body. Chapter 1, Unit 1 Essays

development: (1) Cell division, growth, and differentiation of cells from embryonic layers into all the tissues and organs of the body; (2) later changes with age, including reproductive maturity, with its effects on appearance and body function. Chapter 3, Unit 1; Chapter 13, Unit 5 Essays

developmental biologist: Chapter 2, Unit 1

diastole (dy AS tuh lee): The stage of the cardiac cycle in which the heart muscle is relaxed, allowing the chamber to fill with blood. (Compare with *systole*.) Chapter 6, Unit 2

differentiation: Specialization, as when developing cells become ordered into certain tissues and organs. Chapter 13, Unit 5

diffusion (dih FYOO zhun): The movement of a substance down its concentration gradient from a more concentrated area to a less concentrated area. Chapter 4, Unit 2 Essays

dihybrid (DI HI brid) cross: A genetic cross between individuals differing in two alleles. Chapter 11, Unit 4

diploid (DIH ployd): A cell containing both members of every chromosome pair characteristic of a species (2n). Chapter 11, Unit 4 Essays

diuretic (di yer RET ik): Any substance or agent that promotes the increased formation and excretion of urine. Chapter 4, Unit 2

division: The second largest grouping, after kingdom, in the biological classification system for plants. Chapter 3, Unit 1 Essays

DNA (deoxyribonucleic [dee OK sih ry boh noo KLEE ik] acid): The hereditary material of most organisms. DNA makes up the genes. These nucleic acids contain deoxyribose, a phosphate group, and one of four bases. Chapter 4, Unit 2 Essays; Chapter 11, Unit 4 Essays

DNA ligase: Enzyme that functions during the replication and repair of DNA molecules. Chapter 12, Unit 4 Essays

dominant trait: A trait that is visible in a heterozygous organism. Chapter 11, Unit 4 Essays

E

ecology: The study of living and nonliving components of the environment and of the interactions that affect biological species. Chapter 3, Unit 1

ecosystem (EE koh sis tum): A biological community in its abiotic environment. Chapter 9, Unit 3; Chapter 15, Unit 6

ejaculation: Expulsion of semen (sperm-bearing fluid) from the urethra. Chapter 10, Unit 4 Essays

electron transport system: The process in which electrons are transferred from one carrier molecule to another in photosynthesis and in cellular respiration; results in storage of some of the energy in ATP molecules. Chapter 8, Unit 3 Essays

electrophoresis (eh LEC tro for EE sis): Any of several techniques for separating large molecules, such as proteins or DNA fragments, based on their ability to move through a gel medium subjected to an electric field. Chapter 12, Unit 4

embryo (em BREE o): An organism in its earliest stages of development. Chapter 10, Unit 4 Essays

emigration (em ih GRAY shun): Departure of individuals from a population; decreases the size of the population. Chapter 15, Unit 6

endocrine (EN doh krin) system: The system of glands that secretes their products from their cells directly into the blood. Chapter 5, Unit 2 Essays

endoskeleton (EN doh SKEL eh tun): A hard skeleton buried in the soft tissues of an animal, such as the spicules of sponges and bony skeletons of vertebrates. Chapter 7, Unit 3 Essays

endothermic reaction: Chapter 8, Unit 3

enzyme (EN zime): A protein or part-protein molecule made by an organism and used as a catalyst in a specific biochemical reaction. Chapter 7, Unit 3; Chapter 8, Unit 3 Essays

epididymis (eh pih DID ih mus): A coiled structure along the surface of the testis that provides for the storage, transmission, and maturation of sperm. Chapter 10, Unit 4 Essays

estrogen (ES troh jen): A hormone that stimulates the development of female secondary sexual characteristics. Chapter 10, Unit 4 Essays

ethologists: Chapter 10, Unit 4

eukaryote (yoo KAIR ee oht): An organism whose cells have a membrane-enclosed nucleus and organelles; a protist, fungus, plant, or animal. (Compare with *prokaryote*.) Chapter 3, Unit 1 Essays; Chapter 4, Unit 2 Essays

evidence: Chapter 2, Unit 1

evolution: A cumulative change in the characteristics of organisms or populations from generation to generation. Chapter 3, Unit 1

evolutionary biologist: Chapter 2, Unit 1

exoskeleton (EK soh SKEL eh tun): A hard encasement deposited on the surface of an animal, such as the shell of a mollusk, that provides protection and points of attachment for muscles. Chapter 7, Unit 3 Essays

exothermic reaction: Chapter 8, Unit 3 Essays

exponential growth: Chapter 16, Unit 6 Essays

extinction: Chapter 2, Unit 1 Essays

F

family: The fifth largest grouping after kingdom, phylum or division, class, and order in the biological classification system; a group of related genera. Chapter 3, Unit 1 Essays

feedback system: A relationship in which one activity of an organism affects another, which in turn affects the first, yielding a regulatory balance. Chapter 5, Unit 2 Essays

fermentation (fer men TAY shun): The incomplete breakdown of food molecules, especially sugars, in the absence of oxygen. Chapter 7, Unit 3 Essays

fertilization (fer til iz AY shun): The union of an egg nucleus and a sperm nucleus. Chapter 10, Unit 4

fetus: A vertebrate embryo in later stages of development when it has attained the recognizable structural plan and features of its type. Chapter 10, Unit 4 Essays

filtration: In vertebrate kidneys, filtration takes place when blood pressure forces the blood into the glomerulus of the nephron where blood cells and plasma proteins are separated from the blood's water, nitrogenous wastes, and ions. Most of the liquid filtrate is reabsorbed, but some wastes are secreted from the body in the urine. Chapter 4, Unit 2 Essays

follicle-stimulating hormone (FSH): A substance secreted by the anterior lobe of the pituitary that stimulates the development of an ovarian follicle in a female or the production of sperm cells in a male. Chapter 10, Unit 4 Essays

food: A substance containing energy-rich organic compounds made by organisms and used as a source of energy and matter for life. Chapter 7, Unit 3 Essays

food web: Food chains in an ecosystem taken collectively, showing partial overlapping and competition for many food organisms. Chapter 9, Unit 3

G

gamete (GAM eet): A sex cell, either an egg or a sperm, formed by meiosis, having half the number of chromosomes as body cells. Chapter 10, Unit 4

gas exchange system: Chapter 5, Unit 2 Essays

gene: The fundamental physical unit of heredity, which transmits a set of specifications from one generation to the next. A segment of DNA that codes for a specific product. Chapter 11, Unit 4 Essays

gene expression: The manifestation of the genetic material of an organism as a collection of specific units. Chapter 12, Unit 4 Essays

gene therapy: The introduction of a gene into a cell to correct a hereditary disorder. Chapter 12, Unit 4 Essays

genetic code: The "language" of the genes in which the nucleotide sequence of DNA (in codons) specifies the amino acid sequences of proteins. Chapter 12, Unit 4 Essays

genetic engineering: The experimental technology developed to alter the genome of a living cell for medical or industrial use. Chapter 12, Unit 4 Essays

genotype (JEE noh tipe): The genetic makeup of an organism. Chapter 11, Unit 4 Essays

genus (JEE nus): The next largest grouping after kingdom, phylum or division, class, order, and family in the biological classification system; a group of related species. Chapter 3, Unit 1 Essays

gestation (je STAY shen): Development period between conception and birth that takes place in the uterus. Chapter 10, Unit 4

glans: Rounded gland structure at the tip of the penis, covered by the foreskin. Chapter 10, Unit 4 Essays

glial (GLEE ul) cells: Protection, support, and insulation for neurons. Chapter 5, Unit 2 Essays

glomerulus (glah MER yoo lus): A ball of capillaries surrounded by a capsule in the nephron and serving as the site of filtration in the kidneys. Chapter 4, Unit 2 Essays

glucose: A common 6-carbon sugar. Chapter 4, Unit 2

glycogen (GLY ko jen): The chief carbohydrate used by animals for energy storage. Chapter 8, Unit 3 Essays

glycolysis (gly KA luh sis): The initial breakdown of a carbohydrate, usually glucose, into smaller molecules at the beginning of cellular respiration. Chapter 8, Unit 3 Essays

gonads: The gamete-producing organs. Chapter 10, Unit 4 Essays

growth: Increase in size. In development, the successive rounds of cell division that produce a multicellular organism. Chapter 13, Unit 5 Essays

H

habitat (HA bih tat): Place where an organism lives. Even in the same ecosystem, different organisms differ in their habitats. Chapter 15, Unit 6

haploid (HAP loyd) cell: A cell containing only one member (n) of each chromosome pair characteristic of a species. Chapter 11, Unit 4

helper T-cell: A type of T-cell required by some B-cells to make antibodies, by other T-cells to respond to antigens, or by other T-cells that secrete lymphokines. Chapter 6, Unit 2

hemoglobin (HEE moh gloh bin): The pigment in red blood cells responsible for transporting oxygen. Chapter 12, Unit 4

heterotroph (HET er oh trohf): An organism that obtains carbon and all metabolic energy from organic molecules previously assembled by autotrophs; a consumer. Chapter 8, Unit 3

heterozygous (HET er oh ZY gus): Having two different alleles for a given trait. Chapter 11, Unit 4

hierarchical: Chapter 3, Unit 1

histamine (HISS tuh meen): A substance released by injured cells that causes blood vessels to dilate during an inflammatory response. Chapter 6, Unit 2 Essays

homeostasis (hoh mee oh STAY sis): A fundamental characteristic of living systems; maintaining a stable number of individuals within a population (social); the tendency of an organism to maintain a stable, constant internal environment (physiological). Chapter 5, Unit 2

hominid (HOM ih nid): A primate of the family Hominidae, which includes modern humans, earlier subspecies, and australopithecines. Chapter 2, Unit 1

homogenate (ho MAH jeh nate): A material with uniform consistency. Chapter 5, Unit 2

homozygous (HOH moh ZY gus): Having two identical alleles for a given trait. Chapter 11, Unit 4

hormone: A substance, secreted by cells or glands, that has a regulatory effect on cells and organs elsewhere in the body; a chemical messenger. Chapter 5, Unit 2 Essays

hydrostatic (hi dro STAT ik) skeleton: A mass of fluid enclosed within a muscular wall that provides the support necessary for antagonistic muscle action. Chapter 7, Unit 3

hyperthermia (HI pur THUR mee AH): An abnormally elevated body temperature; fever. Chapter 6, Unit 2

hypertonic (HI pur TAHN ik): A solution where the concentration of solutes outside a cell is greater than the concentration inside. Chapter 4, Unit 2

hypothalamus (HI po THAL uh muss): A part of the brain. In humans, it links the nervous system to the endocrine system. (The endocrine system controls the hormones that regulate many body functions.) Chapter 5, Unit 2 Essays

hypothermia (HI po THIR mee ah): An abnormally lowered body temperature. Chapter 6, Unit 2

hypothesis (hy PA thih sis): A statement that suggests an explanation for an observation or an answer to a scientific problem. Chapter 2, Unit 1 Essays

hypotonic (HI po TAHN ik): A solution where the concentration of solutes outside the cell is less than the concentration inside. Chapter 4, Unit 2

immigration (im ih GRAY shun): Arrival of new individuals into a population; increases the size of a population. Chapter 15, Unit 6

immunity: Disease-resistance, usually specific for one disease or pathogen. Chapter 6, Unit 2

impermeable (im PUR mee uh bul): Not permeable; not possible to pass through. Chapter 4, Unit 2 Essays

incest: Sexual relations between members of the immediate family. Chapter 10, Unit 4 Essays

incomplete dominance: Pattern of gene expression in which the phenotype of a heterozygous individual is intermediate between those of the parents. Chapter 11, Unit 4 Essays

independent assortment: Independent inheritance of the alleles for a trait. Chapter 11, Unit 4 Essays

indicator: Chapter 4, Unit 2

induction: Chapter 13, Unit 5 Essays

inductive reasoning: Chapter 1, Unit 1

inference: Chapter 2, Unit 1

in vitro (in VEE tro): Literally means "in glass"; refers to laboratory procedures done in test tubes or in petri dishes. Chapter 10, Unit 4 Essays

ion: An atom or a molecule that has either gained or lost one or more electrons, giving it a positive or negative charge. Chapter 4, Unit 2 Essays

ionic bond: A chemical bond formed by the attraction between oppositely charged ions. Chapter 8, Unit 3 Essays

isotonic (I suh TA nik): A solution where the concentration of solutes outside a cell equals the concentration inside. Chapter 4, Unit 2

K

killer T-cell: A lymphocyte that is produced in the bone marrow but matures in the thymus. These cells recognize and destroy infected cells, limiting the spread of infection. Chapter 6, Unit 2

kilocalorie (kil o KAL er ee; kcal): A measure of food energy equal to 1,000 calories. Chapter 8, Unit 3

kinetic (KIN et ik) energy: Active energy. Chapter 8, Unit 3 Essays

kingdom: The largest grouping in the biological classification system. Chapter 3, Unit 1 Essays

Krebs cycle: The energy-releasing cycle in cellular respiration that completes the breakdown of intermediate products of glycolysis; also a source of carbon skeletons for use in biosynthesis reactions. Chapter 8, Unit 3 Essays

L

labia (LAE be uh): Folds of skin that protect the female genitals and cover the clitoris and the vaginal and urinary openings. Chapter 10, Unit 4 Essays

larva (LAR vuh): An immature stage of development in offspring of many types of animals. Chapter 1, Unit 1 Essays

limiting factor: An environmental condition such as food, temperature, water, or sunlight that restricts the types of organisms and population numbers that an environment can support. Chapter 15, Unit 6 Essays

linkage: In inheritance, the association of different genes due to their physical proximity on chromosomes. Chapter 11, Unit 4

lipid bilayer: The arrangement of molecules in cellular membranes. Chapter 4, Unit 2 Essays

logistic growth: Chapter 16, Unit 6 Essays

luteinizing (lew TEE ih NY zing) hormone (LH): A hormone secreted by the anterior lobe of the pituitary gland that controls the formation of the corpus luteum in females and the secretion of testosterone in males. Chapter 10, Unit 4 Essays

lymphocyte (LIM foh site): A type of small white blood cell important in the immune response. Chapter 6, Unit 2

lymphokine (LIM foh kine): Any of a class of proteins by which the cells of the vertebrate immune system communicate with one another. Chapter 6, Unit 2

lysosome (LY soh zohm): A cell vesicle that contains digestive enzymes. Chapter 4, Unit 2 Essays

M

macrophage (MAK roh fayj): A large white blood cell that ingests pathogens and dead cells. Chapter 6, Unit 2

meiosis (my OH sis): Two successive nuclear divisions (with corresponding cell divisions) that produce gametes (in animals) or sexual spores (in plants) that have one-half of the genetic material of the original cell. Chapter 10, Unit 4; Chapter 11, Unit 4

memory cell: B- or T-lymphocyte produced in response to a primary immune response. The lymphocyte remains in the circulation and can respond rapidly if the same antigen is encountered in the future. Chapter 6, Unit 2

menopause (MEN oh pawz): In human females, the cessation of menstruation, usually taking place between the ages of 45 and 50. Chapter 10, Unit 4 Essays

menstrual (MEN strew al) cycle: The female reproductive cycle that is characterized by regularly recurring changes in the uterine lining. Chapter 10, Unit 4 Essays

menstruation (men strew AY shun): Periodic sloughing of the blood-enriched lining of the uterus when pregnancy does not occur. Chapter 10, Unit 4 Essays

messenger RNA (mRNA): The RNA complementary to one strand of DNA; transcribed from genes and translated by ribosomes into protein. Chapter 12, Unit 4

metabolism (meh TAB oh liz um): The sum of all the chemical changes taking place in an organism. Chapter 8, Unit 3 Essays

metastasize: To spread, as in the spread of cancer cells. Chapter 13, Unit 5 Essays

mitochondria (my toh KON dree uh): The organelles in eukaryotic cells that carry on cellular respiration, releasing energy from food molecules and storing it in ATP. Chapter 7, Unit 3 Essays

mitosis (my TOH sis): The replication of the chromosomes and the production of two nuclei in one cell; usually followed by cytokinesis. Chapter 10, Unit 4; Chapter 13, Unit 5

model: Chapter 2, Unit 1

monogamy (moh NOG ahm ee): A bond between two individuals. Chapter 10, Unit 4 Essays

monohybrid (mon o HI brid) cross: A genetic cross between individuals differing in one allele. Chapter 11, Unit 4

mons pubis (MONS PYOO bis): A pad of tissue covering the female pubic bone that becomes covered with hair. Chapter 10, Unit 4 Essays

mortality (mor TAL ih tee): Death rate, measured as the proportion of deaths to total population over a given period; often expressed as number of deaths per 1,000 or 10,000 individuals. Chapter 15, Unit 6

mRNA: See messenger RNA. Chapter 12, Unit 4

mutation (myoo TAY shun): A chemical change in a gene, resulting in a new allele, or a change in the portion of a chromosome that regulates the gene. In either case, the change is hereditary. Chapter 11, Unit 4 Essays

mutualism (MYOO tyoo ul is um): Symbiotic relationship that mutually benefits two species. Chapter 15, Unit 6 Essays

N

natality (nay TAL ih tee): The rate at which reproduction increases the population; the birthrate. Chapter 15, Unit 6

negative feedback: A kind of feedback that creates equilibrium between input and output in a system or process. Chapter 5, Unit 2 Essays

nephron (NEF rahn): The functional unit of a kidney. It consists of a long, coiled tubule. One end forms a cup that encloses a mass of capillaries. The other end opens into a duct that collects urine. The entire nephron is surrounded by a network of capillaries. Chapter 4, Unit 2 Essays

nervous system: A coordinating mechanism in all multicellular animals, except sponges, that regulates internal body functions and responses to external stimuli. In vertebrates, it consists of the brain, spinal cord, nerves, ganglia, and parts of receptor and effector organs. Chapter 1, Unit 1 Essays; Chapter 5, Unit 2 Essays

neurobiologist: Chapter 1, Unit 1 Essays

neuron (NOOR ahn): A nerve cell; a name usually reserved for nerve cells in animals that have a complex brain and specialized associative, motor, and sensory nerves. Chapter 1, Unit 1 Essays; Chapter 5, Unit 2 Essays

neurotransmitter (NOOR oh TRANS mit er): A chemical messenger that diffuses across the synapse and transmits a nerve impulse from one neuron to another. Chapter 1, Unit 1 Essays; Chapter 5, Unit 2

niche (NITCH): The sum total of all the adaptations an organism uses to survive in its environment. This includes its role in the community, what it eats, and what interactions it has with other organisms and with its environment. Chapter 15, Unit 6 Essays

nondisjunction (non dis JUNG shun): The failure of a pair of homologous chromosomes to separate during meiosis or mitosis. Chapter 11, Unit 4 Essays

nucleic (noo KLEE ik) acid: DNA or RNA. An organic compound composed of nucleotides, it is important in coding instructions for cell processes. Chapter 12, Unit 4 Essays

nucleotide (NOO klee oh tide): A subunit or building block of DNA or RNA. It is chemically constructed of a 5-carbon sugar, a nitrogen base, and a phosphate group. Chapter 12, Unit 4 Essays

nucleus (NOO klee us): In atoms, the central core, containing positively charged protons and (in all but hydrogen) electrically neutral neutrons. In eukaryotic cells, it is the membranous organelle that houses the chromosomal DNA. Chapter 4, Unit 2 Essays

nymph: Chapter 1, Unit 1 Essays

oncogene: A gene found in viruses or as part of the normal genome that is crucial for triggering cancerous characteristics. Chapter 13, Unit 5 Essays

order: The fourth largest grouping, after kingdom, phylum or division, and class, in the biological classification system; a group of related families. Chapter 3, Unit 1 Essays

organelle (or guh NEL): An organized structure within a cell, with a specific function. A chloroplast and a mitochondrion are examples. Chapter 4, Unit 2

organ system: Chapter 4, Unit 2 Essays

orgasm: Sensory and motor events at the peak of sexual stimulation that result in ejaculation for the male and involuntary contraction of the muscles surrounding the vagina in the female. Chapter 10, Unit 4 Essays

osmosis (os MOH sis): The movement of water across a selectively permeable membrane. Chapter 4, Unit 2 Essays

ova (singular: ovum): Mature female gametes. Chapter 10, Unit 4

ovaries (singular: ovary): The primary reproductive organs of a female; egg-cell-producing organs. Chapter 10, Unit 4 Essays

oviduct (OH vi dukt): A tube leading from an ovary to the uterus. Chapter 10, Unit 4 Essays

ovulation (ahv yoo LAY shun): In vertebrates, the release of one or more eggs from an ovary. Chapter 10, Unit 4 Essays

ozone layer: A triatomic form of oxygen that, in the upper atmosphere, forms a protective layer against excess ultraviolet radiation. Chapter 16, Unit 6

P

paleontologist (PAY lee on TOHL oh jist): A scientist who studies the history of the earth through its geologic history and who learns about the history of life on earth through the study of fossils. Chapter 2, Unit 1

parasitism (PAIR uh sih tiz um): An ecological niche in which one organism is the habitat and the food for another. A parasite lives and feeds on the host organism, usually without killing it. Chapter 15, Unit 6 Essays

passive transport: The diffusion of a substance across a biological membrane through a transport protein in the membrane. Chapter 4, Unit 2 Essays

pathogen (PATH oh jen): A disease-causing organism. Chapter 6, Unit 2

penicillin (pen ih SIL lin): Any of several antibiotic compounds obtained from penicillium mold and used to prevent or treat a wide variety of diseases and infections. Chapter 6, Unit 2

penis: In vertebrates, the male organ through which sperm are passed to the female and through which nitrogenous wastes from the kidneys—in the form of urine—are discharged outside the body. Chapter 10, Unit 4 Essays

permeable: Open to passage or penetration. Chapter 4, Unit 2 Essays

pH: A measure of how acidic a solution is. Chapter 5, Unit 2

phenotype (FEE noh tipe): The expression of a genotype in the appearance or function of an organism; the observed trait. Chapter 11, Unit 4 Essays

pheromone (FARE oh mohn): A small chemical signal that animals produce that can stimulate and influence the physiology and behavior of other individuals of the same species; acts much like hormones. Chapter 1, Unit 1 Essays; Chapter 11, Unit 4

photosynthesis (fo toe SIN thus sis): The process by which living cells that contain chlorophyll use light energy to make organic compounds from inorganic materials. Chapter 8, Unit 3

phylum (FY lum): The second largest grouping, after kingdom, in the biological classification system; for all organisms except plants, which are classified in divisions. Chapter 3, Unit 1 Essays

physical anthropologist: A scientist who studies the biological evolution of humans. Chapter 2, Unit 1

physiological (fiz ee OH laj ih kul) processes: Related to functions of an organism or its parts. Chapter 5, Unit 2 Essays

pituitary (pih TOO ih ter ee): A part of the brain that produces and secretes hormones that regulate a variety of body functions. The pituitary also stores and then releases two hormones produced by cells in the hypothalamus. Chapter 5, Unit 2 Essays

placenta (pluh SEN tuh): A structure in the pregnant uterus for nourishing a fetus with the mother's blood supply, formed from the uterine lining and embryonic membranes. Chapter 10, Unit 4 Essays

plasma (PLAZ muh): The liquid portion of the blood in which the cells are suspended. Chapter 4, Unit 2

plasma cell: An antibody-producing cell that forms as a result of the proliferation of sensitized B-lymphocytes. Chapter 6, Unit 2

plate tectonics (tek TON iks): The theory and study of the movement of the plates that make up the earth's crust. Essay Section, Unit 1

polygamy (puh LIG uh me): Mating strategy whereby one individual mates with more than one individual of the opposite sex. Chapter 10, Unit 4 Essays

polymerase (PAH lce mur ayse) chain reaction (PCR): A technique for amplifying a DNA molecule where after 20 cycles of PCR amplification, more than a million copies of a DNA molecule will have been made. Extremely important in biotechnology and research. Chapter 12, Unit 4 Essays

population: A group of organisms of one species that lives in the same place at the same time. Chapter 2, Unit 1 Essays; Chapter 3, Unit 1

population density: Number of organisms per unit of habitat area. Chapter 15, Unit 6 Essays

positive feedback: A kind of feedback that disturbs or prevents equilibrium between input and output in a system or process. Chapter 5, Unit 2 Essays

potential energy: Chapter 8, Unit 3 Essays

predation (pred EH shun): The killing and consumption of prey. Chapter 2, Unit 1 Essays

predator-prey relationship: The relationship between organisms in which one, the predator, feeds on the other, the prey. Chapter 15, Unit 6 Essays

principle of independent assortment: The inheritance of alleles for one trait does not affect the inheritance of alleles for another trait. Chapter 11, Unit 4 Essays

principle of segregation: During meiosis, chromosome pairs separate so that each of the two alleles for any given trait appears in a different gamete. Chapter 11, Unit 4 Essays

producer: An autotroph. Any organism that produces its own food using matter and energy from the nonliving world. Chapter 9, Unit 3 Essays

progesterone (proh JES tuh rohn): A female hormone secreted by the placenta and the corpus luteum that acts to prepare and maintain the uterus for pregnancy and to prepare the breasts for lactation. Chapter 10, Unit 4 Essays

prokaryote (pro KAIR ee oht): An organism whose cells do not have membrane-enclosed organelles, such as nuclei, mitochondria, and chloroplasts; a bacterium. (Compare with *eukaryote*.) Chapter 3, Unit 1 Essays; Chapter 4, Unit 2 Essays

prostate (PRAH stayt) gland: Male reproductive gland that produces and adds more fluid to the semen. Chapter 10, Unit 4 Essays

protein (PROH teen): An organic compound composed of one or more polypeptide chains of amino acids. Most structural materials and enzymes in a cell are proteins. Chapter 4, Unit 2 Essays

protocol: A plan or procedure for a basic investigation that can answer a testable question; serves as a standard for controlling variables. Chapter 1, Unit 1

puberty (PYOO bur tee): The stage of development in which the reproductive organs become functional. Chapter 10, Unit 4 Essays

pulse: Chapter 6, Unit 2

R

radioactive isotope: A form of a chemical element that emits energetic particles (such as electrons) by the decay of its atomic nucleus. Chapter 2, Unit 1 Essays

reabsorption (REE ab ZORP shun) (in the kidney): Takes place in capillaries outside the glomerulus (in the renal tubule). Water and some dissolved substances that had been filtered from the blood are returned (reabsorbed) to the filtered blood. Chapter 4, Unit 2 Essays

receptor (ree SEP ter): A specialized sensory cell, as in the eye or the skin, that is sensitive to a particular type of stimulus. Chapters 4–5, Unit 2 Essays

recessive (ree SESS iv): A term used to describe an allele or trait that is masked by a dominant allele or trait. Chapter 11, Unit 4

recessive trait: Chapter 11, Unit 4

recombinant (re KOM bin ent) DNA: DNA that incorporates parts of different parent DNA molecules, as formed by natural recombination mechanisms or by recombinant DNA technology. Chapter 12, Unit 4 Essays

recombination (re KOM bin EH shun): The regrouping of genes in an offspring caused by the crossing over of chromosomes during meiosis. Chapter 11, Unit 4 Essays

reflex: An involuntary reaction or response to a stimulus. Chapter 1, Unit 1 Essays

reflex arc: A nerve pathway that forms the structural and functional basis for a reflex. Chapter 1, Unit 1 Essays

replication (rep li KAY shun): The process of making a copy of the chromosome in a cell nucleus as well as other genes in certain organelles outside the nucleus, particularly chloroplasts and mitochondria. The process is unlike duplication in that each gene and each chromosome in the double set is partly new but also includes part of the old gene or chromosome. Chapter 12, Unit 4 Essays

reproduction: Chapter 10, Unit 4

restriction enzyme: An enzyme that recognizes specific nucleotide sequences in DNA and breaks the DNA chain at those points. Chapter 12, Unit 4

ribonucleic (ry boh noo KLEE ik) acid (RNA): The hereditary material of certain viruses, and the material coded by the DNA of other cells to carry out specific genetic functions; for example, messenger RNA and transfer RNA. Chapter 12, Unit 4

ribosomal (RY boh SOHM ul) RNA (rRNA): A class of RNA molecules found, together with characteristic proteins, in ribosomes. Chapter 12, Unit 4 Essays

ribosome (RY boh SOHM): A cell organelle constructed in the nucleus. It consists of two subunits and functions as the site of protein synthesis in the cytoplasm. Chapter 12, Unit 4 Essays

rRNA: See ribosomal RNA. Chapter 12, Unit 4 Essays

S

scrotum: A pouch of skin that encloses the testes. Chapter 10, Unit 4 Essays

secretion: In the kidney, takes place near the end of the renal tubule. Unfiltered wastes are passed from the blood (secreted) into the filtrate, a process that adjusts the blood pH. Chapter 4, Unit 2 Essays

selectively permeable: A property of biological membranes that allows some substances to cross and prevents others from crossing. Chapter 4, Unit 2 Essays

semen (SEE men): In mammalian males, the thick fluid that transports sperm. Chapter 10, Unit 4 Essays

seminal vesicles (SEM in ul VES ih kuls): In the male reproductive system, two small sacs that contribute to semen production. Chapter 10, Unit 4 Essays

senescence: Chapter 13, Unit 5 Essays

sexual reproduction: Reproduction involving the contribution of genetic material from two parents. Chapter 10, Unit 4

sexual selection: Selection based on variation in secondary sexual characteristics, leading to the enhancement of individual reproductive fitness. Chapter 10, Unit 4 Essays

shock: A condition of profound disturbance of the body's vital processes, characterized by failure of the circulatory system to deliver adequate amounts of blood to vital organs. Chapter 6, Unit 2

solute (SAWL yoot): The dissolved substance in a solution. Chapter 4, Unit 2

solution: Two or more substances combined to make a homogeneous mixture. Chapter 4, Unit 2

solvent: The liquid in which the solute is dissolved. Chapter 4, Unit 2

somatic cell: Any nonreproductive cell in an organism. Chapter 10, Unit 4

species (SPEE sheez): All individuals and populations of a particular type of organism, maintained by biological mechanisms that result in their breeding mostly with their type. Chapter 2, Unit 1 Essays; Chapter 3, Unit 1

sperm: A male gamete, usually motile in swimming movements. Its motility increases its chance of encountering and fertilizing an egg. Chapter 10, Unit 4

spores: One-celled reproductive bodies that are usually resistant to harsh environmental conditions and may remain dormant, in a dry covering, for long periods. In some organisms, spores are asexual and may initiate the growth of a new organism under favorable conditions. In other organisms, spores are sexual and must unite with spores of the other sex before producing a new organism. Chapter 10, Unit 4; Chapter 11, Unit 4

starch: A plant polysaccharide composed of glucose. Chapter 4, Unit 2; Chapter 7, Unit 3

stimulus (STIM yoo lus; plural: stimuli): A change or signal in the internal or external environment that causes an adjustment or reaction by an organism. Chapter 1, Unit 1 Essays

stomate (stow MATE): The opening between two guard cells in the epidermis of a plant leaf through which gases are exchanged with the air. Chapter 5, Unit 2 Essays

stop codon (KO don): A special codon in messenger RNA that does not specify an amino acid. When present, the synthesis (translation) of the growing amino acid chain stops. Chapter 12, Unit 4 Essays

strata (STRA tuh; singular: stratum): Layers, usually of deposited earth sediments carried by erosion. Many strata become mineralized into rock layers. Chapter 2, Unit 1

stratigraphy (stra TIG ra fee): A branch of geology that is concerned with the systemized study, description, and classification of stratified rocks. Chapter 2, Unit 1

stressor: A factor capable of stimulating a stress response. Chapter 6, Unit 2 Essays

stroma (STROH muh): The colorless substance in a chloroplast surrounding the thylakoids. The enzymes of the Calvin cycle also are in the stroma. Chapter 8, Unit 3 Essays

substitution mutation: Mutation caused by substituting one small base for the other or one large base for the other during replication. Chapter 12, Unit 4 Essays

substrate (SUB strayt): A molecule on which enzymes act. Chapter 7, Unit 3

symbiosis (sim by OH sis): An ecological relationship between organisms of two different species that benefit from living together in direct contact. Chapter 15, Unit 6 Essays

synapse (SIN aps): An open junction between neurons, across which an impulse is transmitted by a chemical messenger, a neurotransmitter. Chapter 1, Unit 1 Essays

systole (SIS toh lee): The stage of the cardiac cycle in which the heart muscle contracts and the chambers pump blood. (Compare with *diastole*.) Chapter 6, Unit 2

T

T-cell: A lymphocyte that matures in the thymus stimulated by the presence of a particular antigen. It differentiates and divides, producing offspring cells (killer cells) that attack and kill the cells bearing the antigen. Chapter 6, Unit 2

technology: The application of scientific knowledge for practical purposes. Chapter 7, Unit 3

testes: The primary reproductive organs of a male; sperm-cell-producing organs. Chapter 10, Unit 4 Essays

testosterone (tes TOS ter ohn): A male sex hormone secreted by the testes. Chapter 10, Unit 4 Essays

theory: A well-tested hypothesis that organizes knowledge, fits existing data, explains how events or processes are thought to take place, and successfully predicts future observations. Chapter 2, Unit 1 Essays

thylakoid (THY luh koyd): A flattened sac in a chloroplast. Many of the thylakoids are arranged in stacks known as grana. The pigments and enzymes for the light reactions of photosynthesis are embedded in the sac membrane. Chapter 8, Unit 3 Essays

toxin: A substance produced by one organism that is poisonous to another. Chapter 7, Unit 3 Essays

trachea (TRAY kee uh): The windpipe of an air-breathing vertebrate, connecting the air passage in the throat with the lungs. Chapter 13, Unit 5

transcription (tran SKRIP shun): The assembly of an RNA molecule complimentary to a strand of DNA. The product may be messenger RNA, transfer RNA, or ribosomal RNA. Chapter 12, Unit 4 Essays

transgenic (trans JEN ik): Plants or animals that contain genes from unrelated species. Chapter 12, Unit 4 Essays

translation: The assembly of proteins on ribosomes, using messenger RNA to direct the order of amino acids. Chapter 12, Unit 4 Essays

triage (TREE azh): A sorting out and classification of patients according to the seriousness of injuries, urgency of treatment, and place for treatment. Carried out as an emergency procedure during an influx of large numbers of victims of a disaster. Chapter 6, Unit 2

tRNA (transfer RNA): Transfers amino acids to the growing end of a polypeptide chain during translation. Chapter 12, Unit 4

U

umbilical (um BIL ih kul) cord: In placental mammals, a tube connecting the embryo with the placenta. Chapter 10, Unit 4 Essays

ureter (YOO ree ter): A muscular tube that carries urine from the kidney to the urinary bladder. Chapter 4, Unit 2

urethra (yoo REE thruh): In vertebrates, the tube through which urine is carried from the bladder to the outside of the body. Chapter 10, Unit 4 Essays

uterus (YOO ter us): A hollow muscular organ, located in the female pelvis, in which a fetus develops. Chapter 10, Unit 4 Essays

V

vacuole (VAK yoo ohl): A membrane-enclosed structure in the cytoplasm of a cell or a unicellular organism. Different types of vacuoles serve different functions. Chapter 4, Unit 2

vagina (vuh JI nuh): A tubular organ that leads from the uterus to the opening of the female reproductive tract. Chapter 10, Unit 4 Essays

variable: A condition that varies from one organism to another (size, shape, color) or is subject to change for an individual organism (humidity, temperature, light intensity, fatigue). Chapter 4, Unit 2

vas deferens (vas DEF er enz): A tube that leads from the epididymis to the urethra of the male reproductive tract. Chapter 10, Unit 4 Essays

vasopressin (vas O press in): Hormone released by the pituitary in response to the signal of dehydration sent from the hypothalamus. Chapter 5, Unit 2

vegetative reproduction: Asexual reproduction by plants that also may reproduce sexually. Examples include potato plants from "eyes" and grass plants from runners. Chapter 10, Unit 4

vulva (VUL va): External female reproductive organs. Chapter 10, Unit 4 Essays

Z

zygote (ZY goht): The diploid product of the union of haploid gametes in conception; a fertilized egg. Chapter 10, Unit 4

Credits

CHAPTER 5: Opener Person Balancing PhotoDisc; 5.1 BSCS by Carlye Calvin; Thermometer BSCS by Hedi Baxter; 5.2 BSCS by Hedi Baxter; 5.3 BSCS by Carlye Calvin; Teen exercising PhotoDisc; 5.6 BSCS by Carlye Calvin; 5.8 Kendall/Hunt Publishing Company by Jeff Simon; 5.11 Photo of Various Food with Their PH Levels Indicated Comstock; 5.12 BSCS by Tom Bishop.

CHAPTER 6: Opener (patient) PhotoDisc; Canyon trail Corel; Patient on a stretcher DigitalSTOCK; Stethoscope PhotoDisc; Heart rate measurement PhotoDisc; 6.1 (a–c) DigitalSTOCK; Anesthesiologist with patient DigitalSTOCK; 6.2 David M. Dennis/Tom Stack & Associates; "Virus" PhotoDisc; Stressed teens PhotoDisc; 6.4 (a-c) PhotoDisc; 6.5 NIAID; Skier PhotoDisc; Entrepreneur PhotoDisc; Bottles of alcohol PhotoDisc; Blood pressure check PhotoDisc; Doctor discussing birth control options with patient PhotoDisc; Patient undergoing medical treatment DigitalSTOCK; Patient with OB/GYN physician PhotoDisc; Man smoking a cigarette PhotoDisc; Boy getting a vaccine EyeWire; Mother reading to her daughter PhotoDisc.

UNIT TWO ESSAYS
E4.1 BSCS by Janet C. Girard; E4.2 (a) Richard H. Thom/Tom Stack & Associates; Diffusion shown in 3-photo series BSCS ; E4.9 (b) P.M. Motta, A. Caggiati, G. Macchiarelli/Science Photo Library/Photo Researchers; E5.2 Cabisco/Visuals Unlimited; E5.8 (b) David M. Phillips/Visuals Unlimited; E5.9 (EM of alveolar capillaries) Fred Hossler/Visuals Unlimited; E5.11 Corel; E5.12 Corel; E5.14 Corel; E6.3 (a) John Cunningham/Visuals Unlimited, (b) Tom Stack/Tom Stack and Associates; E6.4 BSCS; E6.5 (a, b) Courtesy of Penrose Hospital, Colo. Springs., CO; E6.6 Raymond B. Otero/Visuals Unlimited; E6.7 David M. Phillips/ Visuals Unlimited; E6.8 Lennart Nilsson/Boehringer Ingelheim International GmbH; E6.11 © Bettmann/ CORBIS; E6.13 a) normal human lung, b) lung cancer, and c) emphysema American Lung Association; E6.16 Gerald Bellow/Colorado Springs Police Department; E6.17 BSCS by Carlye Calvin.

Unit 3

Unit Opener (woman racer) Corel.

CHAPTER 7: Opener (amputee) Courtesy of the International Tennis Federation; (kids at ocean) PhotoDisc; (woman biker) EyeWire; U.S. Air Force T-38 supersonic jet trainer BSCS by William J. Cairney; Jet streams BSCS by Bill Beaudin; 7.2 (left) Tom Kimmell/USA Hockey, (middle) EyeWire, (right) BSCS by Hedi Baxter; Woman Eating Pizza, PhotoDisc; Teens eating PhotoDisc; 7.4 BSCS; Flexed arm PhotoDisc; 7.8 (a) Carlye Calvin, (b, c) Corel; Blind skier Courtesy of Brian Santos/USABA.

CHAPTER 8: Opener (sunrays) Comstock; Exhausted athlete Corel; 8.1 Corel; 8.2 Corel; 8.4 BSCS by Carlye Calvin; 8.5 (a, b) BSCS by Hedi Baxter; 8.7 BSCS by Bill Beaudin; 8.8 a) windmills Comstock, b) hydroelectric dam, c) solar plant Corel; 8.9 BSCS by Hedi Baxter; 8.12 Corel; 8.13 BSCS by Bill Beaudin; 8.16 Comstock; Cowboy BSCS by Bill Beaudin; 8.17 Argonne National Laboratory.

CHAPTER 9: Opener BSCS by Bill Beaudin; 9.1 BSCS by Carlye Calvin; 9.2 BSCS by Bill Beaudin; 9.3 (worm) Carlye Calvin, (worms and compost) BSCS by Bill Beaudin; 9.4 BSCS by Bill Beaudin; Cow Corel; 9.5 (wheat in the field) Corel, (grain harvest combine) Corel, (flour and tortillas) BSCS by Bill Beaudin; 9.6 (left) ArtToday, (other photos) BSCS by Bill Beaudin; 9.7 (a, b) Corel, (c, d) BSCS by Bill Beaudin; 9.8 BSCS by Bill Beaudin; 9.9 BSCS by Carlye Calvin; 9.10 BSCS by Bill Beaudin; Finished compost BSCS by Bill Beaudin; 9.11 National Oceanic & Atmospheric Administration (NOAA), NOAA Central Library, Captain Budd Christman, NOAA Corps; Cabin in the snow BSCS by Wilber Fulker; 9.12 Corel.

UNIT THREE ESSAYS
E7.1 (rollerbladers) PhotoDisc, (backpacker) PhotoDisc, (kids studying) EyeWire; E7.2 Dancing Wheels, www.dancingwheels.org. Photo: Al Fuchs © 2001, The Snowman by Sabatino Verlezza; E7.3 ©Mehau Kulyk, Victor de Schwanberg, Science Photo Library, Photo Researchers, Inc.; Japanese food PhotoDisc; Mexican food BSCS by Bill Beaudin; E7.4 U.S.D.A.; E7.12 (a) S. Maslowski/Visuals Unlimited, (b) Corel; E7.15 (a) Milton Rand/Tom Stack & Associates; Male Gymnast, Corel; Man training with power chute Perform Better; www. performbetter.com; BSCS by Carlye Calvin; E7.18 Athletes Training PhotoDisc; Ice melting BSCS by Hedi Baxter; E8.4 BSCS by Fred Baxter; E8.10 Corel; E8.11 (food photo) PhotoDisc; E8.13 (left) Don W. Fawcett/Visuals Unlimited; E8.16 BSCS by Carlye Calvin; Students sitting in a library BSCS by Carlye Calvin; E8.22 (b) George B. Chapman/Visuals Unlimited; E8.24 BSCS by Bill Beaudin; E8.26 Comstock; E8.27 (top) PhotoDisc; E9.1 Bernd Wittich/Visuals Unlimited; E9.2 Corel; E9.3 Corel; E9.5 PhotoDisc.

EXPLAIN SECTION: Opener (scientist working with mapping equipment) U.S. Geological Survey/photo by Michael F. Diggles, (entomologist) Courtesy of Anneke Lisberg, (scientist inspecting air deposition) U.S. Geological Survey/photo by Dave Usher, (scientists studying the Kilauea Volcano) U.S. Geological Survey/photo by J.D. Griggs; **Pregnant teen** PhotoDisc; **Ex.1** Corel; **Ex.2 Photo of scientist working in a lab wearing gloves, safety goggles, and lab coat**, PhotoDisc.

Unit 4

Unit Opener (collage of technology equipment) PhotoDisc.

CHAPTER 10: Opener (human sperm fertilizing an ovum) ©M. Kulyk/Photo Researchers; **Reproduction in three unusual organisms** (moss, bobby birds and beetles) Corel; **Grove of Aspen trees** Comstock; **10.2** Jason Pope/Colorado School for the Deaf and the Blind; **Reproduction in little-known organisms** (puffball) ©Stephen Dalton/Photo Researchers, (lizards) ArtToday/Painet URL: www.painetworks.com; **10.3** (a) Jackie Ott-Rodgers/BSCS, (b) Brian Parker/Tom Stack and Associates; **10.4** BSCS by Hedi Baxter; **10.6** Courtesy of the Lor Family; **10.7** (a, b) PhotoDisc; **10.8** Milton Rand/Tom Stack & Associates.

CHAPTER 11: Opener (large family) CORBIS; **Romanov family** BSCS by Robert F. Schwengel; **Heads side of a coin** Corel; **Bunnies** Dee Wilkins and Lucinda Schirmer; **Fast car** Corel; **11.2** PhotoDisc; **11.5** (top) Heather Harris; **Colored beans** Corel; **Father and baby** PhotoDisc; **Cocker spaniels** Corel; **11.7** © Claude Edelmann/Photo Researchers; **11.8** ©Biophoto Associates/Photo Researchers; **11.10** BSCS by Robert F. Schwengel; **11.13** PhotoDisc; **Two Goldfish in Tank** Corel; **11.14** Comstock; **Cave** Corel; **11.16** Copyright © 2002, www.doctorfungus.org.

CHAPTER 12: Opener (Two Navajos serving with the Marine signal unit) Courtesy of Air Force News Archive, (Navajo Code Talkers being honored by President George Bush) Paul Natonabah, The Navajo Times, (Navajo Code Talkers in the field) © Corbis; **12.1** Barbara McClintock Papers, American Philosophical Society Library; **12.3** Courtesy of Xerox—The Document Company—Xerox and 5900 are Trademarks of Xerox Corporation; **DNA word** PhotoDisc; **12.5** Dr. Leticia Márquez-Magaña/San Francisco University; **12.6** (b) Science Source/Photo Researchers; **Famous geneticist** © Bob Handelman, All Rights Reserved; **Photo of a group of scientists,** PhotoDisc.

UNIT FOUR ESSAYS
E10.1 Corel; **E10.3** (a) M. Siegelman/Visuals Unlimited, (b) Cabisco/Visuals Unlimited, (c) James W. Richardson/Visuals Unlimited; **E10.4** The Roslin Institute, Edinburgh; **E10.6** (c) Ed Reschke; **E10.9** W. Perry Conway/Tom Stack & Associates; **E10.11** J. Terrence McCabe; **E11.9** BSCS by Carlye Calvin; **E11.10** (a) Courtesy of Michael Dougherty, (b) F.R. Turner/Visuals Unlimited; **E11.13** Courtesy of Musée cantonal del Géologie, Lausanne; **E11.18** BSCS by Carlye Calvin; **E12.2** Science/Visuals Unlimited; **E12.3** J.R. Paulsen, U. Laemmli, D.W. Fawcett/Visuals Unlimited; **E12.8** BSCS by Robert F. Schwengel; **Hand holding corn kernels** Comstock; **E12.16** (bottom photo) John Cunningham/Visuals Unlimited; **Kary Mullis** BSCS by Robert F. Schwengel; **E12.19** (a) Comstock, (b) PhotoDisc; **Human hand with superimposed DNA** PhotoDisc; **Globe on house of cards** Comstock.

Unit 5

Unit Opener (photo series of egg to chick development) ©H. Turvey/Photo Researchers, Inc.

CHAPTER 13: Opener (human fetus) Nestle/Petit Format/Photo Researchers, Inc.; **13.1** Corel; **13.3** (a-f) Courtesy of Wilber Fulker; **13.4** Dr. Steven Scadding, Sandra J. Ackerley, Department of Zoology, University of Guelph, Ontario, Canada NIG 2W1; **13.5** BSCS by Carlye Calvin; **Person thinking hard** EyeWire; **13.6** (a, b) Will Allgood, Mark Viner/Media Design Associates; **13.8** PhotoDisc; **13.9** Lochlean Macleay, M.D.; **Doctor talking to patient** DigitalSTOCK; **13.10** Ken Lucas/Visuals Unlimited.

CHAPTER 14: Opener (collage: photos of baby and family) Ms. Lynn Peters Adler, National Centenarian Awareness Project, (photo of centenarian: © William Clark); **14.1** © Ariel Skelley/CORBIS; **14.2** BSCS by Carlye Calvin; **14.3** EyeWire; **Children** Comstock; **Woman with Boy and Girl**, EyeWire; **Senior w/kids** BSCS by Carlye Calvin; **Elderly Indian woman** Corel; **Students debating** BSCS by Carlye Calvin; **Teens from different ethnic backgrounds** Corel.

UNIT FIVE ESSAYS
E13.1 BSCS; **E13.2** (left) Will Allgood/Media Design Associate, (middle) Cabisco/Visuals Unlimited; (right, fetal pig) John D. Cunningham/Visuals Unlimited; **E13.6** (a, b) Media Design Associates; **E13.7** (a) Fred Hossler/Visuals Unlimited, (b) David M. Phillips/Visuals Unlimited, (c) John D. Cunningham/Visuals Unlimited; **E13.12** (a, b) John Moss/Photo Researchers; **E13.13** Courtesy of Phil and Ellen Goulding; **E13.16** K.G. Murti/Visuals Unlimited; **E13.17** PhotoDisc; **E13.19** (a) Cabisco/Visuals Unlimited, (b) Randy Morse/Tom Stack & Associates; **E13.21** (a) Victor Hutchinson/Visuals Unlimited, (b) Corel;

Student recording observations BSCS by Carlye Calvin; **E14.2** Courtesy of Jean and Mina Milani; **Photo of a man helping a girl putt,** EyeWire; **E14.8** BSCS by Carlye Calvin; **E14.9** BSCS by Carlye Calvin; **E14.13** Bayard H. Brattstrom/Visuals Unlimited; **E14.15** D. Long/Visuals Unlimited; **E14.16** D. Long/Visuals Unlimited; **Amish at Open Market** Link/Visuals Unlimited.

Unit 6

Unit Opener (photo collage of various biomes) Desert: Comstock, Alpine: EyeWire, Rainforest: Comstock, Savanna: PhotoDisc, Pine Forest: Comstock.

CHAPTER 15: Opener (Havasupai Indian women playing in the river beneath Havaus Falls) Rich Clarkson; **Girl putting birdseed into a feeder** BSCS by Pam Van Scotter; **15.1** Comstock; **Early Morning Reflections** Corel; **Map of Easter Island** Corel; **15.5** Courtesy of Daryl O'Connor; **15.6** Corel; **15.9** Corel; **Moai of Ahu Akivi** Corel.

CHAPTER 16: Opener (From the Apollo program, taken by the Apollo 8 astronauts) NASA; **16.1** EyeWire; **Scientist taking notes** U.S. Geological Survey/Michael F. Diggles; **Lake** Corel; *Daphnia* Bruce J. Russell/BioMEDIA Associates, *Gammarus* John D. Cunningham/Visuals Unlimited; **16.2** NOAA; **The World** NASA (From the Apollo program, taken by the Apollo 17 astronauts); **16.6** PhotoDisc; **Environmental theme** BSCS by Tom Bishop.

UNIT SIX ESSAYS:
E15.1 Joe McDonald/Visuals Unlimited; **E15.2** David Vessey; **E15.4** (a, b) BSCS by Carlye Calvin; **E16.1** NASA; **E16.2** Carlye Calvin; **E16.3 Photo of Everglades** Corel; **E16.4** BSCS by Robert F. Schwengel; **E16.8** C. Allan Morgan; **E16.9** David S. Addison/Visuals Unlimited; **E16.10** Carlye Calvin.

EVALUATE SECTION: Opener (Collage of scientists conducting experiments) scientist at pond: ArtToday, two scientists testing water quality in Trout Creek: U.S. Geological Survey/photo by Eduardo Patino, scientist weighing a polar bear cub: U.S. Geological Survey/photo by Karen Bollinger, scientist measuring a puffin: U.S. Geological Survey/photo by John Piatt, scientist showing a dragonfly nymph to two young girls: Daniel Martinez; **Ev.3** EyeWire; **Ev.8** (left) Carlye Calvin, (right) BSCS; **Ev.12** Glenn M. Oliver/Visuals Unlimited; **Ev.13** (a) Jack Bostrack/Visuals Unlimited, (b) Gary Robinson/Visuals Unlimited; **Big band** (top) The Bettmann Archive, **Rock concert** (bottom) The Bettmann Archive; **Wetlands** Carlye Calvin; **Portfolios** BSCS by Hedi Baxter.

APPENDIX B: B.8 John Bostrack/Visuals Unlimited; **B.10** BSCS by Jerry Grant.

Index